MODERN GUNS
Identification & Values
3rd Revised Edition

Russell C. Quertermous

Steven C. Quertermous

COLLECTOR BOOKS
Gun Book Division
P.O. Box 3009-G
Paducah, Kentucky 42001

Additional copies of this book may be ordered from:

COLLECTOR BOOKS
P.O. Box 3009
Paducah, Kentucky 42001

@$11.95 Add $1.00 for postage and handling.

Copyright: Steve and Russell Quertermous, 1981
ISBN: 0-89145-146-3

ON THE COVER

Front:
High Standard Model HD Military Semi-automatic pistol
Remington Model 870 Wingmaster Magnum slide action shotgun
Savage Model 840 bolt action rifle
Colt Trooper MK III Revolver

Back:
Smith & Wesson Model 36 Chiefs Special revolver
Smith & Wesson Model 10 Military & Police Revolver
Harrington & Richardson Model 88 single shot shotgun
Browning Sweet Sixteen semi-automatic shotgun
Winchester Model 06 slide action rifle

Acknowledgements

Stackpole Books for use of the following photographs from the BOOK OF PISTOLS & REVOLVERS by W.H.B. Smith: Astra 1924; Bayard 1923; Bayard 1930; CZ 22; CZ 45; Fiala; 94 Japanese; Lignose 2; MAB A; MAB F; Mauser 1; Mauser 2; Sauer 1913; Sauer WTM; Savage 1907, 1915, 1917; Smith & Wesson 32.

The companies included for use of catalogs, advertisements and promotional material.

A special thanks to the following gun manufacturers for additional photos, information and assistance: Beretta Arms Co. Inc. for material on Beretta handguns and shotguns; Browning for material on Browning handguns, rifles and shotguns; Charter Arms Corporation for material on Charter Arms handguns; Colt Industries, Firearms Division for material on Colt handguns and rifles; Commercial Trading Imports, Inc. for material on Baikal shotguns; Harrington & Richardson, Inc. for material on Harrington & Richardson handguns, rifles and shotguns; High Standard Sporting Firearms for material on High Standard handguns; Interarms for material on Mark X rifles, Valmet rifles, Walther handguns and rifles, Star handguns, and Astra handguns; Ithaca Gun Co. for material on Ithaca shotguns; Iver Johnson Arms, Inc. for material on Iver Johnson handguns and Plainfield rifles; Kleinguenther Inc. for materials on Kleinguenther rifles; Mannlicher for materials on Mannlicher rifles; Marlin for material on Marlin and Marlin-Glenfield rifles and shotguns; O.F. Mossberg & Sons Inc., for material on Mossberg and New Haven rifles and shotguns; Remington for material on Remington rifles, shotguns, and handguns; Richland Arms Co. for material on Richland shotguns; Savage Arms for material on Savage rifles and shotguns, Stevens rifles and shotguns; Fox shotguns, and Anschutz rifles; Sears, Roebuck & Co. for material on Sears rifles and shotguns and Ted Williams rifles and shotguns; Smith & Wesson for material on Smith & Wesson handguns, rifles, and shotguns; Speer Inc. Advertising for material on Mossberg firearms; Sterling Arms Corporation for material on Sterling handguns; Universal Firearms for material on Universal rifles; Weatherby, Inc. for material on Weatherby rifles and shotguns; Winchester-Western for material on Winchester rifles and shotguns.

CONTENTS

Introduction

The gun enthusiast, whether he owns several hundred fireamrs or only one relic passed down through his family is in need of a quick, descriptive, handy, and illustrated reference of realistic gun values. With this in mind, *Modern Guns* has been created.

Since entire books have been written about a single firearm, many decisions have had to be made in compiling a book of this type. For this reason we have chosen to deal with the more common varieties of American and foreign firearms produced from about 1900 until the present. This does not mean that all brands, nor even all models of any particular brand are listed. The guns listed here are generally not the rare collector's items that fill so many books and so few gun owner's racks. Also, for the most part, elaborate match style target rifles and handguns have been purposefully omitted. What will be found here is a look at the guns that are currently appearing on the market across the country with a fair market price.

Well over 2,000 guns have been cataloged here, with important identifying information and facts. Illustrations are used to aid in identifying the firearms. They are not intended to be proportional in scale to each other, and the text should be consulted in questions of size.

This book is divided into three main sections for ease in use. The section on shotguns appears first followed by rifles and then handguns. The listings under each heading will be found alphabetically except for American and foreign military rifles. These will all be found under the military heading in the rifle section. Content pages can be found at the beginning of each section for more speedy searching. A glossary of firearms terms can be found in the back for the reader not familiar with some of the terms used.

If an owner believes one of his guns has more value than listed for any reason, he is encouraged to do further research to ascertain its fair value. Likewise, if a particular model is not listed, further research is again necessary to fill the gap in information. An excellent source for material on guns, either recent or older, is company produced catalogs, advertisements, or distributor catalogs. A multi-year look at these materials will give a good view of the trends and production habits of the company in question.

For the purpose of estimating values, the firearm's condition is the first and foremost consideration. Conditions of guns evaluated in this guide are considered to be in accordance with the National Rifle Association (NRA) definitions, taken from its magazine, *The American Rifleman*. This evaluation system is generally accepted in the firearms trade.

New Discontinued—same as new, but discontinued model. The following definitions will apply to all second hand articles:

Perfect—in new condition in every aspect; Excellent—new condition, used but little, no noticeable marring of wood or metal, bluing perfect [except at muzzle or sharp edges]; Very Good—in perfect working condition, no appreciable wear on working surfaces, no corrosion or pitting, only minor surface dents or scratches; Good—in safe working condition, minor wear on working surfaces no broken parts, no corrosion or pitting that will interfere with proper functioning; Fair—in safe working condition, but well worn, perhaps requiring replacment of minor parts or adjustments, no rust but may have corrosion pits which do not render article unsafe or inoperable.

Values in this guide are for guns in the following conditions:

New [Retail]: present suggested retail prices still in production. Excellent and Very Good; or Very Good & Good, for all second hand items. Commemoratives are valued for guns in new, unused condition with original box or case.

The values listed here are considered to be at the retail level. That is, they are prices that a dealer might ask for a particular firearm. Therefore, a dealer would not be expected to buy or trade at these values. Many things affect the value of used guns, such as condition, availability, type, season, geographic area, and the retail price of the firearm. These prices can fluctuate greatly in a relatively short period of time. The prices here are not to be used as a hard fast rule, but rather as a guide to be used in judging the relative worth of a particular gun. We realize that people have different ideas about the value of any used item, and guns are no different. It is wise for the average person to consult an expert when dealing in items or materials with which he is not familiar. And where firearms are concerned, it is wise to investigate the laws concerning buying, selling, and owning.

Some firearms are worth more because of quantities produced, markings, special finishes [such as engraving and inlays] historical value, and factory options. The guns listed here are standard factory issues, unless noted. Options available can change the value of a gun considerably. Some guns are worth more simply because of market popularity or geographic preferance. A gun that is plentiful in one area and demands a low price could be scarce on the market in another area and sell for a high figure.

This material has been compiled for the benefit and enjoyment of the average gun enthusiast, shooter, owner, trader, buyer, and seller, either expert or novice. With this book in hand, he can go into the firearms market well armed.

Shotguns

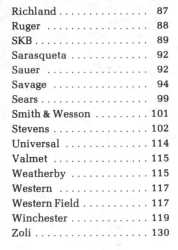

AYA

AYA Matador
Gauge: 10, 12, 16, 20, 20 Magnum
Action: Box lock; top lever break-open; hammerless; selective single trigger and automatic ejector; double barrel
Magazine: None
Barrel: Double barrel, 26", 28", 30" any choke combination.
Finish: Blued; checkered walnut pistol grip stock and beavertail forearm
Approximate wt.: 7 lbs.
Comments: Produced from 1953 until 1963. Replaced by Matador II.
Estimated Value: Excellent: $300.00
Very good: $240.00

AYA Matador II
Same as the Matador with ventilated rib. Produced since the discontinuation of the Matador.
Estimated Value: Excellent: $375.00
Very good: $300.00

AYA Bolero
The same shotgun as the Matador in 28 gauge and .410 gauge. Produced from the mid 1950's until 1963.
Estimated Value: Excellent: $325.00
Very good: $270.00

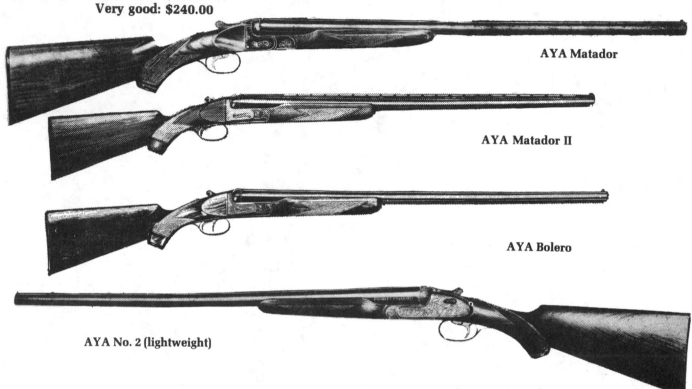

AYA Matador

AYA Matador II

AYA Bolero

AYA No. 2 (lightweight)

AYA Model 56

AYA No. 2 (lightweight)
Similar to AYA No. 1 (lightweight) except no load indicators or folding front trigger.
Estimated Value: Excellent: $700.00
Very good: $575.00

AYA Model 56 and AYA No. 1 (Lightweight)
Gauge: 12, 20 (2¾" chambers standard; 3" on request)
Action: Side lock, top lever break-open; hammerless; double barrel; automatic ejectors; folding front trigger, load indicators
Magazine: None
Barrel: Double barrel; any length and choke combination
Finish: Blued; engraving on receiver; matted rib; custom walnut stock
Approximate wt.: 7 lbs.
Comments: Basically a custom gun in production since early 1970's. Due to its nature, values will vary greatly; made to customer's requirements.
Estimated Value: Excellent: $1,200.00 - $1,800.00
Very good: $1,000.00 - $1,500.00

Armalite

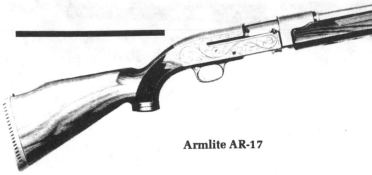

Armlite AR-17

Armalite AR-17
Gauge: 12
Action: Semi-automatic; recoil operated; hammerless
Magazine: 2 shot
Barrel: 24" aluminum alloy; interchangeable choke tubes; improved modified, and full, chokes
Finish: Gold anodized or black anodized; plastic stock and forearm
Approximate wt.: 5 ½ lbs.
Comments: Barrel and receiver housing made of aluminum alloy; Made from about 1963 to 1965. Approximately 2000 manufactured.
Estimated Value: Excellent: $600.00
Very good: $500.00

Baikal

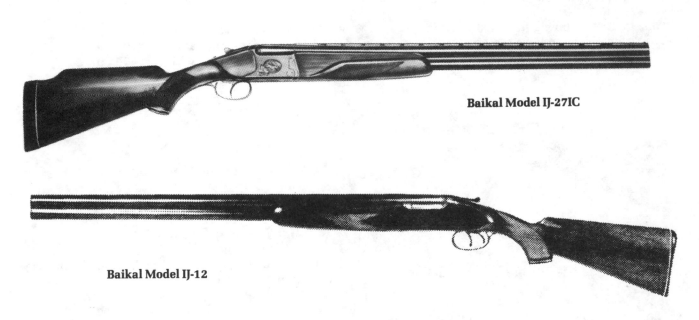

Baikal Model IJ-27IC

Baikal Model IJ-12

Baikal Model IJ-27EIC Silver
Same as the Model IJ-27EIC with silver inlays and fancy engraving.
Estimated Value: New (retail): $585.95
Excellent: $440.00
Very good: $350.00

Baikal Model IJ-12
Less fancy, but similar to the IJ-27IC. No engraving; no recoil pad; 28" barrel only. Imported in the early 1970's.
Estimated Value: Excellent: $190.00
Very good: $150.00

Baikal Model IJ-27IC and IJ-27EIC
Gauge: 12
Action: Box lock; top lever break-open; hammerless; over and under double barrel; selective single trigger
Magazine: None
Barrel: Over and under double barrel; 26", 28", 30" improved cylinder and modified or modified and full chokes; ventilated rib
Finish: Blued; engraved receiver; hand checkered walnut pistol grip stock and forearm
Approximate wt: 7 ½ lbs.
Comments: Made in Soviet Union and imported at present; IJ-27EIC has selective ejectors, add $40.00
Estimated Value: New (retail): $390.00
Excellent: $290.00
Very good: $230.00

Baikal TOZ-66

Baikal TOZ-66
Gauge: 12
Action: Box lock; top lever, break-open; exposed hammers; double barrel
Magazine: None
Barrel: Double barrel; 28" chrome lined, variety of chokes
Finish: Blued; checkered wood, pistol grip stock & short tapered forearm; engraving
Approximate wt.: 8 lbs.
Comments: Imported during the 1970's.
Estimated Value: Excellent: $175.00
 Very good: $140.00

Baikal Model TOZ-34E Souvenir
Gauge: 12, 20, 28
Action: Box lock; top lever, break-open; hammerless; over and under double barrel
Magazine: None
Barrel: Over and under double barrel; 26" or 28" improved cylinder and modified or modified and full; ventilated rib on 12 and 20 gauge; solid rob on 28 gauge
Finish: Blued; select walnut, hand checkered pistol grip stock and forearm; engraved receiver
Approximate wt: 7 lbs.
Comments: Presently imported from the Soviet Union. It features selective ejectors and cocking indicator.
Estimated Value: New (retail): $675.00
 Excellent: $500.00
 Very good: $400.00

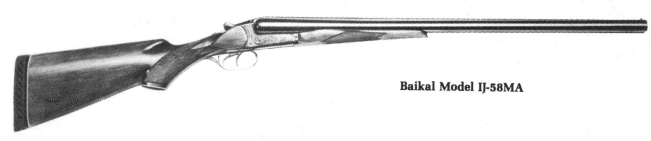

Baikal Model IJ-58MA

Baikal Model IJ-18 and IJ-18E
Gauge: 12, 20
Action: Box lock; top lever, break-open; hammerless; single shot; cocking indicator
Magazine: None
Barrel: 26", 28" modified, 30" full, chokes
Finish: Blued; checkered walnut stained hardwood pistol grip stock & tapered forearm; engraved receiver
Approximate wt: 6 lbs.
Comments: Manufactured at present; IJ-18E has selective ejector; Add $6.00.
Estimated Value: New (retail): $73.50
 Excellent: $60.00
 Very good: $50.00

Baikal IJ-58MA and 58MAE
Gauge: 12, 20 Magnum
Action: Box lock; top lever, break-open; hammerless; double barrel
Magazine: None
Barrel: Double barrel; 26" improved cylinder & modified, 28" modified & full chokes; chrome lined
Finish: Blued; checkered walnut, pistol grip stock & short tapered forearm; engraved receiver; IJ-58 MAE has selective ejectors; Add $28.00
Approximate wt: 7 lbs.
Comments: Made at present.
Estimated Value: New (retail): $239.95
 Excellent: $190.00
 Very good: $150.00

Baikal Model IJ-18

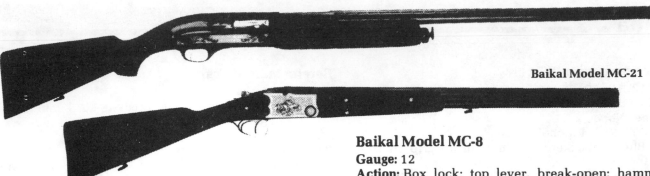

Baikal Model MC-21

Baikal Model MC-5

Baikal Model MC-8
Gauge: 12
Action: Box lock; top lever, break-open; hammerless; over & under double barrel
Magazine: None
Barrel: Over & under double barrel; 26'' skeet, 28'' modified & full, chokes; chrome lined
Finish: Blued; checkered walnut, Monte Carlo, pistol grip stock & forearm; engraved
Approximate wt.: 8 ½ lbs.
Comments: Imported during the 1970's.
Estimated Value: Excellent: $775.00
                    Very good: $625.00

Baikal Model MC-21
Gauge: 12
Action: Semi-automatic; hammerless; side-ejection
Magazine: 5 shot tubular
Barrel: 26'' improved cylinder, 28'' modified, 30'' full, chokes; ventilated rib
Finish: Blued; checkered walnut, pistol grip stock & forearm; cheekpiece
Approximate wt.: 7 ½ lbs.
Comments: Imported in 1970's.
Estimated Value: Excellent: $275.00
                    Very good: $220.00

Baikal Model MC-5
Gauge: 20
Action: Box lock; top lever; break-open; hammerless; over & under double barrel; double triggers
Magazine: None
Barrel: Over & under double barrel; 26'' and 28'' improved cylinder & modified or skeet chokes
Finish: Blued; checkered walnut, pistol grip or straight stock & forearm; engraved; solid rib
Approximate wt: 5 ¾ lbs.
Comments: Imported during the 1970's.
Estimated Value: Excellent: $675.00
                    Very good: $550.00

Baker

Baker Black Beauty Special
Similar to Baker Batavia Leader except higher quality wood and finish. Add $75.00 for automatic extractors.
Estimated Value: Excellent: $500.00
                    Very good: $425.00

Baker Batavia Leader
Gauge: 12, 16, 20
Action: Side lock; hammerless; double barrel
Magazine: None
Barrel: 26'', 28'', 30'', 32'', double barrel; any standard choke combination
Finish: Blued; walnut pistol grip stock & forearm
Approximate wt.: 7-8 lbs.
Comments: Made from about 1900 to 1930. Add $75.00 for automatic extractors.
Estimated Value: Excellent: $300.00
                    Very good: $250.00

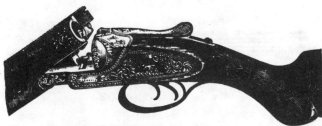

Baker Black Beauty Special

Baker Batavia Leader

Beretta

Beretta Companion FS-1
Gauge: 12, 16, 20, 28, 410
Action: Underlever; hammerless; single shot
Magazine: None
Barrel: 26", 28" full choke
Finish: Blued; checkered walnut, pistol grip stock & forearm
Approximate wt.: 5 lbs.
Comments: A folding shotgun made from about 1960 to the late 1970's.
Estimated Value: Excellent: $95.00
             Very good: $75.00

Beretta Mark II Trap
Gauge: 12
Action: Box lock; top lever, break-open; hammerless; single shot
Magazine: None
Barrel: 32", 34" full choke; ventilated rib
Finish: Blued; checkered walnut, Monte Carlo pistol grip stock & forearm; recoil pad; engraving
Approximate wt.: 8 lbs.
Comments: Made from the mid 1970's to present.
Estimated Value: New (retail): $550.00
             Excellent: $415.00
             Very good: $335.00

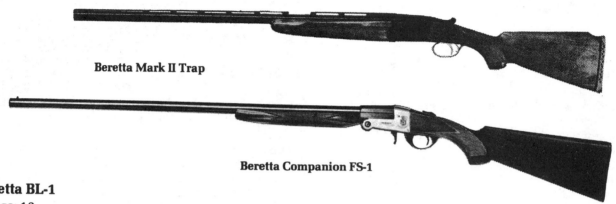

Beretta Mark II Trap

Beretta Companion FS-1

Beretta BL-1
Gauge: 12
Action: Box lock; top lever, break-open; hammerless; over & under double barrel; double triggers
Magazine: None
Barrel: Over & under double barrel; chrome steel; 26"-30" improved cylinder & modified or modified & full, chokes
Finish: Blued; checkered walnut, semi-pistol grip stock & forearm; sights
Comments: Made from about 1969 to early 1970's.
Approximate wt.: 7 lbs.
Estimated Value: Excellent: $325.00
             Very good: $265.00

Beretta BL-2
Similar to the BL-1 with selective single trigger.
Estimated Value: Excellent: $375.00
             Very good: $300.00

Beretta BL-3
Similar to the BL-2 with ventilated rib;
Estimated Value: Excellent: $475.00
             Very good: $380.00

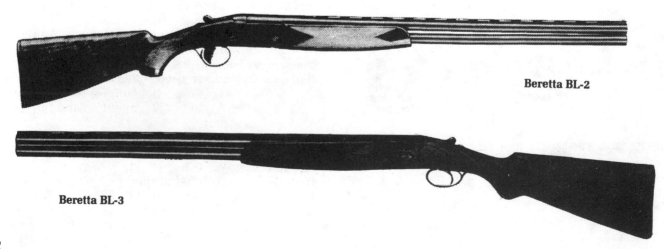

Beretta BL-2

Beretta BL-3

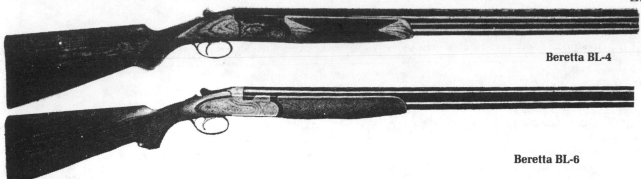

Beretta BL-4

Beretta BL-6

Beretta BL-4

Similar to the BL-3 with deluxe engraving and checkering; automatic ejectors.

Estimated Value: Excellent: $575.00
Very good: $460.00

Beretta BL-6

The finest of the BL line. Highest quality checkering & engraving. Similar to the BL-4.

Estimated Value: Excellent: $850.00
Very good: $725.00

Beretta Silver Snipe

Beretta Silver Snipe

Gauge: 12, 20, regular or magnum
Action: Box lock; top lever, break-open; hammerless; over & under double barrel
Magazine: None
Barrel: 26''-30'' improved cylinder & modified, modified & full, full, or skeet, chokes; ribbed
Finish: Blued; nickel receiver; checkered walnut, pistol grip stock & forearm
Approximate wt.: 7 ½ lbs.
Comments: Made from the mid 1950's to late 1960's. Add $25.00 for single selective trigger.

Estimated Value: Excellent: $385.00
Very good: $310.00

Beretta Golden Snipe

Similar to the Silver Snipe with ventilated rib; automatic ejectors. Discontinued in the mid 1970's.

Estimated Value: Excellent: $425.00
Very good: $350.00

Beretta Asel

Gauge: 12, 20
Action: Box lock; top lever, break-open; hammerless; over & under double barrel; automatic ejectors
Magazine: None
Barrel: Over & under double barrel; 25'', 28'', 30'' improved cylinder & modified or modified & full, chokes
Finish: Blued; checkered walnut, pistol grip stock & forearm
Approximate wt.: 7 lbs.
Comments: Manufactured from the late 1940's to mid 1960's.

Estimated Value: Excellent: $750.00
Very good: $625.00

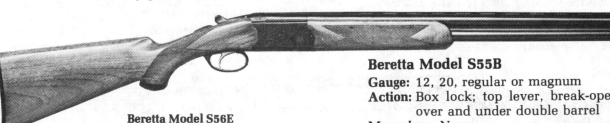

Beretta Model S56E

Beretta Model S56E

Similar to to Model S55B with scroll engraving on the receiver; selective automatic ejectors.

Estimated Value: New (retail): $750.00
Excellent: $565.00
Very good: $455.00

Beretta Model S55B

Gauge: 12, 20, regular or magnum
Action: Box lock; top lever, break-open; hammerless; over and under double barrel
Magazine: None
Barrel: Over and under double barrel; chrome lined; ventilated rib; 26'' improved cylinder and modified; 28'' or 30'' modified and full; 30'' full in 12 gauge.
Finish: Blued; checkered walnut pistol grip stock and beavertail forearm; recoil pad on magnum
Approximate wt: 6-7 lbs.
Comments: Introduced in the late 1970's.

Estimated Value: New (retail): $650.00
Excellent: $490.00
Very good: $395.00

Shotguns

Beretta GR-2

Gauge: 12, 20
Action: Box lock; top lever, break-open; hammerless; double barrel
Magazine: None
Barrel: Double barrel; 26"-30"; variety of choke combinations
Finish: Blued; checkered walnut, semi-pistol grip stock & forearm
Approximate wt.: 6-8 lbs.
Comments: Manufactured from the mid 1970's to late 1970's.
Estimated Value: Excellent: $400.00
Very good: $325.00

Beretta GR-3

Similar to the GR-2 with single selective trigger.
Estimated Value: Excellent: $435.00
Very good: $350.00

Beretta GR-4

Similar to the GR-3 with automatic ejectors; engraving and deluxe wood work.
Estimated Value: Excellent: $550.00
Very good: $445.00

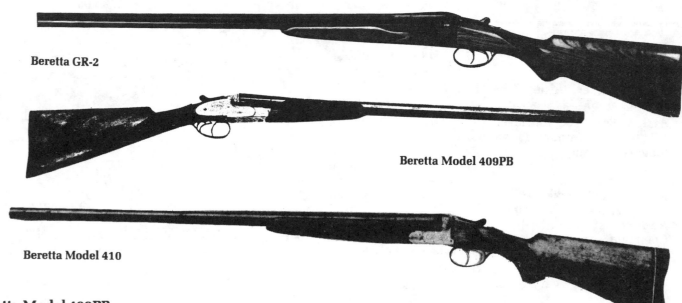

Beretta GR-2

Beretta Model 409PB

Beretta Model 410

Beretta Model 409PB

Gauge: 12, 16, 20, 28
Action: Box lock; top lever, break-open; hammerless; double barrel; double triggers
Magazine: None
Barrel: Double barrel 27½", 28½", 30" improved cylinder & modified or modified & full, chokes
Finish: Blued; checkered walnut, straight or pistol grip stock & small tapered forearm; engraved
Approximate wt.: 6-8 lbs.
Comments: Made from mid 1930's to the mid 1960's.
Estimated Value: Excellent: $450.00
Very good: $360.00

Beretta Model 410E

Similar to the 409PB with higher quality finish and engraving; automatic ejectors.
Estimated Value: Excellent: $525.00
Very good: $420.00

Beretta Model 411E

Similar to 410E with higher quality finish.
Estimated Value: Excellent: $750.00
Very good: $600.00

Beretta Model 410

Gauge: 10 magnum
Action: Box lock; top lever, break-open; hammerless, double barrel; double triggers
Magazine: None
Barrel: Double barrel; 27½", 28½", 30" improved cylinder & modified or modified & full, chokes
Finish: Blued; checkered walnut, stock & short tapered forearm
Approximate wt.: 10 lbs.
Comments: Made from the mid 1930's to present
Estimated Value: New (retail): $1,050.00
Excellent: $ 800.00
Very good: $ 650.00

Beretta Model 410E

Beretta Model 424

Beretta Silver Hawk Featherweight

Gauge: 12, 16, 20, 28
Action: Box lock; top lever, break-open; hammerless; double barrel
Magazine: None
Barrel: 26"-32" variety of chokes; matted rib
Finish: Blued; checkered walnut, pistol grip stock & forearm
Approximate wt.: 7¼ lbs.
Comments: Manufactured from the mid 1950's to late 1960's.
Estimated Value: Excellent: $350.00
      Very good: $280.00

Beretta Silver Hawk Featherweight Magnum

Similar to the Silver Hawk Featherweight in 12 gauge magnum; chrome lined 30" or 32" barrels; ventilated rib; recoil pad.
Estimated Value: Excellent: $400.00
      Very good: $320.00

Beretta Model 424

Gauge: 12, 20
Action: Box lock; top lever, break-open; hammerless; double barrel; double trigger
Magazine: None
Barrel: Double barrel; chrome lined; matted rib; 26" or 28" improved cylinder and modified or modified and full
Finish: Blued; checkered walnut straight grip stock and forearm
Approximate wt: 6 lbs.
Comments: Introduced in the late 1970's.
Estimated Value: New (retail): $782.00
      Excellent: $585.00
      Very good: $475.00

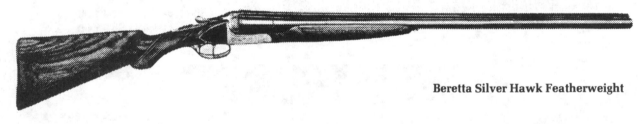

Beretta Silver Hawk Featherweight

Beretta Silver Pigeon

Beretta Silver Pigeon

Gauge: 12
Action: Slide action; hammerless
Magazine: 5 shot tubular
Barrel: 26"-32", various chokes
Finish: Blued; engraved & inlaid with silver pigeon; chrome trigger; checkered walnut, pistol grip stock and slide handle
Approximate wt.: 7 lbs.
Comments: Manufactured from about 1960 for 6 years.
Estimated Value: Excellent: $225.00
      Very good: $190.00

Beretta Gold Pigeon

Similar to the Silver Pigeon with heavy engraving; gold pigeon invalid; ventilated rib; gold trigger.
Estimated Value: Excellent: $475.00
      Very good: $390.00

Berreta Ruby Pigeon

Similar to the Gold Pigeon with deluxe engraving and inlaid pigeon has ruby eye.
Estimated Value: Excellent: $525.00
      Very good: $425.00

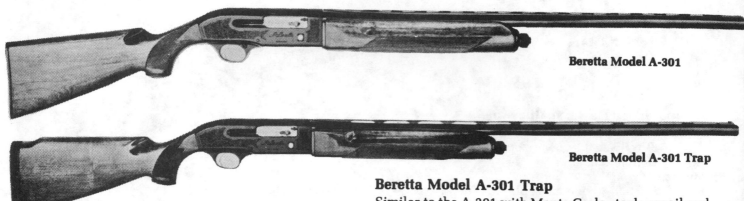

Beretta Model A-301

Beretta Model A-301 Trap

Beretta Model A-301

Gauge: 12, 20 regular or magnum
Action: Gas operated, semi-automatic; hammerless
Magazine: 3 shot tubular
Barrel: 26" improved cylinder; 28" modified or full; 30" full in 12 gauge; ventilated rib; chrome molybendeum
Finish: Blued; checkered walnut pistol grip stock and forearm; decorated alloy receiver; recoil pad on magnum model
Approximate wt: 6¼-7 lbs.
Comments: Introduced in the late 1970's. Add $45.00 for magnum.
Estimated Value: New (retail): $470.00
                 Excellent: $355.00
                 Very good: $285.00

Beretta Model A-301 Trap

Similar to the A-301 with Monte Carlo stock, recoil pad, and gold plated trigger; 12 gauge only; 30" full choke.
Estimated Value: New (retail): $485.00
                 Excellent: $355.00
                 Very good: $285.00

Beretta Model A-301 Skeet

Similar to the A-301 Trap with a 26" skeet choke barrel.
Estimated Value: New (retail): $470.00
                 Excellent: $355.00
                 Very good: $285.00

Beretta Model A-301 Deer Gun

Similar to the A-301 with a 22' slug barrel; 12 gauge only; adjustble open sights.
Estimated Value: New (retail): $470.00
                 Excellent: $355.00
                 Very good: $285.00

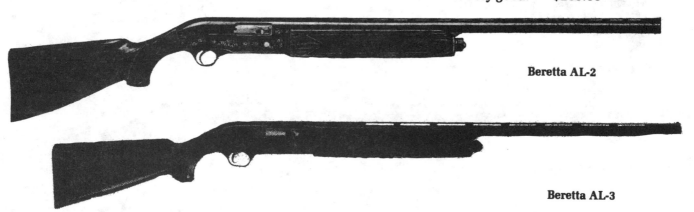

Beretta AL-2

Beretta AL-3

Beretta AL-2

Gauge: 12, 20; regular or magnum
Action: Gas operated, semi-automatic; hammerless
Magazine: 3 shot tubular
Barrel: 26"-30", skeet, improved cylinder, modified, or full, chokes; ventilated rib
Finish: Blued; checkered walnut, pistol grip stock & forearm
Approximate wt.: 6½-7¾ lbs.
Comments: Manufactured from the late 1960's to mid 1970's.
Estimated Value: Excellent: $260.00
                 Very good: $210.00

Beretta AL-3

Similar to the AL-2 with engraved receiver; ventilated rib; recoil pad; chrome lined bores.
Estimated Value: Excellent: $350.00
                 Very good: $275.00

Beretta AL-3 Deluxe

Similar to the AL-3 with trap specifications and Monte Carlo stock.
Estimated Value: Excellent: $375.00
                 Very good: $300.00

Beretta Silver Lark
Gauge: 12
Action: Gas operated, semi-automatic; hammerless
Magazine: 5 shot tubular
Barrel: 26''-32'', improved cylinder, modified or full, chokes
Finish: Blued; checkered walnut, pistol grip stock & forearm
Approximate wt.: 7 lbs.
Comments: Made from the early to late 1960's.
Estimated Value: Excellent: $190.00
**   Very good: $160.00**

Beretta Gold Lark
Similar to the Silver Lark with high quality engraving and ventilated rib.
Estimated Value: Excellent: $325.00
**   Very good: $275.00**

Beretta Ruby Lark
Similar to Silver Lark with deluxe engraving and a stainless steel barrel.
Estimated Value: Excellent: $400.00
**   Very good: $325.00**

Bernardelli

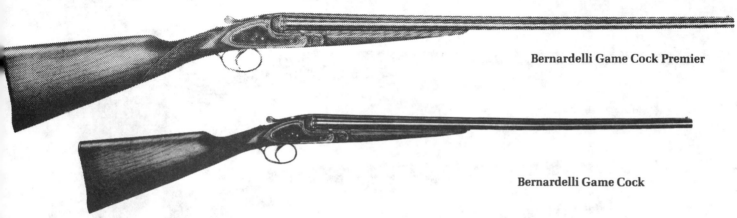

Bernardelli Game Cock Premier

Bernardelli Game Cock

Bernardelli Game Cock
Gauge: 12, 20
Action: Box lock; top lever break-open; double barrel; double trigger, hammerless;
Magazine: None
Barrel: Double barrel, 25'' improved and modified or 28'' modified and full, chokes
Finish: Blued; checkered walnut straight stock and forearm; light engraving
Approximate wt.: 6 ½ lbs.
Comments: Produced in the 1970's.
Estimated Value: Excellent: $660.00
**   Very good: $525.00**

Bernardelli Game Cock Deluxe
Same as the Game Cock with light scroll engraving; single trigger; automatic ejector.
Estimated Value: Excellent: $600.00
**   Very good: $480.00**

Bernardelli Game Cock Premier
Same as the Game Cock with more engraving; selective single trigger; automatic ejector.
Estimated Value: Excellent: $750.00
**   Very good: $600.00**

Bernardelli Roma
Gauge: 12, 16, 20
Action: Anson & Deeley type; top lever break-open; hammerless; double trigger; automatic ejector double barrel
Magazine: None
Barrel: Double barrel; 27 ½'' or 29 ½'' modified and full choke
Finish: Blued; checkered walnut straight or pistol grip stock and forearm
Approximate wt.: 5 to 7 lbs.
Comments: Produced in three grades from the mid 1940's. Add $50.00 for single trigger.

Estimated Value:	Roma 3	Roma 4	Roma 6
Excellent:	$700.00	$1,000.00	$1,050.00
Very good:	$560.00	$ 800.00	$ 850.00

Bernardelli Roma

Shotguns

Bernardelli Italia

Gauge: 12
Action: Top lever break-open; exposed hammer; double barrel; double trigger
Magazine: None
Barrel: Double, chrome lined 30'' modified and full chokes
Finish: Blued; engraving on receiver; checkered walnut straight grip stock and forearm
Approximate wt.: 7 lbs.
Comments: Still in production
Estimated Value: Excellent: $750.00
Very good: $600.00

Bernardelli Brescia

Same as the Italia but available in 28'' barrels or 20 gauge in 26'' barrels, modified and improved cylinder bore.
Estimated Value: Excellent: $650.00
Very good: $525.00

Bernardelli Brescia

Bernardelli Italia

Bernardelli Holland

Bernardelli Holland Deluxe

Bernardelli St. Uberto

Gauge: 12, 16
Action: Box lock; top lever break-open; double barrel; double triggers; hammerless; automatic ejector.
Magazine: None
Barrel: Double barrrel; 26'' to 32'' any choke combination
Finish: Blued; checkered walnut straight or pistol grip stock & forearm
Approximate wt.: 7 lbs.
Comments: Produced from the mid 1940's to the early 1970's.
Estimated Value: Excellent: $425.00
Very good: $350.00

Bernardelli Holland

Gauge: 12
Action: Side lock; top lever break-open; hammerless; double trigger; double barrel; automatic ejectors;
Magazine: None
Barrel: Double barrel, 26'' to 32'' any choke combination
Finish: Blued; straight or pistol grip stock & forearm
Approximate wt.: 7 lbs.
Comments: Produced from the mid 1940's to the early 1970's.
Estimated Value: Excellent: $1,050.00
Very good: $ 890.00

Bernardelli Holland Deluxe

This is the same as the Holland with engraved hunting scene.
Estimated Value: Excellent: $1,375.00
Very good: $1,100.00

Bernardelli St. Uberto

18

Breda

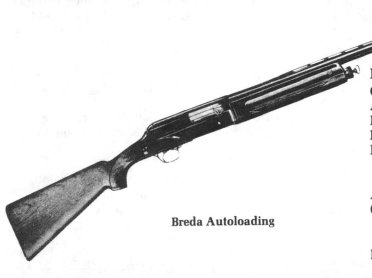

Breda Autoloading

Gauge: 12, 12 magnum
Action: Semi-automatic; hammerless
Magazine: 4-shot tubular
Barrel: 25½" or 27½"
Finish: Blued; checkered walnut, straight or pistol grip stock and forearm; available with ribbed barrel; engraving on grades 1, 2 and 3
Approximate wt.: 7¼ lbs.
Comments: Engraved models worth more depending on grade and quality of engraving. Add $110.00 for magnum.
Estimated Value: Excellent: $300.00
Very good: $240.00

Breda Autoloading

Browning

Browning BT-99 Trap

Browning BT-99 Trap

Gauge: 12
Action: Top lever, break-open; automatic ejector; hammerless; single shot
Magazine: None
Barrel: 32" or 34" full or modified choke
Finish: Blued; wide high ventilated rib; checkered walnut, pistol grip stock and forearm; recoil pad; some engraving
Approximate wt.: 8 lbs.
Comments: Made in Asia, and introduced in the early 1970's.
Estimated Value: New (retail): $599.95
Excellent: $450.00
Very good: $360.00

Browning B-SS

Gauge: 12, 20
Action: Top lever, break-open; double barrel; hammerless; automatic ejectors
Magazine: None
Barrel: Double barrel; in 12 gauge, 30" full & full or modified & full chokes; in 12 & 20 gauge, 28" modified & full chokes; 26" modified and full or improved cylinder & modified chokes
Finish: Blued; checkered walnut, pistol or straight grip stock & forearm
Approximate wt: 7-7½ lbs.
Comments: Made from the early 1970's to present in Asia. Add $60.00 for barrel selector. Add $400.00 for Grade II carving and engraving.
Estimated Value: New (retail): $464.95
Excellent: $350.00
Very good: $280.00

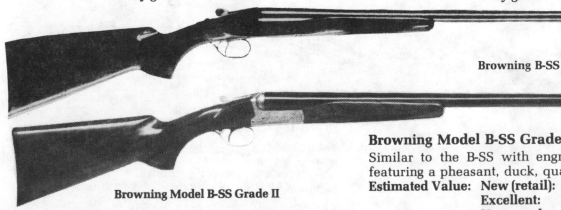

Browning B-SS

Browning Model B-SS Grade II

Browning Model B-SS Grade II

Similar to the B-SS with engraved satin grey frame featuring a pheasant, duck, quail, and dogs.
Estimated Value: New (retail): $825.00
Excellent: $625.00
Very good: $500.00

Shotguns

Browning Superposed Field Grade

Gauge: 12, 20 (added following W.W. II), 28 & 410 (added in early 1960's)

Action: Browning; non-selective trigger; twin single triggers; selective trigger

Magazine: None

Barrel: Over & under double barrel; 26½", 28", 30", 32" choice of chokes; ventilated or matted rib

Finish: Blued; hand checkered, European walnut pistol grip stock & forearm; fluted comb; recoil pad; engraving

Approximate wt: 6-8 lbs.

Comments: This gun first appeared in 1931 and has been made in a dozen different grades. More inlays & engraving is added on higher grades. Discontinued in 1973. Add $500.00 for Grade 1

Estimated Value: Excellent: $800.00 - $1,500.00
Very good: $650.00 - $1,200.00

Browning Superposed Broadway Trap Grade 1

Similar to Superposed Grade 1, but with wide ventilated rib. Introduced in 1960 in many grades.

Estimated Value: Excellent: $1,800.00 - 4,000.00
Very good: $1,400.00 - 3,200.00

Browning Super Light Grade I

Similar to Grade I Superposed except: lightweight; 26½" barrel; straight grip stock. Introduced in the late 1960's in many grades.

Estimated Value: Excellent: $2,000.00 - $4,500.00
Very good: $1,500.00 - $3,500.00

Browning Superposed Magnum Grade I

Same gun as the Superposed Grade I except chambered for 3" magnum 12 gauge and with recoil pad.

Estimated Value: Excellent: $1,600.00 - $3,600.00
Very good: $1,200.00 - $2,800.00

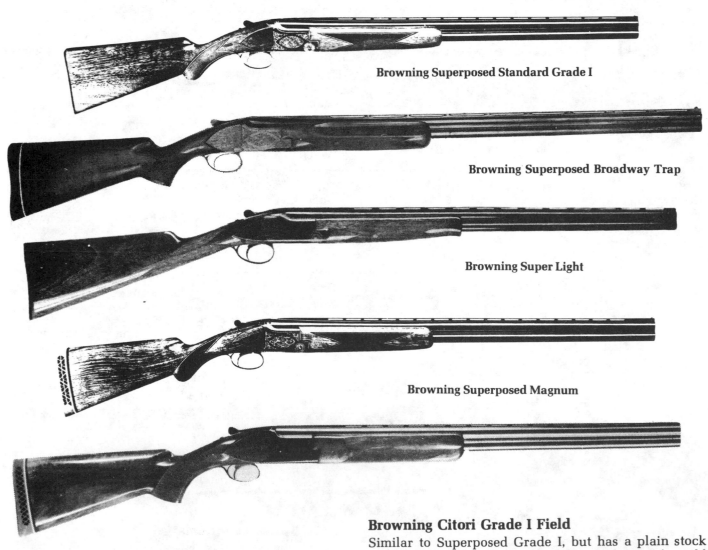

Browning Superposed Standard Grade I

Browning Superposed Broadway Trap

Browning Super Light

Browning Superposed Magnum

Browning Citori Grade I Field

Browning Citori Grade I Field

Similar to Superposed Grade I, but has a plain stock with recoil pad. Introduced in the early 1970's. Add $20.00 for 28 gauge or 410 bore.

Estimated Value: Excellent: $475.00
Very good: $380.00

Browning BPS

Gauge: 12, 12 magnum
Action: Slide action; concealed hammer; bottom ejection
Magazine: 4 shot; 3 shot in magnum
Barrel: 26" improved cylinder bore; 28" modified choke, 30" full choke; ventilated rib
Finish: Blued; checkered walnut pistol grip stock and forearm.
Approximate wt: 7 ½ lbs.
Comments: Produced since the late 1970's. Add $10.00 for Trap Model, $25.00 for Buck Special.
Estimated Value: New (retail): **$299.95**
  Excellent: **$225.00**
  Very good: **$180.00**

Browning B.A.A.C. No. 1 Regular

Gauge: 12
Action: Semi-automatic, hammerless
Magazine: 4 shot
Barrel: 28"
Finish: Blued; walnut straight stock and grooved forearm
Approximate wt.: 7 ¾ lbs.
Comments: This gun was sold in the U.S. for about 3 years from 1902.
Estimated Value: Excellent: **$250.00**
  Very good: **$200.00**

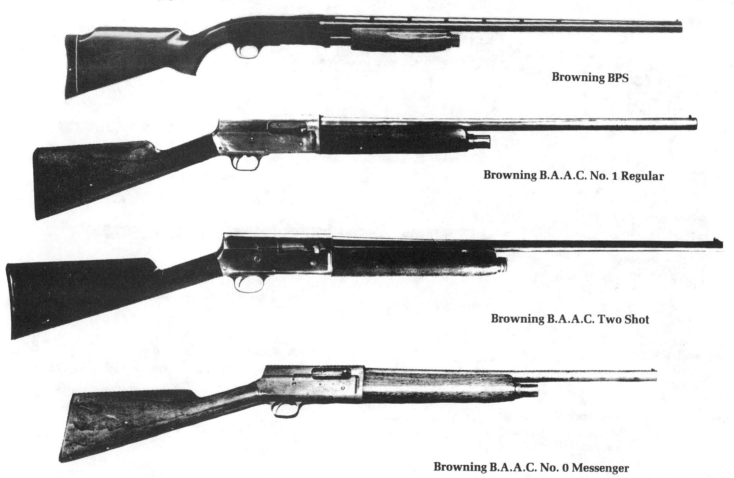

Browning BPS

Browning B.A.A.C. No. 1 Regular

Browning B.A.A.C. Two Shot

Browning B.A.A.C. No. 0 Messenger

Browning B.A.A.C. Two Shot

Similar to the No. 1 in 2 shot model.
Estimated Value: Excellent: **$200.00**
  Very good: **$160.00**

Browning B.A.A.C. No. 0 Messenger

A short, 20" barrel, version of the No. 1, made for bank guards, etc.
Estimated Value: Excellent: **$250.00**
  Very good: **$225.00**

Browning B.A.A.C. No. 2 Trap

Trap grade version of the No. 1 with some checkering.
Estimated Value: Excellent: **$275.00**
  Very good: **$225.00**

F.N. Browning Automatic

Similar to the B.A.A.C. No. 1, sold by F. N. only overseas. Some models carried swivels for sling. Produced until Browning's American sales began in 1931.
Estimated Value: Excellent: **$325.00**
  Very good: **$275.00**

Shotguns

Browning Automatic 5 Standard Grade

Gauge: 12, 16 (16 gauge discontinued in 1964)
Action: Semi-automatic; hammerless; side ejection; recoiling barrel
Magazine: 4 shot, bottom load; 3 shot model also available
Barrel: 26"-32" full choke, modified or cylinder bore; raised matted rib or ventilated rib
Finish: Blued; checkered walnut, pistol grip stock and forearm
Approximate wt.: 7-8 lbs.
Comments: Made from about 1931 to early 1970's.
Estimated Value: Excellent: $390.00
Very good: $320.00

Browning Automatic 5 Grades II, III, IV

Basically the same shotgun as the Standard Grade with engraving and improved quality on higher grades. Discontinued in the early 1940's. Add $25.00 for rib.

Estimated Value:	Gr. II	Gr. III	Gr. IV
Excellent:	$700.00	$850.00	$1000.00
Very good:	$550.00	$600.00	$800.00

Browning Automatic 5 Light 12

Basically the same as the Standard Grade except 12 gauge only and light weight. Made from about 1948 to present.

Estimated Value: New (retail): $479.95
Excellent: $360.00
Very good: $290.00

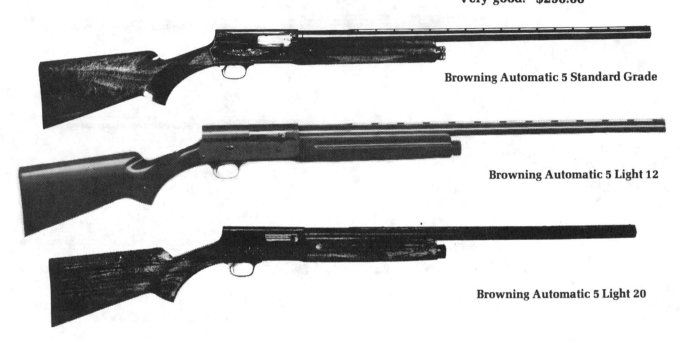

Browning Automatic 5 Standard Grade

Browning Automatic 5 Light 12

Browning Automatic 5 Light 20

Browning Automatic 5 Light 20

Basically the same as the Standard Grade except: 20 gauge only; a lightweight 26" or 28" barrel. Made from the late 1950's to present.

Estimated Value: New (retail): $479.95
Excellent: $360.00
Very good: $290.00

Browning Automatic 5 Skeet

Similar to the Light 12 and Light 20 with 26" or 28" skeet choke barrel.

Estimated Value: New (retail) $479.95
Excellent: $360.00
Very good: $290.00

Browning Automatic 5 Magnum 20

Browning Automatic 5 Magnum 20

Similar to the Standard Model except: 20 gauge magnum; 26" or 28" barrel. Made from the late 1960's to present.

Estimated Value: New (retail) $489.95
Excellent: $375.00
Very good: $300.00

Browning Automatic 5 Trap

Basically the same as the Standard Grade except 12 gauge only; trap stock; 30" full choke; ventilated rib.

Estimated Value: Excellent: $390.00
Very good: $320.00

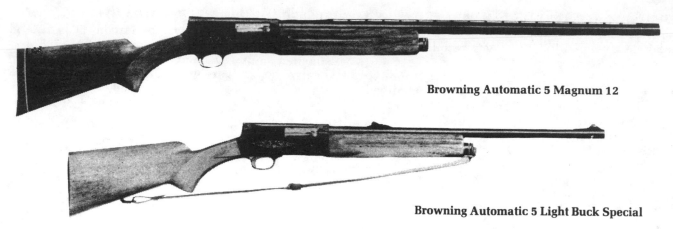

Browning Automatic 5 Magnum 12

Browning Automatic 5 Light Buck Special

Browning Automatic 5 Light Buck Special

Similar to the Standard Model, 12 or 20 gauge; special 24'' barrel choked & bored for rifle slug. Made from the early 1960's to present..
Estimated Value: New (retail):$507.95
                 Excellent: $390.00
                 Very good: $310.00

Browning Automatic 5 Sweet Sixteen

A lightweight 16 gauge version of the Standard Model, made from the late 1930's. Add $30.00 for ventilated rib.
Estimated Value: Excellent: $425.00
                 Very good: $350.00

Browning Automatic 5 Buck Special Magnum

Same as the Buck Special, for 3'' magnum shells, in 12 or 20 gauge.
Estimated Value: New (retail):$517.95
                 Excellent: $395.00
                 Very good: $315.00

Browning Automatic 5 Magnum 12

Similar to the Standard Model except 12 gauge magnum, equipped with recoil pad. Made from the late 1950's to present. Also equipped with a 32'' full choke barrel.
Estimated Value: New (retail):$489.95
                 Excellent: $370.00
                 Very good: $295.00

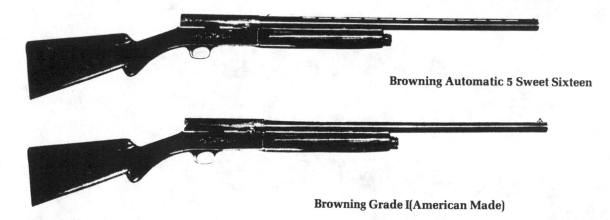

Browning Automatic 5 Sweet Sixteen

Browning Grade I(American Made)

Browning Grade I (American Made)

Similar to Browning Standard Grade. Made by Remington from 1940 until about 1948. World War II forced the closing of the F. N. plant.
Estimated Value: Excellent: $250.00
                 Very good $200.00

Browning Special (American Made)

Similar to Grade I with a matted or ventilated rib.
Estimated Value: Excellent: $280.00
                 Very good: $225.00

Browning Special Skeet (American Made)

Same as the Grade I with a Cutts Compensator.
Estimated Value: Excellent: $265.00
                 Very good: $220.00

Browning Utility (American Made)

Similar to Grade I with Poly Choke.
Estimated Value: Excellent: $260.00
                 Very good: $210.00

Shotguns

Browning Double Automatic Standard

Gauge: 12
Action: 2 shot, semi-automatic, short recoil, side ejection; hammerless
Magazine: 1 shot
Barrel: 30" or 28" full choke; 28" or 26" modified choke; 28" or 26" skeet; 26" cylinder bore or improved cylinder
Finish: Blued; checkered walnut, pistol grip stock & forearm
Approximate wt.: 7 ¾ lbs.
Comments: Made from the mid 1950's to the early 1960's. Add $25.00 for vent rib.
Estimated Value: Excellent: $300.00
Very good: $240.00

Browning Double Automatic Twelvette

Basically the same as the Standard with lightweight aluminum receiver. Made until the early 1970's.
Estimated Value: Excellent: $310.00
Very good: $245.00

Browning Double Automatic Twentyweight

A still lighter version of the Standard with 26 ½" barrel. Made until the early 1970's.
Estimated Value: Excellent: $325.00
Very good: $275.00

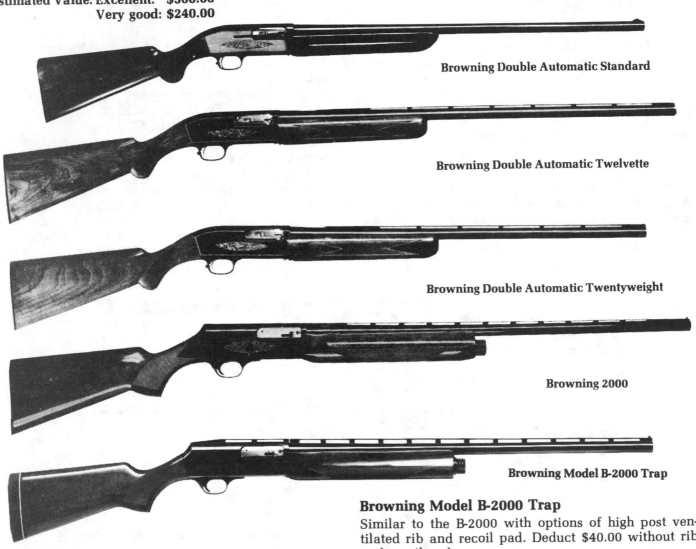

Browning Double Automatic Standard

Browning Double Automatic Twelvette

Browning Double Automatic Twentyweight

Browning 2000

Browning Model B-2000 Trap

Browning Model B-2000 Trap

Similar to the B-2000 with options of high post ventilated rib and recoil pad. Deduct $40.00 without rib and recoil pad.

Estimated Value:	New (retail):	$474.95
	Excellent:	$355.00
	Very good:	$285.00

Browning 2000 or B-2000

Similar to the Automatic 5 shotgun except gas operated. Introduced in the early 1970's in 12 and 20 gauge regular or magnum.

Estimated Value:	New (retail):	$439.95
	Excellent:	$330.00
	Very good:	$265.00

Browning 2000 Buck Special

Similar to the 2000 except: 24" barrel; adjustable rifle sights; swivels.

Estimated Value:	New (retail):	$457.95
	Excellent:	$345.00
	Very good:	$275.00

Charles Daly

Charles Daly Hammerless Double

Gauge: 10, 12, 16, 20, 28, 410
Action: Box lock; top lever, break-open; hammerless; double barrel; automatic ejectors (except Superior)
Magazine: None
Barrel: Double barrel; 26", 28", 30", 32", choice of choke combinations
Finish: Blued; checkered walnut, pistol grip stock & short tapered forearm; engraving
Approximate wt.: 4-8 lbs.
Comments: Manufactured in differing grades, alike except for quality of finish and amount of engraving. Manufactured from about 1920 to 1935.

Estimated Value:

	Excellent	Very good
Diamond	$2000.00	$1600.00
Empire	$1200.00	$ 900.00
Superior	$ 900.00	$ 650.00

Charles Daly Commander 100

Gauge: 12, 16, 20, 28, 410
Action: Box lock; top lever, break-open; hammerless; over & under double barrel; automatic ejectors
Magazine: None
Barrel: Over & under double barrel; 26", 28", 30" improved cylinder & modified or modified & full, chokes
Finish: Blued; checkered walnut, straight or pistol grip stock & forearm; engraved
Approximate wt.: 5-7 ½ lbs.
Comments: Manufactured from the mid 1930's to about 1939.
Estimated Value: Excellent: $600.00
Very good: $500.00

Charles Daly Commander 200

This is a fancier version of the Commander 100 with select wood, more engraving and a higher quality finish.
Estimated Value: Excellent: $650.00
Very good: $550.00

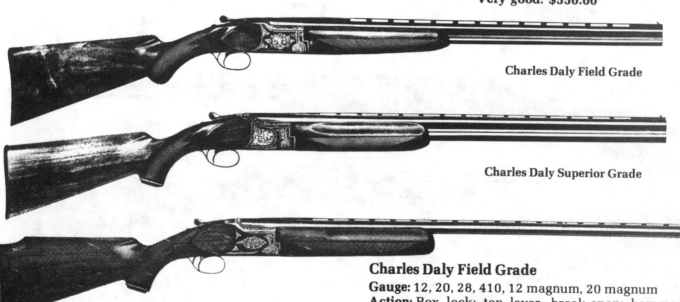

Charles Daly Field Grade

Charles Daly Superior Grade

Charles Daly Single Barrel Trap

Charles Daly Single Barrel Trap

Gauge: 12
Action: Box lock; top lever, break-open; hammerless; automatic ejector
Magazine: None
Barrel: 32" or 34" full choke; ventilated rib
Finish: Blued; checkered walnut Monte Carlo pistol grip stock and beavertail forearm; recoil pad.
Approximate wt: 8 lbs.
Comments: Made from the late 1960's to mid 1970's. This model should not be confused with the Single Barrel Trap Model made in the 1930's that is worth several times more.
Estimated Value: Excellent: $275.00
Very good: $200.00

Charles Daly Field Grade

Gauge: 12, 20, 28, 410, 12 magnum, 20 magnum
Action: Box lock; top lever, break-open; hammerless; over & under double barrel
Magazine: None
Barrel: Over & under double barrel; 26", 28", 30", standard choke combinations; ventilated rib
Finish: Blued; engraved; checkered walnut, pistol grip stock & forearm; 12 gauge magnum has recoil pad
Approximate wt.: 6-8 lbs.
Comments: Manufactured since the early 1960's.
Estimated Value: Excellent: $450.00
Very good: $360.00

Charles Daly Superior Grade

Similar to the Field Grade but not chambered for magnum.
Estimated Value: Excellent: $500.00
Very good: $400.00

Shotguns

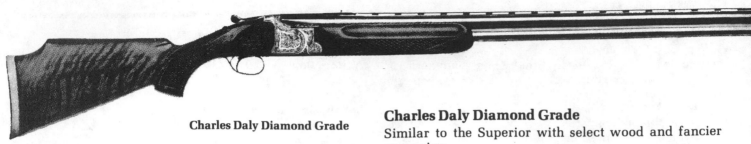

Charles Daly Diamond Grade

Charles Daly Venture Grade

Gauge: 12, 20
Action: Box lock; top lever, break-open; hammerless; over & under double barrel; automatic ejectors
Magazine: None
Barrel: Over & under double barrel; 26", 28", 30", various chokes; ventilated rib
Finish: Blued; checkered walnut, pistol grip stock & forearm
Approximate wt.: 7-8 lbs.
Comments: Manufactured since the early 1970's. Add $25.00 for skeet model, $35.00 for Monte Carlo Trap model.
Estimated Value: Excellent: $420.00
             Very good: $340.00

Charles Daly Diamond Grade

Similar to the Superior with select wood and fancier engraving.
Estimated Value: Excellent: $575.00
             Very good: $450.00

Charles Daly Auto Trap

Gauge: 12
Action: Recoil operated, semi-automatic
Magazine: 5 shot tubular
Barrel: 26" improved cylinder, 28" modified or full, 30" full, chokes; ventilated rib
Finish: Blued; checkered walnut, pistol grip stock & forearm
Approximate wt.: 7 ½ lbs.
Comments: Made in the mid 1970's.
Estimated Value: Excellent: $250.00
             Very good: $200.00

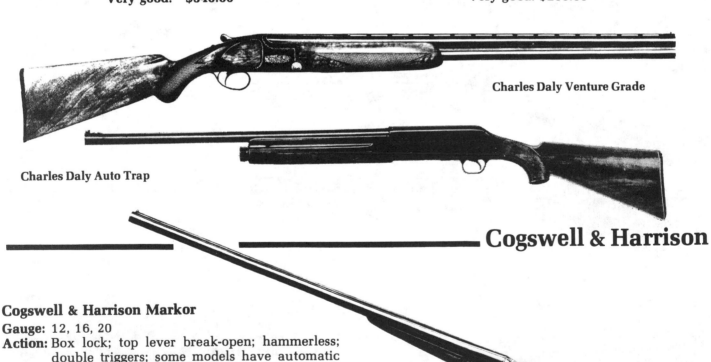

Charles Daly Venture Grade

Charles Daly Auto Trap

Cogswell & Harrison

Cogswell & Harrison Markor

Gauge: 12, 16, 20
Action: Box lock; top lever break-open; hammerless; double triggers; some models have automatic ejectors; double barrel
Magazine: None
Barrel: Double; 27 ½" or 30", any choke combination
Finish: Blued; checkered walnut, straight grip stock and forearm
Approximate wt: 7 ½ lbs.
Comments: Produced in the 1920's. Add $50.00 for automatic ejectors.
Estimated Value: Excellent: $775.00
             Very good: $625.00

Cogswell & Harrison Markor

Colt

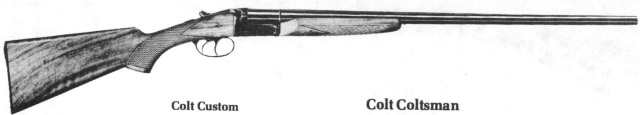

Colt Custom

Colt Custom
Gauge: 12, 16
Action: Box lock, top lever break-open; hammerless; double barrel; double trigger; automatic ejectors
Magazine: None
Barrel: Double barrel; 26" improved and modified, 28" modified and full or 30" full, chokes
Finish: Blued; checkered walnut pistol grip stock and tapered forearm
Approximate wt.: 7 to 8 lbs.
Comments: Produced in the early 1960's.
Estimated Value: Excellent: $270.00
Very good: $215.00

Colt Coltsman
Gauge: 12, 16, 20
Action: Side action
Magazine: 4-shot
Barrel: 26" improved, 28" modified, 30" full, chokes
Finish: Blued; plain walnut pistol grip stock and slide handle.
Approximate wt.: 6 ½ to 7 lbs.
Comments: Produced from the early to mid 1960's in takedown models.
Estimated Value: Excellent: $120.00
Very good: $ 95.00

Colt Coltsman Custom
A fancier version of the Coltsman with checkering and a ventilated rib.
Estimated Value: Excellent: $175.00
Very good: $140.00

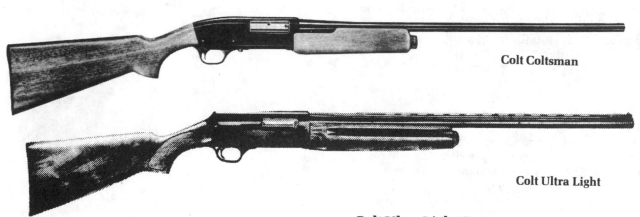

Colt Coltsman

Colt Ultra Light

Colt Ultra Light
Gauge: 12, 20
Action: Semi-automatic
Magazine: 4-shot
Barrel: Chrome lined, 26" improved or modified, 28" modified or full, 30", 32" full, chokes; rib available
Finish: Blued; checkered walnut pistol grip stock and forearm; alloy receiver
Approximate wt.: 6 ½ lbs.
Comments: A takedown shotgun produced during the mid 1960's. Add $15.00 for solid rib, $25.00 for ventilated rib.
Estimated Value: Excellent: $200.00
Very good: $160.00

Colt Ultra Light Custom
This is the same as the Ultra Light Auto with select wood, engraving and ventilated rib.
Estimated Value: Excellent: $260.00
Very good: $210.00

Colt Magnum Auto
Same as the Ultra Light Auto in magnum gauges and heavier. Add $15.00 for solid rib or $25.00 for ventilated rib.
Estimated Value: Excellent: $220.00
Very good: $180.00

Colt Magnum Auto Custom
Same as Magnum Auto with select wood, engraving and ventilated rib.
Estimated Value: Excellent: $275.00
Very good: $225.00

Darne

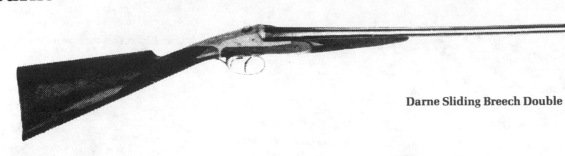

Darne Sliding Breech Double

Darne Sliding Breech Double

Gauge: 12, 16, 20, 28
Action: Sliding breech; selective ejectors; double barrel; double trigger
Magazine: None
Barrel: Double barrel; 25½", 27½" modified and improved cylinder; raised rib
Finish: Blued; checkered walnut straight or pistol grip stock and forearm; case hardened receiver
Approximate wt: 5¾ to 6¼ lbs.
Comments: A French shotgun, still in production.
Estimated Value: New (retail): $900.00 Approx.
Excellent: $675.00
Very good: $550.00

Darne Deluxe

Same as the Sliding Breech Double with engraving and 28" modified and full choke barrels.
Estimated Value: New (retail): $1,050.00 Approx.
Excellent: $ 780.00
Very good: $ 625.00

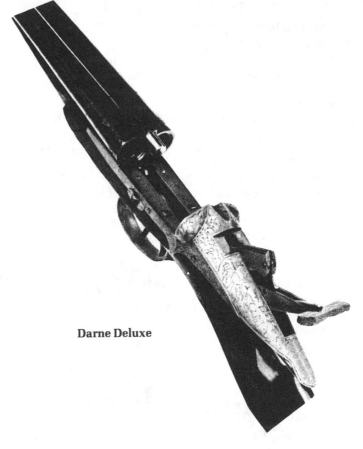

Darne Deluxe

Darne Supreme

Same shotgun as the Darne Deluxe except in 20 or 28 gauge, 25½" barrels, elaborate engraving and swivels.
Estimated Value: Excellent: $900.00
Very good: $720.00

Davidson

Davidson Model 73 Stagecoach

Gauge: 12, 20 magnum
Action: Box lock; top lever break-open; exposed hammers; double barrel.
Magazine: None
Barrel: Double barrel; 20" improved cylinder and modified or modified and full, chokes; matted rib.
Finish: Blued; checkered walnut pistol grip stock and forearm; sights; engraved receiver
Approximate wt.: 7 lbs.
Comments: Produced from early 1970's to late 1970's.
Estimated Value: Excellent: $175.00
Very good: $150.00

Davidson Model 69 SL

Gauge: 12, 20
Action: Side lock; double barrel
Magazine: None
Barrel: Double barrel; 26"-30"; variety of chokes
Finish: Blued and nickel; checkered walnut pistol grip stock and forearm; gold trigger; bead sights; engraved
Approximate wt.: 6 to 7 lbs.
Comments: Produced from early 1960's to late 1970's.
Estimated Value: Excellent: $180.00
Very good: $155.00

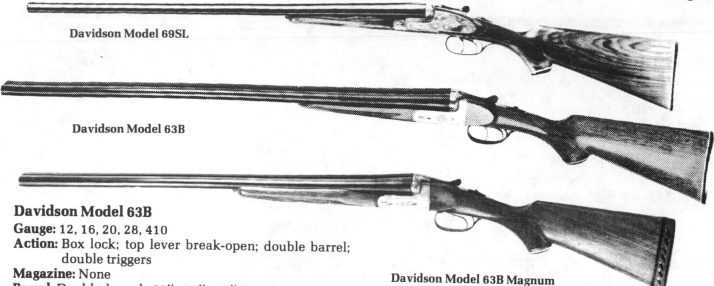

Davidson Model 69SL

Davidson Model 63B

Davidson Model 63B Magnum

Davidson Model 63B

Gauge: 12, 16, 20, 28, 410
Action: Box lock; top lever break-open; double barrel; double triggers
Magazine: None
Barrel: Double barrel; 26", 28", 25" in 410; 30" in 12 gauge; improved cylinder and modified, modified and full, full and full, chokes
Finish: Blued and nickel; checkered walnut pistol grip stock and forearm; bead sights; some engraving
Approximate wt.: 6 to 7 lbs.
Comments: Produced in Spain and sold in the United States from early 1960's to present.
Estimated Value: New (retail): $225.00 Approx.
Excellent: $170.00
Very good: $135.00

Davidson Model 63B Magnum

Same as Model 63B in 10, 12 or 20 gauge magnum. Available with 32" barrel in 10 gauge.
Estimated Value: New (retail): $275.00 Approx.
Excellent: $210.00
Very good: $170.00

Fox

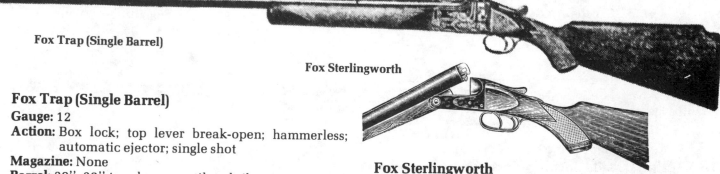

Fox Trap (Single Barrel)

Fox Sterlingworth

Fox Trap (Single Barrel)

Gauge: 12
Action: Box lock; top lever break-open; hammerless; automatic ejector; single shot
Magazine: None
Barrel: 30", 32" trap bore; ventilated rib.
Finish: Blued; checkered walnut, half or full pistol grip stock & large forearm; some with recoil pad; decorated receiver; after 1931 Monte Carlo Stock. Grades differ in quality of craftsmanship and decoration. ME Grade was made to order with inlaid gold and finest walnut wood;
Approximate wt.: 7-8 lbs.
Comments: Produced until the early 1940's. Prices for grades made before 1932 are about 20% less.
Estimated Value:

Grade	Excellent	Very Good
JE	$1,440.00	$1,200.00
KE	$1,675.00	$1,400.00
LE	$2,100.00	$1,800.00
ME	$4,550.00	$4,000.00

Fox Sterlingworth

Gauge: 12, 16, 20
Action: Box lock; top lever break-open; hammerless; double barrel; double trigger or selective single trigger; some with automatic ejectors
Magazine: None
Barrel: Double barrel; 26"-30"; full & full choke; modified & full choke; cylinder & modified choke
Finish: Blued; checkered walnut, pistol grip stock & forearm
Approximate wt.: 5 ¾ -8 lbs.
Comments: Produced until the early 1940's. Add $50.00 for selective single trigger, $75.00 for automatic ejectors.
Estimated Value: Excellent: $390.00
Very good: $325.00

Shotguns

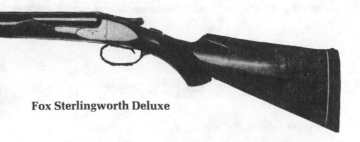

Fox Sterlingworth Deluxe

This is a fancy model Sterlingworth with: ivory bead; recoil pad; 32" barrels; selective single trigger. Add $75.00 for automatic ejectors.
Estimated Value: Excellent: $420.00
Very good: $360.00

Fox Sterlingworth Deluxe

Fox Sterlingworth Skeet

Basically the same as the Sterlingworth with skeet bore; 26" or 28" barrels; straight grip stock. Add $75.00 for automatic ejectors
Estimated Value: Excellent: $425.00
Very good: $365.00

Fox Skeeter

Similar to Sterlingworth with: 28" skeet bored barrels; ventilated rib; invory bead; recoil pad; 12 or 20 gauge; automatic ejectors.
Estimated Value: Excellent: $550.00
Very good: $500.00

Fox Super Fox

Fox Hammerless Double

Gauge: 12
Action: Box lock; top lever break-open; hammerless; double barrel; double trigger; automatic ejectors.
Magazine: None
Barrel: Double barrel; 30" or 32" full choke
Finish: Blued; checkered walnut, pistol grip stock and forearm
Approximate wt.: 7¾-9¾ lbs.
Comments: This is a long range gun produced from the mid 1920's to early 1940's.
Estimated Value: Excellent: $475.00
Very good: $410.00

Fox Hammerless Doubles

These are very similar to the Sterlingworth models, in varying degrees of increased quality. All have automatic ejectors except grade A. Add $50.00 for selective single trigger; $125.00 for ventilated rib.

Estimated Value:	Grade	Excellent	Very Good
	A	$ 475.00	$ 425.00
	AE	$ 560.00	$ 500.00
	BE	$ 720.00	$ 650.00
	CE	$ 960.00	$ 875.00
	DE	$1,450.00	$1,225.00
	FE	$3,000.00	$2,500.00
	XE	$1,575.00	$1,425.00

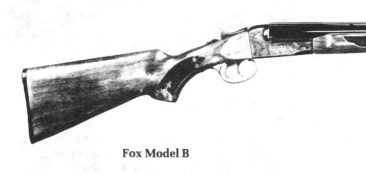

Fox Model B

Fox Model B Lightweight

Same as the Model B with 24" cylinder bore and modified choke barrels in 12 and 20 gauge.
Estimated Value: Excellent: $250.00
Very good: $200.00

Fox Model B, BE

Gauge: 12, 16, 20, 410
Action: Box lock; top lever break-open; hammerless; double barrel; double triggers; plain extractor
Magazine: None
Barrel: Double barrel; 26"-30" full & full choke; modified & full choke; cylinder & modified choke; ventilated rib
Finish: Blued; checkered walnut, pistol grip stock and forearm; case hardened receiver on current model
Approximate wt: 7½ lbs.
Comments: Made from the early 1940's to present. Model BE has automatic ejectors, add $40.00-$45.00.
Estimated Value: New (retail): $273.45
Excellent: $205.00
Very good: $175.00

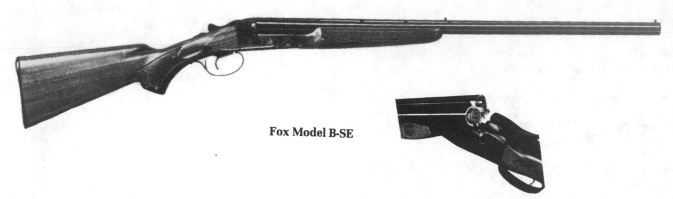

Fox Model B-SE

Fox Model B-SE

Basically the same as the Model B with automatic ejectors and a single trigger. In production from 1968 to the present.
Estimated Value: New (retail): $316.50
                  Excellent: $245.00
                  Very good: $190.00

Fox Model B-ST

This is the same as Model B with gold plated non-selective single trigger. Made from the mid 1950's to mid 1960's.
Estimated Value: Excellent: $250.00
                       Very good: $200.00

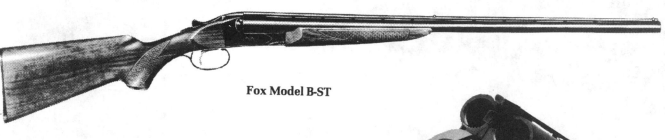

Fox Model B-ST

Fox Model B-DL & B-DE

Similar to the B-ST with chrome frame and beavertail forearm. Made from the early 1960's to early 1970's.
Estimated Value: Excellent: $270.00
                       Very good: $220.00

Fox Model B-DL

Franchi

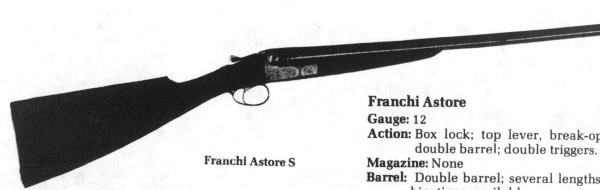

Franchi Astore S

Franchi Astore S

Same as the Astore with higher quality wood and engraving.
Estimated Value: Excellent: $400.00
                       Very good: $320.00

Franchi Astore

Gauge: 12
Action: Box lock; top lever, break-open; hammerless; double barrel; double triggers.
Magazine: None
Barrel: Double barrel; several lengths and choke combinations available
Finish: Blued; checkered walnut, straight grip stock and short tapered forearm
Approximate wt.: 7 lbs.
Comments: Made from the mid 1950's to late 1960's
Estimated Value: Excellent: $375.00
                       Very good: $300.00

Shotguns

Franchi Airon

Gauge: 12
Action: Box lock; top lever, break-open; hammerless; double barrel; automatic ejectors.
Magazine: None
Barrel: Double barrel; several lengths & combinations available.
Finish: Blued; checkered walnut, straight grip stock & short tapered forearm; engraved
Approximate wt: 7 lbs.
Comments: Manufactured from the mid 1950's to late 1960's.
Estimated Value: Excellent: $390.00
Very good: $310.00

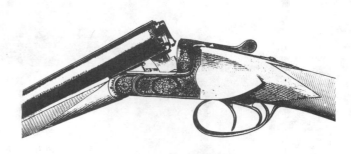

Franchi Airon

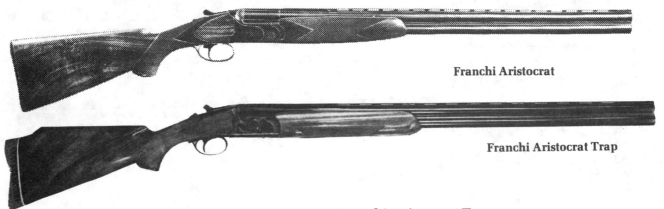

Franchi Aristocrat

Franchi Aristocrat Trap

Franchi Aristocrat

Gauge: 12
Action: Box lock; top lever, break-open; hammerless; over and under double barrel; automatic ejectors
Magazine: None
Barrel: Over and under double barrel; 24" cylinder bore and improved cylinder; 26" improved cylinder and modified; 28", 30" modified and full, chokes; ventilated rib
Finish: Blued; engraved; checkered walnut, pistol grip stock and forearm
Approximate wt.: 7 lbs.
Comments: Made from the early to late 1960's.
Estimated Value: Excellent: $325.00
Very good: $270.00

Franchi Aristocrat Trap

Similar to the Aristocrat with Monte Carlo stock; chrome lined barrels; case hardened receiver; 30" barrels only
Estimated Value: Excellent: $375.00
Very good: $300.00

Franchi Aristocrat Skeet

Same as the Aristocrat Trap with 26" skeet barrels.
Estimated Value: Excellent: $375.00
Very good: $300.00

Franchi Aristocrat Silver King

Similar to the Aristocrat with higher quality finish; select wood; engraving.
Estimated Value: Excellent: $500.00
Very good: $400.00

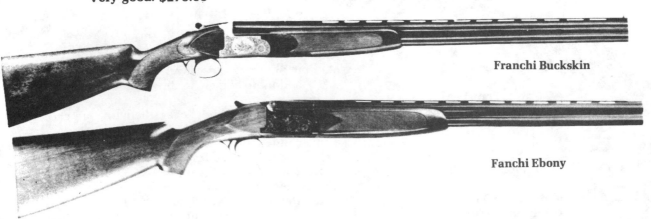

Franchi Buckskin

Fanchi Ebony

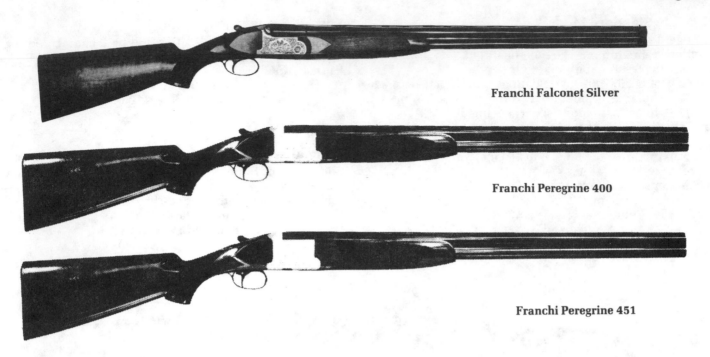

Franchi Falconet Silver

Franchi Peregrine 400

Franchi Peregrine 451

Franchi Falconet Buckskin & Ebony

Gauge: 12, 20
Action: Box lock; top lever, break-open; hammerless; over and under double barrel.
Magazine: None
Barrel: Over and under double barrel; 24''-30'' barrels in several choke combinations; ventilated rib; chrome lined
Finish: Blued; colored frame with engraving; epoxy finished checkered walnut, pistol grip stock and forearm
Approximate wt.: 6-7 lbs.
Comments: Made from about 1970 to late 1970's. Buckskin and Ebony differ only in color of receiver and engraving.
Estimated Value: Excellent: $475.00
Very good: $360.00

Franchi Falconet Silver

Same as the Buckskin and Ebony except: 12 gauge only; pickled silver receiver.
Estimated Value: Excellent: $550.00
Very good: $440.00

Franchi Peregrine 400

Gauge: 12
Action: Box lock; top lever, break-open; hammerless; over and under double barrel
Magazine: None
Barrel: Over and Under double barrel; 26½'', 28'' in various chokes; chrome lined; ventilated rib
Finish: Blued; checkered walnut, pistol grip stock and forearm.
Approximate wt.: 7 lbs.
Comments: Made from the mid to late 1970's.
Estimated Value: Excellent: $500.00
Very good: $400.00

Franchi Peregrine 451

Similar to the 400 except: alloy receiver; light weight.
Estimated Value: Excellent: $420.00
Very good: $340.00

Franchi Standard Model

Shotguns

Franchi Standard Model

Gauge: 12, 20, 28
Action: Semi-automatic; recoil operated
Magazine: 5 shot tubular
Barrel: 24", 26" improved cylinder, modified or skeet chokes; 28" modified or full chokes; ventilated rib on some models; chrome lined
Finish: Blued; checkered walnut, pistol grip stock with fluted forearm
Approximate wt.: 5-6¼ lbs. One of the lightest autoloaders available.
Comments: Manufactured in Italy from about 1950 to present.
Estimated Value: New (retail): $334.95
     Excellent: $260.00
     Very good: $200.00

Franchi Standard Magnum

Similar to the Standard with recoil pad; chambered for magnum shells; 12 or 20 ga.
Estimated Value: New (retail): $349.95
     Excellent: $275.00
     Very good: $210.00

Franchi Slug Gun

Similar to the Standard Model with a 22" cylinder bore barrel; sights; swivels; alloy receiver. Made from the mid 1950's to present; 12 or 20 ga.
Estimated Value: New (retail): $349.95
     Excellent: $275.00
     Very good: $210.00

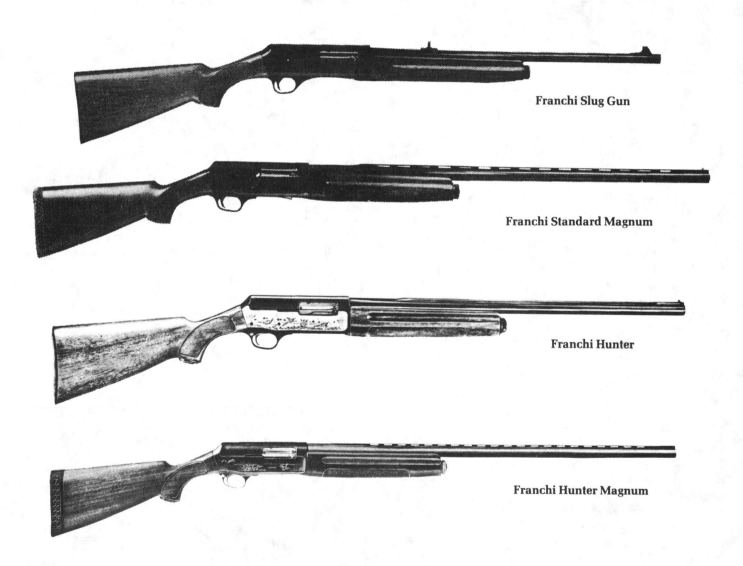

Franchi Slug Gun

Franchi Standard Magnum

Franchi Hunter

Franchi Hunter Magnum

Franchi Hunter

Similar to the Standard Model; 12 or 20 gauge; higher quality wood; engraving; ventilated rib.
Estimated Value: New (retail): $359.95
     Excellent: $280.00
     Very good: $215.00

Franchi Hunter Magnum

Same as the Hunter with recoil pad and chambered for magnum shells.
Estimated Value: Excellent: $300.00
     Very good: $240.00

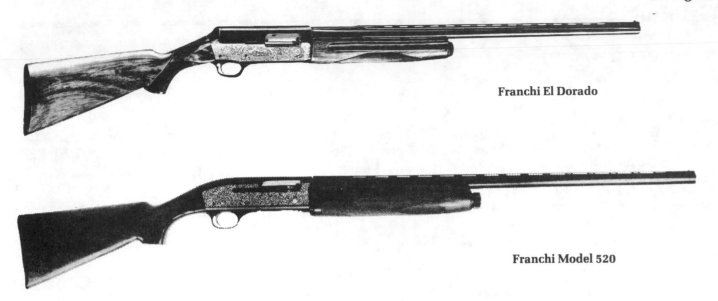

Franchi El Dorado

Franchi Model 520

Franchi El Dorado
Similar to the Standard Model with heavy engraving; select wood; gold trigger; ventilated rib.
Estimated Value: Excellent: $400.00
Very good: $325.00

Franchi Model 500
Similar to the Standard except: gas operated; 12 gauge only; made for fast takedown. Currently manufactured.
Estimated Value: Excellent: $300.00
Very good: $250.00

Franchi Model 520
Similar to the Model 500 with deluxe features.
Estimated Value: Excellent: $350.00
Very good: $280.00

Franchi Model 530 Trap
Similar to the Model 520 with Monte Carlo stock; high ventilated rib; 3 interchangeable choke tubes; currently manufactured.
Estimated Value: New (retail): $695.00
Excellent: $525.00
Very good: $420.00

Greener

Greener Empire

Greener Empire
Gauge: 12 or 12 magnum
Action: Box lock; top lever break-open; hammerless; double barrel
Magazine: None
Barrel: Double barrel; 28″, 30″, 32″, any choke
Finish: Blued; checkered walnut straight or semi-pistol grip stock and forearm
Approximate wt.: 7 ½ lbs.
Comments: Produced from before 1900 until the mid 1960's
Estimated Value: Excellent: $870.00
Very good: $695.00

Greener Empire Deluxe
Same as the Empire Model only fancier.
Estimated Value: Excellent: $950.00
Very good: $765.00

Greener General Purpose
Gauge: 12
Action: Martini action; single shot
Magazine: None
Barrel: 26″, 30″, 32″ modified or full choke
Finish: Blued; checkered walnut straight grip and stock and forearm
Approximate wt.: 6 to 7 lbs.
Comments: Manufactured from the early 1900's to the early 1960's
Estimated Value: Excellent: $200.00
Very good: $160.00

Griefelt

Griefelt Model 22
Gauge: 12, 16
Action: Box lock; top lever break-open; hammerless; double barrel; double trigger
Magazine: None
Barrel: Double barrel; 28" or 30" modified or full choke
Finish: Blued; checkered walnut straight or pistol grip stock and forearm; cheekpiece
Approximate wt.: 7 lbs.
Comments: Produced from late 1940's
Estimated Value: Excellent: $960.00
Very good: $770.00

Griefelt Model 22E
Same as Model 22 with automatic ejectors.
Estimated Value: Excellent: $980.00
Very good: $790.00

Griefelt Model 103
Gauge: 12, 16
Action: Box lock, top lever break-open; hammerless; double barrel; double triggers
Magazine: None
Barrel: Double barrel, 28" or 30" modified and full
Finish: Blued, checkered; walnut straight or pistol grip stock and forearm; cheekpiece
Approximate wt.: 7 lbs
Comments: Produced from late 1940's
Estimated Value: Excellent: $900.00
Very good: $720.00

Griefelt Model 103E
Same as Model 103 with automatic ejectors.
Estimated Value: Excellent: $925.00
Very good: $750.00

Griefelt Model 22

Harrington & Richardson

Harrington & Richardson No. 3
Gauge: 12, 16, 20, 410
Action: Box lock; top lever break-open; hammerless; single shot; automatic ejector
Magazine: None
Barrel: 26"-32" full choke
Finish: Blued; walnut, semi-pistol grip stock and tapered forearm
Approximate wt.: 5½-6½ lbs
Comments: Made from about 1908 to World War II.
Estimated Value: Excellent: $55.00
Very good: $45.00

Harrington & Richardson No. 5
Gauge: 20, 28, 410
Action: Box lock; top lever, break-open; exposed hammer; single shot; automatic ejector
Magazine: None
Barrel: 26", 28" full choke
Finish: Blued; walnut, semi-pistol grip stock and tapered forearm
Approximate wt.: 4½ lbs.
Comments: Made from about 1908 to World War II
Estimated Value: Excellent: $55.00
Very good: $45.00

Harrington & Richardson No. 3

Harrington & Richardson No. 5

Harrington & Richardson No. 6

Harrington & Richardson No. 6
Similar to the No. 5 in 10, 12, 16 and 20 gauge; heavier design and barrel lengths of 28"-36". Weighs 5-8 lbs.
Estimated Value: Excellent: $60.00
Very good: $50.00

Harrington & Richardson No. 8

Harrington & Richardson No. 7

Harrington & Richardson No. 8
Similar to the No. 6 with different style forearm and in 12, 16, 20, 24, 28 or 410 gauge.
Estimated Value: Excellent: $60.00
Very good: $50.00

Harrington & Richardson No. 7 or No. 9
Similar to the No. 8 with smaller forearm and more rounded pistol grip. Not available in 24 gauge.
Estimated Value: Excellent: $55.00
Very good: $45.00

Harrington & Richardson Topper No. 48

Harrington & Richardson Topper No. 48
Similar to the No. 8. Made from the mid 1940's to the late 1950's.
Estimated Value: Excellent: $60.00
Very good: $50.00

Harrington & Richardson Topper No. 488 Deluxe
Similar to the No. 48 with chrome frame; recoil pad; black lacquered stock and forearm.
Estimated Value: Excellent: $55.00
Very good: $45.00

Harrington & Richardson Folding Model

Harrington & Richardson Topper No. 148
Gauge: 12, 16, 20, 410
Action: Box lock; side lever, break-open; exposed hammer; single shot automatic ejector
Magazine: None
Barrel: 28''-36'' full choke
Finish: Blued; walnut, semi-pistol grip stock and forearm; recoil pad
Approximate wt.: 5-6 ½ lbs.
Comments: Manufactured from the late 1950's to early 1960's.
Estimated Value: Excellent: $50.00
Very good: $40.00

Harrington & Richardson Topper Jr. 480
Youth version of the 48; 410 gauge; 26'' barrel; smaller stock
Estimated Value: Excellent: $50.00
Very good: $40.00

Harrington & Richardson Topper Jr. 580
Similar to the Topper Jr. 480 with color finish similar to 188 Deluxe.
Estimated Value: Excellent: $45.00
Very good: $35.00

Harrington & Richardson Folding Model
Gauge: 28, 410 with light frame; 12, 16, 20, 28, 410 with heavy frame
Action: Box lock; top lever, break-open; exposed hammer; single shot
Magazine: None
Barrel: 22'' in light frame; 26'' in heavy frame, full choke
Finish: Blued; walnut, semi-pistol grip stock and tapered forearm; sight
Approximate wt.: 5 ½-6 ¾ lbs.
Comments: This shotgun has a hinged frame. Barrel folds against stock for storage. Made from about 1910 until World War II.
Estimated Value: Excellent: $75.00
Very good: $60.00

Harrington & Richardson Topper 188 Deluxe
Similar to the No. 148 with black, red, blue, green, pink, yellow or purple lacquered finish; chrome plated frame; 410 gauge only
Estimated Value: Excellent: $45.00
Very good: $35.00

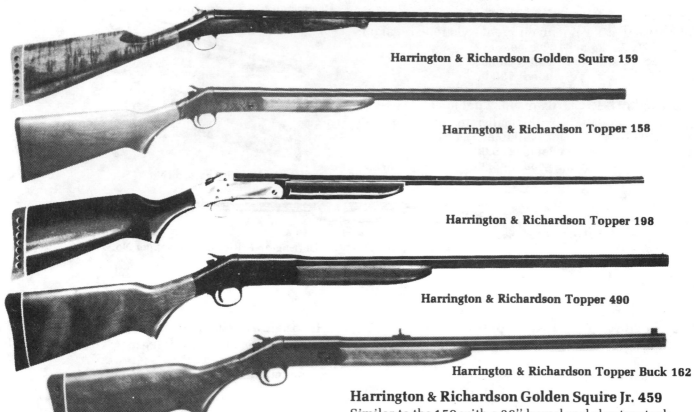

Harrington & Richardson Golden Squire 159

Harrington & Richardson Topper 158

Harrington & Richardson Topper 198

Harrington & Richardson Topper 490

Harrington & Richardson Topper Buck 162

Harrington & Richardson Golden Squire 159

Gauge: 12, 20
Action: Box lock; side lever, break open; exposed hammer; automatic ejector; single shot
Magazine: None
Barrel: 28", 30" full choke
Finish: Blued; wood straight grip stock and lipped forearm; recoil pad
Approximate wt.: 6½ lbs
Comments: Made in the mid 1960's
Estimated Value: Excellent: $60.00
Very good: $50.00

Harrington & Richardson Topper 158 or 058

Gauge: 12, 16, 20, 410
Action: Box lock; side lever, break-open; exposed hammer; single shot
Magazine: None
Barrel: 28"-36" variety of chokes
Finish: Blued; plain wood, straight or semi-pistol grip stock & tapered forearm; recoil pad on early models
Approximate wt.: 5½-6½ lb.
Comments: Made from the early 1960's to mid 1970's as Model 158, mid 1970's to present as 058; currently available in 28 gauge also. Also available is 058 combination with 22" rifle barrel in 22 Hornet and 30-30 Win. (Add $30.00.)
Estimated Value: New (retail): $79.50
Excellent: $60.00
Very good: $50.00

Harrington & Richardson Golden Squire Jr. 459

Similar to the 159 with a 26" barrel and shorter stock.
Estimated Value: Excellent: $50.00
Very good: $40.00

Harrington & Richardson Topper 198 or 098

Similar to the model 158 or 058 except: 20 or 410 gauge only; black lacquered stock and forearm; nickel plated frame.
Estimated Value: New (retail): $79.50
Excellent: $60.00
Very good: $50.00

Harrington & Richardson Topper 490 and 490 Greenwing

A youth version of the Model 158, 058 with 26" barrel; shorter stock; 20, 410, & 28 gauge only. Greenwing has high quality finish. (Add $10.00.)
Estimated Value: New (retail): $79.50
Excellent: $60.00
Very good: $50.00

Harrington & Richardson Topper 590

Similar to the 490 with chrome plated frame and color lacquered stock and forearm. Production ended in the mid 1960's.
Estimated Value: Excellent: $55.00
Very good: $45.00

Harrington & Richardson Topper Buck 162

Similar to the model 158, 058 with a 24" cylinder bore barrel for rifled slugs; equipped with sights
Estimated Value: New (retail): $89.50
Excellent: $65.00
Very good: $50.00

Harrington & Richardson 404

Harrington & Richardson Model 176

Harrington & Richardson Model 176

Gauge: 10, 12, 16, 20 magnum
Action: Box lock; top push lever, break-open; exposed hammer; single shot
Magazine: None
Barrel: 32" or 36" full choke in 10 or 12 gauge; 32" full choke in 16 or 20 gauge
Finish: Blued; case hardened frame; plain hardwood Monte Carlo pistol grip stock and forearm; recoil pad
Approximate wt: 8-10 lbs.
Comments: Introduced in the late 1970's. Add $5.00 for 36" barrel.
Estimated Value: New (retail): $94.50
Excellent: $70.00
Very good: $55.00

Harrington & Richardson Model 404

Gauge: 12, 20, 410
Action: Box lock; top lever, break-open; double barrel
Magazine: None
Barrel: Double barrel; 26",28" variety of choke combinations
Finish: Blued; checkered wood, semi-pistol grip stock & forearm
Approximate wt.: 5 ¾ -7 ½ lbs.
Comments: Made from the late 1960's to early 1970's
Estimated Value: Excellent: $175.00
Very good: $140.00

Harrington & Richardson 404C

Similar to the 404 with Monte Carlo stock.
Estimated Value: Excellent: $180.00
Very good: $145.00

Harrington & Richardson Model 088

Harrington & Richardson Model 1212

Harrington & Richardson Model 1212

Gauge: 12
Action: Box lock; top lever, break-open, over and under double barrel; single selective trigger
Magazine: None
Barrel: Over and under double barrel; 28" improved modified over improved cylinder; ventilated rib
Finish: Blued; decorated frame; checkered walnut pistol grip stock and forearm
Approximate wt: 7 lbs.
Comments: Introduced in the late 1970's. Manufactured in Spain for H & R.
Estimated Value: New (retail): $340.50
Excellent: $250.00
Very good: $200.00

Harrington & Richardson Model 1212 Waterfowl

Similar to the Model 1212 in 12 gauge magnum; 30" full choke over modified barrel; ventilated recoil pad.
Estimated Value: New (retail): $350.50
Excellent: $260.00
Very good: $210.00

Harrington & Richardson Model 088

Gauge: 12, 16, 20, 410, regular or magnum
Action: Box lock; top push lever, break-open; exposed hammer; single shot
Magazine: None
Barrel: 28" modified or full in 12 gauge; 28" modified in 16 gauge; 26" modified or full in 20 gauge; 25" full in 410
Finish: Blued; case hardened frame; plain hardwood semi-pistol grip stock and forearm
Approximate wt: 6 lbs.
Comments: An inexpensive line of all purpose shotguns introduced in the late 1970's.
Estimated Value: New (retail): $68.75
Excellent: $50.00
Very good: $40.00

Harrington & Richardson Model 088 Jr.

Similar to the Model 088 with a scaled down stock and forearm, 25" barrel in 20 or 410 gauge.
Estimated Value: New (retail): $68.75
Excellent: $50.00
Very good: $40.00

Shotguns

Harrington & Richardson Gamester 348
Gauge: 12, 16
Action: Bolt action; repeating
Magazine: 2 shot
Barrel: 28" full choke
Finish: Blued; plain wood, semi-pistol grip stock and forearm
Approximate wt.: 7 lbs.
Comments: Made from about 1950 to 1954
Estimated Value: Excellent: $65.00
Very good: $55.00

Harrington & Richardson Gamester 349 Deluxe
Similar to the 348 model with adjustable choke; 26" barrel; recoil pad.
Estimated Value: Excellent: $80.00
Very good: $65.00

Harrington & Richardson Huntsman 351
Gauge: 12, 16
Action: Bolt action; repeating
Magazine: 2 shot tubular
Barrel: 26" adjustable choke
Finish: Blued; plain Monte Carlo, semi-pistol grip stock & forearm; recoil pad
Approximate wt.: 7 lbs.
Comments: Made from the mid to late 1950's
Estimated Value: Excellent: $70.00
Very good: $60.00

Harrington & Richardson Model 400

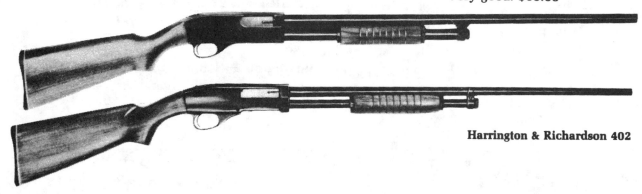

Harrington & Richardson 402

Harrington & Richardson Model 400
Gauge: 12, 16, 20
Action: Slide action; hammerless; repeating
Magazine: 5 shot tubular
Barrel: 28" full choke
Finish: Blued; semi-pistol grip stock and groved slide handle; recoil pad on 12 and 16 gauge
Approximate wt.: 7 ½ lbs.
Comments: Made from the mid 1950's to the late 1960's
Estimated Value: Excellent: $125.00
Very good: $100.00

Harrington & Richardson Model 401
Similar to the 400 with adjustable choke. Made to the early 1960's.
Estimated Value: Excellent: $130.00
Very good: $105.00

Harrington & Richardson Model 402
Similar to the 400 in 410 gauge only.
Estimated Value: Excellent: $130.00
Very good: $110.00

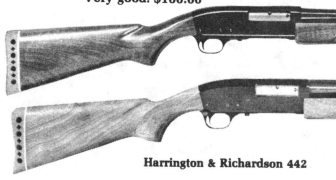

Harrington & Richardson 440

Harrington & Richardson 442

Harrington & Richardson Model 440
Gauge: 12, 16, 20
Action: Slide action; hammerless; repeating
Magazine: 4 shot clip
Barrel: 24"-28" variety of chokes
Finish: Blued; walnut, semi-pistol grip stock & forearm; recoil pad
Approximate wt.: 7 lbs.
Comments: Made from the early to mid 1970's.
Estimated Value: Excellent: $145.00
Very good: $115.00

Harrington & Richardson Model 442
Similar to the 440 with a ventilated rib and checkering.
Estimated Value: Excellent: $160.00
Very good: $125.00

Harrington & Richardson 403

Harrington & Richardson Model 403
Gauge: 410
Action: Semi-automatic
Magazine: 4 shot tubular
Barrel: 26" full choke
Finish: Blued; wood semi-pistol grip stock and fluted forearm
Approximate wt.: 5 ¾ lbs.
Comments: Made in the mid 1960's.
Estimated Value: Excellent: $200.00
Very good: $160.00

High Standard

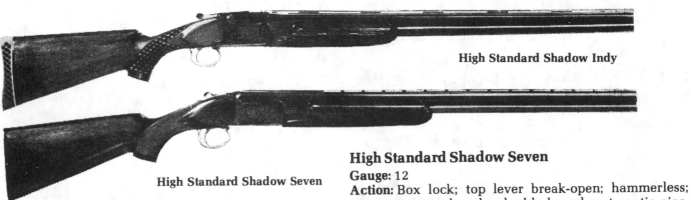

High Standard Shadow Indy

High Standard Shadow Seven

High Standard Shadow Seven
Gauge: 12
Action: Box lock; top lever break-open; hammerless; over and under double barrel; automatic ejectors; single selective trigger
Magazine: None
Barrel: Over and under double barrel; 27 ½", 29 ½"; variety of chokes; ventilated rib
Finish: Blued; checkered walnut, pistol grip stock and forearm; gold plate trigger
Approximate wt.: 8 lbs.
Comments: Manufactured to the late 1970's.
Estimated Value: Excellent: $570.00
Very good: $450.00

High Standard Shadow Indy
Similar to Shadow Seven with higher quality finish; chrome lined barrels; engraving; recoil pad.
Estimated Value: Excellent: $700.00
Very good: $565.00

High Standard Flite-King Field

High Standard Flite-King Special

High Standard Flite-King Field
Gauge: 12, 16, 20, 410
Action: Slide action; hammerless; repeating
Magazine: 5 shot tubular; 4 shot in 20 gauge
Barrel: 26" improved cylinder, 28" modified, 30" full, chokes.
Finish: Blued; plain walnut, semi-pistol grip stock and grooved slide handle.
Approximate wt.: 6-7 ¼ lbs.
Comments: Made from the early 1960's to late 1970's.
Estimated Value: Excellent: $140.00
Very good: $110.00

High Standard Flite-King Special
Similar to Flite-King Field with an adjustable choke and 27" barrel. No 410 gauge.
Estimated Value: Excellent: $145.00
Very good: $115.00

41

Shotguns

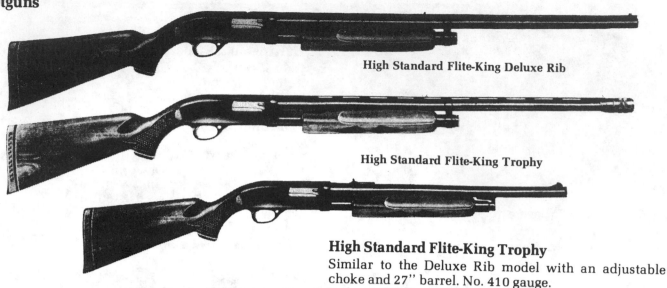

High Standard Flite-King Deluxe Rib

High Standard Flite-King Trophy

High Standard Flite-King Brush

High Standard Flite-King Trophy

Similar to the Deluxe Rib model with an adjustable choke and 27" barrel. No. 410 gauge.

Estimated Value: Excellent: $170.00
Very good: $140.00

High Standard Flite-King Deluxe Rib

Similar to the Flite-King Field with ventilated rib and checkered wood.

Estimated Value: Excellent: $165.00
Very good: $135.00

High Standard Flite-King Brush

Similar to Flite-King Field with an 18" or 20" cylinder bore barrel; rifle sights. 12 gauge only.

Estimated Value: Excellent: $185.00
Very good: $155.00

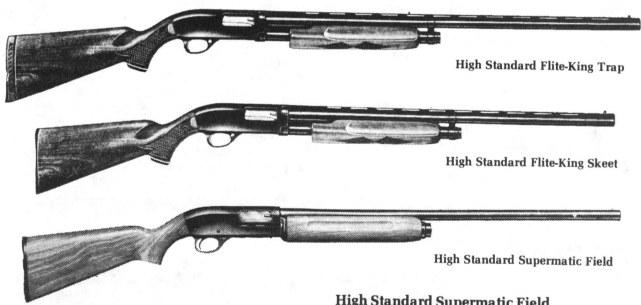

High Standard Flite-King Trap

High Standard Flite-King Skeet

High Standard Supermatic Field

High Standard Flite-King Trap

Similar to the Deluxe Rib model with a 30" full choke barrel; ventilated rib; recoil pad; and trap stock. 26" barrel on 410 gauge.

Estimated Value: Excellent: $190.00
Very good: $155.00

High Standard Flite-King Skeet

Similar to the Deluxe Rib model with a skeet choke; 26" ventilated rib barrel. Not available in 16 gauge.

Estimated Value: Excellent: $180.00
Very good: $145.00

High Standard Supermatic Field

Gauge: 12, 20, 20 magnum
Action: Gas operated, semi-automatic; hammerless
Magazine: 4 shot tubular; 3 shot in 20 magnum
Barrel: In 12 gauge; 26" improved, 28" modified or full, 30" full, chokes. In 20 gauge: 26" improved, 28" modified or full chokes
Finish: Blued; plain walnut, semi-pistol grip stock & fluted forearm
Approximate wt.: 7-7 ½ lbs.
Comments: Available from about 1960 to late 1970's. 20 gauge magnum from 1963 to late 1970's.
Estimated Value: Excellent: $170.00
Very good: $140.00

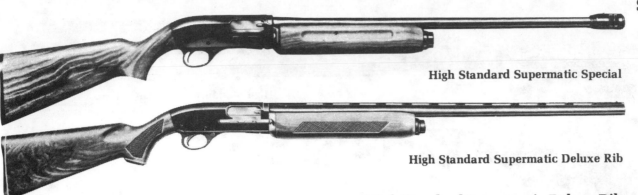

High Standard Supermatic Special

High Standard Supermatic Deluxe Rib

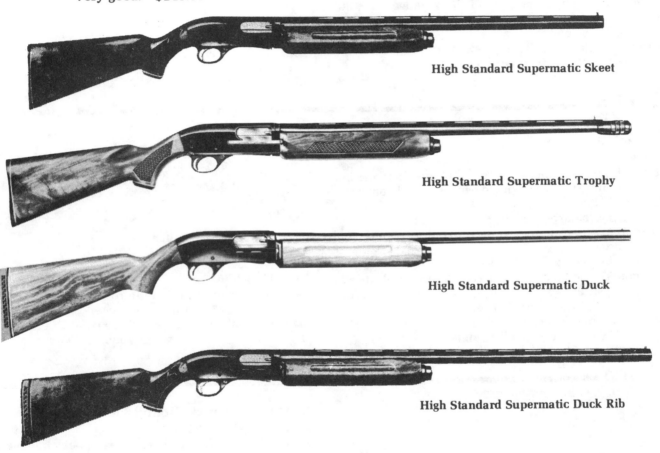

High Standard Supermatic Skeet

High Standard Supermatic Trophy

High Standard Supermatic Duck

High Standard Supermatic Duck Rib

High Standard Supermatic Special

Similar to the Supermatic Field with adjustable choke and 27" barrel.

Estimated Value: Excellent: $175.00
Very good: $145.00

High Standard Supermatic Deluxe Rib

Similar to Supermatic Field with a 28" modified or full choke barrel, (30" in 12 gauge); checkered wood and ventilated rib.

Estimated Value: Excellent: $200.00
Very good: $165.00

High Standard Supermatic Skeet

Similar to Field Model with a 26" ventilated rib barrel; skeet choke; checkered wood.

Estimated Value: Excellent: $200.00
Very good: $165.00

High Standard Supermatic Trophy

Similar to the Supermatic Field with a 27" barrel; adjustable choke; ventilated rib; checkering.

Estimated Value: Excellent: $190.00
Very good: $150.00

High Standard Supermatic Duck

Similar to the Supermatic Field in 12 gauge magnum with a 30" full choke barrel and recoil pad. Made from the early 1960's to mid 1960's.

Estimated Value: Excellent: $200.00
Very good: $170.00

High Standard Supermatic Duck Rib

Similar to the Supermatic Duck with checkered wood and ventilated rib.

Estimated Value: Excellent: $210.00
Very good: $175.00

Shotguns

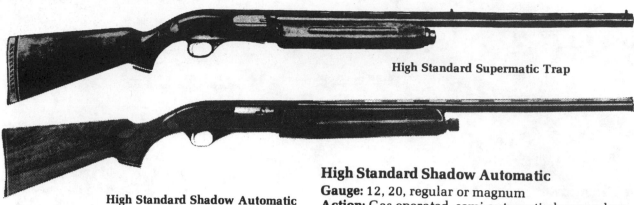

High Standard Supermatic Trap

High Standard Shadow Automatic

High Standard Supermatic Trap

Similar to the Supermatic Field in 12 gauge only; 30"
full choke; ventilated rib; checkered trap stock &
forearm; recoil pad.
Estimated Value: Excellent: **$200.00**
Very good: **$160.00**

High Standard Shadow Automatic

Gauge: 12, 20, regular or magnum
Action: Gas operated, semi-automatic; hammerless
Magazine: 4 shot tubular
Barrel: 26", 28", 30" variety of chokes; rib
Finish: Blued; walnut pistol grip stock and forearm;
sights; recoil pad available
Approximate wt.: 7 lbs.
Comments: Manufactured to the late 1970's.
Estimated Value: Excellent: **$225.00**
Very good: **$190.00**

Hunter

Hunter Fulton

Gauge: 12, 16, 20
Action: Box lock; top lever break-open; hammerless;
double trigger or single trigger; double barrel
Magazine: None
Barrel: Double Barrel; 26" to 32" any choke
Finish: Blued; checkered walnut, pistol grip stock and
forearm
Approximate wt.: 6½ to 7½ lbs.
Comments: Produced from early 1920's until shortly
after World War II in the United States. Add
$25.00 for single trigger.
Estimated Value: Excellent: **$360.00**
Very good: **$290.00**

Hunter Fulton

Hunter Special

Very similar to Hunter Fulton but somewhat higher
quality. Add $25.00 for single trigger.
Estimated Value: Excellent: **$410.00**
Very good: **$335.00**

Ithaca

Ithaca Hammerless Double Field Grade

Ithaca Hammerless Double Field Grade

Gauge: 12, 16, 20, 28, 410
Action: Box lock; top lever, break-open; hammerless;
double barrel
Magazine: None
Barrel: Double barrel; 26"-32"; various chokes
Finish: Blued; checkered walnut, pistol grip stock and
short tapered forearm
Approximate wt.: 6-10 lbs.
Comments: Made in this style from the mid 1920's to
late 1940's. Add $50.00 for automatic ejec-
tors, magnum or ventilated rib. Made in
various grades differing in quality, with
values up to $5000.00. Prices here for stan-
dard grade. Made in 8 grades.
Estimated Value: Excellent: **$500.00 - $650.00**
Very good: **$400.00 - $500.00**

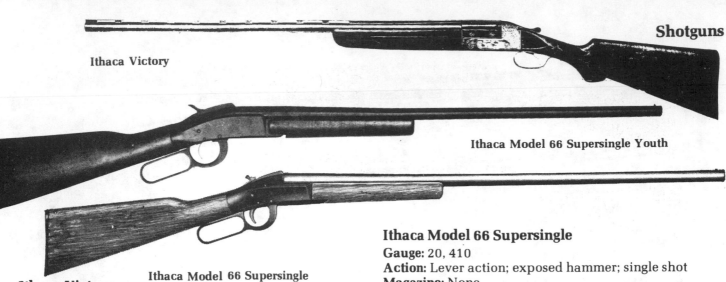

Ithaca Victory

Ithaca Model 66 Supersingle Youth

Ithaca Model 66 Supersingle

Ithaca Victory

Gauge: 12
Action: Box lock; top lever, break-open; hammerless; single shot.
Magazine: None
Barrel: 34" full choke; ventilated rib
Finish: Blued; engraving; checkered pistol grip stock and forearm
Approximate wt.: 8 lbs.
Comments: Made from the early 1920's to World War II. Other grades in higher quality available valued up to $4000. Prices here are for standard grade; Made in 5 grades.
Estimated Value: Excellent: $1,000.00
Very good: $ 800.00

Ithaca Model 66 Supersingle

Gauge: 20, 410
Action: Lever action; exposed hammer; single shot
Magazine: None
Barrel: 26" full choke, 28" full or modified choke, 30" full choke
Finish: Blued; plain or checkered straight stock and forearm
Approximate wt.: 7 lbs.
Comments: Made from the mid 1960's to late 1970's.
Estimated Value: Excellent: $55.00
Very good: $45.00

Ithaca Model 66 Supersingle Youth

Similar to the 66 with shorter stock; 410 gauge; 25" barrel; recoil pad.
Estimated Value: Excellent: $50.00
Very good: $40.00

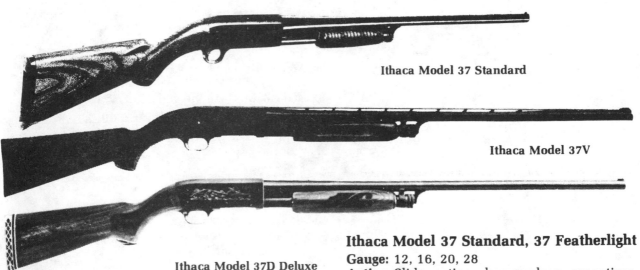

Ithaca Model 37 Standard

Ithaca Model 37V

Ithaca Model 37D Deluxe

Ithaca Model 37V

Similar to the 37 with ventilated rib. Add $65.00 for magnum.
Estimated Value: Excellent: $215.00
Very good: $175.00

Ithaca Model 37D Deluxe

Similar to the 37 with checkered stock and slide handle. Made from the mid 1950's to 1970's.
Estimated Value: Excellent: $200.00
Very good: $160.00

Ithaca Model 37 Standard, 37 Featherlight

Gauge: 12, 16, 20, 28
Action: Slide action; hammerless; repeating; bottom ejection
Magazine: 4 shot tubular
Barrel: 26"-30" various chokes
Finish: Blued; walnut, semi-pistol grip stock and grooved slide handle; some with checkering
Approximate wt.: 6-7 lbs.
Comments: Made from the 1937 to present; Add $65.00 for magnum
Estimated Value: New (retail): $255.00
Excellent: $190.00
Very good: $155.00

Shotguns

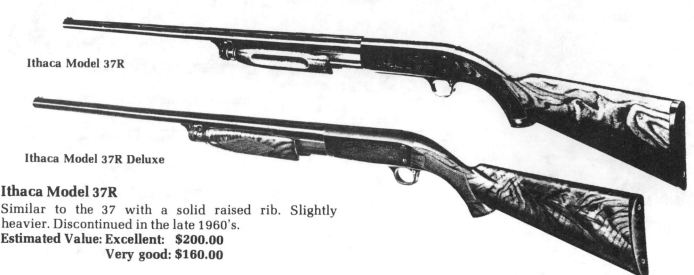

Ithaca Model 37R

Ithaca Model 37R Deluxe

Ithaca Model 37R
Similar to the 37 with a solid raised rib. Slightly heavier. Discontinued in the late 1960's.
Estimated Value: Excellent: $200.00
Very good: $160.00

Ithaca Model 37R Deluxe
Similar to the 37D Deluxe with a raised solid rib. Made to the early 1960's.
Estimated Value: Excellent: $220.00
Very good: $175.00

Ithaca Model 37DV Deluxe
Similar to the 37D with ventilated rib. Currently manufactured.
Estimated Value: New (retail): $305.00
Excellent: $225.00
Very good: $185.00

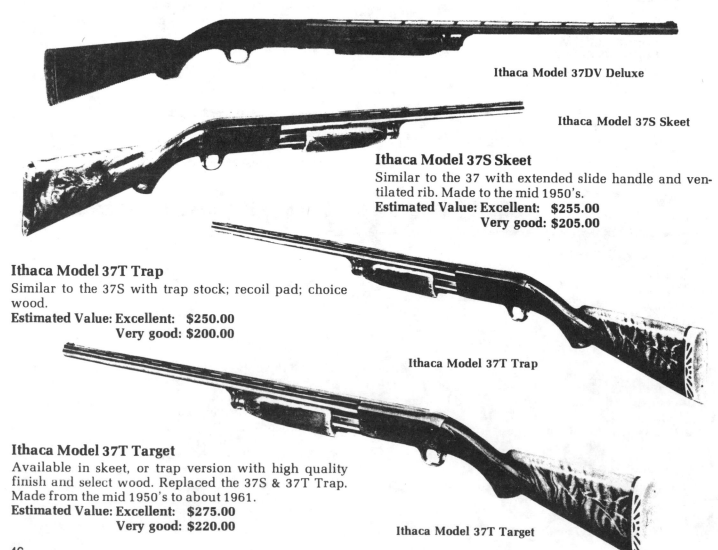

Ithaca Model 37DV Deluxe

Ithaca Model 37S Skeet

Ithaca Model 37S Skeet
Similar to the 37 with extended slide handle and ventilated rib. Made to the mid 1950's.
Estimated Value: Excellent: $255.00
Very good: $205.00

Ithaca Model 37T Trap
Similar to the 37S with trap stock; recoil pad; choice wood.
Estimated Value: Excellent: $250.00
Very good: $200.00

Ithaca Model 37T Trap

Ithaca Model 37T Target
Available in skeet, or trap version with high quality finish and select wood. Replaced the 37S & 37T Trap. Made from the mid 1950's to about 1961.
Estimated Value: Excellent: $275.00
Very good: $220.00

Ithaca Model 37T Target

Ithaca Model 37 Supreme

Similar to the 37T Target. Currently manufactured
Estimated Value: Excellent: $300.00
            Very good: $240.00

Ithaca Model 37 Bicentennial

Limited to 1976, these shotguns have special engraving on the receiver, select wood and recoil pad.
Estimated Value: Excellent: $450.00.
            Very good: $360.00

Ithaca Model 37 Deerslayer

Ithaca Model 37 Ducks Unlimited

A commemorative version of the Model 37; 12 gauge only; 30" full choke barrel; engraving on receiver; ventilated rib; made in 1977.
Estimated Value: Excellent: $200.00
            Very good: $175.00

Ithaca Model 37 Deerslayer

Similar to the Model 37 with a 20" or 26" barrel and rifle sights. Made from the 1960's to present; 12 or 20 gauge
Estimated Value: New (retail): $285.00
            Excellent: $215.00
            Very good: $170.00

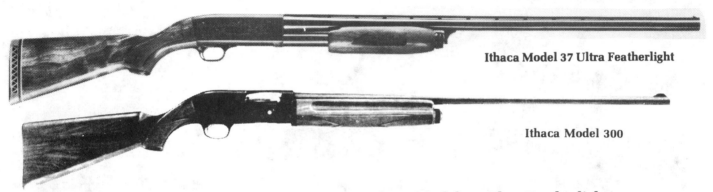

Ithaca Model 37 Ultra Featherlight

Ithaca Model 300

Ithaca Model 37 DSPS

A law enforcement version of the Model 37 Deerslayer; grooved slide handle; available in regular, parkerized, or chrome finished. Add $10.00 for 8 shot magazine, $40.00 for chrome finish.
Estimated Value: New (retail): $256.00
            Excellent: $190.00
            Very good: $150.00

Ithaca Model 37 M&P

Similar to the Model 37 for law enforcement use; 18" or 20" cylinder bore barrel; non glare tung oil finish; parkerized or chrome finish metal; 5 or 8 shot magazine. Add $10.00 for 8 shot magazine, $40.00 for chrome.
Estimated Value: New (retail): $230.00
            Excellent: $170.00
            Very good: $135.00

Ithaca Model 37 Basic Featherlight

Similar to the Model 37 without cosmetic finish; no checkering; finished in non glare tung oil; grooved slide handle; "vapor blasted" metal surfaces with a nonglare finish; add $35.00 for ventilated rib. Introduced in 1979.
Estimated Value: New (retail): $243.00
            Excellent: $180.00
            Very good: $145.00

Ithaca Model 37 Ultra Featherlight

A 20 gauge lightweight version of the Model 37; 25" ventilated rib barrel; recoil pad; gold trigger; special grip cap. Introduced in 1979.
Estimated Value: New (retail): $314.00
            Excellent: $230.00
            Very good: $180.00

Ithaca Model 37 Ultra Deerslayer

Similar to the Ultra Featherlight with a 20" barrel for slugs; sights; recoil pad; swivels.
Estimated Value: New (retail): $295.00
            Excellent: $220.00
            Very good: $175.00

Ithaca Model 300

Gauge: 12, 20
Action: Recoil operated, semi-automatic; hammerless
Magazine: 3 shot tubular
Barrel: 26" improved cylinder, 28" modified or full, 30" full, choke
Finish: Blued; checkered walnut, pistol grip stock & forearm
Approximate wt.: 6½-7 lbs.
Comments: Made from about 1970-1973. Add $10.00 for ventilated rib.
Estimated Value: Excellent: $200.00
            Very good: $160.00

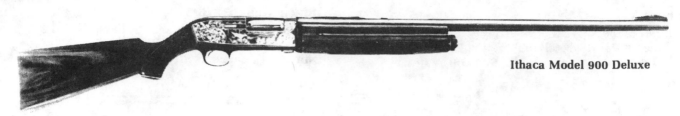

Ithaca Model 900 Deluxe

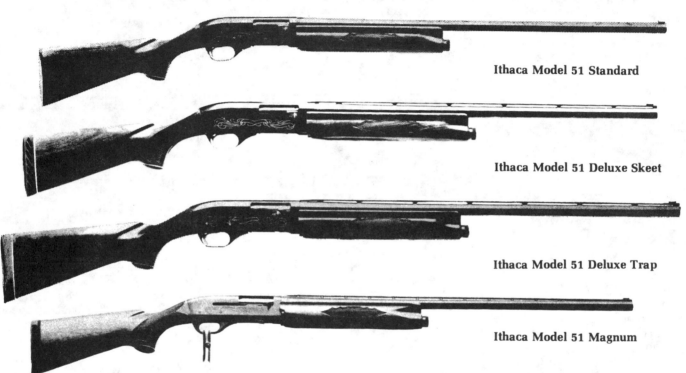

Ithaca Model 51 Standard

Ithaca Model 51 Deluxe Skeet

Ithaca Model 51 Deluxe Trap

Ithaca Model 51 Magnum

Ithaca Model 900 Deluxe Slug

Similar to the 900 Deluxe with a 24" barrel for slugs and rifle sights.
**Estimated Value: Excellent:	$240.00**
Very good: $190.00

Ithaca Model 900 Deluxe

Similar to the 300 except: ventilated rib on all models; gold filled engraving; nameplate in stock; gold trigger.
**Estimated Value: Excellent:	$250.00**
Very good: $200.00

Ithaca Model 51 Deluxe Skeet

Similar to the 51 with recoil pad; ventilated rib; 28" or 29" skeet choke barrel.
Estimated Value: New (retail): $435.00
**Excellent:	$325.00**
**Very good:	$260.00**

Ithaca Model 51 Standard

Gauge: 12, 20
Action: Gas operated, semi-automatic
Magazine: 3 shot tubular
Barrel: 26"-30", various chokes
Finish: Blued; checkered walnut, pistol grip stock & forearm; decorated receiver
Approximate wt.: 7 ½ lbs.
Comments: Currently manufactured. Add $30.00 for ventilated rib.
Estimated Value: New (retail): $329.00
**Excellent:	$240.00**
**Very good:	$200.00**

Ithaca Model 51 Deluxe Trap

Similar to the Model 51 except: 12 gauge only; select wood; 28" or 30" barrel; recoil pad. Add $10.00 for Monte Carlo stock.
Estimated Value: New (retail): $445.00
**Excellent:	$330.00**
**Very good:	$265.00**

Ithaca Model 51 Ducks Unlimited

A commemorative version of the Model 51; 12 gauge only; 30" full choke barrel; iridescent sight; engraving on receiver; ventilated rib. Made in 1979.
**Estimated Value: Excellent:	$250.00**
**Very good:	$225.00**

Ithaca Model 51 Magnum

Similar to the 51 but chambered for magnum shells; ventilated rib.
Estimated Value: New (retail): $384.00
**Excellent:	$290.00**
**Very good:	$230.00**

Ithaca Model 51 Deerslayer

Ithaca Model 51 Deerslayer
Similar to the 51 with 24" barrel for slugs; sights; recoil pad; 12 gauge only.
Estimated Value: New (retail): $348.00
Excellent: $260.00
Very good: $210.00

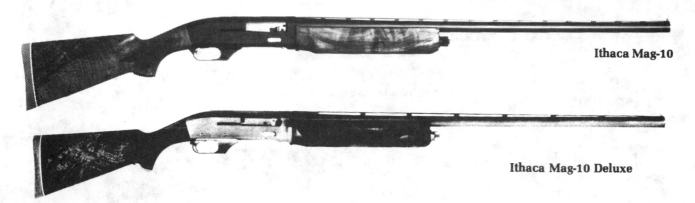

Ithaca Mag-10

Ithaca Mag-10 Deluxe

Ithaca Mag-10 Supreme
Similar to the Magnum 10 Deluxe with higher quality finish and select wood.
Estimated Value: New (retail): $725.00
Excellent: $545.00
Very good: $435.00

Ithaca Mag-10 Roadblocker
A law enforcement version of the Mag-10 with a 20" barrel; plain stock; "vapor blasted" metal finish.
Estimated Value: New (retail): $500.00
Excellent: $375.00
Very good: $300.00

Ithaca Mag-10 Deluxe
Gauge: 10 magnum
Action: Gas operated, semi-automatic
Magazine: 3 shot tubular
Barrel: 32" full choke; ventilated rib
Finish: Blued; checkered walnut pistol grip stock and forearm; recoil pad; swivels
Approximate wt: 11 ½ lbs.
Comments: Currently manufactured. Deduct $90.00 for Ithaca Mag-10 Standard.
Estimated Value: New (retail): $620.00
Excellent: $465.00
Very good: $375.00

Iver Johnson

Iver Johnson Champion

Iver Johnson Matted Rib
Similar to the Champion with a matted rib and checkering. Discontinued in the late 1940's.
Estimated Value: Excellent: $80.00
Very good: $65.00

Iver Johnson Champion
Gauge: 12, 20, 410
Action: Box lock; top lever, break-open; hammerless; automatic ejector; single shot
Magazine: None
Barrel: 26"-30" full choke
Finish: Blued; hardwood, semi-pistol grip stock and short tapered forearm
Approximate wt: 7 lbs.
Comments: Made from about 1910 to late 1970's
Estimated Value: Excellent: $60.00
Very good: $50.00

Shotguns

Iver Johnson Special Trap

Similar to the Champion with a 32" ribbed barrel; checkered stock; 12 gauge only. Manufactured until the late 1940's.

Estimated Value: Excellent: $250.00
Very good: $225.00

Iver Johnson Matted Rib

Iver Johnson Special Trap

Iver Johnson Skeeter

Iver Johnson Hercules

Gauge: 12, 16, 20, 410
Action: Box lock; top lever, break-open; hammerless; double barrel
Magazine: None
Barrel: Double barrel; 26"-32", modified & full or full, chokes
Finish: Blued; checkered walnut, pistol grip stock and tapered forearm
Approximate wt.: 6-8 lbs
Comments: Made from about 1920 to 1949. Available with some extras. Prices are for standard grade. Add $25.00-$35.00 for single trigger or automatic ejectors.

Estimated Value: Excellent: $200.00
Very good: $160.00

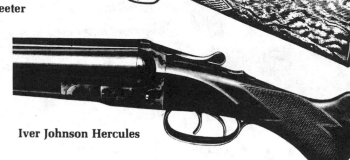

Iver Johnson Hercules

Iver Johnson Skeeter

Similar to the Hercules with addition of 28 gauge; 26"-28" barrels; wide forearm; Add $25.00-$35.00 for automatic ejectors

Estimated Value: Excellent: $375.00
Very good: $300.00

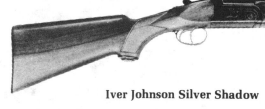

Iver Johnson Silver Shadow

Iver Johnson Silver Shadow

Gauge: 12
Action: Box lock; top lever, break-open; over & under double barrel; hammerless
Magazine: None
Barrel: Over & under double barrel; 28" modified & full choke; ventilated rib
Finish: Blued; checkered walnut, pistol grip stock & forearm
Approximate wt.: 8 ¼ lbs.
Comments: Currently manufactured in Italy for Iver Johnson Add $20.00 for single trigger.

Estimated Value: Excellent: $250.00
Very good: $200.00

Iver Johnson Super Trap

Gauge: 12
Action: Box lock; top lever, break-open; hammerless; double barrel
Magazine: None
Barrel: Double barrel; 32" full choke; ventilated rib
Finish: Blued; checkered wood, pistol grip stock & forearm; recoil pad
Approximate wt.: 8 ½ lbs.
Comments: Production stopped on this model during World War II. Available with some extras. Prices for standard grade, add $25.00-$35.00 for non-selective single trigger, $50.00-$60.00 for selective single trigger.

Estimated Value: Excellent: $450.00
Very good: $375.00

Iver Johnson Super Trap

Kessler 3 shot
Gauge: 12, 16, 20
Action: Bolt action
Magazine: 2 shot detachable box
Barrel: 26", 28" full choke
Finish: Blued; plain pistol grip stock and forearm; recoil pad.
Approximate wt.: 6 to 7 lbs.
Comments: Made only for a few years in the early 1950's.
Estimated Value: Excellent: $75.00
Very good: $65.00

Kessler Lever Matic
Gauge: 12, 16, 20
Action: Lever action
Magazine: 3 shot
Barrel: 26, 28, 30 inch, full choke
Finish: Blued; walnut straight stock and forearm; recoil pad.
Approximate wt.: 7 lbs.
Comments: Produced only for a few years in the early 1950's.
Estimated Value: Excellent: $150.00
Very good: $130.00

Kleinguenther

Kleinguenther Condor

Kleinguenther Condor
Gauge: 12, 20
Action: Double lock; top lever break-open; hammerless; over and under double barrel; selective single trigger; automatic ejectors
Magazine: None
Barrel: Over and under double barrel; ventilated rib; 26" improved and modified or skeet; 28" modified or modified and full; 30" modified and full or full in 12 gauge
Finish: Blued; checkered walnut, pistol grip stock and forearm; recoil pad
Approximate wt.: 7 ½ lbs.
Comments: An Italian shotgun produced in the 1970's.
Estimated Value: Excellent: $450.00
Very good: $380.00

Kleinguenther Condor Skeet
A skeet version of the Condor with a wide rib.
Estimated Value: Excellent: $490.00
Very good: $415.00

Kleinguenther Condor Trap
A trap version of the Condor with a Monte Carlo stock, wide rib and available in 32" barrel.
Estimated Value: Excellent: $490.00
Very good: $415.00

Kleinguenther Brescia
Gauge: 12, 20
Action: Box lock; top lever break-open; hammerless; double barrel; double trigger
Magazine: None
Barrel: Double barrel; chrome lined; 28" improved or modified or modified and full, chokes.
Finish: Blued; checkered walnut, pistol grip stock and tapered forearm.
Approximate wt.: 7 ½ lbs.
Comments: Manufactured in Italy
Estimated Value: Excellent: $240.00
Very good: $200.00

Kleinguenther Brescia

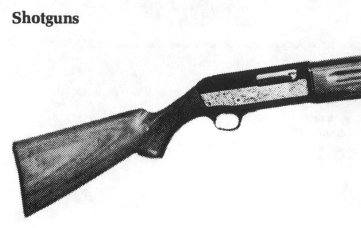

Kleinguenther Semi-Automatic

Kleinguenther Semi-Automatic

Gauge: 12
Action: Semi-automatic; hammerless; side ejection
Magazine: Tubular, 3 shot
Barrel: Chrome line; 25'' skeet, 26'' improved cylinder, 28'' and 30'' full, chokes; ventilated rib.
Finish: Blued; smooth walnut, pistol grip stock and grooved forearm; engraved
Approximate wt.: 7 ½ lbs.
Comments: Produced in the early and mid 1970's
Estimated Value: Excellent: $265.00
**   Very good: $205.00**

L.C. Smith

L.C. Smith Single Barrel

Gauge: 12
Action: Box lock; hammerless; top lever break-open; automatic ejector
Magazine: None; single shot.
Barrel: 32'', 34'' choice of bore; ventilated rib.
Finish: Blued; checkered walnut pistol grip stock & forearm; recoil pad
Approximate wt.: 8 lbs.
Comments: Produced by Hunter Arms until about 1946, and Marlin from about 1946-1950

Estimated Value:	Olympic	Specialty	Crown
Excellent:	$1,450.00	$2,000.00	$3,200.00
Very good:	$1,050.00	$1,450.00	$2,500.00

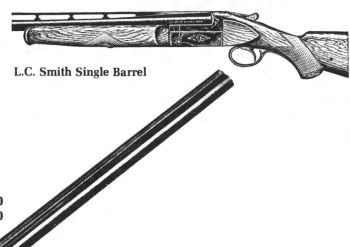

L.C. Smith Single Barrel

L.C. Smith Double Barrel (Hunter Arms)

Gauge: 12, 16, 20, 410
Action: Side lock, top lever break down; hammerles, automatic ejectors ; double or single trigger; double barrel; side by side
Magazine: None
Barrel: 26''-32'', double barrel, any choke
Finish: Depending on grade, walnut checkered, pistol, semi-pistol or straight grip stock & forearm; blued barrels
Approximate wt.: 6 ½ -8 ½ lbs.
Comments: Produced by Hunter Arms until about 1946, and Marlin from 1946 to 1950. Prices for field grade. Others considerably higher due to higher quality workmanship and finish quality.
Estimated Value: Excellent: $600.00
**   Very good: $500.00**

L.C. Smith Double Barrel (Hunter Arms)

L.C. Smith Field Grade (Marlin)

L.C. Smith Field Grade (Marlin)

Same as the Deluxe Model with standard checkered walnut pistol grip stock and forearm and extruded ventilated rib.

Estimated Value: Excellent: $390.00
Very good: $310.00

L.C. Smith Deluxe (Marlin)

Gauge: 12, regular or magnum
Action: Top lever break-open; hammerless; side lock; double barrel; double triggers
Magazine: None
Barrel: Double barrel; 28" modified & full chokes; floating steel ventilated rib
Finish: Top quality, hand fitted, hand checkered walnut, pistol grip stock & beavertail forearm; blued; case hardened side plates
Approximate wt.: 6¾ lbs.
Comments: Produced from about 1968 to mid 1970's
Estimated Value: Excellent: $525.00
Very good: $425.00

Lefever

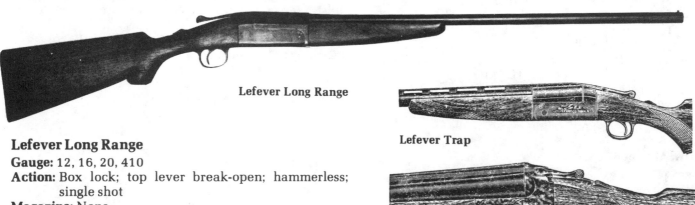

Lefever Long Range

Lefever Trap

Lefever Nitro Special

Lefever Long Range

Gauge: 12, 16, 20, 410
Action: Box lock; top lever break-open; hammerless; single shot
Magazine: None
Barrel: 26", 28", 30", 32" any choke
Finish: Blued; checkered or plain walnut pistol grip stock and forearm; bead sight
Approximate wt.: 5 to 7 lb.
Comments: Produced from the early 1920's to the early 1940's.
Estimated Value: Excellent: $145.00
Very good: $120.00

Lefever Nitro Special

Gauge: 12, 16, 20, 410
Action: Box lock; top lever break-open; hammerless; double barrel; double triggers
Magazine: None
Barrel: Double barrel; 26", 28", 30", 32" any choke
Finish: Blued; checkered walnut pistol grip stock and forearm
Approximate wt.: 5 ½ to 7 lbs.
Comments: Made from the early 1920's to late 1940's. Add $25.00 for single trigger.
Estimated Value: Excellent: $260.00
Very good: $220.00

Lefever Trap

Gauge: 12
Action: Box lock; top lever break-open; hammerless; single shot
Magazine: None
Barrel: 30" or 32" full choke; ventilated rib
Finish: Blued; checkered walnut pistol grip stock and forearm; recoil pad
Approximate wt.: 8 lbs.
Comments: Produced from the early 1920's to the early 1940's.
Estimated Value: Excellent: $300.00
Very good: $260.00

Lefever Excellsior

Similar to Nitro-Special with light engraving and automatic ejector.
Estimated Value: Excellent: $500.00
Very good: $400.00

Marlin

Marlin Model 60

Marlin Model 90

Marlin Model 60

Gauge: 12
Action: Box lock; takedown breech loaded; automatic ejector; exposed hammer
Magazine: Single shot
Barrel: 30'' or 32'' full choke; matted top; 2¾'' chamber
Finish: Blued; walnut pistol grip stock and beavertail forearm
Approximate wt.: 6 ½ lbs.
Comments: This shotgun was made in 1923, a combination of Marlin and Hopkins & Allen parts. Less than 1,000 were manufactured.
Estimated Value: Excellent: $125.00
                     Very good: $105.00

Marlin Model 410

Gauge: 410
Action: Lever action; exposed hammer
Magazine: 5-shot tubular
Barrel: 22'' or 26''; 2 ½'' chamber
Finish: Blued; walnut pistol grip stock & beavertail forearm
Approximate wt.: 6 lbs.
Comments: This solid frame lightweight shotgun was produced from about 1929 to 1932.
Estimated Value: Excellent: $325.00
                     Very good: $275.00

Marlin Model 90

Gauge: 12, 16, 20, 410 (also .22 caliber and .222)
Action: Top lever break down; box lock; double trigger; hammerless; double barrel; (single trigger available prior to W W II). Non-automatic extractors.
Magazine: None
Barrel: Over and under double barrel; 26'', 28'' or 30'' rifle; shotgun barrels available in 26''; 2¾'' chamber, 3'' chamber in 410; full, modified, skeet or improved cylinder choke
Finish: Blued; plain or checkered walnut, pistol grip stock and forearm; recoil pad
Approximate wt.: 6 to 7 ½ lbs.
Comments: This shotgun or combination was manufactured from about 1937 until 1958. Add $40.00 for 410 gauge.
Estimated Value: Excellent: $350.00
                     Very good: $300.00

Marlin Model 55 Hunter

Gauge: 12, 16 or 20
Action: Bolt action
Magazine: 2-shot clip
Barrel: 26'' or 28'' full choke; ''Micro Choke'' available; 2¾'' or 3'' chamber
Finish: Blued; walnut, pistol grip stock and forearm; recoil pad optional
Approximate wt.: 7 ¼ lbs.
Comments: This shotgun was manufactured from about 1950 to 1965.
Estimated Value: Excellent: $75.00
                     Very good: $60.00

Marlin Model 410

Marlin Model 55 Hunter

Marlin 55G, Glenfield 55G and Glenfield 50

This is the same basic shotgun as the Marlin Model 55 Hunter. It was produced from about 1961 to 1966 as the 55G and Glenfield 55G and in 1966 it became the Glenfield 50.

Estimated Value: Excellent: $75.00
Very good: $60.00

Marlin Glenfield 60G

The same shotgun as the Marlin Model 59.

Estimated Value: Excellent: $60.00
Very good: $50.00

Marlin Model 55 Swamp Gun

The same shotgun as the Model 55 except barrel is shortened with "Micro Choke", recoil pad is standard and it has swivels. It weighs about 6½ lbs. and is chambered for 3" 12 gauge magnum shells. It was produced for 2 years beginning in 1963.

Estimated Value: Excellent: $80.00
Very good: $65.00

Marlin Model 55 Goose Gun

The same shotgun as the Model 55 except; it has swivels; extra long 36" barrel; chambered for 3" 12 gauge magnum shells; weighs 7¼ lbs; recoil pad standard. It has been in production since 1966.

Estimated Value: New (retail): $122.95
Excellent: $ 95.00
Very good: $ 75.00

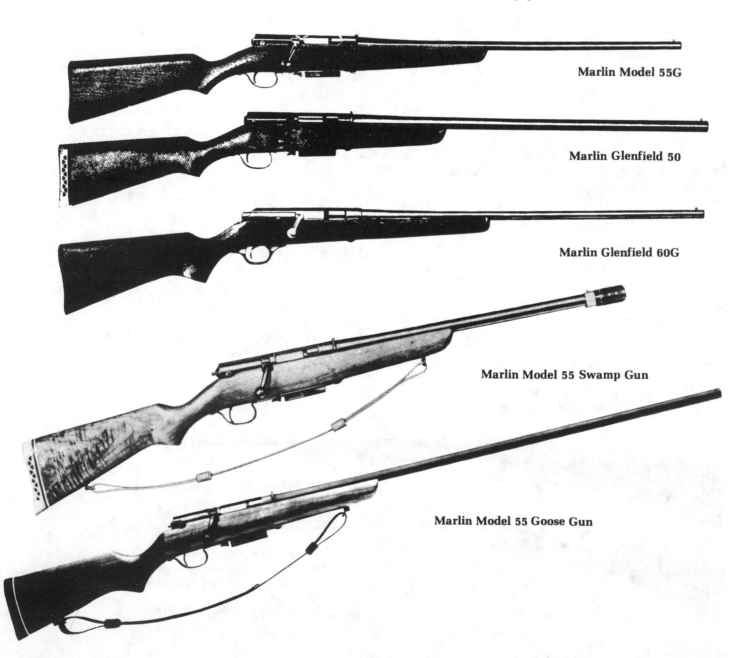

Marlin Model 55G

Marlin Glenfield 50

Marlin Glenfield 60G

Marlin Model 55 Swamp Gun

Marlin Model 55 Goose Gun

Marlin Model 55S Slug Gun

Marlin Model 59

Marlin Model 59, 60G, 61G
Gauge: 410
Action: Bolt action; self-cocking
Magazine: None; single shot
Barrel: 24" full choke; chambered for 2 ½" or 3" shells
Finish: Blued; walnut pistol grip or semi-pistol grip stock & forearm.
Approximate wt.: 5 lbs.
Comments: This takedown model was produced from about 1959 to 1961. It was replaced by Model 60G in 1962 which was replaced by the Model 61G in 1963. In 1966 it was discontinued.
Estimated Value: Excellent: $60.00
Very good: $50.00

Marlin Model 55S Slug Gun
Basically the same as Model 55, this gun has a 24" barrel that is chambered for 2¾" and 3" shells. It has swivels and a recoil pad. In production since 1973.
Estimated Value: Excellent: $90.00
Very good: $75.00

Marlin Model 5510 Supergoose 10

Marlin Model 1898
Gauge: 12 (2¾")
Action: Slide action; exposed hammer; side ejection
Magazine: 5-shot tubular
Barrel: 26", 28", 30" or 32"
Finish: Blued; walnut, pistol grip stock & grooved slide handle
Approximate wt.: 7 ¼ lbs.
Comments: This shotgun was produced for 7 years beginning in 1898.
Estimated Value: Excellent: $240.00
Very good: $200.00

Marlin Model 5510 Supergoose 10
Gauge: 10 gauge magnum
Action: Bolt action
Magazine: 2-shot clip (2 7/8" shells must be loaded single)
Barrel: 34" full choke; chambered for 2 7/8" or 3½".
Finish: Blued; black walnut, semi-pistol grip stock and forearm; swivels; recoil pad
Approximate wt.: 10 ½ lbs.
Comments: This is a more powerful version of the Marlin Goose Gun. It has been in production since 1976.
Estimated Value: New (retail): $190.00
Excellent: $145.00
Very good: $115.00

Marlin Model 1898

Marlin Model 19

Marlin Model 19 and 19G
These shotguns were similar to the Model 1898 with slight improvements. Made from 1906-1907. 19G produced until 1915.
Estimated Value: Excellent: $235.00
Very good: $205.00

Marlin Model 24

Marlin Model 21 "Trap Model"

Marlin Model 26

Marlin Model 16

Marlin Model 16

Gauge: 16 (2¾ inch)
Action: Slide action; exposed hammer
Magazine: 5-shot tubular
Barrel: 26" or 28"
Finish: Blued; walnut pistol grip stock and forearm; some checkered, some with grooved slide handle
Approximate wt.: 6¼ lbs.
Comments: This takedown model was made from about 1904 to 1910
Estimated Value: Excellent: $265.00
Very good: $220.00

Marlin Model 24

This shotgun is an improved version of the Model 19; produced from about 1908 to 1915.
Estimated Value: Excellent: $210.00
Very good: $180.00

Marlin Model 21 "Trap Model"

This shotgun is very similar to the Model 24 with trap specifications.
Estimated Value: Excellent: $250.00
Very good: $215.00

Marlin Model 26

This shotgun is very similar to the Model 24 except: stock is straight grip; solid frame. Made from about 1909 to 1915.
Estimated Value: Excellent: $240.00
Very good: $200.00

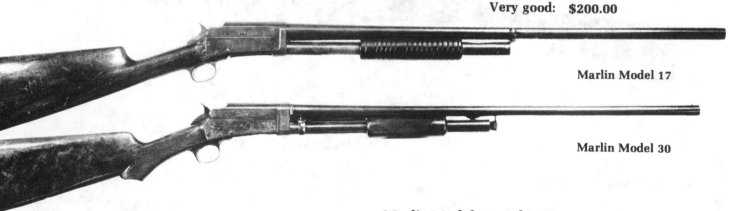

Marlin Model 17

Marlin Model 30

Marlin Model 30 and 30G

Gauge: 16 and 20
Action: Slide action; exposed hammer
Magazine: 5-shot tubular
Barrel: 25, 26, 28 inch modified choke, 2¾" chamber
Finish: Blued; checkered walnut, pistol grip or straight stock, grooved or checkered slide handle
Approximate wt.: 6¾ lbs.
Comments: This shotgun was produced from about 1910 to 1915. In 1915 it was called the Model 30G.
Estimated Value: Excellent: $290.00
Very good: $240.00

Marlin Model 17 and 17G

Gauge: 12
Action: Slide action; exposed hammer
Magazine: 5-shot tubular
Barrel: 30" or 32" full choke (others available by special order).
Finish: Blued; walnut straight grip stock & grooved slide handle.
Approximate wt.: 7½ lbs.
Comments: This solid frame shotgun was made from about 1906 to 1915; from 1908 until 1915 it was produced as Model 17G.
Estimated Value: Excellent: $265.00
Very good: $215.00

Shotguns

Marlin Model 28

Marlin Model 28T

Marlin Model 31

Marlin Model 31A

Marlin Model 28A

Marlin Model 28, 28T, 28TS

Gauge: 12
Action: Slide action; hammerless; side ejection
Magazine: 5-shot tubular
Barrel: 26" or 28" cylinder bore or modified choke; 30" or 32" full choke
Finish: Blued; checkered walnut, pistol grip stock and slide handle
Approximate wt.: 8 lbs.
Comments: This takedown shotgun was produced from about 1913 to just before World War I. The Model 28T and 28TS were trap grade guns with an available straight stock. Add $100.00 for 28T, 28TS.
Estimated Value: Excellent: $325.00
                     Good: $270.00

Marlin Model 28A

Basically the same as the Model 28. It was produced from about 1920 to 1922 and was replaced by the Model 43A
Estimated Value: Excellent: $300.00
                     Very good: $240.00

Marlin Model 31

This shotgun is much like the Model 28 except: 20 gauge or 16 gauge. It was produced from about 1915 to 1917.
Estimated Value: Excellent: $360.00
                     Very good: $300.00

Marlin Model 31A

This shotgun is very similar to the Model 28A in 20 gauge only. It was replaced by the Model 44A
Estimated Value: Excellent: $290.00
                     Very good: $240.00

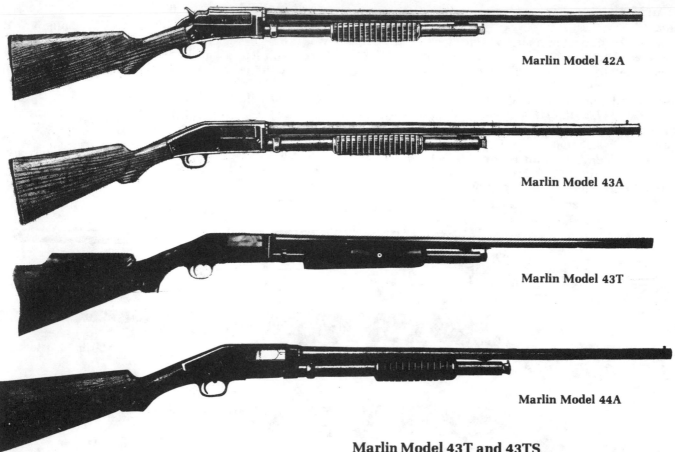

Marlin Model 42A

Marlin Model 43A

Marlin Model 43T

Marlin Model 44A

Marlin Model 42A

Gauge: 12
Action: Slide action; exposed hammer; side ejection
Magazine: 5-shot tubular, bottom load
Barrel: 26'' cylinder bore, 28'' modified, 30'' and 32'' full choke; 2¾'' chamber; round, matted barrel
Finish: Blued; black walnut, semi-pistol grip stock, grooved slide handle
Approximate wt.: 7 ½ lbs.
Comments: This takedown shotgun was manufactured from about 1922 until 1934.
Estimated Value: Excellent: $280.00
Very good: $235.00

Marlin Model 43A

Gauge: 12
Action: Slide action; hammerless; side ejection
Magazine: 5 shot tubular
Barrel: 26'' cylinder bore, 28'' modified, 30'' and 32'' full choke; 2¾'' chamber
Finish: Blued; walnut, full pistol grip stock & grooved slide handle
Approximate wt.: 8 lbs.
Comments: This shotgun was made from abut 1923 until 1930. It was a new style takedown.
Estimated Value: Excellent: $240.00
Very good: $190.00

Marlin Model 43T and 43TS

This is the same basic shotgun as the Model 43A except it has checkered Monte Carlo stock and forearm with recoil pad. The Model 43TS had a choice of many options for the purchaser. Value of the Model 43TS is dependent on the number and type of extras.
Estimated Value: Excellent: $300.00
Very good: $250.00

Marlin Model 44A

Gauge: 20
Action: Slide action; hammerless; side ejection
Magazine: 4-shot tubular; bottom load
Barrel: 25'' or 28'', cylinder bore, modified or full choke; 2¾'' chamber
Finish: Blued; walnut, pistol grip stock & grooved slide handle
Approximate wt.: 6 lbs.
Comments: This is a takedown model that was produced from about 1923 to 1935.
Estimated Value: Excellent: $230.00
Very good: $190.00

Marlin Model 44S

Basically the same shotgun as the Model 44A except it came with either straight or pistol grip checkered stock and forearm.
Estimated Value: Excellent: $260.00
Very good: $220.00

Shotguns

Marlin Model 63A

Gauge: 12
Action: Slide action; hammerless; side ejector
Magazine: 5-shot tubular
Barrel: 26" cylinder bore, 28" modified choke, 30" or 32" full choke
Finish: Blued; plain walnut, pistol grip stock and grooved slide handle
Approximate wt.: 8 lbs.
Comments: This shotgun is an improved version of the Model 43A and was produced from about 1931 to 1935.
Estimated Value: Excellent: $240.00
Very good: $215.00

Marlin Model 63T and 63TS

The Model 63T was basically the same shotgun as the Model 63A except it was only produced in 30" or 32" barrel and had a checkered straight stock. The Model 63TS could be ordered to the buyers specifications. Prices are for standard trap gun.
Estimated Value: Excellent: $325.00
Very good: $300.00

Marlin Model 49

This shotgun is similar to the Model 43A. It was given away with stock in the corporation. It was produced from about 1925 to 1928.
Estimated Value: Excellent: $360.00
Very good: $320.00

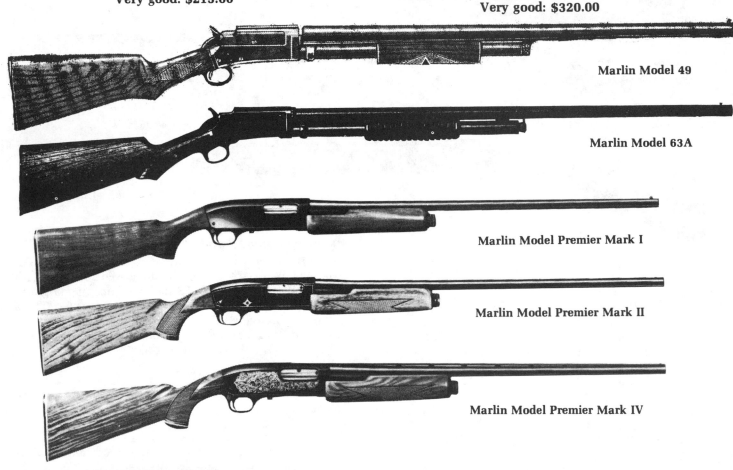

Marlin Model 49

Marlin Model 63A

Marlin Model Premier Mark I

Marlin Model Premier Mark II

Marlin Model Premier Mark IV

Marlin Model Premier Mark I

Gauge: 12
Action: Slide action; hammerless; side ejection
Magazine: 3-shot tubular
Barrel: 26" cylinder bore, 28" modified, 30" full choke; ventilated rib available; 28" slug barrel with rifle sights available; 2¾" chamber
Finish: Blued; walnut pistol grip stock and forearm; recoil pad optional
Approximate wt.: 7 lbs.
Comments: This gun was produced from about 1960 to 1963.
Estimated Value: Excellent: $150.00
Very good: $120.00

Marlin Model Premier Mark II

This is basically the same shotgun as the Premier Mark I except the stock and forearm are checkered and the receiver is engraved.
Estimated Value: Excellent: $205.00
Very good: $170.00

Marlin Model Premier Mark IV

This is basically the same shotgun as the Mark II except the wood is more elaborate and the engraving heavier.
Estimated Value: Excellent: $270.00
Very good: $240.00

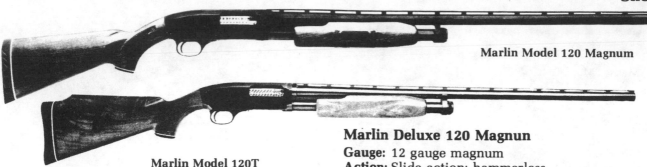

Marlin Model 120 Magnum

Marlin Model 120T

Marlin Model 120T

This is basically the same shotgun as Model 120 with a Monte Carlo stock and 30" full choke or 30" modified trap choke barrel. This gun was offered from 1973 to the late 1970's.

Estimated Value: Excellent: $250.00
Very good: $200.00

Marlin Deluxe 120 Slug Gun

Similar to the Marlin Deluxe 120 with a 20" slug barrel and rifle sights. Introduced in the late 1970's.

Estimated Value: New (retail): $267.95
Excellent: $200.00
Very good: $160.00

Marlin Deluxe 120 Magnun

Gauge: 12 gauge magnum
Action: Slide action; hammerless
Magazine: 5-shot tubular (4-shot with 3" shells)
Barrel: 26" cylinder bore, 28" modified or 30" full choke; chambered for 2¾" or 3"
Finish: Blued; ventilated rib; checkered walnut, pistol grip stock and forearm; recoil pad
Approximate wt: 7¾ lbs.
Comments: This gun was first offered in 1971. In 1973 a 40" MXR Magnum barrel and a choked 26" slug barrel were offered for the first time.

Estimated Value: New (retail): $267.95
Excellent: $200.00
Very good: $160.00

Marlin Glenfield 778

Marlin Glenfield 778

Gauge: 12, regular or magnum
Action: Slide action; hammerless; repeating
Magazine: 5 shot tubular; 4 shot with 3" magnum
Barrel: 26" improved cylinder; 28" modified; 30" full choke; ventilated rib available; 38" MXR full choke barrel available without rib
Finish: Blued; checkered hardwood, semi-pistol grip stock and fluted slide handle; recoil pad
Approximate wt: 7¾ lbs.
Comments: Introduced in the late 970's. Add $25.00 for ventilated rib or MXR barrel.

Estimated Value: New (retail): $194.95
Excellent: $146.00
Very good: $120.00

Marlin Glenfield 778 Slug

Similar to the Glenfield 778 with a 20" slug barrel and rifle sights.

Estimated Value: New (retail): $221.95
Excellent: $170.00
Very good: $135.00

Mauser

Mauser Model 496 Trap

Mauser Model 496 Competition

Mauser Model 496 Trap

Gauge: 12
Action: Box lock; top lever, break open; hammerless; automatic ejector; single shot.
Magazine: None
Barrel: 32" modified or 34" full, chokes; ventilated rib
Finish: Blued; checkered walnut, Monte Carlo pistol grip stock and tapered forearm; engraved; recoil pad
Approximate wt.: 8½ lbs.
Comments: Imported in the 1970's.
Estimated Value: Excellent: $450.00
Very good: $350.00

Mauser Model 496 Competition

Similar to the Model 496 with select wood; higher ventilated rib.

Estimated Value: Excellent: $625.00
Very good: $500.00

Shotguns

Mauser Model 580

Mauser Model 620

Mauser Model 71E

Mauser Model 72E Trap

Mauser Model 610 Phantom

Mauser Model 580

Gauge: 12
Action: Side lock; top lever, break-open; hammerless; double barrel
Magazine: None
Barrel: Double barrel; 28''-30'', various chokes
Finish: Blued; checkered walnut, straight stock and tapered forearm; engraved
Approximate wt: 7 ¾ lbs.
Comments: Imported in the 1970's.
Estimated Value: Excellent: $800.00
 Very good: $650.00

Mauser Model 610 Phantom

Gauge: 12
Action: Box lock; top lever, break-open; hammerless; over & under double barrel
Magazine: None
Barrel: Over & under double barrel; ventilated ribs, between barrels and on top barrel; 30'', 32'' various chokes
Finish: Blued; case hardened frame; checkered walnut, pistol grip stock and forearm; recoil pad
Approximate wt: 8 lbs.
Comments: Imported in the 1970's
Estimated Value: Excellent: $775.00
 Very good: $625.00

Mauser Model 620

Gauge: 12
Action: Box lock; top lever, break-open; hammerless; over & under double barrel; single trigger; automatic ejectors
Magazine: None
Barrel: Over & under double barrel; 28'', 30'' improved cylinder & modified or modified & full, or skeet, chokes; ribbed
Finish: Blued; palin walnut, pistol grip stock & forearm; recoil pad
Approximate wt: 7 ½ lbs.
Comments: Imported from the early to mid 1970's from Germany
Estimated Value: Excellent: $800.00
 Very good: $650.00

Mauser Model 71E

Similar to the Model 620 with double triggers and no recoil pad; 28'' barrel.
Estimated Value: Excellent: $350.00
 Very good: $275.00

Mauser Model 72E Trap

Similar to the Model 71E with large recoil pad; engraving; wide rib.
Estimated Value: Excellent: $480.00
 Very good: $385.00

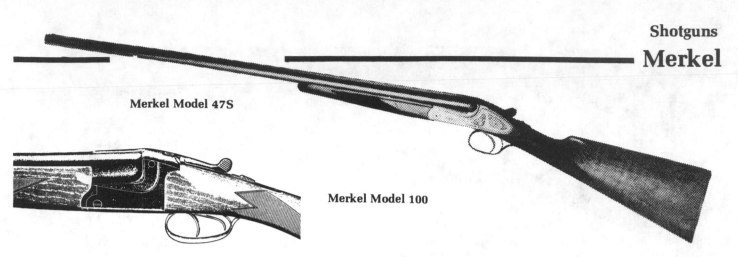

Merkel Model 47S

Merkel Model 100

Merkel Model 100

Gauge: 12, 16, 20
Action: Box lock; top lever, break-open hammerless; over & under double barrel; double triggers
Magazine: None
Barrel: Over & under double barrel; several lengths and chokes available
Finish: Blued; checkered walnut, pistol grip stock & forearm
Approximate wt.: 8 ½ lbs
Comments: A German shotgun produced until World War II. Add $50.00 for ribbed barrel.
Estimated Value: Excellent: $570.00
        Very good: $475.00

Merkel Model 47S

Gauge: 12, 16, 20
Action: Side lock; top lever, break-open hammerless; double barrel
Magazine: None
Barrel: Double barrel; various lengths and chokes
Finish: Blued; checkered walnut, stock & forearm; available with pistol grip or straight stock; engraved.
Approximate wt.: 8 lbs.
Comments: Made from the 1930's to 1970's. Add $50.00 for single trigger.
Estimated Value: Excellent: $1,200.00
        Very good: $1,000.00

Mossberg

Mossberg Model 83D

Mossberg Model 183K

Mossberg Model 83D, 183D

Gauge: 410
Action: Bolt action; repeating
Magazine: 2-shot, top loading; fixed magazine
Barrel: 23" on 83D; 24" on 183D; interchangeable choke fittings
Finish: Blued; hardwood, Monte Carlo, semi-pistol grip, one piece stock & forearm with grooved grip
Approximate wt.: 5 ½ lbs.
Comments: Made as the 83D from about 1940 to 1947, and as the 183D from 1948 until the early 1970's.
Estimated Value: Excellent: $60.00
        Very good: $50.00

Mossberg Model 183K

Similar to the 183D with adjustable choke and recoil pad. Manufactured from the early 1950's to present.
Estimated Value: New (retail): $96.50
        Excellent: $70.00
        Very good: $55.00

Shotguns

Mossberg Model 185K

Mossberg Model 190K

Mossberg Model 190K

Similar to the 183K in 16 gauge. Made from the mid 1950's to the early 1960's
Estimated Value: Excellent: $60.00
Very good: $50.00

Mossberg Model 185K

Similar to the 183K in 20 gauge. Made from about 1950 to the early 1960's.
Estimated Value: Excellent: $60.00
Very good: $50.00

Mossberg Model 195K

Similar to the 183K in 12 gauge. Manufactured from the mid 1950's to early 1960's.
Estimated Value: Excellent: $65.00
Very good: $55.00

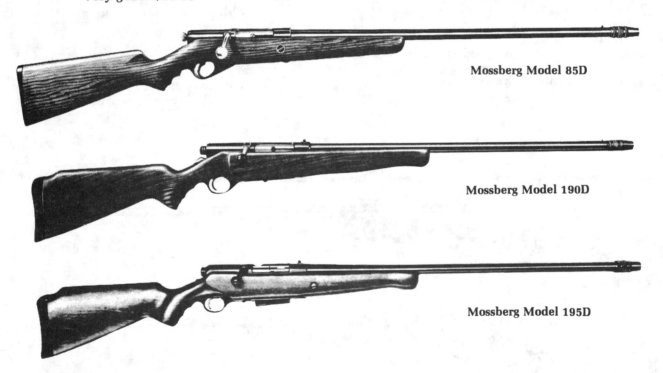

Mossberg Model 85D

Mossberg Model 190D

Mossberg Model 195D

Mossberg Model 85D, 185D

Gauge: 20
Action: Bolt Action; repeating
Magazine: 2-shot detachable box
Barrel: 25" on 85D, 26" on 185D; interchangeable choke fittings
Finish: Blued; hardwood, pistol grip, one piece stock & forearm
Approximate wt.: 6 ½ lbs.
Comments: Made as the 85D from about 1940 to 1948, and as 185D from 1948 to the early 1970's
Estimated Value: Excellent: $85.00
Very good: $65.00

Mossberg Model 190D

Similar to the 185 D in 16 gauge. Made from the mid 1950's to the early 1960's
Estimated Value: Excellent: $75.00
Very good: $60.00

Mossberg Model 195D

Similar to the 185D in 12 gauge. Manufactured from the mid 1950's to the early 1970's.
Estimated Value: Excellent: $80.00
Very good: $60.00

Mossberg Model 385K

Mossberg Model 390 K

Mossberg Model 395K

Mossberg Model 390 K

Similar to 385K with a 28" barrel in 16 gauge. Discontinued in the late 1970's.
Estimated Value: Excellent: **$75.00**
             Very good: **$60.00**

Mossberg Model 395K

Similar to the 385K in 12 gauge. Weighs 7 ½ lbs.
Estimated Value: New (retail): $111.50
             Excellent: **$ 85.00**
             Very good: **$ 65.00**

Mossberg Model 385K

Gauge: 20
Action: Bolt action; repeating
Magazine: 2-shot detatchable box
Barrel: 26" adjustable choke
Finish: Blued; wood, Monte Carlo, semi-pistol grip, one piece stock & tapered forearm; recoil pad
Approximate wt.: 6 ½ lbs.
Comments: Made from the early 1960's to present
Estimated Value: New (retail): $104.95
             Excellent: **$ 80.00**
             Very good: **$ 60.00**

Mossberg Model 200D

Mossberg Model 200K

Mossberg Model 500 Field

Mossberg Model 500 Field

Gauge: 12, 16, 20
Action: Slide action; hammerless; repeating
Magazine: 6-shot tubular
Barrel: 26" adjustable choke or improved cylinder; 28" modified or full; 30" full choke in 12 gauge only.
Finish: Blued; walnut, pistol grip stock and grooved slide handle; recoil pad
Approximate wt: 6-8 lbs.
Comments: Manufactured from about 1960 to the late 1970's.
Estimated Value: **Excellent:**   **$160.00**
                Very good: **$120.00**

Mossberg Model 200D

Gauge: 12
Action: Slide action; hammerless; repeating; slide handle is metal cover over wood forearm
Magazine: 3-shot detatchable box
Barrel: 28" interchangeable choke fittings
Finish: Blued; wood Monte Carlo, semi-pistol grip, one piece stock and forearm
Approximate wt: 7 ½ lbs.
Comments: Manufactured fromt he mid to late 1950's
Estimated Value: **Excellent:**   **$100.00**
                Very good: **$ 80.00**

Mossberg Model 200K

Similar to the 200D with adjustable choke
Estimated Value: Excellent: $120.00
                 Very good: $ 95.00

Shotguns

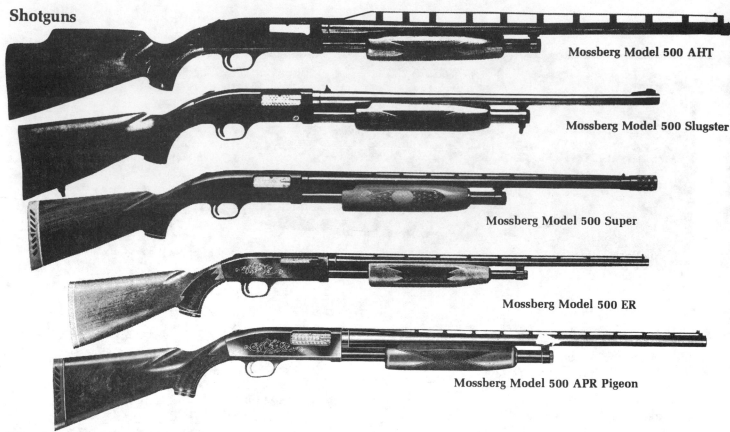

Mossberg Model 500 AHT

Mossberg Model 500 Slugster

Mossberg Model 500 Super

Mossberg Model 500 ER

Mossberg Model 500 APR Pigeon

Mossberg Model 500 Persuader

Similar to the Model 500, built for law enforcement use in five models. Each is 12 gauge, regular or magnum with cylinder bore 20'' barrel, swivels, and recoil pad. 500 ATP-8SP has non-glare barrel, 7 shot magazine (6 in magnum) bead sight; 500ATP-8S has rifle sights, blued barrel; 500 ATP-8 has blued barrel with bead sight; 500 ATP-6S had 5 shot magazine (4 in magnum) and rifle sights; 500 ATP-6 has 5 shot magazine (4 in magnum) and bead sight.

Estimated Value: New (retail): $186.95 - $222.95
                    Excellent: $140.00 - $165.00
                    Very good: $110.00 - $130.00

Mossberg Model 500 ALMR Duck Gun

Similar to 500 in 12 gauge with 30'' or 32'' vent rib barrel for 3'' magnum.

Estimated Value: New (retail): $235.50
                  Excellent: $175.00
                  Very good: $140.00

Mossberg Model 500 Slugster

Similar to 500 with 18'' or 24'' slug barrel and rifle sights. Add $50.00 for removable choke.

Estimated Value: New (retail): $213.95
                  Excellent: $160.00
                  Very good: $125.00

Mossberg Model 500 Hi Rib Trap AHTD, AHT

Similar to 500 with high rib barrel and Monte Carlo stock. AHT full choke; AHTD has adjustable choke. 28'' or 30'' barrel.

Estimated Value: New (retail): $336.95
                  Excellent: $250.00
                  Very good: $200.00

Mossberg Model 500 ALDR, CLDR

Similar to 500 in 12 gauge (ALDR) and 20 gauge (CLDR) with removable choke.

Estimated Value: New (retail): $229.95
                  Excellent: $170.00
                  Very good: $130.00

Mossberg Model 500 Super

Similar to the 500 Field with checkered stock and slide handle & ventilated rib. 12 gauge magnum.

Estimated Value: Excellent: $175.00
                  Very good: $135.00

Mossberg Model 500 ER, ELR

Similar to the 500 Field in 410 gauge; 26'' barrel; skeet version has checkering and ventilated rib (Add $50.00). Currently called ELR.

Estimated Value: New (retail) $219.95
                  Excellent: $165.00
                  Very good: $125.00

Mossberg Model 500 APR Pigeon

Similar to the 500 Field except: engraving; ventilated rib. Made from the late 1960's to late 1970's.

Estimated Value: Excellent: $180.00
                  Very good: $140.00

Mossberg Model 500 APTR Trap

Similar to the 500 APR with a 30'' full choke barrel; Monte Carlo stock. Discontinued in the late 1970's.

Estimated Value: Excellent: $190.00
                  Very good: $150.00

New Haven (Mossberg)

New Haven Model 273

New Haven Model 290

New Haven Model 285

New Haven Model 495

New Haven Model 273

Gauge: 20
Action: Bolt action; hammerless; single shot
Magazine: None
Barrel: 24" full choke
Finish: Blued; plain walnut, Monte Carlo, semi-pistol grip, one-piece stock & forearm
Approximate wt.: 6 ¼ lbs.
Comments: Manufactured in the early 1960's
Estimated Value: Excellent: $50.00
**   Very good: $40.00**

New Haven Model 290

Gauge: 16
Action: Bolt action; hammerless; repeating
Magazine: 2-shot detatchable box
Barrel: 28" removeable full choke
Finish: Blued; walnut, Monte Carlo, pistol grip, one-piece stock & tapered forearm
Approximate wt.: 6 ½ lbs.
Comments: Made in the early 1960's.
Estimated Value: Excellent: $60.00
**   Very good: $50.00**

New Haven Model 285

A 20 gauge version of the 290 with 24" barrel
Estimated Value: Excellent: $60.00
**   Very good: $50.00**

New Haven Model 283, 283T

A 410 gauge version of the 290 with a 24" barrel. Currently called 283T.
Estimated Value: New (retail): $85.00
**   Excellent: $65.00**
**   Very good: $50.00**

New Haven Model 295

A 12 gauge version of the 290.
Estimated Value: Excellent: $65.00
**   Very good: $55.00**

New Haven Model 495, 495T

Gauge: 12
Action: Bolt action; hammerless; repeating
Magazine: 2-shot detatchable box
Barrel: 28" full choke
Finish: Blued; walnut, Monte Carlo, semi-pistol grip stock and tapered forearm
Approximate wt.: 7 ½ lbs.
Comments: Manufactured from the mid 1960's. Currently called 495T.
Estimated Value: New (retail): $99.00
**   Excellent: $70.00**
**   Very good: $55.00**

New Haven 485T

A 20 gauge version of the Model 495.
Estimated Value: New (retail): $93.00
**   Excellent: $70.00**
**   Very good: $55.00**

Shotguns

New Haven Model 600

New Haven Model 600 AST

Similar to Model 600 with 24" barrel and rifle sights.
Estimated Value: New (retail): $174.95
           Excellent: $130.00
           Very good: $100.00

New Haven Model 600, 600 AT30F

Gauge: 12, 20, 410; 600 AT30F - 12 gauge only
Action: Slide action; hammerless; repeating
Magazine: 6 shot tubular
Barrel: 26" improved cylinder, 28" modified or full, 30" full, choked; 600 AT30F full choke only.
Finish: Blued; walnut, semi-pistol grip stock & slide handle
Approximate wt: 7 ½ lbs.
Comments: Made from the early 1960's to present. Currently called 600 AT30F..5
Estimated Value: New (retail): $164.95
           Excellent: $125.00
           Very good: $ 95.00

Noble

Noble Model 420

Noble Model 420

Gauge: 12, 16, 20
Action: Box lock; top lever break-open; hammerless; double barrel; double triggers
Magazine: None
Barrel: Double barrel; 28" modified and full choke
Finish: Blued; checkered walnut pistol grip stock and forearm
Approximate wt.: 6 ¾ lbs.
Comments: Made from the late 1950's to the early 1970's.
Estimated Value: Excellent: $180.00
           Very good: $145.00

Noble Model 420 EK

A fancy version of the Model 420 with automatic ejectors; select walnut; recoil pad; engraving; sights; gold inlay. Made in the late 1960's.
Estimated Value: Excellent: $215.00
           Very good: $175.00

Noble Model 450E

Very similar to Model 420EK. Produced from late 1960's to early 1970's.
Estimated Value: Excellent: $200.00
           Very good: $160.00

Noble Model 40

Noble Model 50

Basically the same gun as the Model 40 without recoil pad or multi-choke.
Estimated Value: Excellent: $100.00
           Very good: $ 80.00

Noble Model 40

Gauge: 12
Action: Slide action; hammerless
Magazine: 5-shot tubular
Barrel: 28" with multi-choke
Finish: Blued; plain walnut pistol grip stock and grooved slide handle; recoil pad
Approximate wt.: 7 ½ lbs.
Comments: Made from the early to mid 1950's.
Estimated Value: Excellent: $120.00
           Very good: $100.00

Noble Model 60

Gauge: 12, 16
Action: Slide action; hammerless
Magazine: 5-shot tubular
Barrel: 28", with variable choke
Finish: Blued; plain walnut pistol grip stock and grooved slide handle; recoil pad
Approximate wt.: 7 ½ lbs.
Comments: Manufactured in takedown version from the mid 1950's to late 1960's.
Estimated Value: Excellent: $110.00
Very good: $ 90.00

Noble Model 60 AF

A fancier version of the Model 60 with special steelbarrel; select wood; fluted comb. Made only during the mid 1960's.
Estimated Value: Excellent: $130.00
Very good: $110.00

Noble Model 60 ACP

Very similar to Model 60 with a ventilated rib. Made from late 1960's to early 1970's.
Estimated Value: Excellent: $120.00
Very good: $100.00

Noble Model 160 Deer Gun, 166L Deer Gun

Very similar to the Model 60 with a 24" barrel, sights; swivels. Made in the mid 1960's as 160 and from late 1960's to early 1970's as 166L.
Estimated Value: Excellent: $125.00
Very good: $105.00

Noble Model 65

Basically the same as the Model 60 without the recoil pad or adjustable choke.
Estimated Value: Excellent: $100.00
Very good: $ 80.00

Noble Model 60

Noble Model 60 AF

Noble Model 160 Deer Gun

Noble Model 65

Noble Model 66 RCLP

Noble Model 66 RCLP

Similar to the Model 60 ACP with a fancier checkered stock.
Estimated Value: Excellent: $135.00
Very good: $110.00

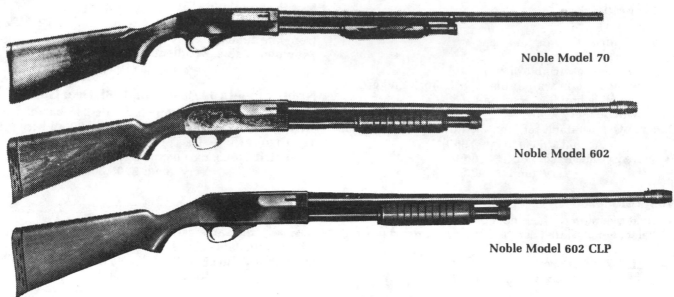

Noble Model 70

Noble Model 602

Noble Model 602 CLP

Noble Model 70 and 70X

Gauge: 410
Action: Slide action; hammerless
Magazine: 5-shot tubular
Barrel: 26'' modified or full choke
Finish: Blued; checkered walnut pistol grip stock and slide handle
Approximate wt.: 6 lbs.
Comments: Produced from the late 1950's to late 1960's as Model 70, from the late 1960's to early 1970's as 70X.
Estimated Value: Excellent: $125.00
                      Very good: $100.00

Noble Model 602

Similar to Model 70 in 20 gauge and 28'' barrel; weighs 6½ lbs. Grooved slide handle.
Estimated Value: Excellent: $130.00
                      Very good: $110.00

Noble Model 602 CLP, 602 RCLP, 602 RLP

602 CLP is same as 602 with adjustable choke and recoil pad; 602 RCLP is same as 602 with recoil pad; 602 RLP is same as 602 with recoil pad and ventilated rib; Add $20.00 for ventilated rib.
Estimated Value: Excellent: $140.00
                      Very good: $120.00

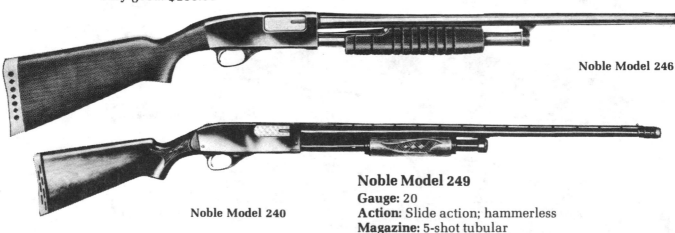

Noble Model 246

Noble Model 240

Noble Model 249

Gauge: 20
Action: Slide action; hammerless
Magazine: 5-shot tubular
Barrel: 28'' modified or full choke
Finish: Blued; checkered walnut, pistol grip stock and slide handle; recoil pad
Approximate wt.: 6½ lbs.
Comments: Produced in the early 1970's
Estimated Value: Excellent: $125.00
                      Very good: $100.00

Noble Model 243

Same as 249 with ventilated rib
Estimated Value: Excellent: $145.00
                      Very good: $115.00

Noble Model 240

Same as 249 with adjustable choke and ventilated rib.
Estimated Value: Excellent: $150.00
                      Very good: $120.00

Noble Model 246

Same as 249 with adjustable choke
Estimated Value: Excellent: $130.00
                      Very good: $110.00

Noble Model 449

Similar to Model 249 without recoil pad and in 410 gauge

Estimated Value: Excellent: $130.00
Very good: $105.00

Noble Model 446

Similar to Model 246 without recoil pad and in .410 gauge.

Estimated Value: Excellent: $135.00
Very good: $110.00

Noble Model 443

Similar to Model 243 without recoil pad and in .410 gauge.

Estimated Value: Excellent: $150.00
Very good: $120.00

Noble Model 440

Similar to Model 240 without recoil pad and in .410 gauge.

Estimated Value: Excellent: $150.00
Very good: $120.00

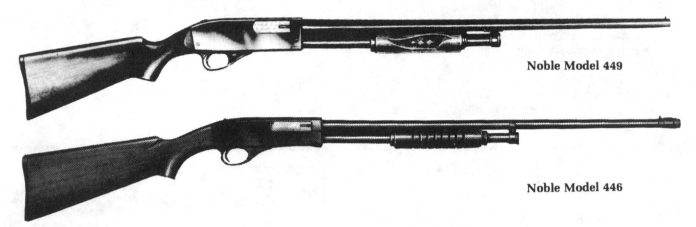

Noble Model 449

Noble Model 446

Noble Model 339

Gauge: 12, 16
Action: Slide action; hammerless
Magazine: 6-shot tubular
Barrel: 28" modified or full choke
Finish: Blued; checkered walnut pistol grip stock and slide handle
Approximate wt.: 7 ½ lbs.
Comments: Made in the early 1970's.
Estimated Value: Excellent: $130.00
Very good: $105.00

Noble Model 390 Deer Gun

Similar to Model 339 with a 24" rifle slug barrel; sights; swivels

Estimated Value: Excellent: $140.00
Very good: $110.00

Noble Model 336

Same as Model 339 with recoil pad and adjustable choke.

Estimated Value: Excellent: $135.00
Very good: $110.00

Noble Model 333

Same as 339 with recoil pad and ventilated rib.

Estimated Value: Excellent: $150.00
Very good: $120.00

Noble Model 330

Same as 333 with adjustable choke.

Estimated Value: Excellent: $150.00
Very good: $120.00

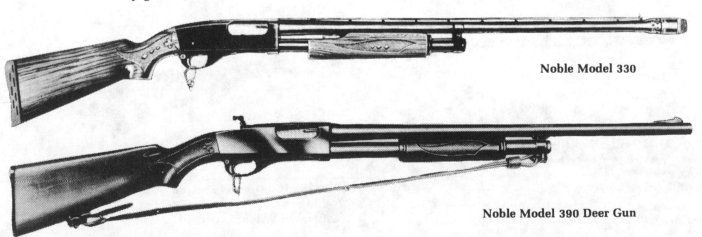

Noble Model 330

Noble Model 390 Deer Gun

Noble Model 80

Noble Model 757
Gauge: 20
Action: Slide action; hammerless
Magazine: 5-shot tubular
Barrel: 28'' aluminum; adjustable choke
Finish: Black anodized aluminum; decorated receiver; checkered walnut, pistol grip stock and slide handle; recoil pad
Approximate wt.: 4 ½ lbs.
Comments: A very light gun made in the early 1970's.
Estimated Value: Excellent: $145.00
Very good: $115.00

Noble Model 80
Gauge: 410
Action: Semi-automatic; hammerless
Magazine: 5-shot tubular
Barrel: 26'' full choke
Finish: Blued; plain walnut, pistol grip stock and forearm
Approximate wt.: 6 lbs.
Comments: Made in the mid 1960's
Estimated Value: Excellent: $175.00
Very good: $140.00

Parker

Parker Single Barrel Trap
Gauge: 12
Action: Single shot; hammerless; top lever break-open; box lock
Magazine: None
Barrel: 30'', 32'', 34'' any choke; ventilated rib
Finish: Straight, semi-pistol grip or full pistol grip; checkered walnut stock; blued
Approximate wt.: 6 ½-7 ½ lbs.
Comments: Grades differ according to workmanship, checkering, and engraving. Made from about 1917 to 1941. Manufacture of Parker guns was taken over by Remington in 1934 and this gun was called Remington Parker Model 930. There is a wide range of values for this gun.
Estimated Value: Excellent: $3,000.00 - $12,000.00
Very good: $2,000.00 - $10,000.00

Parker Single Barrel Trap

Parker Trojan
Gauge: 12, 16, 20
Action: Top lever, break-open; hammerless; box lock; double barrel
Magazine: None
Barrel: Double barrel; 26'', 28'', 30'', full & full or modified & full, chokes
Finish: Blued; checkered walnut, pistol grip stock and forearm
Approximate wt.: 6 ½-8 lbs.
Comments: Made from about 1915 to 1939
Estimated Value: Excellent: $600.00 - $1,200.00
Very good: $475.00 - $1,000.00

Parker Trojan

Parker Hammerless Double

Gauge: 10, 12, 16, 20, 23, 410
Action: Top lever break-open; hammerless; box lock; double barrel; selective trigger and automatic ejectors after 1934
Magazine: None
Barrel: 26", 28", 30", 32" any choke combination; double barrel
Finish: Blued; straight, semi-pistol grip or full pistol grip, checkered walnut stock and forearm
Approximate wt.: 6½-8½ lbs.
Comments: Grades vary according to workmanship, checkering, and engraving. Manufacture of Parker guns was taken over by Remington in 1934 and this gun was called Remington Parker Model 920 until it was discontinued in 1941.
Estimated Value: Excellent: $2,100.00 - $16,000.00
Very good: $1,800.00 - $15,000.00

Parker Hammerless Double G.H.E.

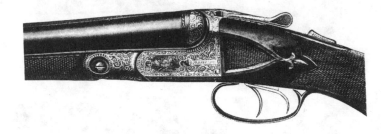

Parker Hammerless Double A.H.E.

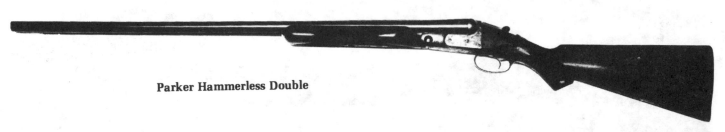

Parker Hammerless Double

Pedersen

Pedersen Model 2000 Grade II

Gauge: 12, 20
Action: Box lock; top lever break-open; hammerless; double barrel; automatic ejectors; single selective trigger
Magazine: None
Barrel: Double barrel; length to customer's specifications
Finish: Blued; checkered walnut, pistol grip stock and tapered forearm; engraved
Approximate wt.: 7½ lbs.
Comments: Produced in the mid 1970's
Estimated Value: Excellent: $550.00
Very good: $450.00

Pedersen Model 2000 Grade I

Similar to Grade II with fancier engraving, gold filling on receiver, select walnut.
Estimated Value: Excellent: $1,075.00
Very good: $ 900.00

Pedersen Model 2500

A field version of the 2000; no engraving; beavertail forearm
Estimated Value: Excellent: $300.00
Very good: $200.00

Pedersen 2500

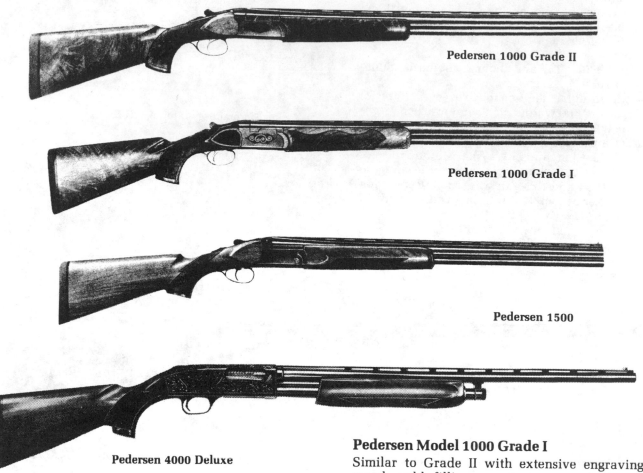

Pedersen 1000 Grade II

Pedersen 1000 Grade I

Pedersen 1500

Pedersen 4000 Deluxe

Pedersen Model 1000 Grade I

Similar to Grade II with extensive engraving, select wood, gold filling on receiver; made to customers specifications; in hunting skeet or trap models.
Estimated Value: Excellent: **$1,800.00**
                  Very good: **$1,500.00**

Pedersen Model 1000 Grade III

Gauge: 12, 20
Action: Box lock; top lever break-open; hammerless; automatic ejectors; single selective trigger; over and under double barrel
Magazine: None
Barrel: Over and under double barrel; length made to customers specifications; ventilated rib
Finish: Blued; checkered walnut, pistol grip stock and forearm; recoil pad
Approximate wt.: 7 ½ lbs.
Comments: Produced in the mid 1970's.
Estimated Value: Excellent: $540.00
                Very good: $450.00

Pedersen Model 1500

A field version of the 1000 with standard barrel lengths only, (26'', 28'', 30'', or 32'')
Estimated Value: Excellent: $420.00
                Very good: $340.00

Pedersen Model 4000 Deluxe

Gauge: 12, 10, 410
Action: Slide action; hammerless; side ejection
Magazine: Tubular
Barrel: 26'', 28'', 30'' variety of chokes; ventilated rib.
Finish: Blued; checkered walnut, pistol grip stock and slide handle; recoil pad; floral engraving on receiver
Approximate wt.: 6 ¾ lbs.
Comments: Made in the mid 1970's.
Estimated Value: Excellent: $275.00
                Very good: $225.00

Pedersen Model 1000 Grade II

Similar to Grade III with engraving and fancier wood; made to customer's specifications. Add $15.00 for magnum.
Estimated Value: Excellent: **$1,450.00**
                Very good: **$1,175.00**

Premier Regent

Gauge: 12, 16, 20, 28, 410
Action: Box locks; top lever break-open; hammerless; double barrel; double triggers
Magazine: None
Barrel: Double barrel; 26", 28" modified and full chokes; matted rib
Finish: Blued; checkered walnut pistol grip stock and tapered forearm.
Approximate wt.: 7 lbs.
Comments: Produced currently
Estimated Value: New (retail): $250.00 Approx.
          Excellent: $185.00
          Very good: $150.00

Premier Brush King

Similar to Regent in 12 and 20 gauge only; 22" improved cylinder and modified choke barrels; straight stock. Still in production.
Estimated Value: New (retail): $270.00
          Excellent: $200.00
          Very good: $160.00

Premier Magnum

Similar to Regent except: 10 gauge magnum with 32 inch barrels or 12 gauge magnum with 30 inch barrels; both gauges in full and full choke; recoil pad; beavertail forearm. Add $25.00 for 10 gauge magnum.
Estimated Value: New (retail): $280.00
          Excellent: $210.00
          Very good: $165.00

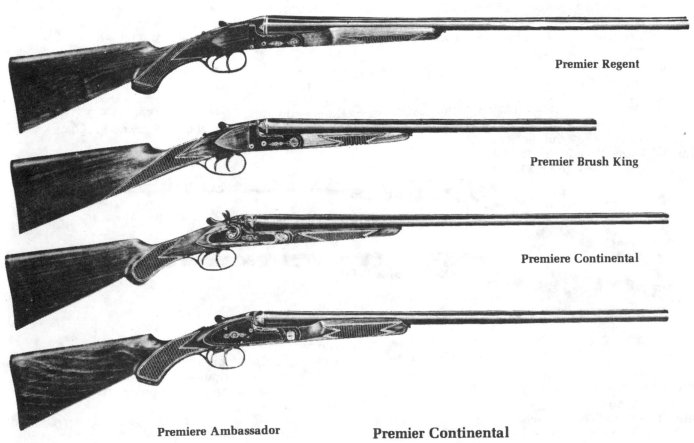

Premier Regent

Premier Brush King

Premiere Continental

Premiere Ambassador

Premier Ambassador

A hammerless version of the Continental. Also available in 410 gauge.
Estimated Value: Excellent: $175.00
          Very good: $150.00

Premier Continental

Gauge: 12, 16, 20
Action: Side lock; top lever break-open; exposed hammer; double barrel; double triggers
Magazine: None
Barrel: 26" modified and full choke
Finish: Blued; checkered walnut, pistol grip stock and tapered forearm
Approximate wt.: 7 lbs.
Comments: Produced in the 1970's.
Estimated Value: Excellent: $225.00
          Very good: $190.00

Remington

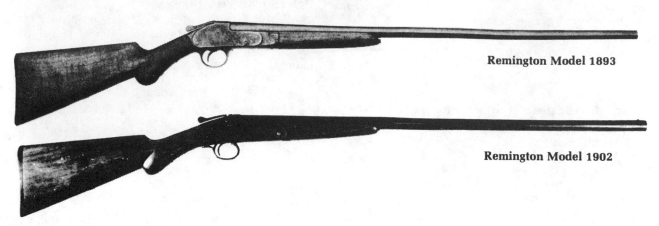

Remington Model 1893

Remington Model 1902

Remington Model 1893

Gauge: 10, 12, 16, 20
Action: Top lever, break-open; semi-hammer (cocking lever on left), takedown (single shot)
Magazine: None
Barrel: 28", 30", 32" or 34"; plain barrel with bead at muzzle in standard chokes
Finish: Blued; case hardened receiver; smooth walnut, half pistol grip stock and forearm
Approximate wt.: 5½-6½ lbs.
Comments: Made from about 1893 to 1906. Approximately 25000 were produced. Also known as the No. 3 and the '93.
Estimated Value: Excellent: $150.00
Very good: $125.00

Remington Model 1902

Similar to Model 1893 except improved with automatic ejector. Made from about 1902 to 1912. Last Single shot shotgun made by Remington.
Estimated Value: Excellent: $180.00
Very good: $150.00

Remington Parker 930

Remington took over production of the Parker shotguns in 1934.
Estimated Value: Excellent: $500.00-$1200.00
Very good $400.00-$1100.00

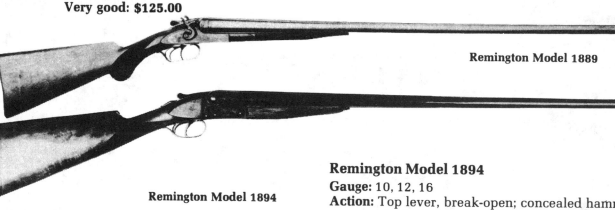

Remington Model 1889

Remington Model 1894

Remington Model 1894

Gauge: 10, 12, 16
Action: Top lever, break-open; concealed hammers; triple lock; double triggers; some models have automatic ejectors, double barrel
Magazine: None
Barrel: Double barrel; 26-32" tapered barrels; full, modified or cylinder bore; ordnance steel or Damascus barrels with concave matted rib.
Finish: Blued; checkered walnut, semi-pistol grip or straight grip stock and short tapered forearm; special engraving and inlays on higher grades
Approximate wt.: 7½-8½"
Comments: Manufactured from about 1894 to 1910 in 7 grades. Receivers marked Remington Arms Co. on left side. Prices for Standard Grade. Deduct $150.00-$125.00 for Damascus barrels.
Estimated Value: Excellent: $725.00
Very good: $600.00

Remington Model 1889

Gauge: 10, 12, 16
Action: Top lever break-open; side lock; breech loading black powder; exposed hammer; double trigger; double barrel
Magazine: None
Barrel: Double barrel; 28"-32" full, modified or cylinder chokes; Damascus or steel
Finish: Blued; Checkered walnut, semi-pistol grip stock and short forearm;
Approximate wt.: 7½-9 lbs.
Comments: Manufactured from about 1889 to 1909 in 7 grades. Approximately 30000 produced. Prices for Standard Grade
Estimated Value: Excellent: $420.00
Very good: $375.00

Remington Model 1900

Remington Parker Model 920

Remington took over production of the Parker shotguns in 1934.

Estimated Value: Excellent: **$750.00**
         Very good: **$675.00**

Remington Model 1900

Gauge: 12, 16
Action: Top lever, break-open; concealed hammers; double triggers; automatic ejectors optional; double barrel
Magazine: None
Barrel: Double barrel; 28" or 32" steel or Damascus in standard chokes; matted rib
Finish: Checkered walnut pistol grip stock and short tapered forearm with gap at front for disassembly
Approximate wt.: 8-9 lbs.
Comments: Similar to Model 1894 except lower grade; takedown model; internal forearm release; Made from about 1900 to 1910. Deduct $100.00 for Damascus barrels.
Estimated Value: Excellent: **$350.00**
         Very good: **$315.00**

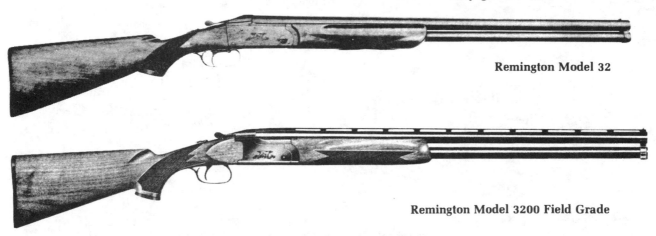

Remington Model 32

Remington Model 3200 Field Grade

Remington Model 32

Gauge: 12
Action: Top Lever, break-open; concealed hammers; single selective trigger; automatic ejectors; over & under double barrel
Magazine: None
Barrel: Over & under double barrel; 26"-32" plain, solid or ventilated rib; full and modified choke standard, but any combination available
Finish: Blued; engraved receiver; checkered walnut, pistol grip stock and forearm
Approximate wt.: 7¾-8½ lbs.
Comments: One of the first modern American over & under double barrel shotguns produced. Manufactured from about 1932 to 1942. Made in about six grades, higher grades with fancier wood and engravings. Add $35.00 for solid rib, $50.00 for ventilated rib.
Estimated Value: Excellent: **$1,000.00**
         Very good: **$ 900.00**

Remington Model 3200 Field Grade

Gauge: 12
Action: Top lever, break-open; concealed hammers; over & under double barrel; selective single trigger; automatic ejectors.
Magazine: None
Barrel: 26"-30" over & under double barrel; ventilated rib; modified & full choke or improved cylinder and modified, chokes
Finish: Blued; Pointing dogs engraved on the receiver; checkered walnut, pistol grip stock and matching forearm
Approximate wt.: 7¾-8¼ lbs.
Comments: A modern version of the Model 32 started back in production in the early 1970's. Still available in Trap and Skeet models. Other models valued higher than Field Grade.
Estimated Value: Excellent: **$695.00**
         Very good: **$575.00**

Shotguns

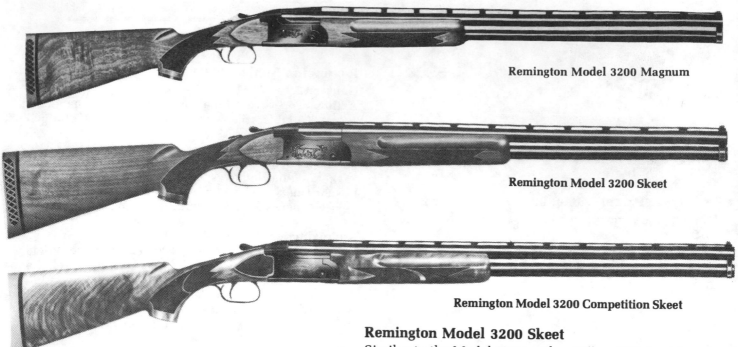

Remington Model 3200 Magnum

Remington Model 3200 Skeet

Remington Model 3200 Competition Skeet

Remington Model 3200 Skeet

Similar to the Model 3200 with a 26" or 28" skeet barrel; ventilated rib only; recoil pad; Monte Carlo stock.

Estimated Value: New (retail): $1,125.00
Excellent: $ 850.00
Very good: $ 700.00

Remington Model 3200 Magnum

Similar to the Model 3200 Field Grade except: chambered for 12 gauge magnum; 30" barrels in full & full chokes or modified & full chokes; receiver decorated with engraved scrollwork.

Estimated Value: Excellent: $720.00
Very good: $600.00

Remington Model 3200 Competition Skeet

Similar to the Model 3200 Skeet with a higher quality finish

Estimated Value: New (retail): $1,350.00
Excellent: $1,025.00
Very good: $ 850.00

Remington Model 3200 Special Trap

Similar to the Model 3200 with a 32" barrel; ventilated rib only; Monte Carlo stock available; recoil pad.

Estimated Value: New (retail): $1,200.00
Excellent: $ 950.00
Very good: $ 775.00

Remington Model 3200 Competetion Trap

Similar to the Model 3200 Special Trap with a higher quality finish.

Estimated Value: New (retail): $1,350.00
Excellent: $1,050.00
Very good: $ 850.00

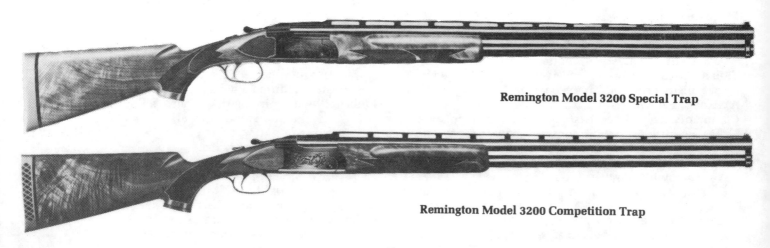

Remington Model 3200 Special Trap

Remington Model 3200 Competition Trap

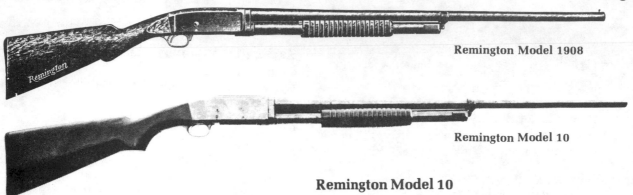

Remington Model 1908

Remington Model 10

Remington Model 1908

Gauge: 12
Action: Slide action; hammerless; bottom ejection; repeating
Magazine: 5-shot tubular
Barrel: 26''-32'' steel barrel in full, modified or cylinder bore
Finish: Blued; plain or checkered, straight or pistol grip walnut stock and forearm
Approximate wt.: 7½-8 lbs.
Comments: Manufactured from about 1908 to 1910 in 6 grades with fancy checkering and engraving on higher grades. Markings on top of barrel "Remington Arms Co." and patent date. About 10,000 made.
Estimated Value: Excellent: $300.00
Very good: $250.00

Remington Model 10

Gauge: 12
Action: Slide action; hammerless; bottom ejection; repeating
Magazine: 5-shot tubular
Barrel: 26''-32'' steel barrel in full, modified or cylinder bore
Finish: Blued; plain or checkered, straight or pistol grip, walnut stock and grooved or checkered forearm
Approximate wt.: 7½-8 lbs.
Comments: Produced from about 1910 to 1928, this is an improved version of the Model 1908. Made in 7 grades with fancy checkering and engraving on higher grades. Also produced in 20'' barrel riot gun. Solid rib optional from 1910-1922. Ventilated rib optional from 1922-1928. Prices for standard grade.
Estimated Value: Excellent: $240.00
Very good: $195.00

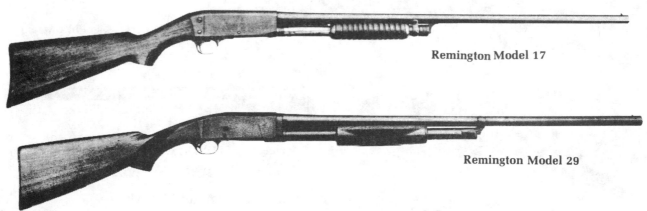

Remington Model 17

Remington Model 29

Remington Model 17

Gauge: 20
Action: Slide action; hammerless; bottom ejection; repeating
Magazine: 3-shot tubular
Barrel: 26''-32'' steel in full, modified or cylinder bore; matted sighting groove on receiver or optional solid rib; 20'' barrel on riot gun
Finish: Blued; plain or checkered, straight or pistol grip, walnut stock and forearm
Approximate wt.: 7½-8 lbs.
Comments: Made from about 1917 to 1933 in 7 grades. Higher grades have higher quality finish.
Estimated Value: Excellent: $265.00
Very good: $215.00

Remington Model 29

Gauge: 12
Action: Slide action; hammerless; bottom ejection; repeating
Magazine: 5-shot tubular
Barrel: 28''-32'' steel in full, modified or cylinder bore; optional solid or ventilated rib; 20'' barrel on riot gun
Finish: Blued; plain or checkered, straight or pistol grip, walnut stock and forearm
Approximate wt.: 7½-8 lbs.
Comments: Made from about 1929 to 1933 in 9 grades. Higher grades have higher quality finish. Prices are for standard.
Estimated Value: Excellent: $200.00
Very good: $170.00

Shotguns

Remington Model 31

Remington Model 31 Skeet

Similar to Model 31 except: 12 gauge only, 26" barrel, solid or ventilated rib; skeet choke. Add $20.00 for ventilated rib.

Estimated Value: Excellent: $375.00
Very good: $330.00

Remington Model 31 R Riot Gun

Similar to Model 31 in 12 gauge only, with 20" plain barrel.

Estimated Value: Excellent: $190.00
Very good: $165.00

Remington Model 31

Gauge: 12, 16, 20
Action: Slide action; hammerless; side ejection; repeating
Magazine: 3 or 5 shot tubular
Barrel: 26", 32", steel; full, modified, cylinder or skeet chokes; optional solid or ventilated rib
Finish: Blued; sighting groove on receiver; plain or checkered, pistol grip stock and forearm; forearm checkered or grooved
Approximate wt: 6½-8 lbs.
Comments: Manufactured from about 1931 to 1949 in 8 grades. Higher grades differ in quality of finish. Prices for standard grades. Add $20.00 for solid rib, $25.00 for ventilated rib.

Estimated Value: Excellent: $240.00
Very good: $200.00

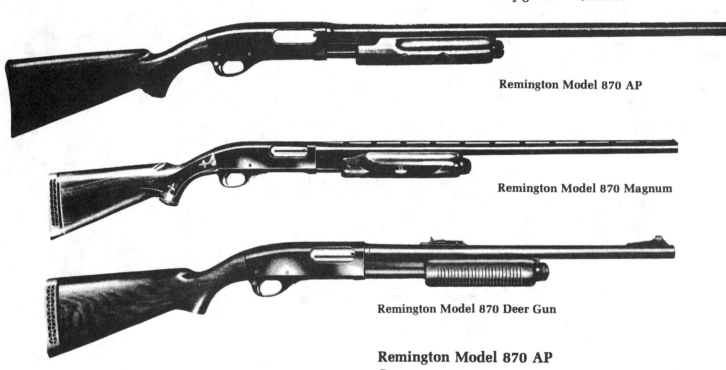

Remington Model 870 AP

Remington Model 870 Magnum

Remington Model 870 Deer Gun

Remington Model 870 Magnum

Similar to Model 870 AP except: 12 gauge magnum; 30" full choke barrel; recoil pad. Produced from about 1955 to 1964. Add $25.00 for ventilated rib.

Estimated Value: Excellent: $210.00
Very good: $175.00

Remington Model 870 Deer Gun

Similar to the Model 870 AP except: 12 gauge only; 26" barrel for slugs; rifle type adjustable sights. Produced from about 1959 to 1964.

Estimated Value: Excellent: $180.00
Very good: $145.00

Remington Model 870 AP

Gauge: 12, 16, 20
Action: Slide action; hammerless; side ejection; repeating
Magazine: 4-shot tubular
Barrel: 26, 28, 30" in 12 gauge; 26 or 28" in 16 & 20 gauge; full, modified or improved cylinder chokes; plain or ventilated rib
Finish: Blued; plain or fancy; fluted comb, pistol grip stock and grooved slide handle
Approximate wt: 6½-8 lbs.
Comments: Made in many styles, grades, and variations from about 1950 to 1964. Higher grades have higher quality finish. Prices for standard grade. Add $25.00 for ventilated rib.

Estimated Value: Excellent: $190.00
Very good: $160.00

Remington Model 870 Riot Gun

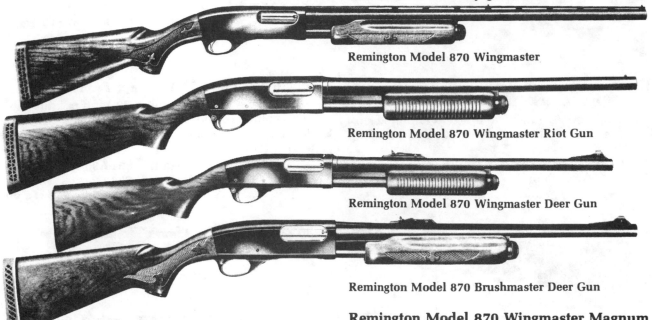

Remington Model 870 Wingmaster

Remington Model 870 Wingmaster Riot Gun

Remington Model 870 Wingmaster Deer Gun

Remington Model 870 Brushmaster Deer Gun

Remington Model 870 Riot Gun

Same as the Model 870AP except: 12 gauge only; 20''
plain barrel; improved cylinder bore.
Estimated Value: Excellent: $170.00
Very good: $140.00

Remington Model 870 Wingmaster Field Gun

Gauge: 12, 16, 20 from 1964 to preset; 28 410 from
1969 to present
Action: Slide action; hammerless; side ejection;
repeating
Magazine: 4-shot tubular
Barrel: 26-30'' in 12 gauge; 26'' or 28'' in 16 & 20 gauge;
25'' in 28 and 410 gauge; full, modified or im-
proved cylinder bore; plain barrel or ventilated
rib
Finish: Blued; checkered walnut, pistol grip stock with
matching forearm; recoil pad
Approximate wt: 5½-7¼ lbs.
Comments: Improved version of the Model 870AP.
Made in many grades and styles from about
1965 to present. Left hand models available
and also lightweight models. Prices for stan-
dard grades. Add $35.00 for ventilated rib.
Add $15.00 for left hand.
Estimated Value: New (retail): $268.95
Excellent: $200.00
Very good: $165.00

Remington Model 870 Wingmaster Riot Gun

Similar to to Model 870 Wingmaster except: 12 gauge
only; 18'' or 20'' improved cylinder barrel; plain stock &
grooved slide handle; designed for law enforcement
use. Add $20.00 for rifle sights.
Estimated Value: New (retail): $247.95
Excellent: $185.00
Very good: $150.00

Remington Model 870 Wingmaster Magnum

Same as the Model 870 Field Grade except: 12 or 20
magnum gauge only; full or modified choke. Add
$35.00 for ventilated rib.
Estimated Value: New (retail): $296.95
Excellent: $220.00
Very good: $180.00

Remington Model 870 Wingmaster Deer Gun

Same as the Model 870 Wingmaster except: 12 gauge or
20 gauge lightweight; 20'' barrel; rifle sights; Produced
from 1964 to present. Plain stock & grooved forearm;
checkering on later models. Add $20.00 for lightweight.
Estimated Value: New (retail): $269.95
Excellent: $205.00
Very good: $160.00

Remington Model 870 Brushmaster Deer Gun

Same as the Model 870 Wingmaster Deer Gun except:12
& 20 gauge; checkered stock & slide handle; recoil pad.
Estimated Value: New (retail): $287.95
Excellent: $215.00
Very good: $175.00

Remington Model 870 Bicentennial

Similar to the Model 870 Wingmaster except: 12 gauge
only; skeet grade (26'' skeet choke) and trap grade (30''
full choke); ventilated rib. Manufactured in 1976 as a
commemorative gun with special Bicentennial engraving on receiver.

Estimated Value:	Skeet	Trap
Excellent:	$250.00	$275.00
Very good:	$195.00	$210.00

Shotguns

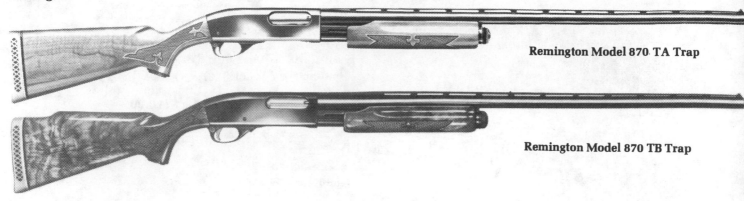

Remington Model 870 TA Trap

Remington Model 870 TB Trap

Remington Model 870SA Skeet

Similar to the Model 870 in skeet choke; ventilated rib only; recoil pad. Made from the late 1970's to present; 25" or 26" barrel.

Estimated Value: New (retail): $311.95
Excellent: $235.00
Very good: $190.00

Remington Model 870 TB Trap, TA Trap

Similar to the Model 870 with a 30" full or trap choke barrel; ventilated rib only; recoil pad; choice of Monte Carlo stock on TB Model; add $10.00 for Monte Carlo

Estimated Value:	T A	T B
New (retail):	$317.95	$353.95
Excellent:	$240.00	$270.00
Very good:	$195.00	$215.00

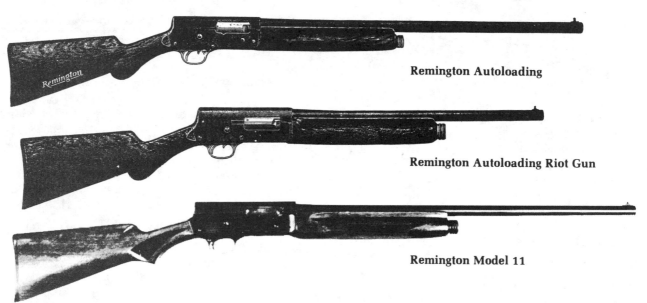

Remington Autoloading

Remington Autoloading Riot Gun

Remington Model 11

Remington Autoloading

Gauge: 12
Action: Semi-automatic; concealed hammer
Magazine: 5-shot tubular
Barrel: 26", 28" steel; full, modified or cylinder bore
Finish: Blued; matted sight groove; plain or checkered, straight or pistol grip, stock and forearm
Approximate wt.: 7 ¾ lbs.
Comments: Made from about 1905 to 1910 in 6 grades. Prices for Standard Grade
Estimated Value: Excellent: $180.00
Very good: $135.00

Remington Autoloading Riot Gun

Similar to the Standard Grade except: 20" barrel and weighs 6 ¾ lbs.
Estimated Value: Excellent: $160.00
Very good: $130.00

Remington Model 11

Gauge: 12 only to 1931; 1931-1948, 12, 16, 20
Action: Semi-automatic; concealed hammer; side ejection; repeating
Magazine: 4-shot, bottom load
Barrel: 26 or 28" to 1931; 1931 to 1948, 26, 28, 30, 32"; full, modified or cylinder
Finish: Blued; wood semi-pistol grip stock; straight grip on trap grades; checkering and fancy wood on higher grades
Approximate wt.: 7 ½-8 ½ lbs.
Comments: Made from about 1911 to 1948 in 6 grades. Optional solid or ventilated rib available; rounded grip ends on stock from 1911 to 1916. Prices are for standard grade. Add $15.00 for ribbed barrel.
Estimated Value: Excellent: $215.00
Very good: $180.00

Remington Model 11 Sportsman

Remington Model 11 Riot Gun

Remington Model 11 Sportsman

Same as the Model 11 with a 2-shot magazine. Made from about 1931 to 1948 in 6 grades. Prices for the standard grade. Add $15.00 for solid rib, $25.00 for ventilated rib.
Estimated Value: Excellent: $270.00
Very good: $220.00

Remington Model 11 Riot Gun

Same as the Model 11 except with a 20" plain barrel.
Estimated Value: Excellent: $180.00
Very good: $150.00

Remington Model 11-48

Remington Model 11-48

Gauge: 12, 16, 20; 28 after 1952; 410 after 1954
Action: Semi-automatic; hammerless; side ejection; take down; cross bolt safety
Magazine: 4-shot; 3-shot in 28 and 410 gauge; tubular
Barrel: 26, 28, 30" in 12, 16, & 20 gauge; 25" in 28 and 410 gauge; Full, modified or improved cylinder
Finish: Checkered walnut, pistol grip stock with fluted comb, matching semi-beavertail forearm; higher grades fancier
Approximate wt.: 6½-7½ lbs.
Comments: Made from about 1949 to 1968 in about 7 grades. This gun replaced the Model 11. It had an improved action and the rear of the receiver was rounded off flush with the stock. Prices for standard model. Add $30.00 for ventilated rib.
Estimated Value: Excellent: $220.00
Very good: $185.00

Remington 11-48 Riot Gun

Same general specifications as the Model 11-48 except: 12 gauge only; 20" plain barrel. Made from about 1954-1968.
Estimated Value: Excellent: $195.00
Very good: $150.00

Remington Model 48

Remington Model 48

Similar to the Model 11-48 except: 2-shot magazine; 12, 16, 20 gauge; Made in several grades to replace the Model 11 Sportsman from about 1948-1959. Prices for standard model. Add $30.00 for ventilated rib.
Estimated Value: Excellent: $175.00
Very good: $145.00

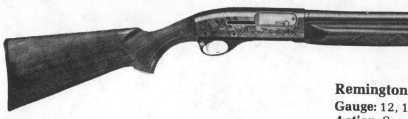

Remington Sportsman 58

Remington Sportsman 58 Rifled Slug Special

Same as the Sportsman 58 except: 12 gauge only; 26" barrel for slugs; equipped with rifle sights.
Estimated Value: Excellent: $215.00
Very good: $180.00

Remington Sportsman 58 Magnum

Similar to the Sportsman 58 except 12 gauge magnum; 30" barrel; recoil pad. Made from the late 1950's to early 1960's. Add $30.00 for ventilated rib.
Estimated Value: Excellent: $250.00
Very good: $200.00

Remington Sportsman 58

Gauge: 12, 16, 20
Action: Semi-automatic; hammerless; side ejection; solid breech; gas operated sliding bolt; fixed barrel
Magazine: 2-shot tubular
Barrel: 26", 28", 30"; plain or ventilated rib; full, modified, improved cylinder or skeet chokes
Finish: Blued; checkered walnut pistol grip, fluted comb stock, with matching semi-beavertail forearm
Approximate wt.: 6½-7½ lbs.
Comments: Manufactured from about 1956 to 1963. Prices for standard model. Add $30.00 for ventilated rib.
Estimated Value: Excellent: $250.00
Very good: $200.00

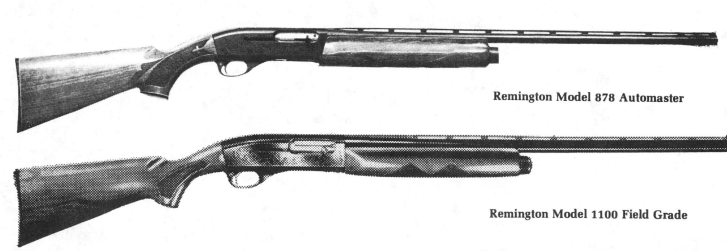

Remington Model 878 Automaster

Remington Model 1100 Field Grade

Remington Model 878 Automaster

Gauge: 12
Action: Semi-automatic; gas operated; hammerless
Magazine: 2-shot tubular
Barrel: 26-30" full, modified, improved cylinder or skeet chokes
Finish: Blued; plain or checkered, pistol grip wood stock and forearm
Approximate wt.: 7 lbs.
Comments: Made similar to the Sportsman 58 to fill in the sales line with a lower priced plain standard grade shotgun. Manufactured from about 1959 to 1962 in two grades. Prices for standard model. Add $30.00 for ventilated rib.
Estimated Value: Excellent: $180.00
Very good: $145.00

Remington Model 1100 Field Grade

Gauge: 12, 16, 20; after 1970 added 28 and 410 gauge
Action: Semi-automatic; gas operated sliding bolt; fixed barrel; solid breech; hammerless; takedown
Magazine: 4-shot tubular
Barrel: 26, 28" in 16 & 20 gauge; 26, 28, 30" in 12 gauge; 25" in 28 & 410 gauge; full, modified, improved cylinder & skeet chokes
Finish: Blued; checkered wood, pistol grip stock with fluted comb and matchig forearm; engraved receiver
Approximate wt: 6½-7½ lbs.
Comments: An improved low-recoil shotgun to replace the 58, 11-48 and 878. Manufactured from about 1963 to present in several grades. Add $35.00 for ventilated rib, $10.00 for left hand model.

Estimated Value:	Regular Wt.	Light Wt.
New (retail):	$340.95	$344.95
Excellent:	$255.00	$260.00
Very good:	$205.00	$210.00

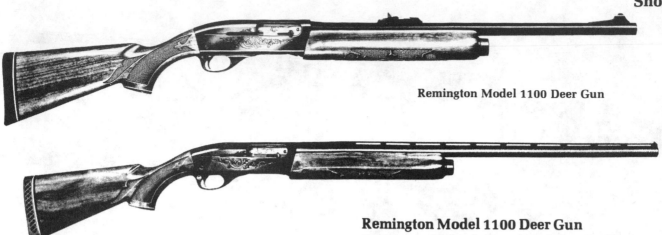

Remington Model 1100 Deer Gun

Remington Model 1100 Magnum

Remington Model 1100 Deer Gun

Similar to the Model 1100 with a 22" plain barrel and adjustable rifle sights; bored for rifle slugs; 12 or 20 gauge lightweight

Estimated Value: New (retail): $377.95
Excellent: $285.00
Very good: $230.00

Remington Model 1100 Bicentennial

Similar to the Model 1100 in 12 gauge only; ventilated rib; skeet grade 26" skeet choke barrel or trap grade 30" full choke barrel. Made in 1976 as a commemorative gun with a special Bicentennial engraving on the receiver. Add $25.00 for Trap grade.

Estimated Value: Excellent: $360.00
Very good: $300.00

Remington Model 1100 Magnum

Similar to the Model 1100 except; 12 or 20 gauge magnum; 28 or 30" barrel; full or modified chokes; recoil pad. Add $37.50 for ventialted rib, $12.00 for lightweight model in 20 gauge. Right or left hand model available.

Estimated Value: New (retail): $376.95
Excellent: $285.00
Very good: $230.00

Remington Model 1100 LT 20 Limited

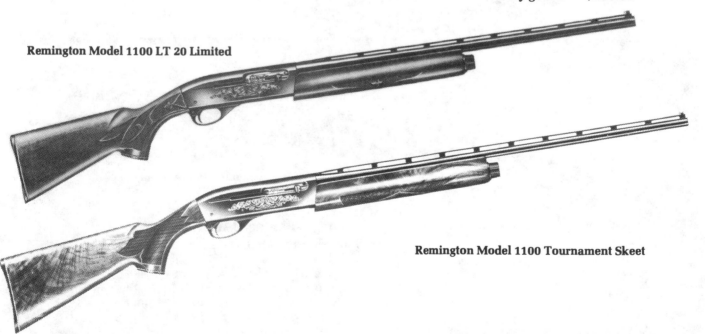

Remington Model 1100 Tournament Skeet

Remington Model 1100 Tournament Skeet

Similar to the Model 1100SA Skeet with higher quality finish.

Estimated Value: New (retail): $459.95
Excellent: $350.00
Very good: $280.00

Remington Model 1100 LT 20 Limited

A scaled down version of the Model 1100 for young shooters; 20 gauge only; introduced in 1980.

Estimated Value: New (retail): $378.95
Excellent: $290.00
Very good: $235.00

Shotguns

Remington Model 1100 TA Trap

Remington Model 1100 TA Monte Carlo

Remington Model 1100 Tournament Trap

Remington Model 1100 Tournament Trap Monte Carlo

Remington Model 1100SA Skeet

Remington Model 1100TA Trap

Similar to the Model 1100 with a 30'' full or modified trap barrel; ventilated rib only; recoil pad; choice of Monte Carlo stock. Add $10.00.

Estimated Value:	New (retail):	$397.95
	Excellent:	$300.00
	Very good:	$240.00

Remington Model 1100SA Skeet

Similar to the Model 1100 with a 25'' or 26'' skeet choke barrel; ventilated rib only; scroll receiver; made from the late 1970's to present.

Estimated Value:	New (retail):	$389.95
	Excellent:	$295.00
	Very good:	$235.00

Remington Model 1100 Tournament Trap

Similar to the Model 1100 TA Trap with higher quality finish.

Estimated Value:	New (retail):	$480.95
	Excellent:	$365.00
	Very good:	$290.00

Richland Model 200

Gauge: 12, 16, 20, 28 410
Action: Box lock; top lever, break-open; hammerless; double trigger; doubel barrel
Magazine: None
Barrel: Double barrel; 22' improved cylinder and modified in 20 gauge; 26", 28" improved & modified or modified & full choke
Finish: Blued; checkered walnut pistol grip stock and tapered forearm; cheekpiece; recoil pad
Approximate wt: 6 to 7 lbs.
Comments: Manufactured from the early 1960's to present.
Estimated Value: New (retail): $428.00
Excellent: $320.00
Very good: $255.00

Richland Model 200

Richland Model 202

This is the same shotgun as the Model 200 with an extra set of barrels in the same gauge. Produced until the mid 1970's.
Estimated Value: Excellent: $400.00
Very good: $320.00

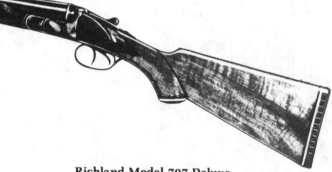

Richland Model 707 Deluxe

Gauge: 12, 20
Action: Box lock; top lever break-open; hammerless; double barrel; double trigger
Magazine: None
Barrel: Double barrel; 26", 28", 30" variety of chokes
Finish: Blued; checkered walnut pistol grip stock and tapered forearm; recoil pad
Approximate wt.: 7 lbs.
Comments: Produced from the mid 1960's to the mid 1970's.
Estimated Value: Excellent: $290.00
Very good: $235.00

Richland Model 707 Deluxe

Richland Model 711 Long Range Waterfowl

Gauge: 10, 12 magnum
Action: Box lock; top lever, break-open; hammerless; double barrel; double trigger
Magazine: None
Barrel: Double barrel; 30", 32" full choke
Finish: Blued; checkered walnut pistol grip stock and tapered forearm
Approximate wt: 8 tp 10 lbs.
Comments: Produced from the early 1960's. Add $50.00 for 10 gauge.
Estimated Value: New (retail): $455.00
Excellent: $340.00
Very good: $275.00

Richland Model 711 Long Range Waterfowl

Shotguns

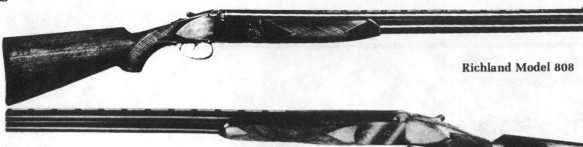

Richland Model 808

Richland Model 808

Gauge: 12

Action: Box lock; top lever break-open; hammerless; over and under double barrel; non-selective single trigger.

Magazine: None

Barrel: Over & under double barrel; 26" improved cylinder and modified; 28" modified and full; 30" full and full choke

Finish: Blued; checkered walnut pistol grip stock and forearm; ribbed barrel

Approximate wt.: 7 lbs.

Comments: Made from the early to late 1960's.

Estimated Value: Excellent: $300.00
Very good: $250.00

Richland Model 828

Richland Model 828

Gauge: 28

Action: Box lock; top lever break-open; hammerless; over and under double barrel

Magazine: None

Barrel: Over and under double barrel; 26" improved and modified, 28" modified and full, chokes

Finish: Blued; case hardened receiver; checkered walnut pistol grip stock and forearm; ribbed barrel

Approximate wt.: 7 lbs.

Comments: Produced from the early 1970's

Estimated Value: Excellent: $350.00
Very good: $300.00

Richland Model 844

Gauge: 12, magnum

Action: Box lock; top lever break-open; hammerless; over and under double barrel; non-selective single trigger

Magazine: None

Barrel: Over and under double barrel; 26" improved cylinder and modified; 28" modified and full, 30" full choke

Finish: Blued; checkered walnut pistol grip stock and forearm

Approximate wt.: 7 lbs.

Comments: Produced from early 1970's.

Estimated Value: Excellent: $250.00
Very good: $200.00

Richland Model 844

Ruger

Ruger Over & Under

Ruger Over & Under

Gauge: 20, regular or magnum

Action: Box lock; top lever, break-open, over and under double barrel; hammerless

Magazine: None

Barrel: Over and under double barrel; 26" or 28" variety of choke combinations; ventilated rib

Finish: Checkered walnut pistol grip stock and semi-beavertail forearm; pistol grip cap; recoil pad

Approximate wt: 7 lbs.

Comments: Introduced in the late 1970's.

Estimated Value: New (retail): $675.00
Excellent: $510.00
Very good: $410.00

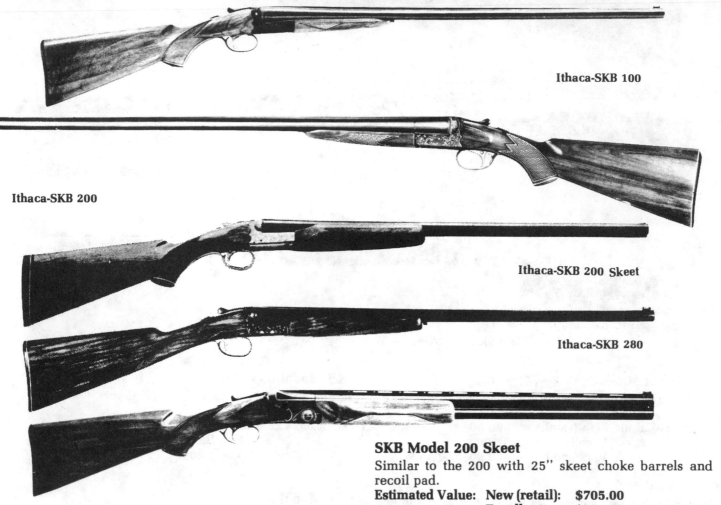

Ithaca-SKB 100

Ithaca-SKB 200

Ithaca-SKB 200 Skeet

Ithaca-SKB 280

Ithaca-SKB 500

SKB Model 100

Gauge: 12, 12 magnum, 20
Action: Box lock; top lever, break-open; hammerless; doubel barrel; single slective trigger
Magazine: None
Barrel: Double barrel; 26", 28" improved cylinder & modified chokes, or 30" full choke in 12 gauge
Finish: Blued; checkered hardwood, pistol grip stock and short tapered forearm
Approximate wt: 6-7 lbs.
Comments: Made from the mid 1960's to present.
Estimated Value: New (retail): $490.00
Excellent: $370.00
Very good: $295.00

SKB Model 200

Similar to the SKB 100 with engraved silverplate frame; wide forearm; select walnut; automatic selective ejectors. Add $21.00 for magnum.
Estimated Value: New (retail): $678.00
Excellent: $510.00
Very good: $425.00

SKB Model 200 Skeet

Similar to the 200 with 25" skeet choke barrels and recoil pad.
Estimated Value: New (retail): $705.00
Excellent: $525.00
Very good: $425.00

SKB Model 280

Similar to the 200 without silver frame; has straight grip stock.
Estimated Value: New (retail): $718.00
Excellent: $530.00
Very good: $430.00

SKB Model 500

Gauge: 12, 20, 12 magnum, 28, 410
Action: Box lock; top lever, break-open; hammerless; over and under double barrel
Magazine: None
Barrel: Over and under double barrel; 26" improved cylinder & modified; 28, 30" modified & full; ventilated rib; chrome lined.
Finish: Blued; checkered walnut, pistol grip stock and forearm; recoil pad on magnum; front sight; engraved receiver.
Approximate wt: 6½-8 lbs.
Comments: Made from the mid 1960's to present; Add $19.00 for magnum.
Estimated Value: New (retail): $680.00
Excellent: $520.00
Very good: $435.00

Shotguns

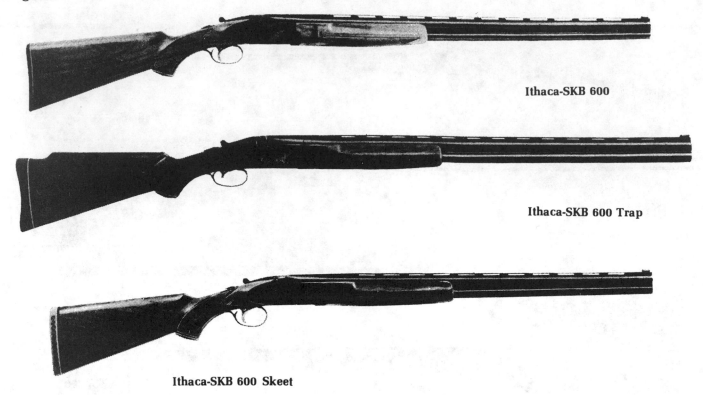

Ithaca-SKB 600

Ithaca-SKB 600 Trap

Ithaca-SKB 600 Skeet

SKB Model 500 Skeet
Similar to the Model 500 with 26" or 28" skeet choke barrels.

Estimated Value:	New (retail):	$690.00
	Excellent:	$520.00
	Very good:	$420.00

SKB Model 600
Similar to the 500 with select wood; trigger mounted barrel selector; silverplate frame; middle sight.

Estimated Value:	New (retail):	$815.00
	Excellent:	$620.00
	Very good:	$490.00

SKB Model 600 Trap
Similar to the 600 with regular or Monte Carlo stock; 12 gauge only; recoil pad; 30" or 32" full choke barrels.

| Estimated Value: | Excellent: | $630.00 |
| | Very good: | $500.00 |

SKB Model 600 Skeet
Similar to the 600 with 26" or 28" skeet choke barrels and recoil pad.

Estimated Value:	New (retail):	$839.00
	Excellent:	$625.00
	Very good:	$500.00

SKB Model 680
Similar to the 600 with a straight grip stock.

| Estimated Value: | Excellent: | $630.00 |
| | Very good: | $490.00 |

SKB Model 700
Similar to the 600 with higher quality finish and more extensive engraving.

| Estimated Value: | Excellent: | $720.00 |
| | Very good: | $575.00 |

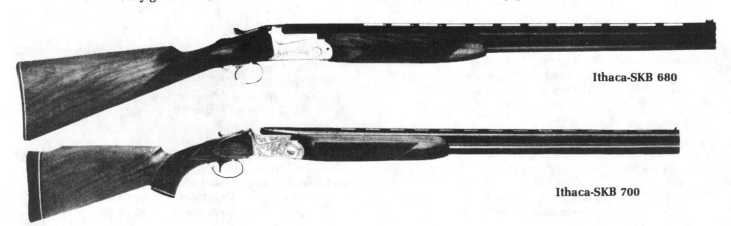

Ithaca-SKB 680

Ithaca-SKB 700

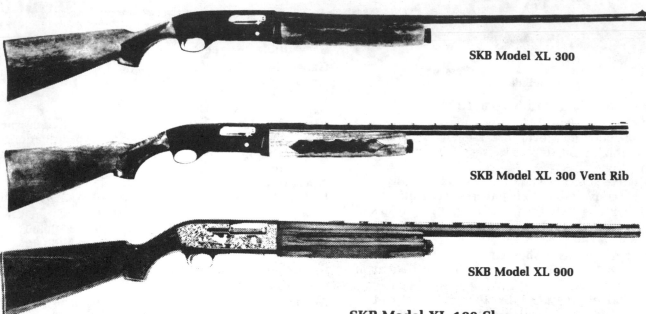

SKB Model XL 300

SKB Model XL 300 Vent Rib

SKB Model XL 900

SKB Model 7300

Gauge: 12 or 20, regular or magnum
Action: Slide action; hammerless
Magazine: 4 shot tubular
Barrel: 26" improved cylinder; 28" modified; 28" or 30" full; ventilated rib; 24" slug barrel available
Finish: Blued; checkered pistol grip stock and slide handle; recoil pad
Approximate wt: 7 lbs.
Comments: Currently manufactured.
Estimated Value: New (retail): $310.00
Excellent: $235.00
Very good: $200.00

SKB XL 300

Gauge: 12, 20
Action: Gas operated, semi-automatic; hammerless
Magazine: 5 shot tubular
Barrel: 26" improved cylinder or skeet, 28" modified or full, 30" modified or full, chokes
Finish: Blued; decorated receiver; checkered walnut, pistol grip stock & forearm
Approximate wt.: 6-7 lbs
Comments: Made from the early 1970's to late 1970's.
Estimated Value: Excellent: $225.00
Very good: $180.00

SKB XL 300 Vent Rib

Similar to the XL 300 with front sights and ventilated rib.
Estimated Value: Excellent: $250.00
Very good: $200.00

SKB Model XL 100 Slug

A no frills slug gun with 20" barrel; rifle sights; swivels; similar to the XL 300.
Estimated Value: New (retail): $275.00
Excellent: $205.00
Very good: $165.00

SKB XL 900

Similar to the XL 300 vent rib with engraved silverplated receiver; gold trigger & name plate.
Estimated Value: New (retail): $371.00
Excellent: $275.00
Very good: $225.00

SKB XL 900 Slug

Similar to the XL 900 with a 24" barrel for slugs; rifle sights; swivels.
Estimated Value: Excellent: $270.00
Very good: $220.00

SKB XL 900 Trap

Similar to the XL 900 with middle sights; no silver receiver; recoil pad; choice of regular or Monte Carlo stock.
Estimated Value: Excellent: $260.00
Very good: $210.00

SKB XL 900 Skeet

Similar to the XL 900 Trap with skeet stock and skeet choke barrel.
Estimated Value: New (retail): $393.00
Excellent: $290.00
Very good: $235.00

SKB Model XL900 MR

Similar to the XL 900 for 3" magnum shells; recoil pad; deduct $35.00 for slug model.
Estimated Value: New (retail): $407.00
Excellent: $305.00
Very good: $245.00

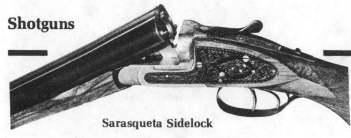

Sarasqueta Sidelock

Sarasqueta Sidelock Grades 4 to 12

Gauge: 12, 16, 20, 28
Action: Sidelock; top lever break-open; hammerless; double barrel; double triggers
Magazine: None
Barrel: Double barrel; standard barrel lengths and chokes available to customers specifications
Finish: Blued; checkered walnut straight grip or pistol grip stock and forearm
Approximate wt.: Varies
Comments: A Spanish shotgun still in production. Grades differ as to quality and extent of engraving.

Estimated Value:	Grade	Excellent	Very Good
	4	$ 330.00	$ 265.00
	5	$ 375.00	$ 290.00
	6	$ 400.00	$ 320.00
	7	$ 450.00	$ 360.00
	8	$ 675.00	$ 540.00
	9	$ 800.00	$ 650.00
	10	$ 930.00	$ 745.00
	11	$1,200.00	$ 975.00
	12	$1,500.00	$1,200.00

Sarasqueta Folding Shotgun

Gauge: 410
Action: Box lock; top lever break-open, exposed hammer; double barrel
Magazine: None
Barrel: Double barrel; 26'' choice of chokes
Finish: Blued; case hardened frame; walnut pistol grip stock & forearm
Approximate wt.: Varies
Comments: A "folding" shotgun in production since early 1970's
Estimated Value: Excellent: $95.00
Very good: $80.00

Sarasqueta Model 2 & 3

Gauge: 12, 16, 20, 28
Action: Box lock; top lever break-open; hammerless; double barrel; double trigger
Magazine: None
Barrel: Double barrel; standard barrel lengths and chokes available to customer's specifications
Finish: Blued; checkered walnut straight grip stock and forearm
Approximate wt.: Varies
Comments: Produced from the mid 1930's. Grades differ only in engraving style.
Estimated Value: Excellent: $250.00 to $300.00
Very good: $200.00 to $250.00

Sarasqueta Over & Under Deluxe

Gauge: 12
Action: Side lock; top lever break-open; hammerless; double barrel (over and under) double triggers, automatic ejectors
Magazine: None
Barrel: Over and under double barrel; lengths and chokes made to customer's specifications
Finish: Blued; checkered walnut pistol grip stock and forearm
Approximate wt.: Varies
Comments: Produced from the mid 1930's.
Estimated Value: Excellent: $1,000.00
Very good: $ 800.00

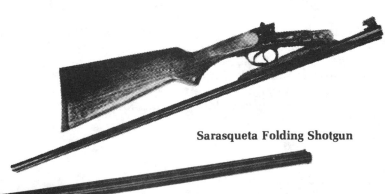

Sarasqueta Folding Shotgun

Sauer

Sauer Royal

Sauer Royal

Gauge: 12, 20
Action: Box lock; top lever, break-open; hammerless; double barrel; single selective trigger; automatic ejectors
Magazine: None
Barrel: Double barrel; 28'' modified and full, 26'' improved and modified in 20 gauge, 30'' full in 12 gauge
Finish: Blued; engraved frame; checkered walnut psitol grip stock and tapered forearm; recoil pad
Approximate wt: 6 to 7 lbs.
Comments: Produced in Germany from the mid 1950's.
Estimated Value: Excellent: $600.00
Very good: $520.00

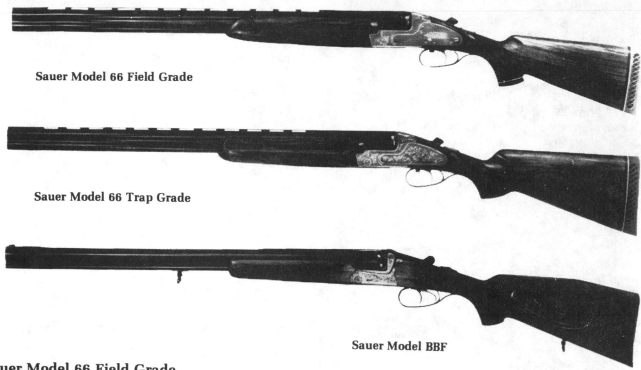

Sauer Model 66 Field Grade

Sauer Model 66 Trap Grade

Sauer Model BBF

Sauer Model 66 Field Grade

Gauge: 12
Action: Purdey action; hammerless; single selective trigger; automatic ejectors; over and under double barrel
Magazine: None
Barrel: Over and under double barrel; 28" modified and full choke; ventilated rib.
Finish: Blued; checkered walnut pistol grip stock and forearm; recoil pad; engraving
Approximate wt.: 7 lbs.
Comments: Produced from the mid 1950's. Prices are for Grade I. Fancier Grades II & III differ in quality and extent of engraving.
Estimated Value: Excellent: $1,100.00
                   Very good: $ 925.00

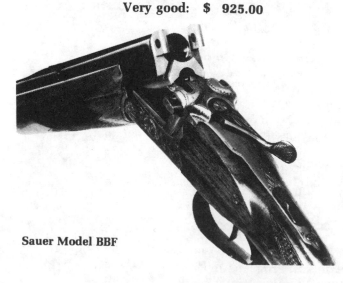

Sauer Model BBF

Sauer Model 66 Trap Grade

This is basically the same as the Field Grade with 30" barrels and a trap stock. Also produced in 3 grades.
Estimated Value: Excellent: $1,250.00
                   Very good: $1,050.00

Sauer Model 66 Skeet

This is basically the same as the Trap Model with 25" barrel in shkeet choke.
Estimated Value: Excellent: $1,200.00
                   Very good: $1,000.00

Sauer Model BBF

Gauge: 16
Caliber: 30-30, 30-06, 7 x 65
Action: Kersten lock; Blitz action; top lever break open; hammerless; over and under combination double barrel; double trigger
Magazine: None
Barrel: Over and under rifle-shotgun combination; 25" Krupp barrels; rifle barrel and full choke shotgun barrel
Finish: Blued; checkered walnut, Monte Carlo pistol grip, stock and forearm; engraved; sights; swivels
Approximate wt.: 6 lbs.
Comments: Produced from the mid 1950's. Also available in deluxe model with extensive engraving.
Estimated Value: Excellent: $1,250.00
                   Very good: $1,025.00

Savage

Savage Model 220

Gauge: 12, 16, 20, 28, 410
Action: Top lever, break-open; single shot; hammerless; automatic ejector
Magazine: None (single shot)
Barrel: Full choke; in 12 & 16 gauge; 28", 30", 32"; in 20 gauge: 26", 28", 30", 32"; in 28 gauge: 28", 30"; in 410 bore: 26", 28"
Finish: Blued; plain wood, pistol grip stock and forearm
Approximate wt.: 6 lbs.
Comments: Made from 1930's until late 1940's. Reintroduced in the mid 1950's with 36" barrel. Replaced by 220L in mid 1960's
Estimated Value: Excellent: $60.00
Very good: $50.00

Savage Model 220P

Basically the same as 220 except no 410 gauge, has "Poly-Choke" and recoil pad
Estimated Value: Excellent: $65.00
Very good: $55.00

Savage Model 220L

Similar to Model 220 except has side lever. Made from mid 1960's to early 1970's.
Estimated Value: Excellent: $50.00
Very good: $40.00

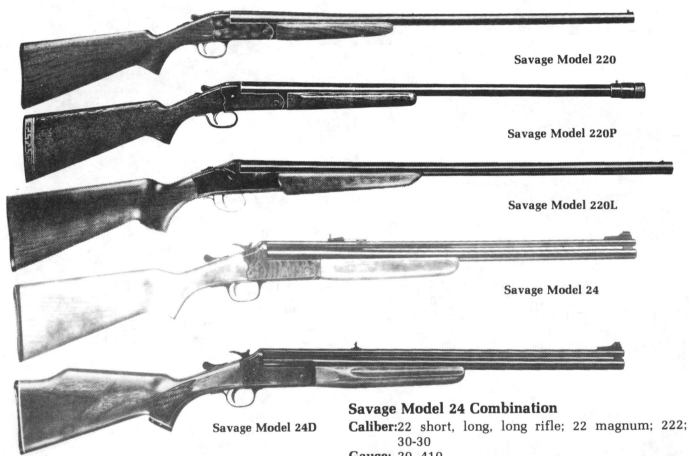

Savage Model 220

Savage Model 220P

Savage Model 220L

Savage Model 24

Savage Model 24D

Savage Model 24V

Similar to the Model 24 in caliber 357, 222, 223, 30-30. Introduced in 1979.
Estimated Value: New(retail): $155.48
Excellent: $120.00
Very good: $100.00

Savage Model 24D

Deluxe version of the Model 24.
Estimated Value: New(retail): $131.00
Excellent: $100.00
Very good: $ 80.00

Savage Model 24 Combination

Caliber: 22 short, long, long rifle; 22 magnum; 222; 30-30
Gauge: 20, 410
Action: Over and under double barrel; rifle barrel over shotgun barrel; exposed hammer; top lever, break-open; single trigger
Magazine: None
Barrel: 24" rifle barrel over shotgun barrel
Finish: Blued; checkered walnut finish hardwood pistol grip stock and forearm; sporting rear, ramp front sights; case hardened reciever
Approximate wt: 6 lbs.
Comments: Produced from the early 1950's to present.
Estimated Value: New (retail): $127.40
Excellent: $100.00
Very good: $ 80.00

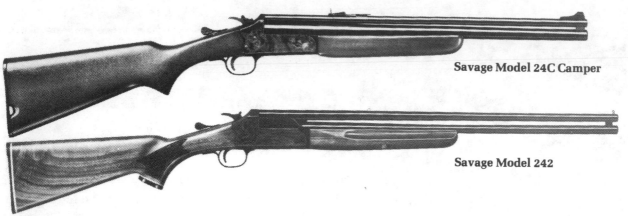

Savage Model 24C Camper

Savage Model 242

Savage Model 24C Camper

A shorter version of the Model 24; 20" barrel; 5¾ lbs.; buttplate swings to expose storage area.

Estimated Value:	New (retail):	$140.25
	Excellent:	$110.00
	Very good:	$ 85.00

Savage Model 242

Similar to the Model 24 with 410 gauge over and under shotgun barrels; full choke; bead sights; introduced in 1979.

Estimated Value:	New (retail):	$156.20
	Excellent:	$125.00
	Very good:	$105.00

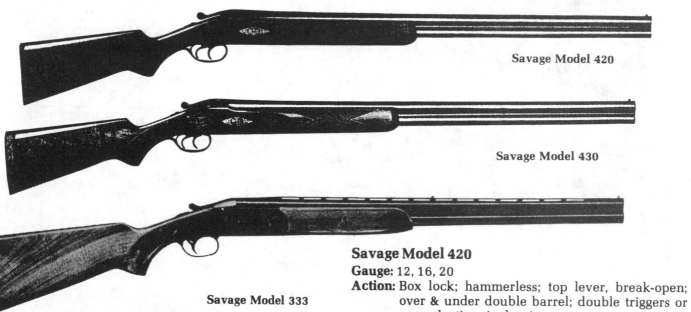

Savage Model 420

Savage Model 430

Savage Model 333

Savage Model 333

Gauge: 12, 20

Action: Hammerless; top lever, break-open; over & under double barrel

Magazine: None

Barrel: Over & under double barrel; 26"-30" variety of chokes

Finish: Blued; checkered walnut, pistol grip stock and forearm

Approximate wt: 6¼-7¼ lbs.

Comments: Made from the early 1970's to late 1970's.

Estimated Value:	Excellent:	$515.00
	Very good:	$425.00

Savage Model 420

Gauge: 12, 16, 20

Action: Box lock; hammerless; top lever, break-open; over & under double barrel; double triggers or non-selective single trigger

Magazine: None

Barrel: Over and under double barrel; 26" to 30" modified and full choke or cylinder bore and modified

Finish: Blued; plain walnut, pistol grip stock and forearm

Approximate wt.: 6¾ to 7¾ lbs.

Comments: Produced from the mid 1930's until World War II. Add $25.00 for single trigger.

Estimated Value:	Excellent:	$300.00
	Very good:	$240.00

Savage Model 430

This is the same shotgun as Model 420 with special checkered walnut stock and forearm; matted upper barrel; recoil pad. Add $25.00 for single trigger.

Estimated Value:	Excellent:	$325.00
	Very good:	$275.00

Shotguns

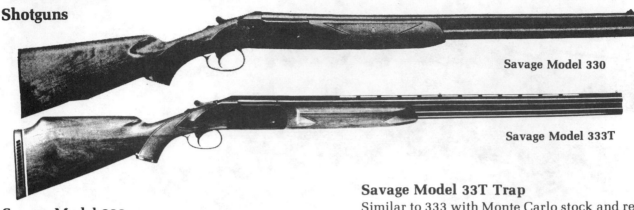

Savage Model 330

Savage Model 333T

Savage Model 330
Similar to 333 without ventilated rib.
Estimated Value: Excellent: $405.00
                 Very good: $325.00

Savage Model 33T Trap
Similar to 333 with Monte Carlo stock and recoil pad in 12 gauge, 30'' barrel.
Estimated Value: Excellent: $505.00
                 Very good: $420.00

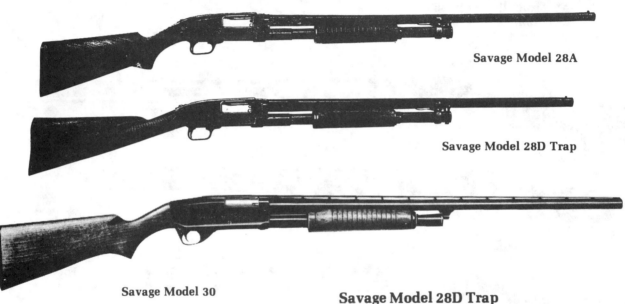

Savage Model 28A

Savage Model 28D Trap

Savage Model 30

Savage Model 28A & B Standard
Gauge: 12
Action: Slide action; hammerless; solid breech; side ejection
Magazine: 5-shot tubular
Barrel: 26'', 28'', 30'', or 32'' cylinder, modified, or full choke; raised rib on 28B
Finish: Blued; checkered wood, pistol grip stock & grooved slide handle
Approximate wt.: 7 ½ lbs.
Comments: Produced from late 1920's until mid 1930's. Add $10.00 for matted rib.
Estimated Value: Excellent: $150.00
                 Very good: $120.00

Savage Model 28C Riot
Basically the same as 28A except with a 20'' cylinder bore barrel. This was for use by police, bank guards, and etc., for protection.
Estimated Value: Excellent: $130.00
                 Very good: $105.00

Savage Model 28D Trap
Basically the same as 28B except; special straight checkered walnut stock and checkered slide handle; 30'' full choke barrel
Estimated Value: Excellent: $180.00
                 Very good: $145.00

Savage Model 28S Special
Basically the same as 28B except: ivory bead front sight; checkered pistol grip stock; checkered forearm.
Estimated Value: Excellent: $190.00
                 Very good: $150.00

Savage Model 30
Gauge: 12, 20, 410
Action: Slide action; hammerless
Magazine: 4-shot tubular
Barrel: 26'', 28'', 30'', cylinder bore, modified or full choke; ventilated rib
Finish: Blued; decorated receiver; walnut pistol grip stock & grooved slide handle
Approximate wt.: 6 ½ lbs.
Comments: Made from late 1950's to late 1960's
Estimated Value: Excellent: $160.00
                 Very good: $125.00

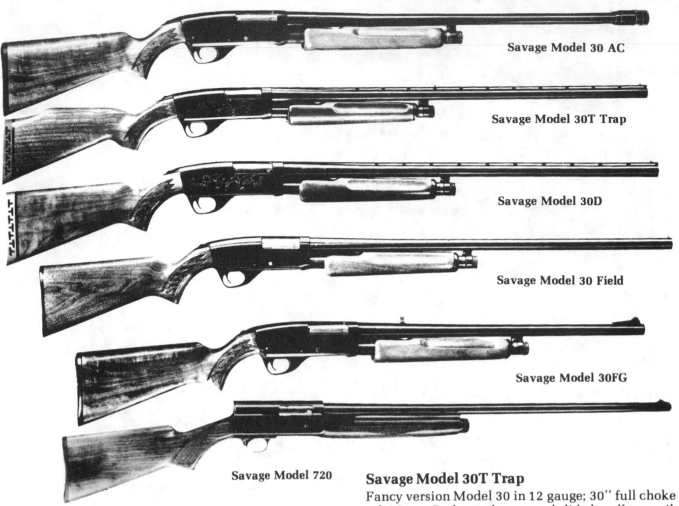

Savage Model 30 AC

Savage Model 30T Trap

Savage Model 30D

Savage Model 30 Field

Savage Model 30FG

Savage Model 720

Savage Model 30 FG (Field Grade)
Similar to Model 30 with plain receiver, no ventilated rib and horizontal groove in slide handle.
Estimated Value: Excellent: $130.00
Very good: $105.00

Savage Model 30FG Slug Gun
Same as Model 30FG with 22'' barrel and rifle sights, 12 gauge. Introduced 1971, discontinued in the late 1970's.
Estimated Value: Excellent: $145.00
Very good: $120.00

Savage Model 30D (Deluxe)
1970's version of the Model 30 with recoil pad and horizontal groove in slide handle. Discontinued in the late 1970's.
Estimated Value: Excellent: $170.00
Very good: $135.00

Savage Model 30 AC
Same as Model 30 with adjustable choke.
Estimated Value: Excellent: $165.00
Very good: $130.00

Savage Model 30T Trap
Fancy version Model 30 in 12 gauge; 30'' full choke barrel; Monte Carlo stock; grooved slide handle; recoil pad; Introduced in mid 1960's.
Estimated Value: Excellent: $175.00
Very good: $140.00

Savage Model 720
Gauge: 12
Action: Browning patent; autoloader; hammerless
Magazine: 4-shot tubular
Barrel: Round 28'', 30'' or 32'' cylinder bore, modified or full choke
Finish: Blued; checkered walnut, pistol grip stock and forearm; after 1940, engraved receiver
Approximate wt.: 8 ½ lbs.
Comments: Originally a Springfield shotgun, this takedown model was made from about 1930 until the late 1940's. In the early 1940's Model 720R (Riot Gun) was introduced with a 20'' barrel
Estimated Value: Excellent: $180.00
Very good: $145.00

Savage Model 720-P
Basically the same as 720 with "Poly-Choke" produced from the late 1930's to 1940's; 3 or 5-shot; 12 gauge only
Estimated Value: Excellent: $185.00
Very good: $150.00

Shotguns

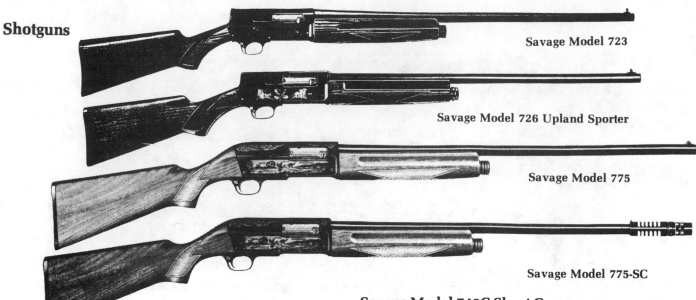

Savage Model 723

Savage Model 726 Upland Sporter

Savage Model 775

Savage Model 775-SC

Savage Model 721
Same as 720 with matted rib
Estimated Value: Excellent: $190.00
Very good: $150.00

Savage Model 722
Same as 720 except has ventilated rib.
Estimated Value: Excellent: $200.00
Very good: $160.00

Savage Model 723
Same as 720 except no 32" barrel, available in 16 gauge. Weighs about 7 ½ lbs.
Estimated Value: Excellent: $170.00
Very good: $135.00

Savage Model 724
Same as 723 except has matted rib.
Estimated Value: Excellent: $180.00
Very good: $145.00

Savage Model 725
Same as 723 except with ventilated rib.
Estimated Value: Excellent: $195.00
Very good: $160.00

Savage Model 726 Upland Sporter
Basically the same as 720 except no 32" barrel; 2-shot tubular magazine; available in 16 gauge; decorated receiver
Estimated Value: Excellent: $180.00
Very good: $145.00

Savage Model 727 Upland Sporter
Same as Model 726 except with matted rib.
Estimated Value: Excellent: $195.00
Very good: $155.00

Savage Model 728 Upland Sporter
Same as model 726 except with ventilated rib.
Estimated Value: Excellent: $200.00
Very good: $160.00

Savage Model 740C Skeet Gun
Basically the same as Model 726 with a skeet stock and "Cutts Compensator". Discontinued in the late 1940's.
Estimated Value: Excellent: $190.00
Very good: $150.00

Savage Model 745 Lightweight
Similar to Model 720 with light alloy receiver. Made from late 1930's to 1940's; 3 or 5-shot; 12 gauge only
Estimated Value: Excellent: $195.00
Very good: $155.00

Savage Model 755
Gauge: 12, 16
Action: Semi-automatic; hammerless
Magazine: 4-shot tubular; 3-shot tubular
Barrel: 26" cylinder bore, 28" full or modified, 30" full choke
Finish: Blued; checkered walnut, pistol grip stock and forearm
Approximate wt.: 8 lbs.
Comments: Produced from the late 1940's until late 1950's; top of receiver flush with stock.
Estimated Value: Excellent: $180.00
Very good: $140.00

Savage Model 755 - SC
Similar to 755 with Savage "Super Choke".
Estimated Value: Excellent: $190.00
Very good: $150.00

Savage Model 775 Lightweight
Similar to 755 with alloy receiver. Produced until mid 1960's.
Estimated Value: Excellent: $170.00
Very good: $135.00

Savage Model 775 - SC
Basically the same as Model 755 with Savage Super choke and 26" barrel.
Estimated Value: Excellent: $190.00
Very good: $150.00

Savage Model 750

Gauge: 12
Action: Browning patent; semi-automatic; hammerless
Magazine: 4-shot tubular
Barrel: 26" cylinder bore; 28" full or modified
Finish: Blued; checkered walnut, pistol grip stock and forearm; decorated receiver
Approximate wt.: 7 ¼ lbs.
Comments: Produced from early to late 1960's
**Estimated Value: Excellent: $240.00
                  Very good: $195.00**

Savage Model 750 SC

Model 750 with Savage "Super Choke". Produced from 1962 for 2 years.
**Estimated Value: Excellent: $260.00
                  Very good: $210.00**

Savage Model 750 AC

Model 750 with adjustable choke. Made during mid 1960's.
**Estimated Value: Excellent: $250.00
                  Very good: $200.00**

Savage Model 750

Savage Model 750 AC

Sears

Sears Single Barrel

Gauge: 12, 20 410
Action: Box lock; top lever, break-open; exposed hammer; automatic ejector
Magazine: None
Barrel: Full choke; 26" in 410; 28" in 20; 30" in 12
Finish: Blued; wood, pistol grip stock & forearm
Approximate wt: 7 lbs.
Comments: Presently manufactured.
**Estimated Value: New (retail): $59.99
                    Excellent: $45.00
                    Very good: $35.00**

Sears Double Barrel

Gauge: 12, 20
Action: Box lock; top lever, break-open; hammerless; double barrel; double triggers
Magazine: None
Barrel: 28" double barrel side by side; variety of chokes
Finish: Blued; epoxied black frame; walnut, pistol grip stock & forearm
Approximate wt: 7 ½ lbs.
Comments: Presently manufactured
**Estimated Value: New (retail): $189.99
                    Excellent: $150.00
                    Very good: $120.00**

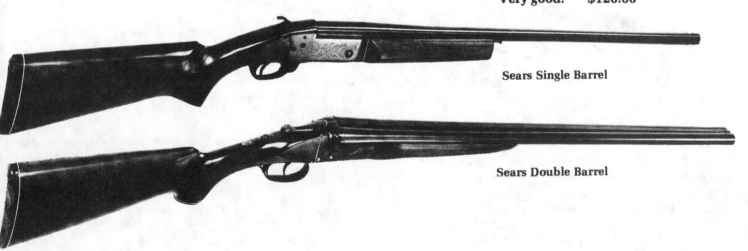

Sears Single Barrel

Sears Double Barrel

Shotguns

Sears Ted Williams Over & Under

Gauge: 12, 20
Action: Box lock; top lever, break-open; hammerless; over & under doubel barrel selective trigger; automatic ejector
Magazine: None
Barrel: Over & under double barrel; 26'', 28'' in standard chokes; ventilated rib; chrome lined
Finish: Blued; engraved steel receivers; checkered walnut, pistol grip stock & forearm; recoil pad
Approximate wt: 6¾ lbs.
Comments: Produced to the late 1970's.
Estimated Value: Excellent: $320.00
Very good: $260.00

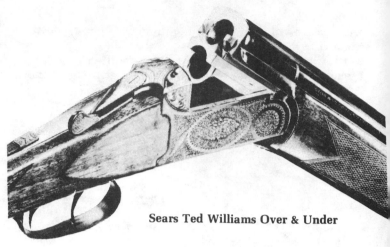

Sears Ted Williams Over & Under

Sears Bolt Action

Gauge: 410
Action: Bolt; repeating
Magazine: 3-shot detachable clip
Barrel: 24'' full choke
Finish: Blued; wood, pistol grip stock & forearm
Approximate wt: 5½ lbs.
Comments: Made to the late 1970's.
Estimated Value: Excellent: $65.00
Very good: $50.00

Sears Model 140

Gauge: 12, 20
Action: Bolt action; repeating
Magazine: 2-shot detachable clip
Barrel: 25'' adjustable choke
Finish: Blued; wood, pistol grip stock & forearm
Approximate wt: 7 lbs.
Comments: Made to the late 1970's.
Estimated Value: Excellent: $70.00
Very good: $55.00

Sears Model 140

Sears Bolt Action

Sears Model 200

Sears Ted Williams 200

Sears Ted Williams 200

A fancier version of the 200 with checkered wood.
Estimated Value: New (retail): $209.95
Excellent: $150.00
Very good: $120.00

Sears Model 200

Gauge: 12, 20
Action: Slide action; hammerless; repeating
Magazine: 4-shot tubular
Barrel: 28'' full or modified, chokes
Finish: Blued; alloy receiver; wood pistol grip stock & forearm; recoil pad
Approximate wt: 6½ lbs.
Comments: Manufactured currently. Add $20.00 for variable choke.
Estimated Value: New (retail): $129.95
Excellent: $105.00
Very good: $ 85.00

Sears Ted Williams 300

Gauge: 12, 20
Action: Gas operated, semi-automatic; hammerless
Magazine: Tubular
Barrel: 27" adjustable choke, 28" modified or full, chokes; ventilated rib
Finish: Blued; checkered waknut, pistol grip stock and forearm; recoil pad
Approximate wt: 7 lbs.
Comments: Manufactured at present. Add $10.00 for variable choke.
Estimated Value: New (retail): $259.99
Excellent: $200.00
Very good: $160.00

Sears Ted Williams 300

Smith & Wesson

Smith & Wesson Model 916

Smith & Wesson Model 916 Vent Rib

Smith & Wesson Model 1000

Smith & Wesson Model 916

Gauge: 12
Action: Slide action; hammerless; side ejection
Magazine: 5-shot tubular
Barrel: 20" cylinder bore; 26" improved cylinder, 28" modified, full or cylinder chokes;
Finish: Blued; satin finish receiver; walnut, semi-pistol grip stock & grooved slide handle; recoil pad available
Approximate wt: 7 lbs.
Comments: Manufactured from the early 1970's to present. Add $39.00 for ventialted rib and recoil pad. Add $20.00 for Deer Model.
Estimated Value: New (retail): $167.50
Excellent: $125.00
Very good: $100.00

Smith & Wesson Model 1000

Gauge: 12, 20, regular and magnum
Action: Gas operated, semi-automatic; hammerless; side ejection
Magazine: 3-shot tubular
Barrel: 26", 28", 30" variety of chokes; ventilated rib
Finish: Blued; engraved alloy receiver; checkered walnut, pistol grip stock & forearm; sights.
Approximate wt: 7½ lbs.
Comments: Manufactured from the early 1970's to present. Add $36.00 for magnum.
Estimated Value: New (retail): $380.95
Excellent: $285.00
Very good: $225.00

Smith & Wesson Model 1000S Superskeet

Similar to the Model 1000 with 25" skeet choke barrel.
Estimated Value: New (retail): $210.00
Excellent: $160.00
Very good: $130.00

Stevens Model No. 93

Stevens Models No. 93, 97 Nitro Special

Gauge: 12, 16
Action: Top lever, break-open; exposed hammer; Model 97 has automatic ejector
Magazine: None; single shot
Barrel: Special steel; 28", 30", or 32"
Finish: Blued; nickel plated, case hardened frame; plain walnut pistol grip stock & lipped forearm
Approximate wt.: 7 to 7 ½ lbs.
Comments: These guns were produced from the early 1900's until World War I.
Estimated Value: Excellent: $60.00
Very good: $50.00

Stevens Model No. 97 Nitro Special

Stevens Models No. 100, 110, 120

Gauge: 12, 16, 20
Action: Top lever, break-open; automatic ejector, exposed hammer; single shot
Magazine: None; single shot
Barrel: 28", 30" or 32"
Finish: Blued; case hardened frame; walnut pistol grip stock and forearm; No. 100 no checkering; 110 and 120 checkered walnut
Approximate wt.: 6 to 7 lbs.
Comments: Produced around the turn of the Century for about 1 to 2 years
Estimated Value: Excellent: $70.00
Very good: $60.00

Stevens Model No. 120

Stevens Model No. 140

This gun is similar to Model 120 except it is hammerless and has an automatic safety.
Estimated Value: Excellent: $90.00
Very good: $75.00

Stevens Model No. 140

Stevens Models No. 160, 165, 170

Gauge: 12, 16, 20
Action: Break-open; exposed hammer; automatic ejector except on 160
Magazine: None; single shot
Barrel: 26", 28", 30" or 32"
Finish: Blued; case hardened frame; checkered walnut, pistol grip stock and forearm except 160 (plain)
Approximate wt.: 6 to 7 lbs.
Comments: Manufactured around the turn of the century for about 5 years.
Estimated Value: Excellent: $55.00
Very good: $45.00

Stevens Model No. 170

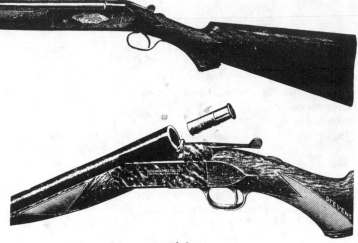

Stevens Model No. 182 Trap Gun

Stevens Model No. 180
Gauge: 12, 16, 20
Action: Top lever, break-open; hammerless; automatic ejector
Magazine: None; single shot
Barrel: 26", 28", 30" modified; 32" or 36" full choke
Finish: Blued; case hardened frame; checkered walnut, pistol grip stock & forearm
Approximate wt.: 6 ½ lbs.
Comments: Produced from around 1900 until World War I.
Estimated Value: Excellent: $90.00
Very good: $75.00

Stevens Model No. 180

Stevens Model No. 185, 190, 195
Gauge: 12
Action: Top lever, break-open; hammerless; automatic shell ejector; automatic safety
Magazine: None; single shot
Barrel: Round with octagon breech; 20" or 32"
Finish: Blued; case hardened frame; checkered walnut, pistol grip stock and forearm; frame engraved on No. 190-195
Approximate wt.: 7 to 8 lbs.
Comments: These guns differ in quality of finish and engraving and were produced briefly around the turn of the Century.
Estimated Value: Excellent: $150.00
Very good: $130.00

Stevens Model No. 970
Similar to the 185, this 12 gauge was made from around 1910 until World War I.
Estimated Value: Excellent: $60.00
Very good: $50.00

Stevens Model No. 182 Trap Gun
Similar to Model No. 180 except; Trap grade; 12 gauge only; matted top of barrel; scroll work on frame. Made from around 1910 to World War I.
Estimated Value: Excellent: $130.00
Very good: $110.00

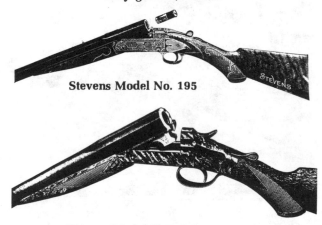

Stevens Model No. 195

Stevens Model No. 970

Stevens Model No. 85, Dreadnaught

Stevens Model No. 89 Dreadnaught

Stevens Model No. 85, Dreadnaught
Gauge: 12
Action: Top lever, break-open; exposed hammer
Magazine: None; single shot
Barrel: 28", 30" or 32" full chokes
Finish: Blued; case hardened frame; plain walnut, pistol grip stock and lipped forearm
Approximate wt.: 7 ½ lbs.
Comments: Made from around 1910 to mid 1920's.
Estimated Value: Excellent: $60.00
Very good: $50.00

Stevens Model No. 89 Dreadnaught
Same as the No. 85 with automatic ejector. Made until mid 1930's.
Estimated Value: Excellent: $60.00
Very good: $50.00

103

Shotguns

Stevens Models No. 105

Stevens Models No. 105, 107, 115 & 125
Gauge: 12, 16, 20, 28
Action: Top lever, break-open; exposed hammer; automatic ejector on all but Model 105
Magazine: None; single shot.
Barrel: 26" or 28"
Finish: Blued; case hardened frame; checkered walnut, pistol grip stock and forearm except No. 107 (plain)
Approximate wt.: 5 ½ lbs.
Comments: This was a light-weight series of shotguns produced until about World War II for Model 105; 1950's for Model 107 and 1920's for Models 115 and 125
Estimated Value: Excellent: $60.00
Very good: $50.00

Stevens Springfield Model No. 95
Very similar to Model 107. Produced from the mid 1920's until the early 1930's.
Estimated Value: Excellent: $55.00
Very good: $45.00

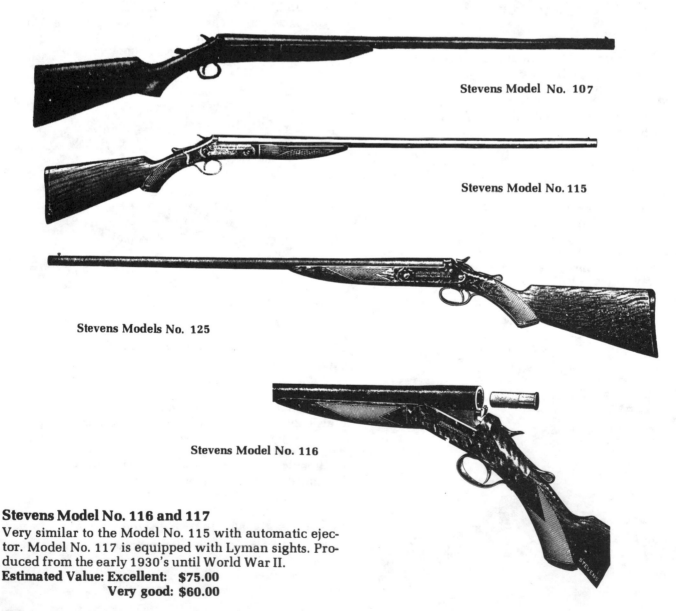

Stevens Model No. 107

Stevens Model No. 115

Stevens Models No. 125

Stevens Model No. 116

Stevens Model No. 116 and 117
Very similar to the Model No. 115 with automatic ejector. Model No. 117 is equipped with Lyman sights. Produced from the early 1930's until World War II.
Estimated Value: Excellent: $75.00
Very good: $60.00

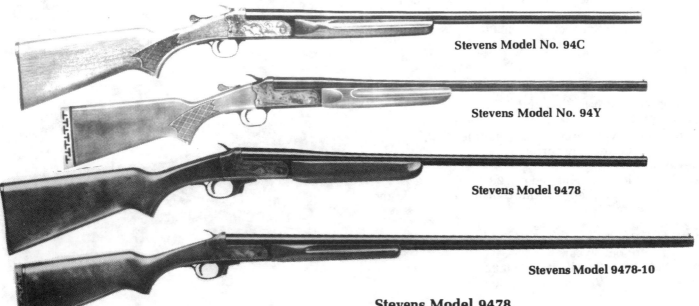

Stevens Model No. 106

Stevens Model No. 106

Gauge: 410
Action: Top lever, break-open; exposed hammer
Magazine: None; single shot
Barrel: 26" or 30"
Finish: Blued; case hardened frame; plain walnut, pistol grip stock and forearm
Approximate wt.: 4 ½ lbs.
Comments: This lightweight, light gauge gun was made from around 1910 until the 1930's.
Estimated Value: Excellent: $60.00
Very good: $50.00

Stevens Model No. 108

Same as the No. 106 with automatic ejector.
Estimated Value: Excellent: $70.00
Very good: $60.00

Stevens Springfield Model No. 958

Very similar to Model No. 108. Produced from mid 1920's until early 1930's.
Estimated Value: Excellent: $60.00
Very good: $50.00

Stevens Model No. 94C

Stevens Model No. 94Y

Stevens Model 9478

Stevens Model 9478-10

Stevens Model No. 94C

Gauge: 12, 16, 20, 410
Action: Top lever, break-open; exposed hammer
Magazine: None
Barrel: 26", 28", 30", 36" full choke
Finish: Blued; case hardened frame; checkered walnut, semi-pistol grip stock and grooved forearm
Approximate wt: 6-8 lbs.
Comments: Produced from mid 1960's to present. Add $3.00 for 36" barrel.
Estimated Value: New (retail): $72.90
Excellent: $50.00
Very good: $45.00

Stevens Model No. 94Y, 9478Y

Similar to 94C in youth version. Shorter stock; recoil pad; 26" barrel; 20 gauge modified or 410 full choke.
Estimated Value: New (retail): $82.50
Excellent: $60.00
Very good: $50.00

Stevens Model 9478

Similar to the Model 94C with lever release on the trigger guard; no checkering.
Estimated Value: New (retail): $70.50
Excellent: $55.00
Very good: $45.00

Stevens Model 9478-10

Similar to the Model 9478 with a 36" full choke barrel: 10 gauge only; recoil pad;
Estimated Value: New (retail): $91.95
Excellent: $70.00
Very good: $55.00

Stevens Model 9478-Y

Similar to the Model 9478 in 410 full or 20 Modified gauges; 26" barrel; short stock with rubber buttplate.
Estimated Value: New (retail): $75.75
Excellent: $60.00
Very good: $50.00

Shotguns

Stevens Model No. 250

Gauge: 12
Action: Top lever, break-open; exposed hammers; double trigger; double barrel
Magazine: None
Barrel: 28", 30", 32" double barrel
Finish: Blued; checkered walnut, pistol grip stock and forearm
Approximate wt.: 8 lbs.
Comments: Made around the turn of the century for about 5 years.
Estimated Value: Excellent: $190.00
　　　　　　　　　Very good: $175.00

Stevens Model No. 250

Stevens Model No. 350

Stevens Models No. 260 and 270

Similar to Model 250 with special Damascus or Twist barrels and available in 16 gauge. Manufactured briefly around the turn of the century.
Estimated Value: Excellent: $180.00
　　　　　　　　　Very good: $165.00

Stevens Model No. 355

Stevens Models No. 350, 360, 370

Gauge: 12, 16
Action: Top lever, break-open; double trigger, hammerless; double barrel
Magazine: None
Barrel: Double barrel, matted rib, 28", 30", or 32"·
Finish: Blued; checkered walnut, pistol grip stock and forearm
Approximate wt.: 7½ to 8½ lbs.
Comments: Produced around the turn of the century for about 5 years
Estimated Value: Excellent: $150.00
　　　　　　　　　Very good: $120.00

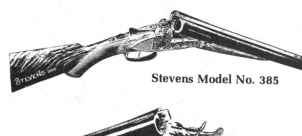

Stevens Model No. 385

Stevens Model No. 235

Stevens Model No. 255

Stevens Models No. 355, 365, 375, 385

Gauge: 12, 16
Action: Top lever, break-open; double trigger; hammerless; double barrel
Magazine: None
Barrel: Double barrel; Krupp steel; matted rib; 28", 30", 32"
Finish: Blued; checkered walnut, straight or pistol grip, stock and forearm; 355 and 365 plain, 375 some engraving, 385 engraved frame
Approximate wt.: 7 to 8½ lbs.
Comments: Produced from the early 1900's. 355 discontinued in World War I. All others before World War I.
Estimated Value: Excellent: $175.00
　　　　　　　　　Very good: $150.00

Stevens Model No. 235, 255, 265

Gauge: 12, 16
Action: Top lever, break-open; exposed hammers; double triggers; box lock; double barrel
Magazine: None
Barrel: Double barrel; matted rib, 28", 30" or 32"
Finish: Blued; checkered walnut, pistol grip stock and forearm; case hardened frame; No. 255 has checkered buttplate
Approximate wt.: 7 to 8½ lbs.
Comments: Produced from around 1907 until the 1920's. 255 stopped around World War I.
Estimated Value: Excellent: $180.00
　　　　　　　　　Very good: $160.00

Stevens Riverside Model No. 215

Gauge: 12 or 16
Action: Top lever, break-open; exposed hammer; double trigger; double barrel
Magazine: None
Barrel: Double barrel; 26'', 28'', 30'', 32''; matted rib; left barrel full choke, right barrel modified
Finish: Blued; case hardened frame; checkered walnut, pistol grip stock and forearm
Approximate wt.: 7 ½ to 8 ½ lbs.
Comments: Produced from around 1910 to World War II.
Estimated Value: Excellent: $180.00
Very good: $160.00

Stevens Riverside Model No. 215

Stevens Riverside Model No. 315

Gauge: 12, 16
Action: Top lever, break-open; hammerless; double trigger; double barrel
Magazine: None
Barrel: Double barrel; matted rib; right barrel modified, left full choke; 26'', 28'', 30'' or 32''
Finish: Blued; case hardened frame; checkered walnut, semi-pistol grip stock and forearm
Approximate wt.: 7 to 7 ½ lbs.
Comments: This gun was made from around 1910 until the late 1930's.
Estimated Value: Excellent: $175.00
Very good: $150.00

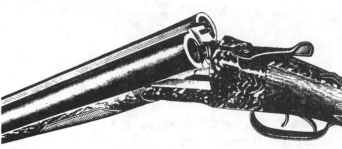

Stevens Riverside Model No. 315

Stevens Model No. 335

This gun is similar to the 315. Produced from around 1910 to the late 1920's.
Estimated Value: Excellent: $165.00
Very good: $140.00

Stevens Model No. 335

Stevens Model No. 345

Very similar to the No. 335 in 20 gauge. Made from around 1910 until the mid 1920's.
Estimated Value: Excellent: $180.00
Very good: $155.00

Stevens Model No. 345

Stevens Model No. 330

Stevens Model No. 330

Gauge: 12, 16, 20, 410
Action: Top lever, break-open; hammerless; double trigger, double barrel; takedown
Magazine: None
Barrel: Double barrel; 26''-32''; right modified, left full choke; both full choke in 410
Finish: Blued; case hardened frame; checkered black walnut, pistol grip stock and forearm.
Approximate wt.: 5 ¾ -7 ¾ lbs.
Comments: This shotgun was in production from the mid 1920's until the mid 1930's.
Estimated Value: Excellent: $165.00
Very good: $135.00

Stevens Springfield Model No. 311

Stevens Springfield Model No. 315

Stevens Springfield Model No. 311
Springfield Hammerless
Gauge: 12, 16, 20, 410
Action: Top lever, break-open; hammerless; double trigger; double barrel; takedown
Magazine: None
Barrel: Double barrel; 26" - 32"; right barrel modified, left full choke, except 32" 12 gauge and .410 (full choked); matted rib
Finish: Blued; case hardened frame; smooth walnut, semi-pistol grip stock and forearm
Approximate wt.: 5 ½ -7 ¾ lbs.
Comments: Produced from the early 1930's to present; presently sold as Savage-Stevens Model 311. Add $30.00 for single-selective single trigger.
Estimated Value: New (retail): $202.35
                 Excellent: $150.00
                 Very good: $130.00

Stevens Springfield Model No. 315
A higher quality version of the Model 311; discontinued.
Estimated Value: Excellent: $175.00
                 Very good: $145.00

Stevens Model No. 530
Gauge: 12, 16, 20, 410
Action: Top lever, break-open; hammerless; box lock; double trigger; double barrel;
Magazine: None
Barrel: Double barrel; 26"-32"; right modified choke, left full choke, except 32" 12 gauge and 410 (full choke).
Finish: Blued; case hardened frame; checkered walnut, pistol grip stock and forearm; recoil pad on early model
Approximate wt.: 6-7 ½ lbs.
Comments: Produced from mid 1930's till early 1950's
Estimated Value: Excellent: $165.00
                 Very good: $145.00

Stevens Model No. 530 ST
Same as 530 with non-selective single trigger.
Estimated Value: Excellent: $190.00
                 Very good: $165.00

Stevens Model No. 530M
Same as 530 with plastic stock. Discontinued in late 1940's.
Estimated Value: Excellent: $150.00
                 Very good: $125.00

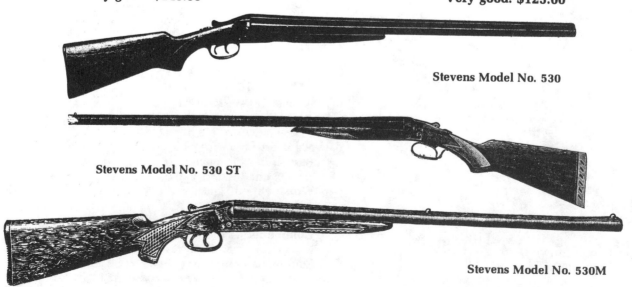

Stevens Model No. 530

Stevens Model No. 530 ST

Stevens Model No. 530M

Stevens Model 511

Stevens Model 511
Gauge: 12, 20 regular or magnum
Action: Box lock; top lever, break-open; double barrel; double trigger
Magazine: None
Barrel: Double barrel; 28" modified and full chokes
Finish: Blued; checkered hardwood, semi-pistol grip stock and small forearm; case hardened frame
Approximate wt: 7¾ lbs.
Comments: Produced in the late 1970's.
Estimated Value: Excellent: $170.00
Very good: $140.00

Stevens-Springfield Model No. 22-410

Stevens Model No. 240

Stevens-Springfield Model No. 22-410
Gauge: 410 and 22 caliber rifle
Action: Top lever, break-open; exposed hammer; single trigger; over and under; separate extractors
Magazine: None
Barrel: Over and under; 22 rifle over 410 shotgun; 24"
Finish: Blued; case hardened frame; plastic semi-pistol grip stock and forearm; open rear and ramp front sights
Approximate wt.: 6 lbs.
Comments: Produced from late 1930's until about 1950. Later produced as Savage.
Estimated Value: Excellent: $120.00
Very good: $100.00

Stevens Model No. 240
Gauge: 410
Action: Top lever, break-open; exposed hammer; double trigger; takedown over & under
Magazine: None
Barrel: Over and under, double barrel; both barrels 26" full choke
Finish: Blued; checkered plastic or wood pistol grip stock and forearm
Approximate wt.: 6½ lbs.
Comments: Produced from the late 1930's until World War II.
Estimated Value: Excellent: $210.00
Very good: $175.00

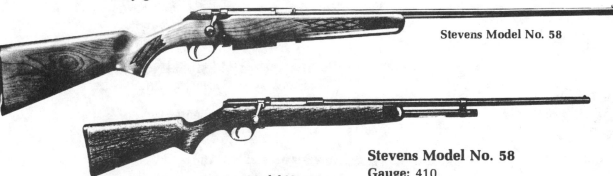

Stevens Model No. 58

Stevens Model No. 59

Stevens Model No. 58
Gauge: 410
Action: Bolt-action
Magazine: 3-shot detatchable box
Barrel: 24" full choke
Finish: Blued; plain walnut, one-piece pistol grip stock and forearm
Approximate wt: 5½ lbs.
Comments: Made from late 1930's to late 1970's. Later versions have checkering.
Estimated Value: Excellent: $60.00
Very good: $50.00

Stevens Model No. 59
Very similar to No. 58 except with a 5-shot tubular magazine. Discontinued in the early 1970's.
Estimated Value: Excellent: $75.00
Very good: $60.00

Shotguns

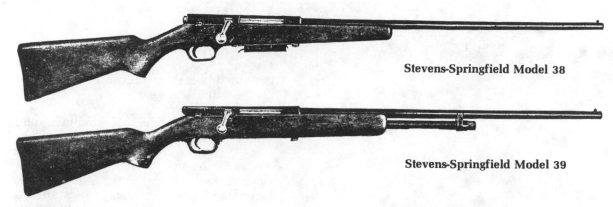

Stevens-Springfield Model 38

Stevens-Springfield Model 39

Stevens-Springfield Model 38
Very similar to Stevens Model No. 58.
Estimated Value: Excellent: $55.00
Very good: $45.00

Stevens-Springfield Model 39
Very similar to Stevens Model No. 59.
Estimated Value: Excellent: $60.00
Very good: $50.00

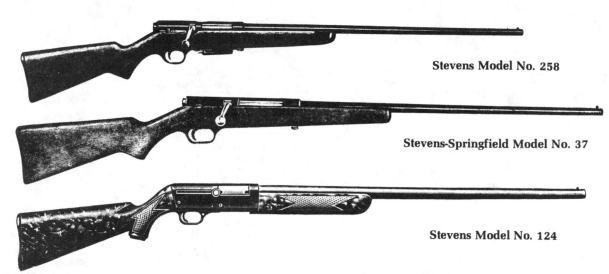

Stevens Model No. 258

Stevens-Springfield Model No. 37

Stevens Model No. 124

Stevens Model No. 258
Gauge: 20
Action: Bolt action; repeating
Magazine: 2-shot detachable box
Barrel: 26'' full choke
Finish: Blued; plain walnut, one-piece pistol grip stock and forearm
Approximate wt.: 6 ¼ lbs.
Comments: This takedown shotgun was produced from the late 1930's until the mid 1960's.
Estimated Value: Excellent: $60.00
Very good: $50.00

Stevens Model No. 254
This is a single shot version of the Model 258.
Estimated Value: Excellent: $45.00
Very good: $35.00

Stevens-Springfield Model 238
Very similar to Stevens Model 258.
Estimated Value: Excellent: $55.00
Very good: $45.00

Stevens-Springfield Model 237
Very similar to Stevens Model No. 254.
Estimated Value: Excellent: $50.00
Very good: $40.00

Stevens-Springfield Model No. 37
Similar to Stevens-Springfield Model 237, except in 410 gauge.
Estimated Value: Excellent: $65.00
Very good: $55.00

Stevens Model No. 124
Gauge: 12
Action: Cross-bolt; side ejection; hammerless
Magazine: 2-shot tubular
Barrel: 28'' improved cylinder, modified, or full choke
Finish: Blued; checkered plastic, pistol grip stock and forearm.
Approximate wt.: 7 lbs.
Comments: Manufactured from late 1940's until mid 1950's.
Estimated Value: Excellent: $60.00
Very good: $50.00

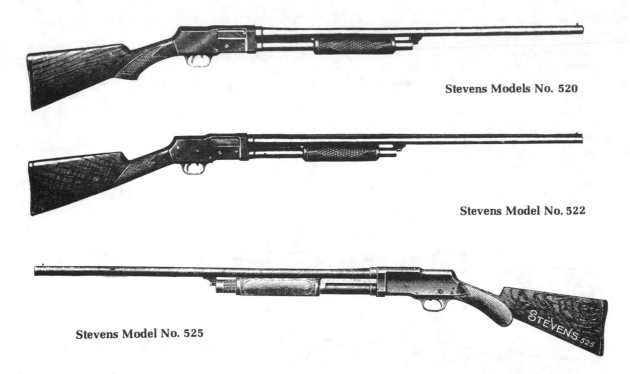

Stevens Models No. 520

Stevens Model No. 522

Stevens Model No. 525

Stevens Models No. 520, 521, 522

Gauge: 12
Action: Browning Patent; slide action; takedown; side ejection; hammerless.
Magazine: 5-shot tubular
Barrel: 26", 28", 30", 32", full choke, modified or cylinder; matted rib on 521
Finish: Blued; walnut pistol grip stock & grooved slide handle; checkered straight grip on 522
Approximate wt.: 8 lbs.
Comments: Produced from early 1900's until World War II; 522 discontinued in the 1920's.
Estimated Value: Excellent: $150.00
Very good: $125.00

Stevens Models No. 525, 530, and 535

Similar to 520-22 except fancier grades. 525 is custom built; 530 custom built with engraved receiver and rib; 535 custom built, heavily engraved. Discontinued by World War I.
Estimated Value: Excellent: $180.00
Very good: $150.00

Stevens Models No. 535

Stevens Model No. 200

Gauge: 20
Action: Pedersen patent slide action; hammerless; side ejection; takedown
Magazine: 5-shot tubular
Barrel: Full choke; modified or cylinder bore; 26", 28", 30" or 32"
Finish: Blued; walnut pistol grip stock, grooved slide handle
Approximate wt.: 6½ lbs.
Comments: Produced from around 1910 until World War I.
Estimated Value: Excellent: $155.00
Very good: $130.00

Stevens Model No. 200

Shotguns

Stevens Model No. 620

Gauge: 12, 16, 20
Action: Slide-action; hammerless; side ejection
Magazine: 5-shot tubular
Barrel: 26", 28", or 30", or 32"; full choke, modified or cylinder bore
Finish: Blued; checkered walnut, pistol grip stock and slide handle
Approximate wt.: 6-7 ¾ lbs.
Comments: This takedown shotgun was manufactured for about 30 years beginning in the late 1920's.
Estimated Value: Excellent: $155.00
                        Very good: $120.00

Stevens Model No. 620-P

Same as Model No. 620 with "Poly-Choke".
Estimated Value: Excellent: $170.00
                        Very good: $135.00

Stevens Model No. 621

Same as No. 620 with matted rib. Discontinued after about 10 years.
Estimated Value: Excellent: $180.00
                        Very good: $145.00

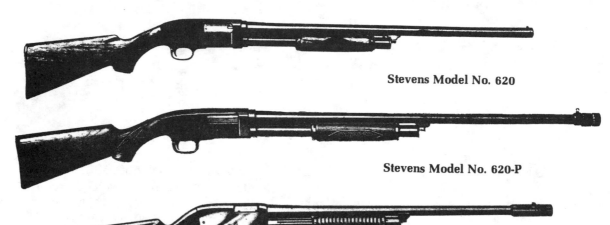

Stevens Model No. 620

Stevens Model No. 620-P

Stevens Model No. 820-SC

Stevens Model No. 820

Gauge: 12
Action: Slide action; hammerless; side ejection
Magazine: 5-shot tubular
Barrel: 28" improved cylinder, modified or full choke
Finish: Blued, plain walnut, semi-pistol grip stock and grooved slide handle
Approximate wt.: 7 ½ lbs.
Comments: Produced for about 5 years beginning in 1949.
Estimated Value: Excellent: $140.00
                        Very good: $120.00

Stevens Model No. 820-SC

Same as No. 820 with Savage "Super Choke."
Estimated Value: Excellent: $150.00
                        Very good: $130.00

Stevens Model No. 77

Stevens Model No. 77

Gauge: 12, 16
Action: Slide-action; hammerless; side ejection
Magazine: 5-shot tubular
Barrel: 26" or 28" improved cylinder, modified or full choke
Finish: Blued; plain walnut, pistol grip stock and grooved slide handle
Approximate wt.: 7 lbs.
Comments: This shotgun was produced from the mid 1950's to early 1970's.
Estimated Value: Excellent: $145.00
                        Very good: $120.00

Stevens Model No. 77-SC

Same as 77 with Savage "Super choke" and recoil pad.
Estimated Value: Excellent: $180.00
                        Very good: $145.00

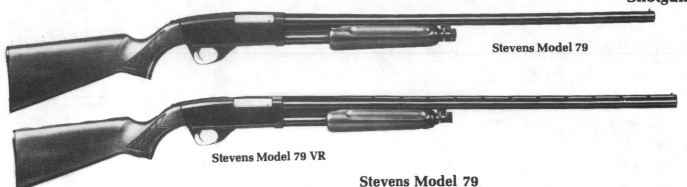

Stevens Model 79

Stevens Model 79 VR

Stevens Model 79 VR
Similar to the Model 79 with a ventilated rib.
Estimated Value: New (retail): $173.75
 Excellent: $130.00
 Very good: $105.00

Stevens Model 79 Slug
Similar to the Model 79 with a 21" barrel for slugs; rifle sights.
Estimated Value: Excellent: $155.00
 Very good: $130.00

Stevens Model 79
Gauge: 12, 20, 410, regular & magnum
Action: Slide action; hammerless; side ejection; repeating
Magazine: 4 shot tubular; 3 shot in magnum
Barrel: 28" modified or 30" full in 12 gauge; 28" modified or full in 20 gauge; 26" full in 410
Finish: Blued; checkered hardwood semi-pistol grip stock and fluted slide handle
Approximate wt: 7 lbs.
Comments: Produced in the late 1970's.
Estimated Value: Excellent: $125.00
 Very good: $100.00

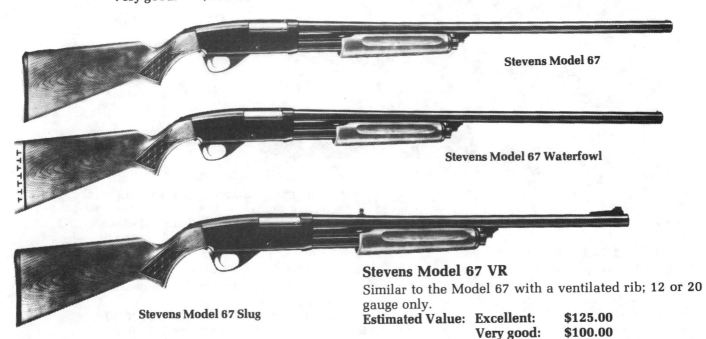

Stevens Model 67

Stevens Model 67 Waterfowl

Stevens Model 67 Slug

Stevens Model 67
Gauge: 12, 29, or 410, regular or magnum
Action: Slide action; hammerless; side ejecting; repeating
Magazine: 4 shot tubular; 3 shot in magnum
Barrel: 28" modified or full; 26" full in 410
Finish: Blued; checkered hardwood semi-pistol grip stock and fluted slide handle
Approximate wt: 6¾ lbs.
Comments: Produced in the late 1970's to present.
Estimated Value: New (retail): $145.25
 Excellent: $110.00
 Very good: $ 90.00

Stevens Model 67 VR
Similar to the Model 67 with a ventilated rib; 12 or 20 gauge only.
Estimated Value: Excellent: $125.00
 Very good: $100.00

Stevens Model 67 Waterfowl
Similar to the Model 67 with a 30" full choke barrel; 12 gauge only; recoil pad.
Estimated Value: Excellent: $160.00
 Very good: $130.00

Stevens Model 67 Slug
Similar to the Model 67 with a 21" barrel for slugs and rifle sights; 12 gauge only.
Estimated Value: Excellent: $145.00
 Very good: $120.00

Universal _____

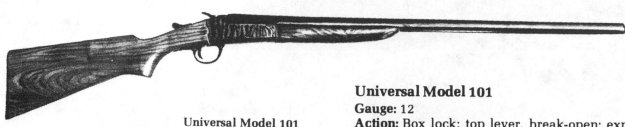

Universal Model 101

Universal Single Wing

Similar to the Model 101 with automatic ejector. Made from the early to mid 1970's.
Estimated Value: Excellent: $65.00
Very good: $55.00

Universal Model 101

Gauge: 12
Action: Box lock; top lever, break-open; exposed hammer; single shot
Magazine: None
Barrel: 28'', 30'' full choke
Finish: Blued; plain wood, pistol grip stock & tapered forearm
Approximate wt.: 7 ½ lbs.
Comments: Manufactured in the late 1960's.
Estimated Value: Excellent: $60.00
Very good: $50.00

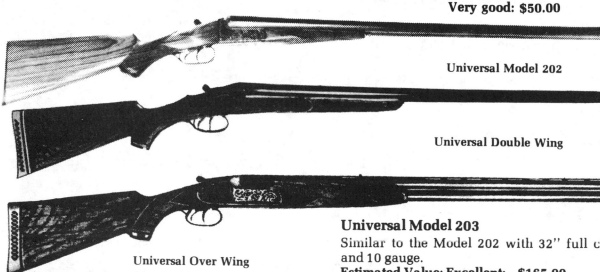

Universal Model 202

Universal Double Wing

Universal Over Wing

Universal Model 202

Gauge: 12, 20, 410
Action: Box lock; top lever, break-open; hammerless; double barrel; double triggers
Magazine: None
Barrel: Double barrel; 26'' improved cylinder & modified, 28'' modified & full, chokes
Finish: Blued; checkered walnut, pistol grip stock & forearm
Approximate wt.: 7 lbs.
Comments: Manufactured in the late 1960's. Add $20.00 for 410 gauge.
Estimated Value: Excellent: $140.00
Very good: $110.00

Universal Double Wing

Similar to the Model 202 with recoil pad. Made from about 1970-1975; 12 or 20 gauge magnum.
Estimated Value: Excellent: $160.00
Very good: $130.00

Universal Model 203

Similar to the Model 202 with 32'' full choke barrels and 10 gauge.
Estimated Value: Excellent: $165.00
Very good: $135.00

Universal Model 2030

Similar to the Double Wing with 32'' full choke barrels and 10 gauge.
Estimated Value: Excellent: $190.00
Very good: $160.00

Universal Over Wing

Gauge: 12, 20
Action: Box lock; top lever, break-open; hammerless; over & under double barrel
Magazine: None
Barrel: Over & under double barrel; 26'', 28'', 30'', ventilated rib
Finish: Blued; checkered walnut, pistol grip stock & forearm; sights; recoil pad; engraving available
Approximate wt.: 8 lbs.
Comments: Manufactured from about 1970 to 1975. Add $50.00 for single trigger.
Estimated Value: Excellent: $250.00
Very good: $200.00

Universal Auto Wing

Universal Duck Wing

Universal Auto Wing
Gauge: 12
Action: Semi-automatic; hammerless
Magazine: 5 shot tubular
Barrel: 26", 28", 30", variety of chokes; ventilated rib
Finish: Blued; checkered walnut, pistol grip stock & forearm; sights
Approximate wt.: 8 lbs.
Comments: Manufactured from about 1970 to 1975.
Estimated Value: Excellent: $210.00
                Very good: $175.00

Universal Duck Wing
Similar to the Auto Wing with 28" or 30" full choke barrel, Teflon coated. Discontinued in the early 1970's.
Estimated Value: Excellent: $225.00
                Very good: $185.00

Valmet

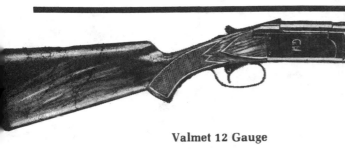

Valmet 12 Gauge

Valmet 12 Gauge
Gauge: 12
Action: Box lock; top lever, break-open; single selective trigger; double barrel; over and under
Magazine: None
Barrel: Over and under double barrel; 26" improved cylinder and modified; 28" modified and full; 30" modified and full, or full chokes
Finish: Blued; checkered walnut, pistol grip stock and wide forearm
Approximate wt.: 7 lbs.
Comments: Produced from the late 1940's to the late 1960's in Finland.
Estimated Value: Excellent: $300.00
                Very good: $245.00

Weatherby

Weatherby Regency

Weatherby Regency
Gauge: 12, 20
Action: Box lock; top lever, break-open; hammerless; automatic ejectors; over & under double barrel; single selective trigger
Magazine: None
Barrel: Over & under double barrel; 26", 28" variety of chokes; ventilated rib
Finish: Blued; checkered walnut, pistol grip stock & forearm; recoil pad; sights; decorated receiver
Approximate wt: 7-7½ lbs.
Comments: Manufactured from the early 1970's to present. Add $50.00 for Trap.
Estimated Value: New (retail): $1,098.95
                Excellent: $ 825.00
                Very good: $ 660.00

Weatherby Regency Skeet
Similar to the Regency in skeet chokes with a 26" or 28" barrel.
Estimated Value: New (retail): $1,098.95
                Excellent: $ 825.00
                Very good: $ 660.00

Weatherby Regency Trap
Similar to the Regency with a wide ventilated rib barrel; 30" or 32" full and full, full and improved modified , or full and modified chokes; choice of regular or Monte Carlo stock; 12 gauge only.
Estimated Value: New (retail): $1,198.95
                Excellent: $ 900.00
                Very good: $ 725.00

Shotguns

Weatherby Olympian

Weatherby Olympian Skeet

Similar to the Olympian with 26'' or 28'' skeet choke barrel.

Estimated Value:

New (retail):	$749.95
Excellent:	$565.00
Very good:	$455.00

Weatherby Olympian Trap

Similar to the Olympian; ventilated rib between barrels; 30'' or 32'' full and modified or full and improved modified chokes; Monte Carlo stock.

Estimated Value:

New (retail):	$829.95
Excellent:	$625.00
Very good:	$500.00

Weatherby Olympian

Gauge: 12 or 20
Action: Box lock; top lever, break-open, over and under double barrel; selective automtic ejectors
Magazine: None
Barrel: 26'' or 28'' full and modified; 26'' or 28'' modified and improved cylinder; 30'' full and modified; ventilted rib
Finish: Blued; checkered walnut pistol grip stock and fluted forearm; recoil pad
Approximate wt: 7-8 lbs.
Comments: Made from the 1970's to present.

Estimated Value:

New (retail):	$749.95
Excellent:	$565.00
Very good:	$455.00

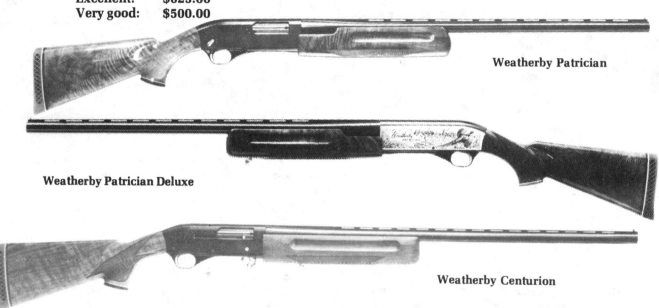

Weatherby Patrician

Weatherby Patrician Deluxe

Weatherby Centurion

Weatherby Centurion and Centurion II

Gauge: 12; Centurion II 12 gauge magnum
Action: Gas operated, semi-automatic; hammerless
Magazine: Tubular
Barrel: 26'', 28'', 30'' variety of chokes; ventilated rib
Finish: Blued; checkered walnut, pistol grip stock & grooved forearm; recoil pad
Approximate wt: 7½ lbs.
Comments: Produced from the early 1970's to present. Add $30.00 for Trap.

Estimated Value:

New (retail):	$399.95
Excellent:	$330.00
Very good:	$260.00

Weatherby Centurion Deluxe

Similar to the Centurian with a decorated satin silver receiver and higher quality wood.

Estimated Value:

New (retail):	$469.95
Excellent:	$355.00
Very good:	$285.00

Weatherby Patrician and Patrician II

Gauge: 12; Patrician II 12 gauge magnum
Action: Slide action; hammerless; side ejection
Magazine: Tubular
Barrel: 26'', 28'', 30'', variety of chokes; ventialted rib
Finish: Blued; checkered walnut, pistol grip stock & grooved slide handle; recoil pad
Approximate wt: 7½ lbs.
Comments: Produced from the early 1970's to present. Add $30.00 for Trap.

Estimated Value:

New (retail):	$379.95 Approx.
Excellent:	$290.00
Very good:	$235.00

Weatherby Patrician Deluxe

Similar to the Patrician with decorated stain silver receiver and higher quality wood.

Estimated Value:

New (retail):	$449.95
Excellent:	$335.00
Very good:	$270.00

Western

Western Long Range

Gauge: 12, 16, 20, 410
Action: Box lock; top lever break-open; hammerless; double barrel; double or single trigger
Magazine: None
Barrel: Double barrel 26", 32" modified and full choke
Finish: Blued; plain walnut, pistol grip stock and forearm.
Approximate wt.: 7 lbs.
Comments: Produced from the mid 1920's until the early 1940's by Western Arms Corp. which was later bought by Ithaca Arms Company. Add $25.00 for single triger.
Estimated Value: Excellent: $210.00
Very good: $175.00

Western Long Range

Western Field

Western Field Model 100

Gauge: 12, 16, 20, 410
Action: Box lock; thumb sliding, break-open; hammerless; automatic ejector; single shot
Magazine: None
Barrel: 26"-30", full choke
Finish: Blued; wood, semi-pistol grip stock & tapered forearm
Approximate wt.: 6¼-7 lbs.
Comments: Manufactured to the mid 1970's.
Estimated Value: Excellent: $50.00
Very good: $40.00

Western Field Standard Double

Gauge: 12, 16, 20, 410
Action: Box lock; top lever, break-open; hammerless; double barrel
Magazine: None
Barrel: Double barrel; 26"-30" modified & full, or full, chokes; ribbed barrels
Finish: Blued; wood, semi-pistol grip stock and short tapered forearm
Approximate wt.: 6½-7 lbs.
Comments: Made to the middle 1970's.
Estimated Value: Excellent: $160.00
Very good: $125.00

Western Field Model 100

Western Field Standard Double

Western Field Model 150C

Western Field Model 150C

Gauge: 410
Action: Bolt action; repeating
Magazine: 3-shot; top loading
Barrel: 25", full choke; 3" chamber
Finish: Blued; wood, Monte Carlo, pistol grip, one piece stock & forearm
Approximate wt: 5½ lbs.
Comments: Currently manufactured
Estimated Value: New (retail): $79.99
Excellent: $60.00
Very good: $45.00

Shotguns

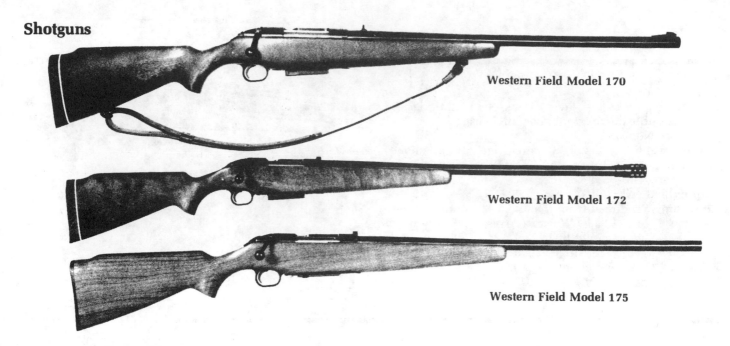

Western Field Model 170

Western Field Model 172

Western Field Model 175

Western Field Model 170

Gauge: 12
Action: Bolt action; repeating
Magazine: 3 shot detachable box
Barrel: 28"
Finish: Blued; hardwood Monte Carlo one piece stock and forearm; recoil pad; sights; swivels
Approximate wt: 7lbs.
Comments: Made to the late 1970's.
Estimated Value: Excellent: $75.00
Very good: $60.00

Western Field Model 172

Similar to the Model 170 without sights and swivels; adjustable choke.
Estimated Value: Excellent: $60.00
Very good: $50.00

Western Field Model 175

Similar to Models 170 and 172 in 20 gauge with a 26" barrel.
Estimated Value: Excellent: $60.00
Very good: $50.00

Western Field Bolt Action

Gauge: 12, 20, regular or magnum
Action: Bolt action; repeating
Magazine: 3 shot detachable box
Barrel: 28" full choke; blued
Finish: Smooth walnut finish hardwood, one piece pistol grip stock and forearm
Approximate wt: 6½ lbs.
Comments: Currently manufactured.
Estimated Value: New (retail): $89.99
Excellent: $70.00
Very good: $55.00

Western Field Model 550

Western Field Model 550 Deluxe

Gauge: 12, 20, regular or magnum
Action: Slide action; hammerless; repeating
Magazine: 5 shot tubular; 4 shot in magnum
Barrel: 28" with 3 interchangeable Accu-choke tubes; ventilated rib
Finish: Blued; checkered hardwood pitol grip stock and slide handle; chrome damascened finish on bolt; recoil pad; engraved receiver
Approximate wt: 7¼ lbs.
Comments: Presently manufactured.
Estimated Value: New (retail): $199.99
Excellent: $150.00
Very good: $120.00

Western Field Model 550

Gauge: 12, 20, 410, regular or magnum
Action: Slide action; hammerless; repeating
Magazine: 4 shot magnum, 5 shot regular; tubular
Barrel: 26" (410 gauge) 28", 30" (12 gauge); full or modified choke
Finish: Blued; smooth hardwood pistol grip, fluted comb stock, grooved slide handle
Approximate wt: 6½ lbs.
Comments: Presently manufactured; add $30.00 for ventilated rib and $10.00 for variable choke.
Estimated Value: New (retail): $129.99
Excellent: $100.00
Very good: $ 80.00

Winchester Model 20

Winchester Model 37

Winchester Model 20

Gauge: 410
Action: Top lever, break-open; box lock; exposed hammer; single shot
Magazine: None
Barrel: 26" full choke
Finish: Blued; plain or checkered wood, pistol grip stock and lipped forearm
Approximate wt: 6 lbs.
Comments: Made from about 1920 to 1925.
Estimated Value: Excellent: $200.00
Very good: $175.00

Winchester Model 37

Gauge: 12, 16, 20, 28, 410
Action: Top lever, break-open; single shot, partially visible hammer; automatic ejector
Magazine: None
Barrel: 26", 28" 30", or 32", full choke, modified or cylinder bore
Finish: Blued; plain walnut, semi-pistol grip stock & forearm
Approximate wt: 6 lbs.
Comments: Made from the late 1930's to mid 1960's. Add $20.00 for 410 gauge.
Estimated Value: Excellent: $95.00
Very good: $75.00

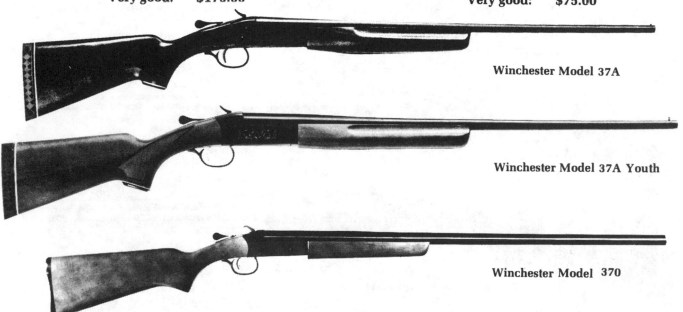

Winchester Model 37A

Winchester Model 37A Youth

Winchester Model 370

Winchester Model 370

Gauge: 12, 16, 20, 28, 410
Action: Top lever, break-open; box lock; single shot; exposed hammer; automatic ejector
Magazine: None
Barrel: 26-32" or 36" full choke; modified on 20 gauge
Finish: Blued; plain wood, semi-pistol grip stock & forearm
Approximate wt: 5¼-6¼ lbs.
Comments: ,ade from the late 1960's tomid 1970's.
Estimated Value: Excellent: $60.00
Very good: $50.00

Winchester Model 37A

Similar to the Model 370 but also available in 36" waterfowl barrel; has checkered stock, grooved forearm; engraved receiver gold plated trigger. Manufactured to the late 1970's. Add $5.00 for 36" barrel.
Estimated Value: Excellent: $60.00
Very good: $50.00

Winchester Model 37A Youth

Similar to the 37A with a recoil pad; 26" barrel.
Estimated Value: Excellent: $65.00
Very good: $55.00

Shotguns

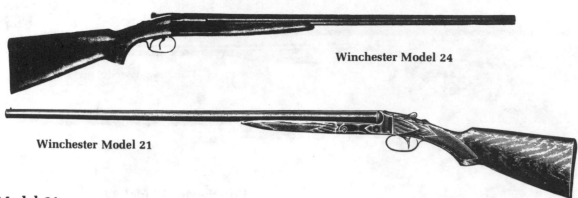

Winchester Model 24

Winchester Model 21

Winchester Model 21

Gauge: 12, 16, 20, 28
Action: Box lock; top lever, break-open; hammerless; double barrel
Magazine: None
Barrel: 26, 28, 30, 32" double barrel; matted or ventilated rib; full, modified or cylinder bore

Finish: Checkered walnut pistol grip stock & forearm
Approximate wt: 7 lbs.
Comments: Made in this grade from 1930 to late 1950's. Fancier grades were produced and some are still available, priced up to several hundred dollars or more. Prices here are for field grade.

Estimated Value: Excellent: $1,000.00
                Very good: $ 800.00

Winchester Model 24

Gauge: 12, 16, 20
Action: Box lock; top lever, break-open; hammerless; double barrel; automatic ejectors; doubel triggers
Magazine: None
Barrel: Double barrel; 28" cylinder bore and modified choke in 12 gauge; others modified & full choke; raised matted rib
Finish: Blued; plain or checkered walnut, pistol grip stock and forearm
Approximate wt: 7 ½ lbs.
Comments: Madde from the late 1930's to the late 1950's.

Estimated Value: Excellent: $300.00
                Very good: $250.00

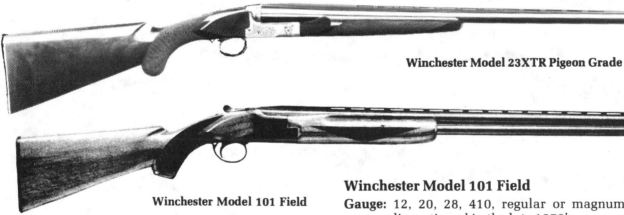

Winchester Model 23XTR Pigeon Grade

Winchester Model 101 Field

Winchester Model 23XTR Pigeon Grade

Gauge: 12, 20, regular or magnum
Action: Box lock; top lever, break-open; hammerless double barrel; selective automatic ejector
Magazine: None
Barrel: Double barrel; 26" improved cylinder and modified; 28" modified and full choke; tapered ventilated rib
Finish: Blued; checkered walnut semi-pistol grip stock and forearm; engraved silver grey satin receiver
Approximate wt: 6 ½-7 lbs.
Comments: Introduced in the late 1970's.

Estimated Value: New (retail): $980.00
                Excellent: $750.00
                Very good: $625.00

Winchester Model 101 Field

Gauge: 12, 20, 28, 410, regular or magnum; 28, 410 discontinued in the late 1970's.
Action: Box lock; top lever, break-open; hammerless; over & under double barrel
Magazine: None
Barrel: Over & under double barrel; 26"-30", various chokes; ventilated rib
Finish: Blued; checkered walnut, pistol grip stock and wide forearm; recoil pad on magnum; engraved receiver; single trigger; automatic ejector
Approximate wt.: 6 ½-7 ½ lbs.
Comments: Made from the mid 1960's to present. Add $30.00 for 410 or 28 gauge, $10.00 for magnum.

Estimated Value: New (retail): $1,115.00
                Excellent: $ 840.00
                Very good: $ 670.00

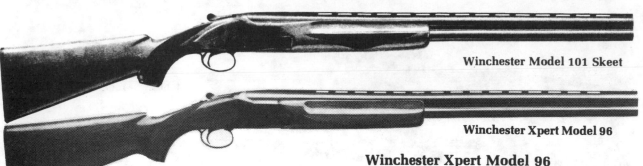

Winchester Model 101 Skeet

Winchester Xpert Model 96

Winchester Xpert Model 96

This is a low cost version of the Winchester Model 101. It lacks engraving as well as some of the internal and external extras. Introduced in the late 1970's.
Estimated Value: New (retail): $726.00
Excellent: $550.00
Very good: $445.00

Winchester Xpert Model 96 Trap

Similar to the Xpert Model 96 with Monte Carlo stock and 30" barrel.
Estimated Value: New (retail): $764.00
Excellent: $575.00
Very good: $465.00

Winchester Model 101 Skeet

Similar to the Model 101 with skeet stock and choke. Add $30.00 for 410 or 28 gauge.
Estimated Value: Excellent: $860.00
Very good: $700.00

Winchester Model 101 Trap

Similar to the Model 101 with regular or Monte Carlo stock; recoil pad; 30"-32" barrels; 12 gauge only.
Estimated Value: Excellent: $850.00
Very good: $690.00

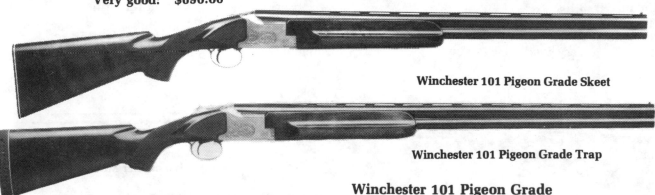

Winchester 101 Pigeon Grade Skeet

Winchester 101 Pigeon Grade Trap

Winchester 101 Pigeon Grade Skeet

Similar to the Pigeon Grade with 27" or 28" skeet choke barrels; front and center sighting beads; 410 or 28 gauge available.
Estimated Value: New (retail): $1,170.00
Excellent: $ 925.00
Very good: $ 750.00

Winchester 101 Pigeon Grade Trap

Similar to the Pigeon Grade with a 30" or 32" barrel; recoil pad; regular or Monte Carlo stock.
Estimated Value: New (retail): $1,170.00
Excellent: $ 925.00
Very good: $ 750.00

Winchester 101 Pigeon Grade

Gauge: 12, 20, regular or magnum
Action: Box lock; top lever, break-open; over and under double barrel; selective automatic ejectors; single selective trigger
Magazine: None
Barrel: Over & under double barrel; 26" improved cylinder & modified; 28" modified & full; ventilated rib
Finish: Blued; checkered walnut pistol grip stock and fluted forearm; engraved silver grey satin finish reciever; recoil pad in magnum
Approximate wt: 7 ¼ lbs.
Comments: Introduced in the late 1970's.
Estimated Value: New (retail): $1,115.00
Excellent: $ 850.00
Very good: $ 700.00

Winchester Model 1901

Gauge: 10
Action: Lever action; repeating
Magazine: 4-shot tubular
Barrel: 30", 32" full choke, modified, or cylinder bore
Finish: Blued; walnut, pistol grip stock & forearm
Approximate wt: 8-9 lbs.
Comments: Made from 1901 to about 1920. This was an improved version of the Model 1887.
Estimated Value: Excellent: $450.00
Very good: $375.00

Winchester Model 1901

Shotguns

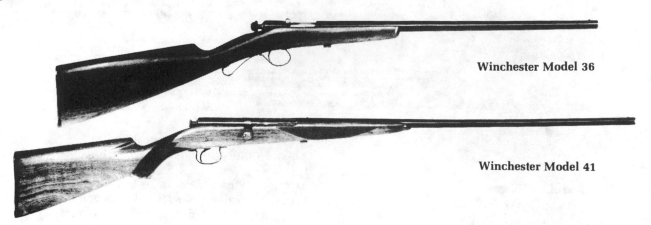

Winchester Model 36

Winchester Model 41

Winchester Model 36
Gauge: 9mm shot or ball cartridges
Action: Bolt action; single shot; rear cocking piece
Magazine: None
Barrel: 18"
Finish: Blued; straight grip, one piece stock & forearm
Approximate wt: 3 lbs.
Comments: Made from the early to late 1920's.
Estimated Value: Excellent: **$200.00**
Very good: **$175.00**

Winchester Model 41
Gauge: 410
Action: Bolt action; single shot; rear cocking piece
Magazine: None
Barrel: 24" full choke
Finish: Blued; plain or checkered, straight or pistol grip, one piece stock & forearm
Approximate wt: 5 lbs.
Comments: Made from about 1920 for 15 years.
Estimated Value: Excellent: **$185.00**
Very good: **$160.00**

Winchester Model 97

Winchester Model 97 Riot Gun

Winchester Model 97 Trench

Winchester Model 97
Gauge: 12, 16
Action: Slide action; exposed hammer; repeating
Magazine: 5-shot tubular
Barrel: 26", 28", 30" 32" modified, full choke or cylinder bore
Finish: Blued; plain wood semi-pistol grip stock & grooved slide handle
Approximate wt: 7 ¾ lbs.
Comments: Made from 1897 to late 1950's. This shotgun was an improved version of the Model 1893.
Estimated Value: Excellent: **$350.00**
Very good: **$300.00**

Winchester Model 97 Riot
Similar to the Model 97 with a 20" cylinder bore barrel.
Estimated Value: Excellent: $240.00
Very good: **$220.00**

Winchester Model 97 Trench
Similar to the 97 Riot Gun with a handguard and bayonet. Used in World War I, 1917-1918.
Estimated Value: Excellent: $420.00
Very good: **$375.00**

Winchester Model 12 Pre-'65

Winchester Model 12 Skeet Pre-'65

Winchester Model 12 Trap Pre-'65

Winchester Model 12 Duck Pre-'65

Winchester Model 12 Field After '72

Winchester Model 12 Super Pigeon After '72

Winchester Model 12 Trap After '72

Winchester Model 12

Gauge: 12, 16, 20, 28
Action: Slide action; hammerless; repeating
Magazine: 6-shot tubular
Barrel: 26"-32", standard chokes available
Finish: Blued; plain or checkered, pistol grip stock & slide handle (wood) some slide handles grooved
Approximate wt: 6 ½-7 ½ lbs.
Comments: Made in various grades: Featherweight, Rib Barrel, Riot Gun, Duck, Skeet, Trap, Pigeon, Super Pigeon from 1912 to about 1965. In 1972 Field Gun, Skeet and Trap were reissued. In 1963, Model 12 was offered with Hydro-coil recoil reducing system. Prices for Field Grade.
Estimated Value: Excellent: **$475.00**
               Very good: **$400.00**

Shotguns

Winchester Model 42

Winchester Model 42 Skeet

Winchester Model 42

Gauge: 410
Action: Slide action; hammerless; repeating
Magazine: 5 & 6 shot tubular
Barrel: 26'', 28'' modified, full choke, or cylinder bore
Finish: Blued; plain walnut, pistol grip, wood stock and grooved slide handle
Approximate wt: 6 lbs.
Comments: ,ade from the mis 1930's to mid 1960's.
Estimated Value: Excellent: $450.00
Very good: $400.00

Winchester Model 42 Skeet

Similar to the Model 42, available in straight stock; has matted rib and skeet choke barrel.
Estimated Value: Excellent: $525.00
Very good: $475.00

Winchester Model 42 Deluxe

Similar to the Model 42 with higher quality finish; ventilated rib; select wood; checkering
Estimated Value: Excellent: $650.00
Very good: $600.00

Winchester Model 25

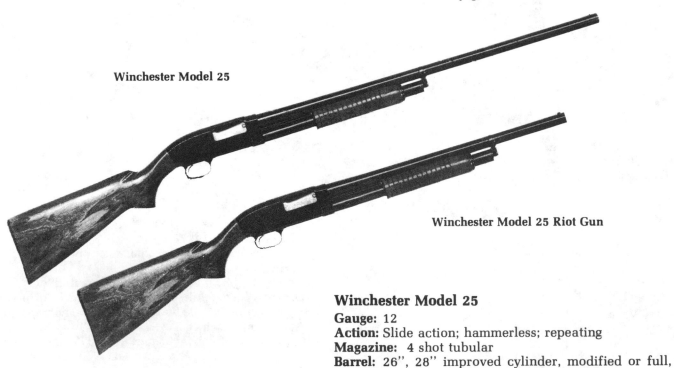

Winchester Model 25 Riot Gun

Winchester Model 25

Gauge: 12
Action: Slide action; hammerless; repeating
Magazine: 4 shot tubular
Barrel: 26'', 28'' improved cylinder, modified or full, chokes
Finish: Blued; plain walnut, semi-pistol grip stock & grooved slide handle; sights
Approximate wt: 7½ lbs.
Comments: Made from the late 1940's to mid 1950's.
Estimated Value: Excellent: $235.00
Very good: $190.00

Winchester Model 25 Riot Gun

Similar to the Model 25 with a 25'' cylinder bore barrel.
Estimated Value: Excellent: $200.00
Very good: $160.00

Winchester Model 1200

Winchester Model 1200 Deer

Winchester Model 1200 Skeet

Winchester Model 1200 Trap

Winchester Model 1200 Trap Monte Carlo

Winchester Model 1200 Field

Gauge: 12, 16, 20, regular or magnum; (16 gauge dropped in mid 1970's)

Action: Front lock; rotary bolt; slide action; repeating

Magazine: 4-shot tubular

Barrel: 26-30" various chokes or adjustable choke (Winchoke)

Finish: Blued; checkered walnut, pistol grip stock & slide handle; recoil pad; alloy receiver

Approximate wt: 6½-7½ lbs.

Comments: Made from the mid 1960's to the late 1970's. Add $15.00 for magnum, $5.00 for adjustable choke, $25.00 for ventilated rib.

Estimated Value: Excellent: $165.00
Very good: $130.00

Winchester Model 1200 Deer

Similar to the 1200 with 22" barrel, rifle-type sights. Made from the mid 1960's to mid 1970's.

Estimated Value: Excellent: $175.00
Very good: $140.00

Winchester Model 1200 Skeet

Similar to 1200 except: 12 & 20 gauge only; 26" skeet choke; ventilated rib barrel. Made to the mid 1970's.

Estimated Value: Excellent: $185.00
Very good: $150.00

Winchester Model 1200 Trap

Similar to the 1200 with a 30" full choke; ventilated rib; regular or Monte Carlo stock. Made to the mid 1970's.

Estimated Value: Excellent: $190.00
Very good: $155.00

Shotguns

Winchester Model 1300 XTR

Winchester Model 1300XTR Deer Gun

Winchester Model 1300 XTR

Gauge: 12, 20, regular or magnum
Action: Slide action; hammerless; repeating
Magazine: 3 shot tubular
Barrel: 26", 28", 30", improved cylinder, modified, or full choke; ventilated rib available
Finish: Blued; checkered walnut pistol grip stock & slide handle
Approximate wt: 6½ lbs.
Comments: Introduced in the late 1970's. Add $25.00 for ventilated rib.
Estimated Value: New (retail): $242.00
Excellent: $185.00
Very good: $150.00

Winchester Model 1300XTR Deer Gun

Similar to the Model 1300XTR with a 22" barrel, rifle sights, sling, and recoil pad. Intoduced in 1980; 12 gauge only.
Estimated Value: New (retail): $270.00
Excellent: $205.00
Very good: $165.00

Winchester Model 1300XTR Winchoke

Similar to the Model 1300 XTR with removable choke tube system; 28" barrel only; add $25.00 for ventilated rib.
Estimated Value: New (retail): $257.00
Excellent: $195.00
Very good: $160.00

Winchester Model 1911

Winchester Model 40 Skeet

Winchester Model 1911

Gauge: 12
Action: Semi-automatic; hammerless
Magazine: 4 shot tubular
Barrel: 26", -32" various chokes
Finish: Blued; plain or checkered, semi-pistol grip stock & forearm
Approximate wt: 8 lbs.
Comments: Made from 1911 to the mid 1920's.
Estimated Value: Excellent: $350.00
Very good: $300.00

Winchester Model 40

Gauge: 12
Action: Semi-automatic; hammerless
Magazine: 4 shot tubular
Barrel: 28", 30" modified or full choke
Finish: Blued; plain walnut pistol grip stock & forearm
Approximate wt: 8 lbs.
Comments: Made in the early 1940's.
Estimated Value: Excellent: $285.00
Very good: $240.00

Winchester Model 40 Skeet

Similar to the Model 40 with a 24" skeet barrel; checkering; "Cutts Compensator."
Estimated Value: Excellent: $300.00
Very good: $250.00

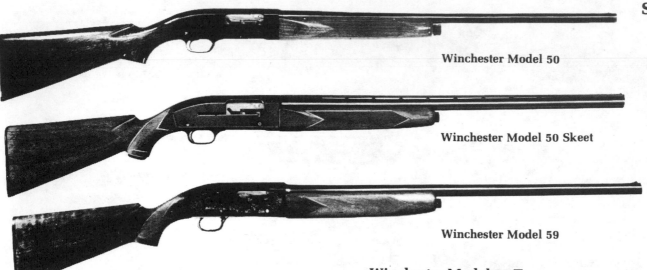

Winchester Model 50

Winchester Model 50 Skeet

Winchester Model 59

Winchester Model 50

Gauge: 12, 20
Action: Semi-automatic; non recoiling barrel; hammerless
Magazine: 2 shot tubular
Barrel: 26"-30", variety of chokes
Finish: Blued; checkered walnut pistol grip stock & forearm
Comments: Made from the mid 1950's to early 1960's. Add $25.00 for ventilated rib.
Estimated Value: Excellent: $240.00
                  Very good: $190.00

Winchester Model 50 Skeet

Similar to the Model 50 with a skeet stock 26" skeet choke; ventilated rib barrel.
Estimated Value: Excellent: $260.00
                  Very good: $210.00

Winchester Model 50 Trap

Similar to the Model 50 except 12 gauge only; Monte Carlo stock; 30" full choke; ventilated rib;
Estimated Value: Excellent: $325.00
                  Very good: $275.00

Winchester Model 59

Gauge: 12
Action: Semi-automatic; hammerless; non recoiling barrel
Magazine: 2-shot tubular
Barrel: 26"-30" variety of chokes. Steel and glass fiber composition; interchangeable choke tubes available.
Finish: Blued; checkered walnut, pistol grip stock & forearm; alloy receiver
Approximate wt: 6½ lbs.
Comments: Made from the late 1950's to mid 1960's.
Estimated Value: Excellent: $300.00
                  Very good: $250.00

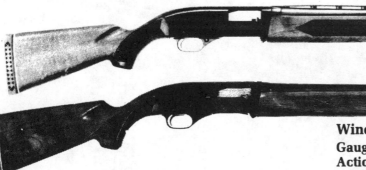

Winchester Model 1400

Winchester Model 1400 Mark II

Winchester Model 1400, 1400 Winchoke

Gauge: 12, 16, 20
Action: Gas operated, semi-automatic
Magazine: Two shot tubular
Barrel: 26", 28", 30", variety of chokes, or adjustable choke; all 1979 models have adjustable choke
Finish: Blued; checkered walnut pistol grip stock and forearm; recoil pad available; Cycolak stock available with recoil reduction system until late 1970's.
Approximate wt: 7½ lbs.
Comments: Made from the mid 1960's to late 1970's. Add $25.00 for ventilated rib or cycolak stock and recoil reduciton system.
Estimated Value: Excellent: $210.00
                  Very good: $165.00

Winchester Model 1400 Mark II

Similar to the 1400 except lighter weight and with minor improvements. Introduced in the late 1960's.
Estimated Value: Excellent: $200.00
                  Very good: $165.00

Shotguns

Winchester Model 1400 Deer

Winchester Model 1400 Skeet

Winchester Model 1400 Trap

Winchester Model 1400 Trap

Similar to the 1400 in 12 gauge with a 30" full choke, ventilated rib barrel. Available with Monte Carlo stock. Add $25.00 for recoil reduction system.
Estimated Value: Excellent: $260.00
Very good: $210.00

Winchester Model 1400 Skeet

Similar to the 1400 in 12 or 20 gauge; 26" barrel with ventilated rib. Add $25.00 for recoil reduction system.
Estimated Value: Excellent: $250.00
Very good: $200.00

Winchester Model 1400 Deer Gun

Similar to the 1400 with a 22" barrel for slugs, and sights.
Estimated Value: Excellent: $215.00
Very good: $170.00

Western Model 1500 XTR

Winchester Model 1500 XTR Winchoke

Similar to the Model 1500XTR with removable choke tube system, 28" barrel only; add $25.00 for ventilated rib.

Estimated Value:	New (retail):	$319.00
	Excellent:	$240.00
	Very good:	$195.00

Winchester Model 1500 XTR

Gauge: 12, 20, regular or magnum
Action: Gas operated semi-automatic
Magazine: 3 shot tubular
Barrel: 26", 28", 30", improved cylinder, modified, or full choke; ventilated rib available
Finish: Blued; checkered walnut pistol grip stock and forearm; alloy receiver
Approximate wt: 6½-7 lbs.
Comments: Introduced in the late 1970's. Add $25.00 for ventilated rib.

Estimated Value:	New (retail):	$304.00
	Excellent:	$235.00
	Very good:	$190.00

Winchester Super X Model 1

Winchester Super X Model 1 Skeet

Winchester Super X Model 1 Trap

Winchester Super X Model 1, Super X Model 1 XTR
Gauge: 12
Action: Gas operated; Semi-automatic
Magazine: 4-shot tubular
Barrel: 26"-30¼" various chokes; ventilated rib
Finish: Blued; scroll engraved alloy receiver; checkered walnut, pistol grip stock and forearm
Approximate wt: 8¼ lbs.
Comments: Currently sold as Super X 1 XTR. Introduced in the mid 1970's.
Estimated Value: New (retail): $500.00
 Excellent: $375.00
 Very good: $300.00

Winchester Super X Model 1 Skeet
Similar to the Super X Model 1 with skeet stock and 26" skeet choke; ventilated rib barrel.
Estimated Value: New (retail): $576.00
 Excellent: $430.00
 Very good: $345.00

Winchester Super X Model 1 Trap
Similar to the Super X Model 1 with regular or Monte Carlo stock; 30" full choke barrel; recoil pad
Estimated Value: New (retail): $589.00
 Excellent: $440.00
 Very good: $350.00

Zoli

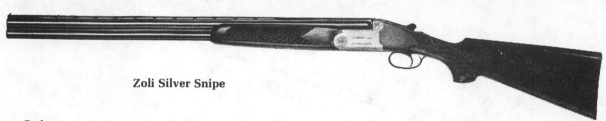

Zoli Silver Snipe

Zoli Silver Snipe

Gauge: 12, 20
Action: Box lock; top lever, break-open; hammerless; over & under double barrel; single trigger
Magazine: None
Barrel: Over & under doubel barrel; 26", 28", 30" ventilated rib; chrome lined; 3" chambers.
Finish: Blued; checkered waknut,pistol grip stock & forearm
Approximate wt: 7 lbs.
Comments: Currently manufactured in Italy.
Estimated Value: New (retail): $500.00 Approx.
Excellent: $385.00
Very good: $310.00

Zoli Golden Snipe

Similar to the Silver Snipe with selective automatic ejectors.
Estimated Value: New (retail): $575.00 Approx.
Excellent: $450.00
Very good: $360.00

Zoli 300 Gray Eagle

Gauge: 12
Action: Box lock; top lever, break-open; hammerless; over & under double barrel
Magazine: None
Barrel: Over & under double barrel; 26", 28"; ventilated rib; chrome lined; 3" chambers.
Finish: Blued; checkered walnut pistol grip stock and forearm.
Approximate wt: 7 lbs.
Comments: Currently manufactured in Italy.
Estimated Value: Excellent: $375.00
Very good: $300.00

Zoli 302 Gray Eagle

Similar to the 300 in 20 gauge. Weight about 6 ¼ lbs.
Estimated Value: Excellent: $390.00
Very good: $315.00

Zoli 302 Gray Eagle

Rifles

Anschutz Model 64

Anschutz Model 64S

Anschutz Mark 12 Target

Anschutz Model 1407

Anschutz Model 64 & 64L Match

Caliber: 22 long rifle
Action: Bolt action; single shot
Magazine: None
Barrel: 26'' blued
Sights: None
Stock & Forearm: Match style; checkered walnut, pistol grip, one piece stock and forearm; thumb rest; cheek piece; adjustable butt plate; foreward swivel
Approximate wt.: 7¾ lbs.
Comments: A match rifle made from about 1967 to present. Add $10.00-$15.00 for left hand action (64L)
Estimated Value: New (retail): $305.70
          Excellent: $230.00
          Very good: $185.00

Anschutz Model 64S & 64SL Match

Similar to Model 64 & 64L with special match sights. Add $20.00 - $30.00 for left hand version (64SL).
Estimated Value: New (retail): $418.63
                Excellent: $315.00
                Very good: $250.00

Anschutz Mark 12 Target

Similar to the Model 64 with a heavy barrel; non-adjustable buttplate; handstop; tapered stock & forearm; introduced in the late 1970's.
Estimated Value: New (retail): $140.70
                Excellent: $105.00
                Very good: $ 85.00

Anschutz Model 1407 & 1407L

Caliber: 22 long rifle
Action: Bolt action; single shot
Magazine: None
Barrel: 26'' blued
Sights: None
Stock & Forearm: Walnut, pistol grip, one-piece stock and wide forearm; thumb rest; cheekpiece; adjustable butt plate; forward swivel
Approximate wt.: 10 lbs.
Comments: A match rifle made from about 1967 to present. Add $15.00-$20.00 for left hand action (1407L)
Estimated Value: New (retail): $616.60
              Excellent: $465.00
              Very good: $370.00

Anschutz Models 1407L, 1807

Left hand version of the Model 1407.
Estimated Value: New (retail): $678.75
                Excellent: $520.00
                Very good: $420.00

Anschutz Model 184

Caliber: 22 long rifle
Action: Bolt action; repeating
Magazine: 5-shot detatchable clip
Barrel: 21½'' blued
Sights: Folding leaf rear, hooded ramp front
Stock & Forearm: Checkered walnut, Monte Carlo pistol grip, one piece stock and lipped forearm; swivels
Approximate wt.: 6 lbs.
Comments: Made from the mid 1960's to mid 1970's
Estimated Value: Excellent: $175.00
               Very good: $140.00

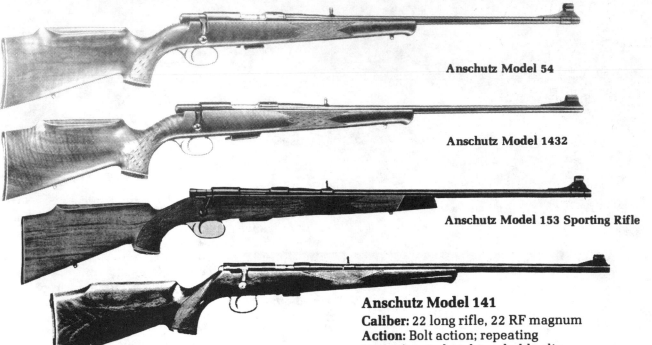

Anschutz Model 54

Anschutz Model 1432

Anschutz Model 153 Sporting Rifle

Anschutz Model 164

Anschutz Model 54

Caliber: 22 long rifle
Action: Bolt action; repeating
Magazine: 5 or 10 shot detatchable clip
Barrel: 24" blued
Sights: Folding leaf rear, hooded ramp front
Stock & Forearm: Checkered walnut, Monte Carlo pistol grip, one piece stock and lipped forearm
Approximate wt.: 6¾ lbs
Comments: Made from the late 1960's to present.
Estimated Value: New (retail): $576.10
        Excellent: **$430.00**
        Very good: **$345.00**

Anschutz Model 54M

Similar to Model 54 in 22 Winchester magnum with a 4-shot clip
Estimated Value: New (retail): $590.40
        Excellent: **$445.00**
        Very good: **$355.00**

Anschutz Model 1432

Caliber: 22 Hornet
Action: Bolt action; bottom load; repeating
Magazine: 5-shot clip
Barrel: 24" blued
Sights: Folding leaf rear, hooded ramp front
Stock & Forearm: Checkered walnut, Monte Carlo pistol grip, one piece stock and lipped forearm; swivels
Approximate wt.: 6¾ lbs.
Comments: Currently manufactured.
Estimated Value: New (retail): $632.95
        Excellent: **$475.00**
        Very good: **$380.00**

Anschutz Model 141

Caliber: 22 long rifle, 22 RF magnum
Action: Bolt action; repeating
Magazine: 5-shot detatchable clip
Barrel: 24" blued
Sights: Folding leaf rear, hooded ramp front
Stock & Forearm: Checkered walnut, Monte Carlo pistol grip, one piece stock and forearm
Approximate wt.: 6 lbs
Comments: Made from the middle to late 1960's
Estimated Value: Excellent: **$190.00**
        Very good: $150.00

Anschutz Model 153

Similar to Model 141 with abrupt ended forearm trimmed in different wood. Made from the middle to late 1960's.
Estimated Value: Excellent: **$200.00**
        Very good: $160.00

Anschutz Model 164

Caliber: 22 long rifle
Action: Bolt action; repeating
Magazine: 5 or 10 shot clip
Barrel: 23" blued
Sights: Folding leaf rear, hooded ramp front
Stock & Forearm: Checkered walnut, Monte Carlo pistol grip, one piece stock and lipped forearm
Approximate wt.: 6 lbs.
Comments: Manufactured from the late 1960's to present.
Estimated Value: New (retail): $326.40
        Excellent: **$245.00**
        Very good: **$195.00**

Anschutz Model 164M

Similar to Model 164 in 22 Winchester magnum, with a 4 shot clip.
Estimated Value: New (retail): $333.50
        Excellent: **$250.00**
        Very good: **$200.00**

Anschutz Model 64MS

Anschutz Model 1411

Anschutz Model 64MS

Caliber: 22 long rifle
Action: Bolt action; single shot; adjustable, two stage trigger
Magazine: None
Barrel: 21¾" medium heavy
Sights: None; tapped for scope
Stock & Forearm: Silhouette style one piece stippled pistol grip stock and forearm.
Approximate wt: 8 lbs.
Comments: A silhouette style rifle currently produced.
Estimated Value: New (retail): $310.90
Excellent: $235.00
Very good: $195.00

Anschutz Model 1418

Caliber: 22 long rifle
Action: Bolt action; repeating; double set or single set trigger
Magazine: 5 or 10 shot clip
Barrel: 19¾" blued
Sights: Folding leaf rear, hooded ramp front
Stock & Forearm: Checkered European Monte Carlo stock and full length forearm; cheekpiece; swivels
Approximate wt: 5½ lbs.
Comments: Introduced in the late 1970's.
Estimated Value: New (retail): $462.65
Excellent: $350.00
Very good: $280.00

Anschutz Model 1518

Similar to the Model 1418 in 22 WMR only; 4 shot clip magazine.
Estimated Value: New (retail): $471.10
Excellent: $355.00
Very good: $290.00

Anschutz Model 1411

Caliber: 22 long rifle
Action: Bolt action; single shot
Magazine: None
Barrel: 27½" heavy
Sights: None; tapped for scope
Stock & Forearm: Select walnut, one piece Monte Carlo pistol grip stock and forearm; adjustable cheekpiece; hand rest swivel; adjustable buttplate
Approximate wt: 12 lbs.
Comments: A match style rifle currently produced.
Estimated Value: New (retail): $669.75
Excellent: $510.00
Very good: $415.00

Anschutz Model 1811

A left hand version of the Model 1411.
Estimated Value: New (retail): $737.10
Excellent: $560.00
Very good: $460.00

Armalite

Armalite AR-180 Sporter

Armalite AR-180 Sporter

Caliber: 223
Gauge: Gas operated, semi-automatic
Magazine: 5-shot detachable box
Barrel: 18" blued
Sights: Adjustable rear and front; scope available
Stock & Forearm: Pistol grip; nylon folding stock; fiberglass forearm
Approximate wt: 6½ lbs.
Comments: Made from the early 1970's to late 1970's.
Estimated Value: Excellent: $275.00
Very good: $220.00

Armalite AR-7 Explorer

Armalite AR-7 Custom

Armalite AR-7 Explorer

Caliber: 22 long rifle
Action: Semi-automatic
Magazine: 8-shot clip
Barrel: 16" aluminum & steel lined
Sights: Peep rear, blade front
Stock & Forearm: Fiberglass, pistol grip stock (no forearm). Stock acts as case for gun when dismantled.
Approximate wt.: 2¾ lbs.
Comments: A lightweight alloy rifle designed to float & break down to fit into stock. Made from the 1960's until the 1970's. After about 1973 also marketed as Charter Arms AR-7.
Estimated Value: New (retail): $98.00
Excellent: $70.00
Very good: $55.00

Armalite AR-7 Custom

A sport version of the Explorer with a walnut, Monte Carlo pistol grip, one piece stock and forearm. Slightly heavier.
Estimated Value: Excellent: $85.00
Very good: $70.00

Browning

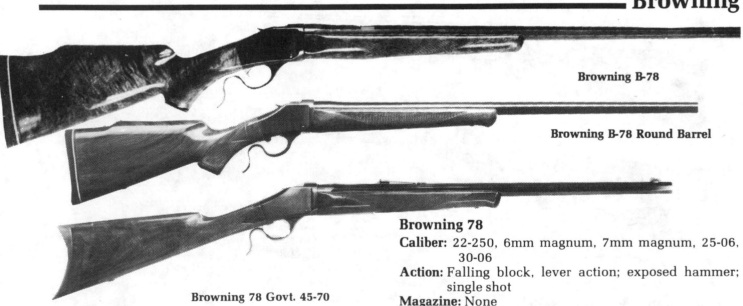

Browning B-78

Browning B-78 Round Barrel

Browning 78 Govt. 45-70

Browning 78

Caliber: 22-250, 6mm magnum, 7mm magnum, 25-06, 30-06
Action: Falling block, lever action; exposed hammer; single shot
Magazine: None
Barrel: Blued; 26" round or octagon
Sights: None
Stock & Forearm: Checkered walnut, Monte Carlo pistol grip stock and forearm
Approximate wt.: 7¾ to 8½ lbs.
Comments: A replica of John Browning's first patent rifle in 1878. Produced from the mid 1970's to present. Asian manufacture.
Estimated Value: New (retail): $399.95
Excellent: $300.00
Very good: $240.00

Browning 78 Govt. 45-70

Similar to 78 in Government 45-70 caliber with iron sights and straight grip stock, octagonal bull barrel.
Estimated Value: New (retail): $399.95
Excellent: $300.00
Very good: $240.00

Rifles

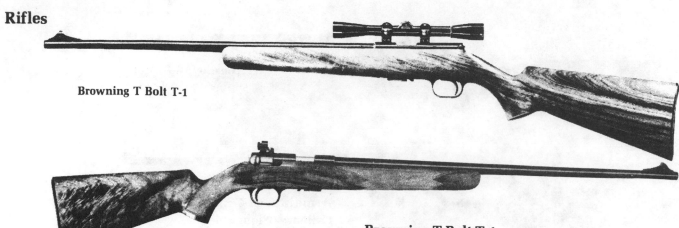

Browning T Bolt T-1

Browning T Bolt T-2

Browning T Bolt T-1

Caliber: 22 short, long, long rifle
Action: Bolt action; hammerless; side ejection; repeating; single shot conversion
Magazine: Removable 5-shot box
Barrel: 22'' blued
Sights: Peep rear, ramp front
Stock & Forearm: Walnut pistol grip, one piece stock & forearm.
Approximate wt.: 6 lbs.
Comments: Manufactured from the mid 1960's to the mid 1970's
Estimated Value: Excellent: $90.00
Very good: $75.00

Browning T Bolt T-2

A fancy version of the T-1 with checkered stock and forearm
Estimated Value: Excellent: $125.00
Very good: $100.00

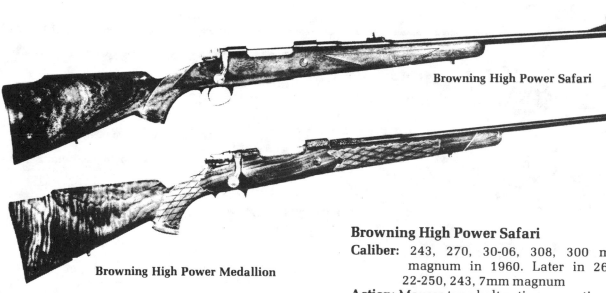

Browning High Power Safari

Browning High Power Medallion

Browning High Power Medallion

A higher grade version of the Safari with more engraving and higher quality wood.
Estimated Value: Excellent: $750.00
Very good: $600.00

Browning High Power Olympian

Highest grade of High Power models with complete engraving and some gold inlay.
Estimated Value: Excellent: $1,325.00
Very good: $1,050.00

Browning High Power Safari

Caliber: 243, 270, 30-06, 308, 300 magnum, 375 magnum in 1960. Later in 264, 338, 222, 22-250, 243, 7mm magnum
Action: Mauser type bolt action; repeating
Magazine: 3 or 5 shot, depending on caliber
Barrel: 22'' or 24'' blued
Sights: Adjustable sporting rear, hooded ramp front
Stock & Forearm: Checkered walnut, Monte Carlo pistol grip one piece stock and forearm; magnum calibers have recoil pad; swivels
Approximate wt.: 6 to 8 lbs.
Comments: This rifle was made from about 1960 through the mid 1970's. Short or medium action worth $10.00-$15.00 less.
Estimated Value: Excellent: $625.00
Very good: $500.00

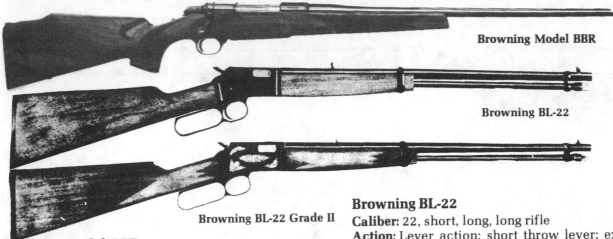

Browning Model BBR

Browning BL-22

Browning BL-22 Grade II

Browning Model BBR

Caliber: 30-06 Sprg., 270 Win., 25-06 Rem., 7mm Rem. magnum, 300 Win. magnum

Action: Bolt action; short throw; cocking indicator; repeating

Magazine: 4 shot; 3 shot in magnum; hinged floorplate, detachable box

Barrel: 24" floating barrel, recessed muzzle

Sights: None; tapped for scope

Stock & Forearm: Checkered walnut Monte Carlo, one piece pistol grip stock and forearm; cheekpiece; low profile sling studs; recoil pad on magnum

Approximate wt: 8 lbs.

Comments: A high powered hunting rifle introduced in the late 1970's.

Estimated Value: New (retail): $399.95
　　　　　　　　　Excellent: $300.00
　　　　　　　　　Very good: $250.00

Browning BL-22

Caliber: 22, short, long, long rifle

Action: Lever action; short throw lever; exposed hammer

Magazine: Tubular, 15 long rifles, 17 longs, 22 shorts

Barrel: 20" blued

Sights: Folding adjustable rear, bead front

Stock & Forearm: Plain walnut, straight grip stock & forearm; barrel band

Approximate wt.: 5 lbs.

Comments: A small, lightweight, 22 caliber rifle produced from 1970 to present in Asia.

Estimated Value: New (retail): $189.95
　　　　　　　　　Excellent: $145.00
　　　　　　　　　Very good: $115.00

Browning BL-22 Grade II

Similar to BL-22 with engraving; gold plated trigger; checkered stock & forearm.

Estimated Value: New (retail): $214.95
　　　　　　　　　Excellent: $160.00
　　　　　　　　　Very good: $130.00

Browning BLR

Browning Model 92

Browning BLR

Caliber: 243, 308, 358

Action: Lever action; exposed hammer; repeating

Magazine: 4-shot removable box

Barrel: 20" blued

Sights: Adjustable rear, hooded ramp front

Stock & Forearm: Checkered walnut, straight grip stock and forearm; recoil pad; barrel band

Approximate wt.: 7 lbs.

Comments: A carbine produced from early 1970's to present. Asian manufacture

Estimated Value: New (retail): $329.95
　　　　　　　　　Excellent: $250.00
　　　　　　　　　Very good: $200.00

Browning Model 92

Caliber: 44 magnum

Action: Lever action; exposed three position hammer; repeating

Magazine: 11 shot tubular

Barrel: 20" round

Sights: Adjustable cloverleaf rear, blade front

Stock & Forearm: Plain walnut straight grip stock and forearm; barrel band

Approximate wt: 5 ½ lbs.

Comments: An authentic remake of the 1892 Winchester designed by John Browning. Introduced in the late 1970's.

Estimated Value: New (retail): $264.95
　　　　　　　　　Excellent: $200.00
　　　　　　　　　Very good: $160.00

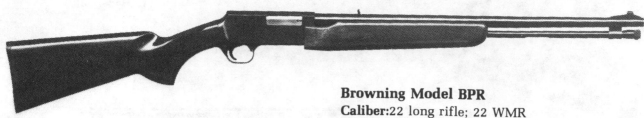

Browning Model BPR

Browning Model BPR

Caliber: 22 long rifle; 22 WMR
Action: Slide action; hammerless; repeating; slide release on trigger guard
Magazine: 15 shot tubular; 11 shot on magnum model
Barrel: 20¼''
Sights: Adjustable folding leaf rear, gold bead front
Stock & Forearm: Checkered walnut pistol grip stock and slide handle
Approximate wt: 6¼ lbs.
Comments: Introduced in the late 1970's. Add $20.00 for magnum.
Estimated Value: New (retail): $209.00
Excellent: $160.00
Very good: $125.00

Browning Model BPR Grade II

Similar to the BPR in magnum only; engraved squirrels and rabbits on receiver.
Estimated Value: New (retail): $329.95
Excellent: $250.00
Very good: $200.00

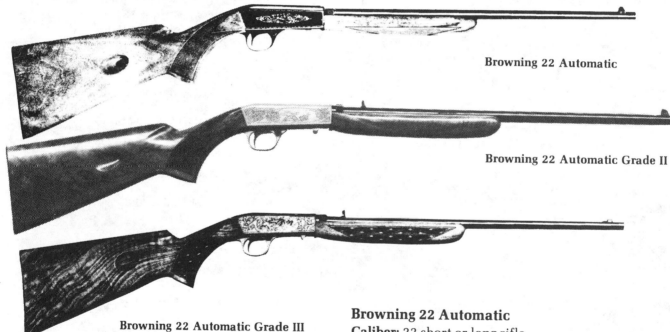

Browning 22 Automatic

Browning 22 Automatic Grade II

Browning 22 Automatic Grade III

Browning 22 Automatic Grade II

Similar to the 22 Automatic with chrome plated receiver and gold plated trigger. Receiver is engraved with squirrel scene.
Estimated Value: New (retail): $314.95
Excellent: $240.00
Very good: $190.00

Browning 22 Automatic Grade III

This is the same rifle as the Grade II except engraving is of bird dog and birds.
Estimated Value: New (retail): $699.95
Excellent: $525.00
Very good: $425.00

Browning 22 Automatic

Caliber: 22 short or long rifle
Action: Browning semi-automatic; hammerless; bottom ejection
Magazine: Tubular in stock; 11 shot in long rifle; 16 shot in short
Barrel: Blued; 22¼'' in long rifle; 19¼'' in short
Sights: Adjustable rear, dovetail bead front
Stock & Forearm: Hand checkered walnut, pistol grip stock and tapered forearm
Approximate wt.: 4¾ lbs.
Comments: This takedown model is made in three grades that differ in quality of finish. All have been in production since the mid 1950's.
Estimated Value: New (retail): $214.95
Excellent: $160.00
Very good: $130.00

Browning BAR Grade I

Caliber: 243, 270, 308, 30-06, 7mm magnum, 300 magnum, 338
Action: Gas operated semi-automatic; side ejection; hammerless
Magazine: 4-shot removable box; 3-shot in magnum
Barrel: 22" or 24" blued
Sights: Folding rear, hooded ramp front
Stock & Forearm: Checkered walnut, pistol grip stock and forearm
Approximate wt.: 7-8 ¼ lbs.
Comments: Made from the late 1960's to present. Add $40.00 for magnum calibers.
Estimated Value: New (retail): $479.95
Excellent: $360.00
Very good: $290.00

Browning BAR Grade II

Engraved version of BAR. Discontinued in the early 1970's.
Estimated Value: Excellent: $450.00
Very good: $375.00

Browning BAR Grade III

Similar to Grade I with elaborate engraving featuring antelope head. Discontinued early 1970's. Reintroduced in 1979 with rams and elk engravings; add $30.00 to $50.00 for magnum.
Estimated Value: New (retail): $900.00
Excellent: $675.00
Very good: $550.00

Browning BAR Grade IV

Similar to Grade I with elaborate engraving featuring two running antelope and running deer. Current Grade IV features running deer. Magnum has moose engraving. Add $40.00 for magnum caliber. Still manufactured.
Estimated Value: New (retail): $1,700.00
Excellent: $1,275.00
Very good: $1,050.00

Browning BAR Grade V

Similar to other grades of BAR. This is the fanciest model, discontinued in the early 1970's.
Estimated Value: Excellent: $1,600.00
Very good: $1,325.00

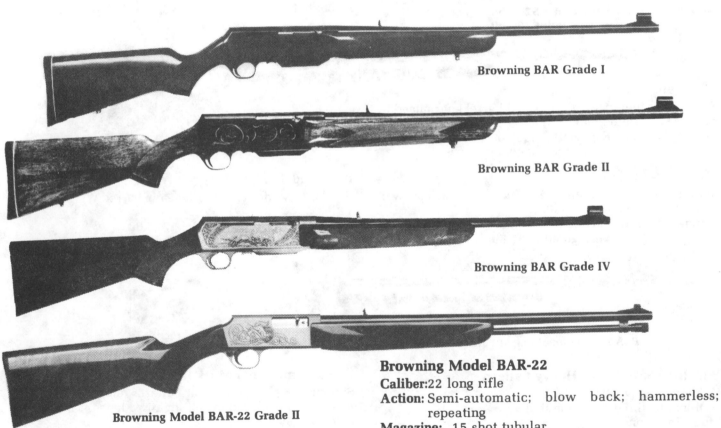

Browning BAR Grade I

Browning BAR Grade II

Browning BAR Grade IV

Browning Model BAR-22 Grade II

Browning Model BAR-22 Grade II

Similar to the BAR-22 with engraved receiver, squirrels and rabbits.
Estimated Value: New (retail): $309.95
Excellent: $235.00
Very good: $190.00

Browning Model BAR-22

Caliber: 22 long rifle
Action: Semi-automatic; blow back; hammerless; repeating
Magazine: 15 shot tubular
Barrel: 20"
Sights: Adjustable folding leaf rear, gold bead front
Stock & Forearm: Checkered walnut pistol grip stock and forearm; fluted comb
Approximate wt: 6 ¼ lbs.
Comments: Introduced in the late 1970's.
Estimated Value: New (retail): $209.95
Excellent: $160.00
Very good: $125.00

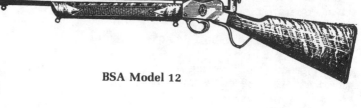

BSA Model 12

Caliber: 22 long rifle
Action: Martini type; single shot
Magazine: None
Barrel: 29" blued
Sights: Match sights; some with open sights
Stock & Forearm: Walnut, straight grip stock and checkered forearm; swivels
Approximate wt.: 9 lbs.
Comments: Made from about 1910 to 1930.
Estimated Value: Excellent: $200.00
Very good: $160.00

BSA Model 12

BSA Model 13

Similar to Model 12 with a 25" barrel. Weighs about 6 lbs.
Estimated Value: Excellent: $180.00
Very good: $145.00

BSA Model 13 Sporting

Similar to Model 13 in 22 Hornet caliber.
Estimated Value: Excellent: $200.00
Very good: $160.00

BSA Model 15

Caliber: 22 long rifle
Action: Martini type; single shot
Magazine: None
Barrel: 29" blued
Sights: Special BSA match sights
Stock & Forearm: Walnut stock and forearm; cheekpiece; swivels
Approximate wt.: 9 ½ lbs
Comments: A match rifle made from about 1915 to the early 1930's.
Estimated Value: Excellent: $225.00
Very good: $180.00

BSA Centurian

Similar to Model 15 with a special barrel guaranteed to produce accurate groups.
Estimated Value: Excellent: $300.00
Very good: $240.00

BSA Model 12/15

BSA Model 12/15

Similar to Model 12 and 15 in pre-war and post-war models. Made to about 1950.
Estimated Value: Excellent: $190.00
Very good: $155.00

BSA Model 12/15 Heavy Barrel

Similar to Model 12/15 with heavy barrel. Weighs about 11 lbs.
Estimated Value: Excellent: $225.00
Very good: $185.00

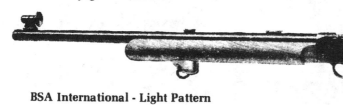

BSA International - Light Pattern

BSA International — Heavy Pattern

Caliber: 22 long rifle
Action: Martini type; single shot
Magazine: None
Barrel: 29" heavy, blued
Sights: Special Parker-Hale match sights
Stock & Forearm: Match style, pistol grip stock with cheekpiece, wide forearm; hand stop; swivels
Approximate wt.: 13 ¾ lbs.
Comments: A target rifle made in the early 1950's.
Estimated Value: Excellent: $275.00
Very good: $220.00

BSA International Mark II

Similar to Heavy and Light Patterns (choice of barrel). Stock and forearm changed slightly. Made from the early to late 1950's.
Estimated Value: Excellent: $300.00
Very good: $240.00

BSA International — Light Pattern

Similar to Heavy Pattern but lighter weight with a 26" barrel
Estimated Value: Excellent: $260.00
Very good: $210.00

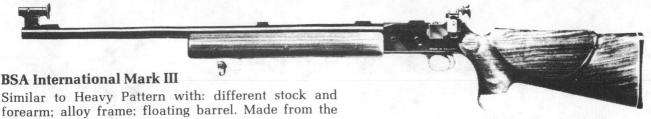

BSA International Mark III

Similar to Heavy Pattern with: different stock and forearm; alloy frame; floating barrel. Made from the late 1950's to late 1960's.

Estimated Value: Excellent: $290.00
**   Very good: $235.00**

BSA International Mark III

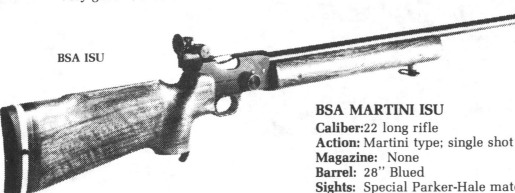

BSA ISU

BSA MARTINI ISU

Caliber: 22 long rifle
Action: Martini type; single shot
Magazine: None
Barrel: 28" Blued
Sights: Special Parker-Hale match sights
Stock & Forearm: Match style, walnut pistol grip, adjustable buttplate
Approximate wt: 10½ lbs.
Comments: A match rifle.
Estimated Value: Excellent: $425.00
**   Very good: $350.00**

BSA Mark V

Similar to ISU with a heavy barrel. Weighs about 12½ lbs.

Estimated Value: Excellent: $400.00
**   Very good: $320.00**

BSA Majestic Deluxe

BSA Majestic Deluxe Featherweight

BSA Monarch Deluxe

BSA Majestic Deluxe

Caliber: 22 Hornet, 222, 243, 30-06, 308 Winchester, 7 x 57 mm
Action: Mauser type bolt action; repeating
Magazine: 4-shot box
Barrel: 22" blued
Sights: Folding leaf rear, hooded ramp front
Stock & Forearm: Checkered walnut, Monte Carlo pistol grip, one piece stock & lipped forearm; swivels; cheekpiece; recoil pad.
Approximate wt.: 7½ lbs.
Comments: Made from the early to mid 1960's.
Estimated Value: Excellent: $200.00
**   Very good: $160.00**

BSA Monarch Deluxe

Similar to Majestic Deluxe with stock and forearm changed slightly and recoil pad. Made from mid 1960's to late 1970's.

Estimated Value: Excellent: $190.00
**   Very good: $150.00**

BSA Majestic Deluxe Featherweight

Similar to Deluxe with: recoil reducer in barrel; available in some magnum calibers.

Estimated Value: Excellent: $210.00
**   Very good: $170.00**

Rifles

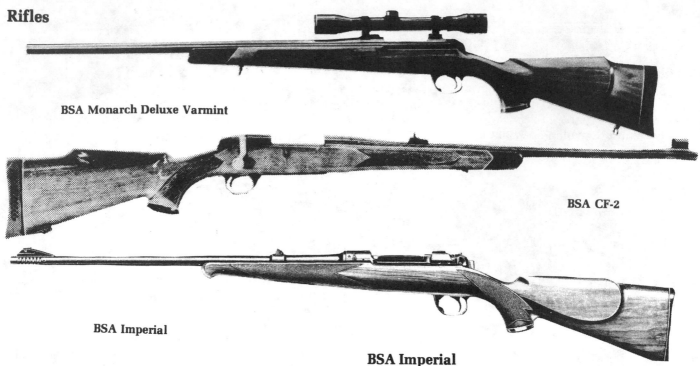

BSA Monarch Deluxe Varmint

BSA CF-2

BSA Imperial

BSA CF-2
Similar to Monarch Deluxe with slightly different forearm, 23½" barrel and adjustable rear sight.
Estimated Value: Excellent: $275.00
Very good: $215.00

BSA Monarch Deluxe Varmint
Similar to Monarch Deluxe with a heavier 24" barrel.
Estimated Value: Excellent: $200.00
Very good: $160.00

BSA Imperial
Caliber: 22 Hornet, 222, 243, 257 Roberts, 270 Winchester, 7 x 57 mm, 300 Savage, 30-06, 308 Winchester
Action: Bolt action; repeating
Magazine: 4-shot box
Barrel: 22" blued; recoil reducer
Sights: Open rear, ramp front
Stock & Forearm: Checkered walnut, Monte Carlo pistol grip one piece stock and lipped forearm; cheekpiece
Approximate wt.: 7 lbs.
Comments: Made in the early 1960's
Estimated Value: Excellent: $225.00
Very good: $185.00

Carl Gustaf

Carl Gustaf Grade II

Carl Gustaf Grade II Magnum

Carl Gustaf Grade II Magnum
Similar to Grade II except magnum calibers; recoil pad; 3-shot magazine.
Estimated Value: Excellent: $425.00
Very good: $350.00

Carl Gustaf Grade II
Caliber: 22-250, 243, 25-06, 270, 6.5x55, 30-06, 308
Action: Bolt action; repeating
Magazine: 5-shot staggered column
Barrel: 23½" blued
Sights: Leaf rear, hooded ramp front
Stock & Forearm: Checkered walnut, Monte Carlo pistol grip, one-piece stock & forearm; swivels
Approximate wt.: 7 lbs.
Comments: Manufactured in Sweden.
Estimated Value: Excellent: $400.00
Very good: $320.00

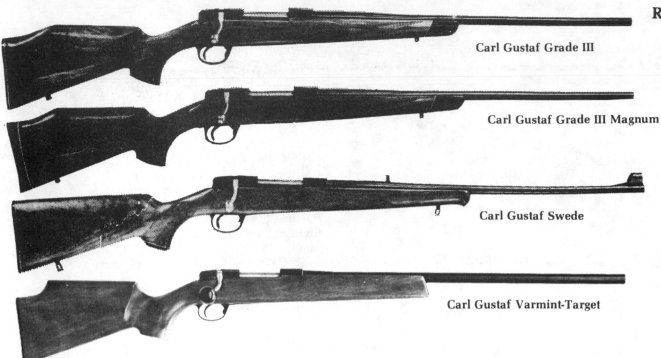

Carl Gustaf Grade III

Carl Gustaf Grade III Magnum

Carl Gustaf Swede

Carl Gustaf Varmint-Target

Carl Gustaf Grade III

Similar to Grade II with: select wood; more checkering; high quality finish; no sights.
Estimated Value: Excellent: $500.00
Very good: $400.00

Carl Gustaf Grade III Magnum

Similar to Grade II Magnum with: select wood; more checkering; high quality finish; no sights.
Estimated Value: Excellent: $525.00
Very good: $420.00

Carl Gustaf Swede

Similar to Grade II without Monte Carlo comb and has a lipped forearm.
Estimated Value: Excellent: $350.00
Very good: $275.00

Carl Gustaf Swede Deluxe

Similar to Grade III with lipped forearm
Estimated Value: Excellent: $475.00
Very good: $385.00

Carl Gustaf Varmint-Target

Caliber: 22-250, 222, 243, 6.5x55
Action: Bolt action; repeating; large bolt knob
Magazine: 5-shot staggered column
Barrel: 27'' blued
Sights: None
Stock & Forearm: Plain walnut, Monte Carlo pistol grip, one piece stock & forearm
Approximate wt.: 9½ lbs.
Comments: Currently manufactured.
Estimated Value: Excellent: $425.00
Very good: $360.00

Charles Daly

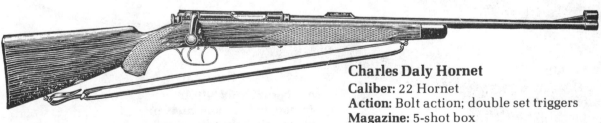

Charles Daly Hornet

Charles Daly Hornet

Caliber: 22 Hornet
Action: Bolt action; double set triggers
Magazine: 5-shot box
Barrel: 24''
Sights: Hooded ramp front; leaf rear
Stock & Forearm: Checkered walnut, one-piece stock & forearm
Approximate wt.: 7¾ lbs.
Comments: Made during the 1930's. Also marketed under the name Herold Rifle.
Estimated Value: Excellent: $570.00
Very good: $460.00

143

Colt

Colt Colteer 1-22

Colt Colteer 1-22
Caliber: 22, short, long, long rifle
Action: Bolt action; hammerless; single shot.
Magazine: None
Barrel: 20'', 22'' blued
Sights: Open rear, ramp front
Stock & Forearm: Plain walnut, Monte Carlo pistol grip
   stock and forearm
Approximate wt.: 5 lbs.
Comments: Made for 10 years from about 1957.
Estimated Value: Excellent: $55.00
Very good: $45.00

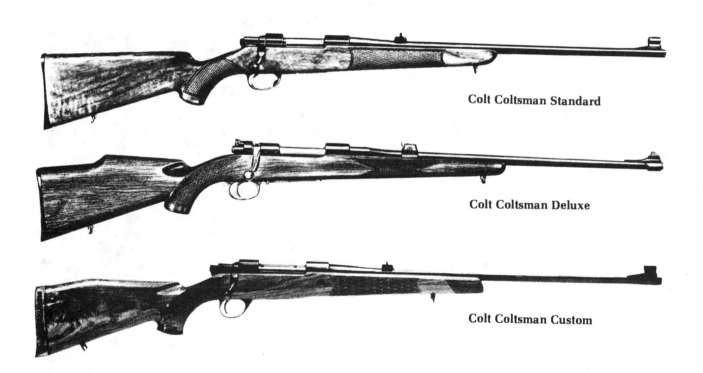

Colt Coltsman Standard

Colt Coltsman Deluxe

Colt Coltsman Custom

Colt Coltsman Standard

Caliber: 300 H & H Magnum, 30-06
Action: Mauser type, bolt action; repeating
Magazine: 5-shot box
Barrel: 22'' blued
Sights: No rear, ramp front
Stock & Forearm: Checkered walnut, pistol grip, one
   piece stock and tapered forearm;
   swivels
Approximate wt.: 7 lbs.
Comments: Made from about 1957 to the early 1960's
Estimated Value: Excellent: $300.00
Very good: $250.00

Colt Coltsman Deluxe

Similar to standard with: higher quality wood and
finish; adjustable rear sight; Monte Carlo stock.
Estimated Value: Excellent: $330.00
Very good: $275.00

Colt Coltsman Custom

Similar to the deluxe with: select wood; cheekpiece;
engraving
Estimated Value: Excellent: $390.00
Very good: $320.00

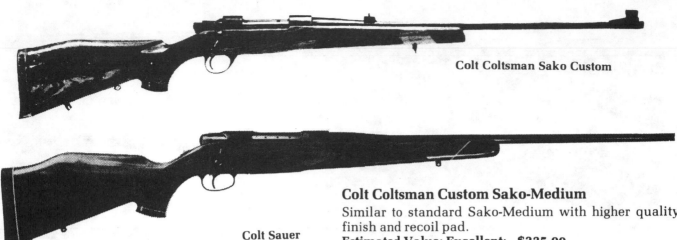

Colt Coltsman Sako Custom

Colt Sauer

Colt Coltsman Sako-Short

Caliber: 222, 222 magnum, 243, 308
Action: Short Sako type bolt action; repeating
Magazine: 5-shot box
Barrel: 22" blued
Sights: Open rear, hooded ramp front
Stock & Forearm: Checkered walnut, Monte Carlo pistol grip, one piece stock and tapered forearm; swivels
Approximate wt.: 7 lbs.
Comments: Made from the late 1950's to mid 1960's
Estimated Value: Excellent: $270.00
           Very good: $215.00

Colt Coltsman Deluxe Sako-Short

Similar to Standard Sako with: adjustable rear sight; higher quality finish; in calibers 243, 308; discontinued in the early 1960's.
Estimated Value: Excellent: $300.00
           Very good: $240.00

Colt Coltsman Custom Sako-Short

Similar to Deluxe Sako-Short with: select wood; cheekpiece; engraving. Made until mid 1960's.
Estimated Value: Excellent: $360.00
           Very good: $290.00

Colt Coltsman Sako-Medium

Caliber: 243, 308 Winchester
Action: Medium stroke, Sako type bolt action; repeating
Magazine: 5-shot box
Barrel: 24" blued
Sights: Folding leaf rear, hooded ramp front
Stock & Forearm: Checkered walnut, Monte Carlo pistol grip, one piece stock and tapered forearm.
Approximate wt.: 7 lbs.
Comments: Made from the early to mid 1960's
Estimated Value: Excellent: $270.00
           Very good: $215.00

Colt Coltsman Custom Sako-Medium

Similar to standard Sako-Medium with higher quality finish and recoil pad.
Estimated Value: Excellent: $325.00
           Very good: $270.00

Colt Coltsman Sako-Long

Caliber: 264, 270 Winchester, 300 H&H, 30-06, 375 H&H
Action: Long stroke, Sako-type bolt action; repeating
Magazine: 5-shot box
Barrel: 24" blued
Sights: Folding leaf rear, hooded ramp front
Stock & Forearm: Checkered walnut, pistol grip, one piece stock and tapered forearm; swivels
Approximate wt.: 7 lbs.
Comments: Made from early to mid 1960's
Estimated Value: Excellent: $275.00
           Very good: $225.00

Colt Coltsman Custom Sako-Long

Similar to Sako-Long with: higher quality finish; recoil pad; Monte Carlo stock.
Estimated Value: Excellent: $325.00
           Very good: $270.00

Colt Sauer

Caliber: 25-06, 270, 30-06, 300 Winchester magnum, 7mm Rem. magnum, 300 Weatherby magnum.
Action: Long stroke, Sauer type bolt action; repeating
Magazine: 3 shot detachable box
Barrel: 24" blued
Sights: None, tapped for scope
Stock & Forearm: Checkered walnut, Monte Carlo pistol grip, one piece stock and tapered forearm; swivels; recoil pad
Approximate wt: 7 ½ to 8. lbs.
Comments: Made from early 1970's to present. Add $30.00 for magnum.
Estimated Value: New (retail): $889.95
           Excellent: $725.00
           Very good: $600.00

Colt Sauer Grand Alaskan

Similar to the Colt Sauer; chambered for 375 H&H; adjustable rear, hooded ramp front sights.
Estimated Value: New (retail): $944.95
           Excellent: $765.00
           Very good: $620.00

Rifles

Colt Sauer-Short

Colt Sauer Grand African

Colt Lightning

Colt Courier

Colt Stagecoach

Colt Sauer-Short

Similar to Sauer with: short stroke action; chambered for 22-250, 243, 308 calibers. Made from mid 1970's to present; 7½ to 8½ lbs.

Estimated Value: New (retail): **$889.95**
Excellent: **$725.00**
Very good: **$600.00**

Colt Sauer Grand African

Similar to Sauer with: higher quality finish; adjustable sights; 458 Win. caliber only; 10 lbs.

Estimated Value: New (retail): **$989.95**
Excellent: **$800.00**
Very good: **$650.00**

Colt Lightning

Caliber: 22 short, long
Action: Slide action; exposed hammer; repeating
Magazine: Tubular, 15 longs, 16 shorts
Barrel: 24'' round or octagon, blued
Sights: Open rear, bead front
Stock & Forearm: Plain walnut, straight grip stock & checkered slide handle
Approximate wt.: 5¾ lbs.
Comments: Made from the 1880's to about 1905.
Estimated Value: Excellent: **$350.00**
Very good: **$290.00**

Colt Courier

Caliber: 22 long rifle
Action: Semi-automatic
Magazine: 15-shot tubular
Barrel: 19½'' blued
Sights: Open rear, hooded ramp front
Stock & Forearm: Plain walnut, straight grip stock and forearm; barrel band
Approximate wt.: 5 lbs.
Comments: Made from the mid 1960's to late 70's.
Estimated Value: Excellent: **$75.00**
Very good: **$60.00**

Colt Stagecoach

Similar to the Courier with: engraving; 16½'' barrel; saddle ring with leather string. Made from mid 1960's to 1976.

Estimated Value: Excellent: **$70.00**
Very good: **$55.00**

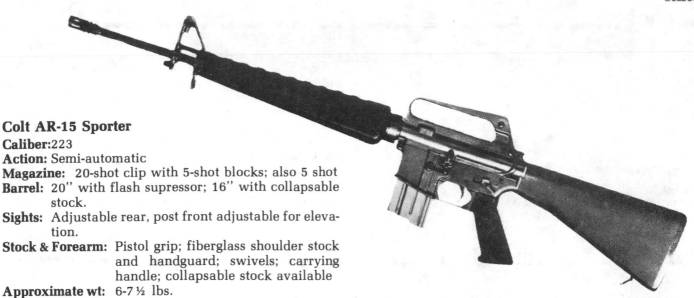

Colt AR-15 Sporter

Caliber: 223
Action: Semi-automatic
Magazine: 20-shot clip with 5-shot blocks; also 5 shot
Barrel: 20" with flash supressor; 16" with collapsable stock.
Sights: Adjustable rear, post front adjustable for elevation.
Stock & Forearm: Pistol grip; fiberglass shoulder stock and handguard; swivels; carrying handle; collapsable stock available
Approximate wt: 6-7 ½ lbs.
Comments: Made from the mid 1960's to present. Add $40.00 for collapsable stock.
Estimated Value: New (retail): $424.95
Excellent: $340.00
Very good: $275.00

Colt AR-15 Sporter

FN

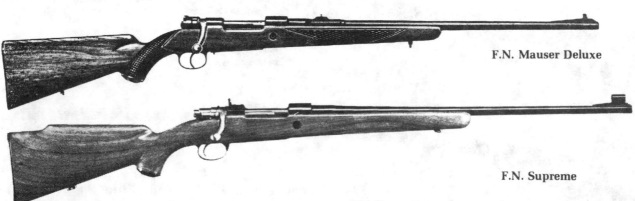

F.N. Mauser Deluxe

F.N. Supreme

F.N. Mauser Deluxe

Caliber: 220, 243, 244, 250-3000, 270, 7mm, 300, 308, 30-06
Action: Mauser type, bolt action; repeating
Magazine: 5-shot box
Barrel: 24" blued
Sights: Adjustable rear, hooded ramp front
Stock & Forearm: Checkered pistol grip, one piece stock & forearm; swivels
Approximate wt.: 7 ½ -8 lbs.
Comments: Made from World War II to the early 1960's.
Estimated Value: Excellent: $330.00
Very good: $265.00

F.N. Mauser Deluxe Presentation

Similar to the Deluxe with Monte Carlo stock; engraving; select wood.
Estimated Value: Excellent: $540.00
Very good: $435.00

FN Supreme

Caliber: 243, 270, 7mm, 30-06, 308
Action: Mauser type, bolt action; repeating
Magazine: 5-shot box, 4-shot box in 308 or 243 calibers
Barrel: 22", 24" blued
Sights: Adjustable rear, hooded ramp front
Stock & Forearm: Checkered wood, Monte Carlo pistol grip, one-piece stock & tapered forearm; cheekpiece; swivels
Approximate wt.: 8 lbs.
Comments: Made from the late 1950's to the mid 1970's.
Estimated Value: Excellent: $390.00
Very good: $315.00

FN Supreme Magnum

Similar to the Supreme in magnum calibers and 3-shot box magazine
Estimated Value: Excellent: $420.00
Very good: $335.00

Haenel

Haenel Sporter M-88
Caliber: 7x57mm, 8x57mm, 9x57mm
Action: Mauser bolt action; double set trigger
Magazine: 5-shot detatchable clip
Barrel: 22'', 24'', half octagon barrel
Sights: Open rear, ramp front
Stock & Forearm: Checkered wood, pistol grip stock & lipped forearm; swivels
Approximate wt.: 7¾ lbs.
Comments: A German sporting rifle, produced from about 1925 to 1940.
Estimated Value: Excellent: $390.00
Very good: $315.00

Haenel M-88
Similar to the Sporter with a box magazine.
Estimated Value: Excellent: $330.00
Very good: $265.00

Harrington & Richardson

Harrington & Richardson 1873 Springfield Commemorative

Harrington & Richardson Little Big Horn Commemorative 174

Harrington & Richardson Cavalry 171 Deluxe Carbine

Harrington & Richardson 1873 Springfield Commemorative
Caliber: 45-70 Gov't.
Action: Trap door; single shot
Magazine: None
Barrel: 32'' blued
Sights: Adjustable rear, blade front
Stock & Forearm: Straight grip, one piece stock & full length forearm; barrel bands; swivels
Approximate wt.: 8¾ lbs.
Comments: Manufactured to the late 1970's; replica of 1873 U.S. Springfield Rifle.
Estimated Value: Excellent: $290.00
Very good: $235.00

Harrington & Richardson Little Big Horn Commemorative 174
Carbine version of the trap door Springfield, 22'' barrel; 7¼ lbs.
Estimated Value: Excellent: $265.00
Very good: $220.00

Harrington & Richardson Cavalry Carbine 171
Similar to the Little Big Horn with saddle ring.
Estimated Value: Excellent: $240.00
Very good: $195.00

Harrington & Richardson Cavalry 171 Deluxe Carbine
Similar to the 171 with engraving.
Estimated Value: Excellent: $260.00
Very good: $215.00

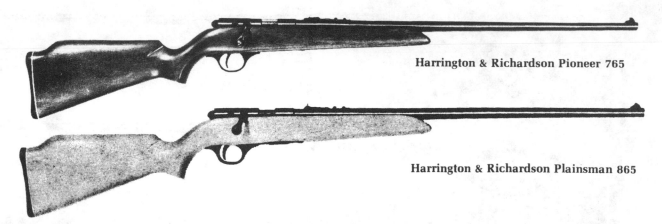

Harrington & Richardson Pioneer 765

Harrington & Richardson Plainsman 865

Harrington & Richardson Pioneer 765

Caliber: 22 short, long, long rifle
Action: Bolt action; single shot
Magazine: None
Barrel: 24'' blued
Sights: Open rear, hooded bead front
Stock & Forearm: Wood, Monte Carlo semi-pistol grip,
one piece stock & forearm
Approximate wt.: 5 lbs.
Comments: Made from the late 1940's to mid 1950's.
Estimated Value: Excellent: $40.00
**   Very good: $30.00**

Harrington & Richardson Plainsman 865

Similar to the 765 with: 5-shot clip; 22'' barrel. Made
from about 1950 to late 1970's.
Estimated Value: Excellent: $60.00
**   Very good: $50.00**

Harrington & Richardson 866

Similar to the 865 with full length forearm. Made in early 1970's.
Estimated Value: Excellent: $65.00
**   Very good: $55.00**

Harrington & Richardson Pioneer 750

Harrington & Richardson Pioneer 750

Similar to the 765. MAde from the mid 1950's to late
1970's.
Estimated Value: Excellent: $50.00
**   Very good: $40.00**

Harrington & Richardson Model 751

Similar to the 750 with full length forearm. Made from
the early to mid 1970's.
Estimated Value: Excellent: $60.00
**   Very good: $50.00**

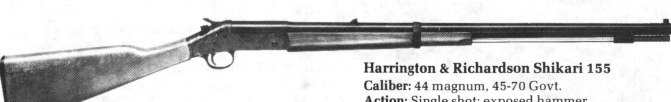

Harrington & Richardson Shikari 155

Harrington & Richardson Shikari 155

Caliber: 44 magnum, 45-70 Govt.
Action: Single shot; exposed hammer
Magazine: None
Barrel: 24'', 28'' blued
Sights: Folding leaf rear, blade front
Stock & Forearm: Wood, straight grip stock & forearm;
barrel band
Approximate wt.: 7-7 ¼ lbs.
Comments: Still manufactured.
Estimated Value: New (retail): $110.00
**   Excellent: $ 85.00**
**   Very good: $ 65.00**

Rifles

Harrington & Richardson 158 Topper

Harrington & Richardson Mustang

Harrington & Richardson Model 157

Harrington & Richardson 158 Topper

Caliber: 22 Hornet, 30-30
Action: Box lock; top lever, break-open; exposed hammer; single shot
Magazine: None
Barrel: 22" blued
Sights: Adjustable rear, ramp front
Stock & Forearm: Hardwood, straight or semi-pistol grip stock & forearm; recoil pad
Approximate wt: 5 lbs.
Comments: Made from the early 1960's to present
Estimated Value: New (retail): $85.00
                Excellent: $65.00
                Very good: $55.00

Harrington & Richardson Model 157

Similar to Model 158 with semi-pistol grip stock, full length forearm and swivels.
Estimated Value: New (retail): $99.50
                Excellent: $75.00
                Very good: $60.00

Harrington & Richardson 158 C & 58 Topper

Similar to the 158 with extra interchangeable 26" 410 or 20 gauge shotgun barrel.
Estimated Value: New (retail): $99.50
                Excellent: $75.00
                Very good: $60.00

Harrington & Richardson Mustang

Similar to the 158 with gold plated trigger & hammer; straight stock. Made in the mid 1960's.
Estimated Value: Excellent: $75.00
                Very good: $60.00

Harrington & Richardson Sahara 755

Harrington & Richardson Model 760

Harrington & Richardson Sahara 755

Caliber: 22 short, long, long rifle
Action: Blow back; hammerless; single shot; automatic ejector
Magazine: None
Barrel: 22" blued
Sights: Open rear, military front
Stock & Forearm: Monte Carlo semi-pistol grip, one piece stock & full length forearm
Approximate wt.: 4 lbs.
Comments: Made from the early 1960's to early 1970's
Estimated Value: Excellent: $60.00
                Very good: $50.00

Harrington & Richardson Model 760

Similar to the 755 with short forearm. Discontinued in 1970.
Estimated Value: Excellent: $50.00
                Very good: $40.00

Harrington & Richardson Medalist 450

Caliber: 22 long rifle
Action: Bolt action; repeating
Magazine: 5-shot detatchable box
Barrel: 26" blued
Sights: None
Stock & Forearm: Target style with pistol grip; swivels
Approximate wt.: 10½ lbs.
Comments: A target rifle made from the late 1940's to early 1960's.
Estimated Value: Excellent: $140.00
                  Very good: $110.00

Harrington & Richardson Medalist 451

Similar to the 450 with extension rear sight and Lyman front sight.
Estimated Value: Excellent: $145.00
                  Very good: $115.00

Harrington & Richardson Sportster 250

Caliber: 22 long rifle
Action: Bolt action; repeating
Magazine: 5-shot detatchable box
Barrel: 23" blued
Sights: Open rear, ramp front
Stock & Forearm: Wood, semi-pistol grip, one piece stock & forearm
Approximate wt.: 6 lbs.
Comments: Made from the late 1940's to the early 1960's.
Estimated Value: Excellent: $60.00
                  Very good: $50.00

Harrington & Richardson 251

Similar to the 250 with a special Lyman rear sight.
Estimated Value: Excellent: $65.00
                  Very good: $55.00

Harrington & Richardson Fieldsman 852

Harrington & Richardson Model 300

Harrington & Richardson Ultra 301 Carbine

Harrington & Richardson Fieldsman 852

Caliber: 22 short, long, long rifle
Action: Bolt action; repeating
Magazine: Tubular, 15 long rifles, 17 long, 21 shorts
Barrel: 24" blued
Sights: Open rear, bead front
Stock & Forearm: Plain wood, semi-pistol grip, one piece stock & forearm
Approximate wt.: 5½ lbs.
Comments: Made in the early 1950's.
Estimated Value: Excellent: $60.00
                  Very good: $50.00

Harrington & Richardson Model 300

Caliber: 22-250 Rem. 243 Win., 270, 308, 30-06, 300 magnum, 7mm magnum
Action: Mauser type, bolt action; repeating
Magazine: 5-shot box, 3-shot in magnum
Barrel: 22" blued
Sights: Open rear, ramp front
Stock & Forearm: Checkered walnut, Monte Carlo pistol grip, one piece stock & forearm; cheekpiece; recoil pad; swivels
Approximate wt.: 7¾ lbs.
Comments: Made from the mid 1960's to present.
Estimated Value: New (retail): $395.00
                  Excellent: $295.00
                  Very good: $235.00

Harrington & Richardson Ultra 301

Similar to the 300 with full length forearm and 18" barrel; no swivels.
Estimated Value: New (retail): $495.00
                  Excellent: $370.00
                  Very good: $300.00

Rifles

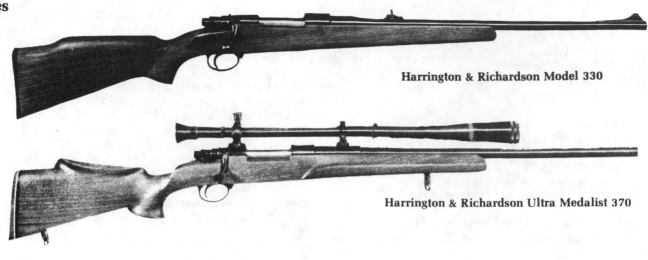

Harrington & Richardson Model 330

Harrington & Richardson Ultra Medalist 370

Harrington & Richardson Ultra Wildcat 317

Harrington & Richardson 317 Presentation

H & R Model 330

Similar to the Model 300 with less fancy finish. Discontinued in the early 1970's.

Estimated Value: Excellent: $250.00
                Very good: $200.00

H & R Model 333

Similar to the Model 330 with no checkering or sights.

Estimated Value: Excellent: $200.00
                Very good: $160.00

Harrington & Richardson Ultra Medalist 370

Caliber: 22-250, 243, 6mm
Action: Sako bolt action; repeating
Magazine: 4-shot box
Barrel: 24'' heavy
Sights: Open
Stock & Forearm: Monte Carlo pistol grip, one piece stock & forearm; cheekpiece; recoil pad; swivels
Approximate wt.: 9 lbs.
Comments: Made from the late 1960's to mid 1970's.
Estimated Value: Excellent: $300.00
                Very good: $240.00

Harrington & Richardson Ultra Wildcat 317

Caliber: 17 Remington, 222, 223, or 17/223 (Handload)
Action: Bolt action, Sako type; repeating
Magazine: 6-shot box
Barrel: 24'' blued
Sights: None
Stock & Forearm: Wood, Monte Carlo, pistol grip, one piece stock & forearm; cheekpiece; recoil pad; swivels
Approximate wt.: 7¾ lbs.
Comments: Made from the mid 1960's to late 1970's
Estimated Value: Excellent: $275.00
                Very good: $220.00

Harrington & Richardson 317 Presentation

Similar to the 317 with select wood, special checkering (basket weave).

Estimated Value: Excellent: $475.00
                Very good: $400.00

Harrington & Richardson Model 422

Harrington & Richardson Model 749

Harrington & Richardson Reising 60

Harrington & Richardson General 65

Harrington & Richardson Leatherneck 165

Harrington & Richardson Model 422

Caliber: 22 short, long, long rifle
Action: Slide action; hammerless; repeating
Magazine: Tubular, 15 long rifles, 17 longs, 21 shorts
Barrel: 24" blued
Sights: Open rear, ramp front
Stock & Forearm: Plain walnut, semi-pistol grip stock & grooved slide handle
Approximate wt.: 6 lbs.
Comments: Made in the mid to late 1950's
Estimated Value: Excellent: $80.00
Very good: $65.00

H & R Model 749

Caliber: 22 short, long, or long rifle
Action: Slide action; exposed hammer; repeating
Magazine: Tubular; 18 shorts, 15 longs, 13 long rifles
Barrel: 19" round, tapered
Sights: Open rear, blade front
Stock & Forearm: Plain hardwood pistol grip stock and tapered slide handle
Approximate wt: 5 lbs.
Comments: Made in the early 1970's.
Estimated Value: Excellent: $75.00
Very good: $60.00

Harrington & Richardson Reising 60

Caliber: 45
Action: Semi-automatic
Magazine: 12 or 20 shot detachable box
Barrel: 18¼" blued
Sights: Open rear, blade front
Stock & Forearm: Plain wood, semi-pistol grip, one piece stock & forearm
Approximate wt.: 7¼ lbs.
Comments: Manufactured during World War II.
Estimated Value: Excellent: $425.00
Very good: $340.00

Harrington & Richardson General 65

Caliber: 22 long rifle
Action: Semi-automatic
Magazine: 10-shot detatchable box
Barrel: Blued, 23"
Sights: Peep rear, covered blade front
Stock & Forearm: Wood, semi-pistol grip, one piece stock & forearm
Approximate wt.: 9 lbs.
Comments: Used as a Marine training rifle during World War II.
Estimated Value: Excellent: $275.00
Very good: $220.00

Harrington & Richardson Leatherneck 165

Lighter version of the 65 with ramp front sight. Made from World War II until the early 1960's.
Estimated Value: Excellent: $125.00
Very good: $100.00

Rifles

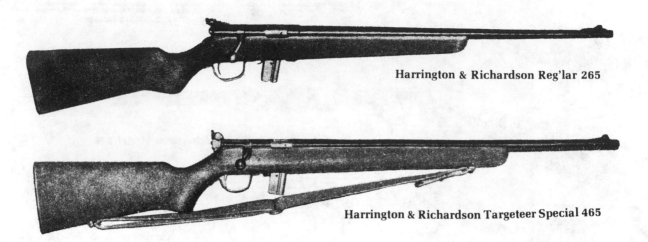

Harrington & Richardson Reg'lar 265

Harrington & Richardson Targeteer Special 465

Harrington & Richardson Reg'lar 265

Similar to the 165 in bolt action with a 22" barrel. Made from World War II until about 1950.
Estimated Value: Excellent: $75.00
Very good: $60.00

Harrington & Richardson Ace 365

Similar to the 265 except single shot. Made in the mid 1940's.
Estimated Value: Excellent: $50.00
Very good: $40.00

Harrington & Richardson Targeteer Jr.

A youth version of the 465 with: short stock; 5-shot magazine; 20" barrel. Made from the late 1940's to early 1950's.
Estimated Value: Excellent: $80.00
Very good: $65.00

Harrington & Richardson Targeteer Special 465

Similar to the 265 with: 25" barrel; swivels; slightly heavier. Made in the mid 1940's.
Estimated Value: Excellent: $75.00
Very good: $60.00

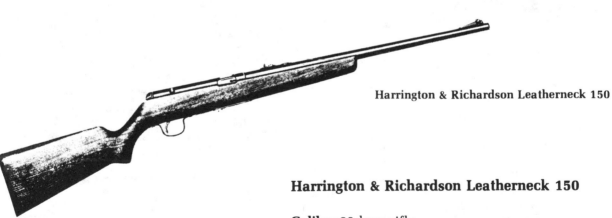

Harrington & Richardson Leatherneck 150

Harrington & Richardson Leatherneck 150

Caliber: 22 long rifle
Action: Semi-automatic; hammerless.
Magazine: 5-shot detachable box
Barrel: 22" blued
Sights: Open rear, ramp front
Stock & Forearm: Wood, semi-pistol grip, one piece stock & forearm
Approximate wt: 7 lbs.
Comments: Made from the late 1940's to early 1950's.
Estimated Value: Excellent: $80.00
Very good: $70.00

Harrington & Richardson Lynx 800

Caliber: 22 long rifle
Action: Semi-automatic; hammerless
Magazine: 10-shot clip
Barrel: 22" blued
Sights: Open rear, ramp front
Stock & Forearm: Walnut, semi-pistol grip, one piece stock & forearm
Approximate wt.: 6 lbs.
Comments: Made from the late 1950's to about 1960.
Estimated Value: Excellent: $75.00
Very good: $60.00

Harrington & Richardson Model 151

Similar to the 150 with a special peep rear sight.
Estimated Value: Excellent: $75.00
Very good: $65.00

Harrington & Richardson Model 308

Harrington & Richardson Model 360

Harrington & Richardson Model 308

Caliber: 264, 308
Action: Gas operated, semi-automatic
Magazine: 3-shot detatchable box
Barrel: 22'' blued
Sights: Adjustable rear, bead front
Stock & Forearm: Checkered walnut, Monte Carlo pistol grip one piece stock & forearm; cheekpiece; swivels
Approximate wt.: 7 lbs.
Comments: Made from the mid 1960's to early 1970's
Estimated Value: Excellent: $250.00
Very good: $200.00

Harrington & Richardson Model 360

Similar to the 308 except 243 caliber .
Estimated Value: Excellent: $260.00
Very good: $210.00

Harrington & Richardson Model 700 Deluxe

H&R Model 700

Caliber: 22 WMRF
Action: Semi-automatic; hammerless
Magazine: 5 or 10 shot detachable
Barrel: 22''
Sights: Adjustable folding leaf rear, ramp blade front
Stock & Forearm: Plain walnut Monte Carlo, one piece pistol grip stock & forearm
Approximate wt: 6 ½ lbs.
Comments: Introduced in the late 1970's.
Estimated Value: New (retail): $179.00
Excellent: $135.00
Very good: $110.00

H & R Model 700 Deluxe

Similar to the Model 700 with select custom finish; checkering; cheekpiece; recoil pad; 4X scope.
Estimated Value: New (retail): $295.00
Excellent: $220.00
Very good: $175.00

High Standard Hi-Power

Caliber: 270, 30-06
Action: Bolt action, Mauser type; repeating
Magazine: 4-shot box
Barrel: 22'' blued
Sights: Folding reaf rear, ramp front
Stock & Forearm: Walnut, semi-pistol grip, one piece stock and tapered forearm
Approximate wt.: 7 lbs.
Comments: Made from the early to mid 1960's.
Estimated Value: Excellent: $240.00
Very good: $195.00

High Standard Hi-Power Deluxe

Similar to Hi-Power with a checkered Monte Carlo stock and swivels.
Estimated Value: Excellent: $270.00
Very good: $220.00

High Standard Flite King

Caliber: 22 short, long, long rifle
Action: Slide-action; hammerless; repeating
Magazine: Tubular, 17 long rifle, 19 long, 24 short
Barrel: 24'' blued
Sights: Adjustable rear, post front
Stock & Forearm: Checkered walnut, Monte Carlo pistol grip stock and grooved slide handle; early models have no checkering
Approximate wt.: 5 ½ lbs.
Comments: Made from about 1962 to the late 1970's.
Estimated Value: Excellent: $ 75.00
Very good: $ 65.00

High Standard Hi-Power

High Standard Hi-Power Deluxe

High Standard Flite King

High Standard Early Sport King

High Standard Sport King Special

High Standard Sport King

Caliber: 22 short, long, long rifle
Action: Semi-automatic
Magazine: Tubular, 15 long rifle, 17 long, 21 short
Barrel: 22¼" blued
Sights: Open rear, post front
Stock & Forearm: Checkered wood, one piece, Monte Carlo pistol grip stock & forearm
Approximate wt.: 5½ lbs.
Comments: Before the mid 1970's, Sport King had no Monte Carlo stock. Field model was made from about 1960 to the late 1970's.
Estimated Value: Excellent: $85.00
Very good: $75.00

High Standard Sport King Special

Similar to Sport King without checkering. Made from the early 1950's to mid 1960's.
Estimated Value: Excellent: $75.00
Very good: $65.00

High Standard Sport King Deluxe

Same specifications as Sport King. Made as Deluxe until mid 1970's.
Estimated Value: Excellent: $85.00
Very good: $75.00

High Standard Sport King Carbine

Carbine version of the Sport King. Straight stock; 18¼" barrel; smaller magazine; swivels. Made from the early 1960's to early 1970's.
Estimated Value: Excellent: $75.00
Very good: $65.00

High Standard Sport King Carbine

High Standard Sport King Deluxe

Husqvarna

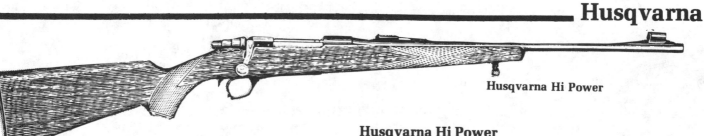

Husqvarna Hi Power

Husqvarna Hi Power

Caliber: 220 Swift, 270, 30-06, 6.5 x 55, 8 x 57, 9.3 x57
Action: Mauser type bolt action; repeating
Magazine: 5-shot box
Barrel: 23¾" blued
Sights: Open rear, hooded ramp front
Stock & Forearm: Checkered beech, pistol grip, one piece stock and tapered forearm; swivels
Approximate wt.: 7¾ lbs.
Comments: Made from the second World War to the late 1950's.
Estimated Value: Excellent: $240.00
Very good: $190.00

Husqvarna 1950 Hi Power

Similar to the Hi Power in 220, 270, and 30-06 calibers only. Made only in the early 1950's.
Estimated Value: Excellent: $350.00
Very good: $300.00

Husqvarna 1951 Hi Power

Husqvarna 1100 Hi Power Deluxe

Husqvarna 3100 Crown Grade

Husqvarna 3000 Crown Grade

Husqvarna P-3000 Presentation

Husqvarna 1951 Hi Power
Similar to the Hi Power with a slightly higher stock. Made only in 1951.
Estimated Value: Excellent: $325.00
Very good: $275.00

Husqvarna 1100 Hi Power Deluxe
Similar to the 1951 Hi Power with walnut stock and forearm. Made from the early to mid 1950's.
Estimated Value: Excellent: $350.00
Very good: $280.00

Husqvarna 1000 Super Grade
Similar to the 1100 with a Monte Carlo stock.
Estimated Value: Excellent: $375.00
Very good: $300.00

Husqvarna 3100 Crown Grade
Caliber: 243, 270. 7mm Remington, 30-06, 308
Action: Mauser type bolt action; repeating
Magazine: 5-shot box
Barrel: 23¾" blued
Sights: Open rear, hooded ramp front
Stock & Forearm: Checkered walnut, pistol, one piece stock and tapered forearm; swivels
Approximate wt.: 7 lbs.
Comments: Made from the mid 1950's to mid 1970's.
Estimated Value: Excellent: $385.00
Very good: $320.00

Husqvarna 3000 Crown Grade
Similar to 3100 with Monte Carlo stock.
Estimated Value: Excellent: $400.00
Very good: $340.00

Husqvarna P-3000 Presentation
A fancy version of the 3000 with: engraving; select wood; adjustable trigger. Made in the late 1960's.
Estimated Value: Excellent: $600.00
Very good: $500.00

Husqvarna 6000 Imperial Custom

Husqvarna 4100 Lightweight

Husqvarna 4000 Lightweight

Husqvarna 456 Lightweight

Husqvarna 7000 Imperial Monte Carlo

Husqvarna 6000 Imperial Custom
Similar to 3000 with: higher quality finish; folding sight; adjustable trigger. Made in the late 1960's.
Estimated Value: Excellent: $475.00
Very good: $400.00

Husqvarna 4100 Lightweight
Caliber: 243, 270, 7mm, 306, 308 Winchester
Action: Mauser type bolt action; repeating
Magazine: 5-shot box
Barrel: 20½'' blued
Sights: Open rear, hooded ramp front
Stock & Forearm: Checkered walnut, pistol grip, one piece stock and tapered forearm
Approximate wt.: 6 lbs.
Comments: Made from the mid 1950's to mid 1970's.
Estimated Value: Excellent: $350.00
Very good: $280.00

Husqvarna 4000 Lightweight
Similar to 4100 with Monte Carlo stock and no rear sight.
Estimated Value: Excellent: $375.00
Very good: $300.00

Husqvarna 456 Lightweight
Similar to 4100 with full length stock and forearm. Made from about 1960 to 1970.
Estimated Value: Excellent: $390.00
Very good: $315.00

Husqvarna 7000 Imperial Monte Carlo
Similar to 4000 with: higher quality wood; lipped forearm; folding sight; adjustable trigger. Made in the late 1960's.
Estimated Value: Excellent: $490.00
Very good: $410.00

Husqvarna 9000 Crown Grade

Husqvarna 8000 Imperial Grade

Husqvarna 610 Varmint

Husqvarna 9000 Crown Grade

Caliber: 270, 30-06, 7mm Remington magnum, 300 Winchester magnum
Action: Bolt action; repeating
Magazine: 5-shot box
Barrel: 23¾" blued
Sights: Leaf rear, hooded ramp front
Stock & Forearm: Checkered walnut, Monte Carlo pistol grip, one piece stock and forearm; swivels
Approximate wt.: 7¼ lbs.
Comments: Made in the early 1970's.
Estimated Value: Excellent: $350.00
Very good: $290.00

Husqvarna 8000 Imperial Grade

Similar to 9000 with: select wood; engraving; no sights.
Estimated Value: Excellent: $460.00
Very good: $390.00

Husqvarna 610 Varmint

Caliber: 222
Action: Short stroke bolt action; repeating
Magazine: 4-shot detatchable box
Barrel: 24¾" blued
Sights: None, tapped for scope
Stock & Forearm: Checkered walnut, Monte Carlo pistol grip, one-piece stock and forearm; cheekpiece.
Approximate wt.: 6½ lbs.
Comments: Made in the late 1960's.
Estimated Value: Excellent: $290.00
Very good: $240.00

Husqvarna 353 Magnum

Caliber: 358 Norma magnum
Action: Bolt action, repeating
Magazine: 3-shot box
Barrel: 25½" blued
Sights: Folding leaf rear, hooded ramp front
Stock & Forearm: Checkered walnut, Monte Carlo pistol grip, one piece stock and forearm; cheekpiece
Approximate wt.: 7¾ lbs.
Comments: Made in the late 1960's.
Estimated Value: Excellent: $320.00
Very good: $275.00

Ithaca Model LSA-55

Ithaca Model LSA-55 Deluxe

Ithaca Model LSA-65

Ithaca Model LSA-65 Deluxe

Ithaca Model LSA-55 Turkey Gun

Ithaca Model LSA-55

Caliber: 222, 22-250, 6mm, 243, 308
Action: Bolt action; repeating
Magazine: 3-shot detatchable box
Barrel: 22'' blued
Sights: Iron; adjustable rear, hooded ramp front
Stock & Forearm: Monte Carlo pistol grip, one-piece stock and tapered forearm
Approximate wt.: 6½ lbs.
Comments: Made from the early 1970s to late 1970's.
Estimated Value: Excellent: $325.00
Very good: $260.00

Ithaca Model LSA-55 Heavy Barrel

Similar to the LSA-55 except: cheekpiece; recoil pad: heavy barrel; weighs 8½ lbs.
Estimated Value: Excellent: $375.00
Very good: $320.00

Ithaca Model LSA-55 Deluxe

Similar to LSA-55 except: checkering; cheekpiece; recoil pad.
Estimated Value: Excellent: $350.00
Very good: $290.00

Ithaca Model LSA-65

Similar to Model LSA-55 in 25-06, 270, 30-06, with a 4-shot magazine and weighs 7 lbs.
Estimated Value: Excellent: $340.00
Very good: $285.00

Ithaca Model LSA-65 Deluxe

Similar to Model LSA-55 Deluxe in same calibers and weight as LSA-65.
Estimated Value: Excellent: $365.00
Very good: $300.00

Ithaca Model LSA-55 Turkey Gun

Caliber: 222 under 12 gauge full choke
Action: Top lever, break-open; exposed hammer
Magazine: None
Barrel: 24½'' rifle under full choke shotgun with matted rib
Sights: Folding rear, dovetail front
Stock & Forearm: Checkered walnut, Monte Carlo pistol grip, stock and forearm; cheekpiece; recoil pad; swivels.
Approximate wt.: 7 lbs.
Comments: An over & under combination manufactured to the late 1970's.
Estimated Value: Excellent: $425.00
Very good: $350.00

Rifles

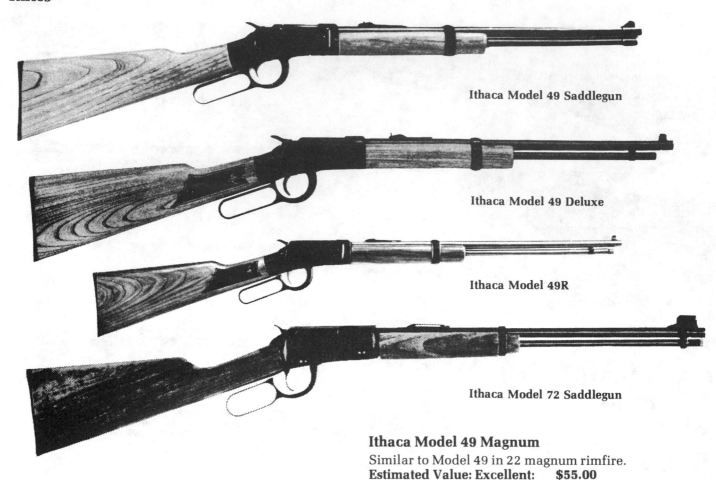

Ithaca Model 49 Saddlegun

Ithaca Model 49 Deluxe

Ithaca Model 49R

Ithaca Model 72 Saddlegun

Ithaca Model 49 Saddlegun

Caliber: 22 short, long, long rifle
Action: Lever action; exposed hammer; single shot
Magazine: none
Barrel: 18" blued
Sights: Adjustable rear, bead front
Stock & Forearm: Plain wood, straight grip stock and forearm; barrel band; late model has checkering
Approximate wt: 5 ½ lbs.
Comments: Made from about 1960 to late 1970's.
Estimated Value: Excellent: $40.00
Very good: $30.00

Ithaca Model 49 Youth

Similar to Model 49 with an abbreviated stock for young shooters.
Estimated Value: Excellent: $40.00
Very good: $30.00

Ithaca Model 49 Deluxe

Similar to Model 49 with checkered stock, gold hammer, gold trigger and swivels. Discontinued in the mid 1970's when standard model was sold with checkering.
Estimated Value: Excellent: $60.00
Very good: $50.00

Ithaca Model 49 Magnum

Similar to Model 49 in 22 magnum rimfire.
Estimated Value: Excellent: $55.00
Very good: $45.00

Ithaca Model 49 Presentation

Similar to Model 49 Deluxe with engraving and nameplate; caliber: 22 short, long, long rifle or 22 RF magnum.
Estimated Value: Excellent: $90.00
Very good: $75.00

Ithaca Model 49R

Similar to Model 49 with a 20" barrel and 15-shot tubular magazine. Sold only in the late 1960's to early 1970's.
Estimated Value: Excellent: $70.00
Very good: $60.00

Ithaca Model 72 Saddlegun

Caliber: 22 long rifle
Action: Lever action; exposed hammer; repeating
Magazine: 15-shot tubular
Barrel: 18½" blued
Sights: Adjustable rear, hooded ramp front
Stock & Forearm: Plain walnut, straight grip stock and forearm; barrel band
Approximate wt: 5 ½ lbs.
Comments: Made from the early 1970's to late 1970's.
Estimated Value: Excellent: $85.00
Very good: $70.00

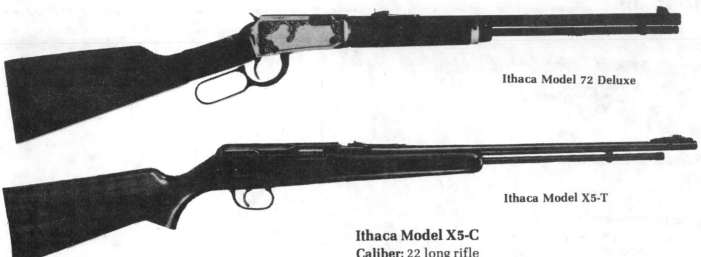

Ithaca Model 72 Deluxe

Ithaca Model X5-T

Ithaca Model X5-C
Caliber: 22 long rifle
Action: Semi-automatic, hammerless
Magazine: 7-shot clip
Barrel: 22" blued
Sights: Open rear, Raybar front
Stock & Forearm: Wood, semi-pistol grip, one piece stock and forearm
Approximate wt.: 6 ¼ lbs.
Comments: Made from the late 1950's to about 1965.
Estimated Value: Excellent: $90.00
Very good: $75.00

Ithaca Model 72 Deluxe
Similar to Model 72 except: brushed silver receiver; engraving; octagon barrel; blade front sight.
Estimated Value: Excellent: $110.00
Very good: $ 90.00

Ithaca Model 72 Magnum
Similar to Model 72 in 22 magnum rimfire. Magazine holds 11 shots.
Estimated Value: Excellent: $100.00
Very good: $ 80.00

Ithaca Model X5-T
Similar to the X5-C with a 16-shot tubular magazine
Estimated Value: Excellent: $100.00
Very good: $ 80.00

Iver Johnson

Iver Johnson Model 2X

Iver Johnson Model X
Caliber: 22 short, long, long rifle
Action: Bolt action; single shot
Magazine: None
Barrel: 22" blued
Sights: Open rear, blade front
Stock & Forearm: Wood, one piece pistol grip stock & forearm
Approximate wt.: 4 lbs.
Comments: Made from the late 1920's to the early 1930's.
Estimated Value: Excellent: $40.00
Very good: $30.00

Iver Johnson Model 2X
Similar to the Model X with a 24" barrel and improved stock. Made from about 1932 to the mid 1950's.
Estimated Value: Excellent: $45.00
Very good: $35.00

Rifles
Johnson

Johnson MMJ Spitfire

Johnson MMJ Spitfire
Caliber: 223
Action: Semi-automatic
Magazine: 5, 15, 30 shot clip
Barrel: 18'' blued
Sights: Adjustable rear, ramp front
Stock & Forearm: Wood, semi-pistol grip, one piece stock & forearm; wood hand guard
Approximate wt.: 5 lbs.
Comments: A conversion of the M1 carbine. Made in the mid 1960's.
Estimated Value: Excellent: $180.00
Very good: $145.00

Johnson Custom Deluxe Sporter
Similar to the MMJ with a Monte Carlo, full pistol grip stock & rear peep sight.
Estimated Value: Excellent: $195.00
Very good: $155.00

Johnson Folding Stock
Similar to the Custom Deluxe Sporter with a special metal folding shoulder stock.
Estimated Value: Excellent: $225.00
Very good: $185.00

Kleinguenther

Kleinguenther K-14

Kleinguenther K-15 Insta-fire

Kleinguenther K-15 Insta-fire
Caliber: 243; 25-06; 270; 30-06; 308 Win.; 308 Norma Mag.; 300 Win. mag.; 7mm Rem. mag.; 375 H&H; 7x57; 270 Weatherby mag; 300 Weatherby mag.; 257 Weatherby mag.
Action: Bolt action; repeating; adjustable trigger
Magazine: 5 shot hidden clip; 3 shot in magnum
Barrel: 24''; 26'' in magnum
Sights: None; tapped for scope
Stock & Forearm: Checkered walnut pistol grip, Monte Carlo, one piece stock and forearm; several shade choices; rosewood forend and cap; swivels; left or right hand model
Approximate wt: 7½ lbs.
Comments: A high powered rifle that is advertised as "the world's most accurate hunting rifle". Currently produced. Engraving and select wood available at additional cost. Add $20.00 for magnum, $50.00 for left hand model.
Estimated Value: New (retail): $699.00
Excellent: $550.00
Very good: $480.00

Kleinguenther K-14
Caliber: Same as MV 2130, also 25-06, 7x57, 375 H&H
Action: Bolt action
Magazine: Hidden clip, 3 shot
Barrel: 24'', 26'' blued
Sights: Open rear, ramp front
Stock & Forearm: Checkered walnut, one piece pistol grip stock and tapered forearm; recoil pad
Approximate wt.: 7¼ lbs.
Comments: Made in the 1970's
Estimated Value: Excellent: $480.00
Very good: $385.00

Kleinguenther MV 2130
Caliber: 243, 270, 30-06, 300 magnum, 308, 7mm Rem.
Action: Mauser type bolt action; repeating
Magazine: 2-shot box
Barrel: 25'' blued
Sights: None; drilled for scope.
Stock & Forearm: Checkered walnut, Monte Carlo pistol grip, one piece stock and tapered forearm; recoil pad
Approximate wt.: 7 lbs.
Comments: Made in the 1970's.
Estimated Value: Excellent: $390.00
Very good: $315.00

Mannlicher-Schoenauer 1905

Mannlicher-Schoenauer High Velocity

Mannlicher-Schoenauer 1950 Sporter

Mannlicher-Schoenauer 1950 Carbine

Mannlicher-Schoenauer 1903

Caliber: 6.5 x 53mm
Action: Bolt action; repeating; double set trigger; "butter-knife" style bolt handle
Magazine: 5-shot rotary
Barrel: 17¾" blued
Sights: Two leaf rear, ramp front
Stock & Forearm: Walnut, semi-pistol grip stock and tapered, full length forearm; swivels; cheekpiece
Approximate wt.: 6½ lbs.
Comments: Made from 1903 to World War II
Estimated Value: Excellent: $600.00
Very good: $480.00

Mannlicher-Schoenauer 1905

Similar to 1903 with a 19¾" barrel and in 9 x 56 mm caliber.
Estimated Value: Excellent: $480.00
Very good: $385.00

Mannlicher-Schoenauer 1908

Similar to the 1903 with a 19¾" barrel and in 7 x 57, and 8 x 56 mm calibers.
Estimated Value: Excellent: $480.00
Very good: $385.00

Mannlicher-Schoenauer 1910

Similar to 1903 with 19¾" barrel and in 9.5 x 57mm caliber.
Estimated Value: Excellent: $450.00
Very good: $360.00

Mannlicher-Schoenauer 1924

Similar to the 1903 with a 19¾" barrel and in 30-06. Made from 1924 to World War II.
Estimated Value: Excellent: $550.00
Very good: $440.00

Mannlicher-Schoenauer High Velocity

Caliber: 7 x 64, 30-06, 8 x 60, 9.3 x 62, 10.75 x 68
Action: Bolt action; repeating; "butter-knife" bolt handle
Magazine: 5-shot rotary
Barrel: 23¾" blued
Sights: 3 leaf rear, ramp front
Stock & Forearm: Checkered walnut, pistol grip, one piece stock and tapered forearm; cheekpiece; swivels
Approximate wt.: 7½ lbs.
Comments: Made from the early 1920's to World ments: War II.
Estimated Value: Excellent: $540.00
Very good: $435.00

Mannlicher-Schoenauer 1950 Sporter

Caliber: 257, 270 Winchester, 30-06
Action: Bolt action; repeating; "butter-knife" bolt handle
Magazine: 5-shot rotary
Barrel: 24" blued
Sights: Folding leaf rear, hooded ramp front
Stock & Forearm: Checkered walnut, pistol grip, one piece stock and tapered forearm; cheekpiece; swivels
Approximate wt.: 7¼ lbs.
Comments: Made in the early 1950's.
Estimated Value: Excellent: $500.00
Very good: $400.00

Mannlicher-Schoenauer 1950 Carbine

Similar to the Sporter with a 20" barrel and a full length forearm.
Estimated Value: Excellent: $525.00
Very good: $420.00

Mannlicher-Schoenauer 1950-6.5

Similar to 1950 Carbine with 18" barrel and in 6.5 x 53 mm caliber.
Estimated Value: Excellent: $490.00
Very good: $395.00

Rifles

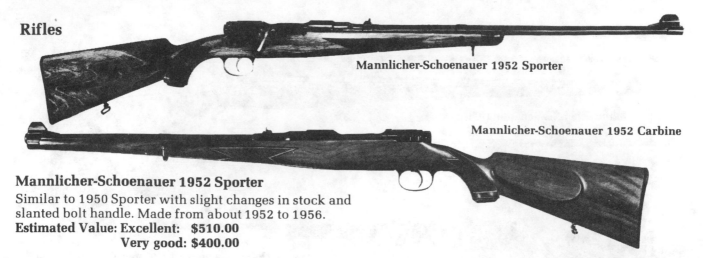

Mannlicher-Schoenauer 1952 Sporter

Mannlicher-Schoenauer 1952 Carbine

Mannlicher-Schoenauer 1952 Sporter

Similar to 1950 Sporter with slight changes in stock and slanted bolt handle. Made from about 1952 to 1956.
Estimated Value: Excellent: $510.00
Very good: $400.00

Mannlicher-Schoenauer 1952 Carbine

Similar to 1952 Sporter with a 20'' barrel, and full length forearm.
Estimated Value: Excellent: $530.00
Very good: $425.00

Mannlicher-Schoenauer 1952-6.5

Similar to 1952 Carbine with 18'' barrel and in 6.5 x 53 mm caliber.
Estimated Value: Excellent: $500.00
Very good: $400.00

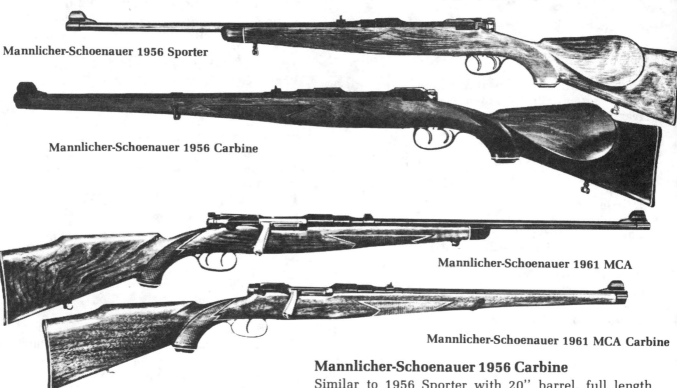

Mannlicher-Schoenauer 1956 Sporter

Mannlicher-Schoenauer 1956 Carbine

Mannlicher-Schoenauer 1961 MCA

Mannlicher-Schoenauer 1961 MCA Carbine

Mannlicher-Schoenauer 1956 Sporter

Caliber: 243, 30-06
Action: Bolt action; repeating; "butter-knife" slanted bolt handle
Magazine: 5-shot rotary
Barrel: 22'' blued
Sights: Folding leaf rear, hooded ramp front
Stock & Forearm: Checkered walnut, pistol grip stock and forearm; high comb; cheekpiece; swivels
Approximate wt.: 7lbs.
Comments: Made from the mid 1950's to about 1960.
Estimated Value: Excellent: $510.00
Very good: $405.00

Mannlicher-Schoenauer 1956 Carbine

Similar to 1956 Sporter with 20'' barrel, full length forearm and addition of 6.5 mm, 257, 270, 7mm and 308 calibers.
Estimated Value: Excellent: $525.00
Very good: $420.00

Mannlicher-Schoenauer 1961 MCA

Similar to 1956 Sporter with Monte Carlo stock. Made from the early 1960's to early 1970's.
Estimated Value: Excellent: $530.00
Very good: $425.00

Mannlicher-Schoenauer 1961 MCA Carbine

Similar to 1956 Carbine with Monte Carlo stock, made from early 1960's to early 1970's.
Estimated Value: Excellent: $550.00
Very good: $440.00

Steyr-Mannlicher Model SL

Steyr-Mannlicher Model SL Varmint

Steyr-Mannlicher Model L

Steyr-Mannlicher Model L Carbine

Steyr-Mannlicher Model SL

Caliber: 222 Remington, 222 magnum, 223, 5.6 x 50
Action: Bolt action; repeating
Magazine: 5-shot rotary
Barrel: 23½ " blued
Sights: Open rear, ramp front
Stock & Forearm: Checkered walnut, Monte Carlo pistol grip, one piece stock and tapered forearm; recoil pad; cheekpiece; swivels
Approximate wt: 5½ lbs.
Comments: Made from the mid 1960's to present
Estimated Value: New (retail): $735.00
Excellent: $555.00
Very good: $445.00

Steyr-Mannlicher Model SL Varmint

Similar to the Model SL with a varmint stock and 26" heavy barrel.
Estimated Value: New (retail): $795.00
Excellent: $600.00
Very good: $485.00

Steyr-Mannlicher SL Carbine

Similar to the SL with a 20" barrel and full length forearm.
Estimated Value: New (retail): $789.00
Excellent: $595.00
Very good: $475.00

Steyr-Mannlicher Model L

Similar to the SL in 22-250, 5.6 x 57, 6 mm, 243; 308
Estimated Value: New (retail): $735.00
Excellent: $555.00
Very good: $445.00

Steyr-Mannlicher Model L Varmint

Similar to the Model L with a varmint stock and 26" heavy barrel.
Estimated Value: New (retail): $795.00
Excellent: $600.00
Very good: $485.00

Steyr-Mannlicher Model L Carbine

Similar to Model L with a 20" barrel and full length forearm.
Estimated Value: New (retail): $789.00
Excellent: $595.00
Very good: $475.00

Rifles

Steyr-Mannlicher Model M

Steyr-Mannlicher Model M

Steyr-Mannlicher Model M Professional

Steyr-Mannlicher S

Steyr-Mannlicher Model S/T

Steyr-Mannlicher Model M

Caliber: 6.5 x 55, 7 x 64, 270 Win., 30-06, 25-06 Rem.; 8 x 57, 9.3 x 62
Action: Bolt action; repeating
Magazine: 5-shot rotary
Barrel: 20'' blued on full stock; 23½'' on half stock
Sights: Open rear, ramp front
Stock & Forearm: Checkered walnut, Monte Carlo pistol grip; choice of standard or full length forearm; cheekpiece; swivels. Left hand model available..
Approximate wt: 6½ lbs.
Comments: Made from the mid 1970's to present. Add $90.00 for left hand model, add $50.00 for full stock.
Estimated Value: New (retail): $735.00
Excellent: $555.00
Very good: $445.00

Steyr-Mannlicher Model M Professional

Similar to the Model M with a parkerized metal finish and ABS Cycolac stock. Add $20.00 for iron sights; 23½'' barrel only.
Estimated Value: New (retail): $558.00
Excellent: $425.00
Very good: $350.00

Steyr-Mannlicher S

Similar to Model M with 26'' barrel in magnum caliber, 7mm Rem., 257 Wby., 264 Win., 300 H & H, 388 Win., 375 H & H, & 458 Win. Half stock only; butt magazine optional. Add $50.00 for buttstock 4 shot magazine.
Estimated Value: New (retail): $848.00
Excellent: $640.00
Very good: $515.00

Steyr-Mannlicher S/T

Similar to the Model S with a heavy barrel. Add $50.00 for buttstock magazine. 375 H & H mag.; 458 Win. mag. calibers.
Estimated Value: New (retail): $848.00
Excellent: $640.00
Very good: $515.00

Mannlicher-Schoenauer M-72 4M Carbine

Mannlicher-Schoenauer M-72 4M Carbine
Similar to M-72 LM with a 20" barrel and full length forearm.
Estimated Value: Excellent: $650.00
Very good: $525.00

Mannlicher-Schoenauer M-72, LM
Caliber: 22-250, 5.6 x 57, 243, 6.5 x 57, 6mm, 7 x 57, 270
Action: Bolt action; repeating
Magazine: 5-shot rotary
Barrel: 23½" blued
Sights: Open rear, ramp front
Stock & Forearm: Checkered walnut, pistol grip, one piece stock and tapered forearm; cheekpiece; recoil pad; swivels
Approximate wt: 7½ lbs.
Comments: Made from mid to late 1970's.
Estimated Value: **Excellent:** $620.00
Very good: $490.00

Steyr-Mannlicher Model SSG Marksman

Steyr-Mannlicher Model SSG Match

Steyr-Mannlicher ML 79 Luxus M
Caliber: 7x57; 7x64; 270 Win.; 30-06 Springfield; others available on request
Action: Bolt action; short stroke; repeating
Magazine: 3 shot detachable; 6 shot available
Barrel: 23½"; 20" on full stock model
Sights: Adjustable V-notch open rear, adjustable hooded ramp front
Stock & Forearm: Checkered European walnut Monte Carlo, one piece, pistol grip stock and forearm; cheekpiece; swivels; full length stock available
Approximate wt: 7 lbs.
Comments: Currently produced. Add $60.00 for full length stock or 6 shot magazine.
Estimated Value: **New (retail):** $925.00
Excellent: $725.00
Very good: $625.00

Steyr-Mannlicher Model SSG Marksman
Caliber: 308 Win; (7.62x51); 243 Win.
Action: Bolt action; repeating
Magazine: 5 shot rotary
Barrel: 25½"
Sights: Folding leaf rear, hooded ramp front
Stock & Forearm: Checkered European walnut one piece stock and forearm; recoil pad; ABS Cycolac stock available
Approximate wt: 8½ lbs.
Comments: Currently produced. Subtract $40.00 for ABS Cycolac stock.
Estimated Value: **New (retail):** $689.00
Excellent: $525.00
Very good: $425.00

Steyr Mannlicher Model SSG Match
A match rifle similar to the SSG Marksman with a heavy barrel; peep sights; stippled checkering; hand stop; weight; 11 lbs; subtract $60.00 for ABS Cycolac stock.
Estimated Value: **New (retail):** $925.00
Excellent: $725.00
Very good: $625.00

Mark X Classic

Mark X Alaskan

Mark X Alaskan

Caliber: 375 H & H, 458 Winchester magnum
Action: Mauser type bolt action; repeating
Magazine: 3-shot box with hinged floor plate
Barrel: 24" blued
Sights: Adjustable rear; hooded ramp front
Stock & Forearm: Checkered, select walnut, Monte Carlo pistol grip, one piece stock & forearm; recoil pad; swivels
Approximate wt.: 8 lbs.
Comments: Currently manufactured.
Estimated Value: New (retail): $389.00
Excellent: $295.00
Very good: $235.00

Mark X Classic

Caliber: 22-250, 25-06, 270, 308, 30-06, 7mm magnum, 7 x 57, 300 magnum
Action: Bolt action, Mauser type; repeating; adjustable trigger
Magazine: 3-shot box with hinged floor plate
Sights: Adjustable rear, hooded ramp front; None on current models
Stock & Forearm: Checkered walnt, Monte Carlo pistol grip, one piece stock & forearm; swivels
Approximate wt.: 7 ½ lbs.
Comments: Currently manufactured. Add $10.00 for magnum and $20.00 for sights.
Estimated Value: New (retail): $319.00
Excellent: $240.00
Very good: $195.00

Mark X Whitworth Express-African

Mark X Marquis

Caliber: 243; 270; 7x57mm; 308; 30-06
Action: Bolt action; Mauser type; repeating
Magazine: 5 shot box with hinged floorplate
Barrel: 20"
Sights: Adjustable rear, hooded ramp front
Stock & Forearm: Checkered walnut Monte Carlo, one piece pistol grip full length stock and forearm; swivels; cheekpiece
Approximate wt: 7 ½ lbs.
Comments: Currently produced.
Estimated Value: New (retail): $369.00
Excellent: $280.00
Very good: $230.00

Mark X Continental

Similar to the Marquis with a "butter knife" bolt handle and double set triggers.
Estimated Value: New (retail): $389.00
Excellent: $295.00
Very good: $235.00

Mark X Whitworth Express-African

Caliber: 7mm Rem. Mag.; 300 Win. mag.; 375 H&H mag.; 458 Win. mag.
Action: Bolt action, Mauser style; repeating
Magazine: 3 shot box with hinged floor plate
Barrel: 24"
Sights: 3 leaf express sights
Stock & Forearm: Checkered European walnut Monte Carlo one piece stock and forearm; cheekpiece; swivels; recoil pad
Approximate wt: 7 ½ lbs.
Comments: Currently produced.
Estimated Value: New (retail): $525.00
Excellent: $400.00
Very good: $320.00

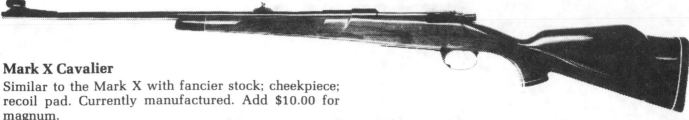

Mark X Cavalier

Similar to the Mark X with fancier stock; cheekpiece; recoil pad. Currently manufactured. Add $10.00 for magnum.

Estimated Value: New (retail): $369.00
     Excellent: $275.00
     Very good: $245.00

Mark X Cavalier

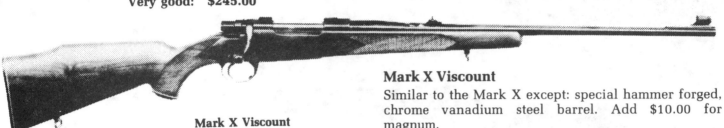

Mark X Viscount

Mark X Viscount

Similar to the Mark X except: special hammer forged, chrome vanadium steel barrel. Add $10.00 for magnum.

Estimated Value: New (retail): $279.00
     Excellent: $210.00
     Very good: $170.00

Marlin

Marlin Model 65

Marlin Model 80

Marlin Model 80E

Marlin Model 65

Caliber: 22 short, long, long rifle
Action: Bolt action; single shot
Magazine: None
Barrel: 24" round
Sights: Open rear, bead front
Stock & Forearm: Pistol grip stock and grooved forearm
Approximate wt.: 5 lbs.
Comments: This is a takedown rifle that was made between 1932 and 1935.
Estimated Value: Excellent: $35.00
     Very good: $30.00

Marlin Model 65E

Same as Model 65 except the front sight is equipped with hood and rear sight is a peep sight.
Estimated Value: Excellent: $40.00
     Very good: $35.00

Marlin Model 80

Caliber: 22 short, long, long rifle
Action: Bolt action; takedown type; repeating
Magazine: 8-shot box (detachable)
Barrel: 24"
Sights: Open rear, bead front
Stock & Forearm: Plain pistol grip stock & forearm
Approximate wt.: 6¼ lbs.
Comments: Production began about 1934, continued until the mid 1940's.
Estimated Value: Excellent: $60.00
     Very good: $50.00

Marlin Model 80E

Same rifle as Model 80 except front sight is hooded and rear sight is a peep sight.
Estimated Value: Excellent: $65.00
     Very good: $55.00

Rifles

Marlin Model 80C

Marlin Model 80 DL

Marlin Glenfield Model 80 G

Marlin Model 81

Marlin Model 81 E

Marlin Model 80C

Basically the same gun as the Model 80 with slight improvements. Forearm is semi-beavertail. Production began in 1946 and continued until it was replaced by the 80 G in 1960.
Estimated Value: Excellent: $65.00
                        Very good: $55.00

Marlin Model 80 DL

Same rifle as Model 80-C except: swivels; front sight is hooded; rear sight is peep sight. Discontinued in 1965.
Estimated Value: Excellent: $70.00
                        Very good: $60.00

Marlin Glenfield Model 80 G

The same rifle as the Marlin Model 80 C. Discontinued about 1966.
Estimated Value: Excellent: $60.00
                        Very good: $50.00

Marlin Model 81

Caliber: 22 short, long, long rifle
Action: Bolt action; repeating
Magazine: 24 shorts, 20 longs, 18 long rifles tubular under barrel
Barrel: 24"
Sights: Open rear, bead front
Stock & Forearm: Plain pistol grip stock & forearm
Approximate wt.: 6¼ lbs.
Comments: This takedown model was produced from 1937 into the 1940's.
Estimated Value: Excellent: $65.00
                        Very good: $55.00

Marlin Model 81 E

Same rifle as Model 81 except front sight is hooded and rear sight is peep sight.
Estimated Value: Excellent: $70.00
                        Very good: $60.00

Marlin Model 81-DL

Marlin Glenfield Model 81 G

Marlin Model 100

Marlin Model 100 SB

Marlin Model 81 C

This is an improved Model 81; forearm is semi-beavertail. It was produced from 1940 to 1970.
Estimated Value: Excellent: $65.00
Very good: $55.00

Marlin Model 81-DL

Same rifle as Model 81-C except it has swivels, front sight is hooded, and rear sight is peep sight.
Estimated Value: Excellent: $70.00
Very good: $60.00

Marlin Glenfield Model 81 G

This is the same basic rifle as the Marlin Model 81 C. It was produced as the 81 G from about 1960 to 1965.
Estimated Value: Excellent: $65.00
Very good: $55.00

Marlin Model 100

Caliber: 22 short, long, long rifle
Action: Bolt action, single shot
Magazine: None
Barrel: 24" round
Sights: Open rear, bead front
Stock & Forearm: Plain pistol grip stock and forearm
Approximate wt.: 4¾ lbs.
Comments: Takedown model, was manufactured from 1936 to 1960. In 1960 it became the Model 100G or Glenfield and was replaced in the mid 1960's by the Glenfield 10.
Estimated Value: Excellent: $35.00
Very good: $30.00

Marlin Model 100S Tom Mix Special

Same rifle as Model 100 except front sight is hooded, rear sight is peep sight. Discontinued 1946.
Estimated Value: Excellent: $75.00
Very good: $65.00

Marlin Model 100 SB

Same rifle as Model 100 except it is smooth bore to use with shot cartridges. Production was stopped in 1941.
Estimated Value: Excellent: $40.00
Very good: $35.00

Rifles

Marlin Glenfield Model 100G

Marlin Model 101

Marlin Glenfield Model 15

Marlin Glenfield Model 100G and Glenfield 10

This is the same basic rifle as Marlin Model 100.
Estimated Value: Excellent: $35.00
**   Very good: $30.00**

Marlin Model 101

Same basic rifle as Model 100 except forearm is beavertail. Weight 5 lbs. Manufactured from 1951 to late 1970's.
Estimated Value: Excellent: $40.00
**   Very good: $30.00**

Marlin Model 101-DL

Same rifle as Model 101 except front sight is hooded, rear sight is peep sight.
Estimated Value: Excellent: $40.00
**   Very good: $30.00**

Marlin Glenfield Model 15

Caliber: 22, short, long or long rifle
Action: Bolt action; single shot
Magazine: None, single shot
Barrel: 22'' round
Sights: Adjustable open rear, ramp front
Stock & Forearm: Checkered hardwood, Monte Carlo, pistol grip one piece stock and forearm
Approximate wt: 5½ lbs.
Comments: Introduced in the late 1970's.
Estimated Value: New (retail): $75.95
**   Excellent: $60.00**
**   Very good: $50.00**

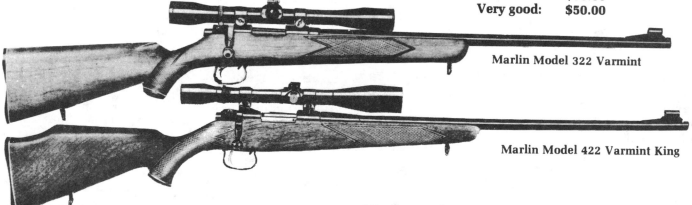

Marlin Model 322 Varmint

Marlin Model 422 Varmint King

Marlin Model 322 Varmint

Caliber: 222 Remington
Action: Bolt action (Sako Short, Mauser); repeating
Magazine: 3-shot clip
Barrel: 24''
Sights: Peep sight rear, hooded ramp front
Stock & Forearm: Checkered hardwood stock & forearm
Approximate wt.: 7½ lbs.
Comments: Produced for only 3 years beginning about 1954.
Estimated Value: Excellent: $200.00
**   Very good: $175.00**

Marlin Model 422 Varmint King

Caliber: 222 Remington
Action: Bolt action repeating
Magazine: 3-shot detachable clip
Barrel: 24'' round
Sights: Peep sight rear, hooded ramp front
Stock & Forearm: Checkered Monte Carlo pistol grip, stock & forearm
Approximate wt.: 7 lbs.
Comments: This rifle replaced Model 322 about 1958 but was discontinued after one year.
Estimated Value: Excellent: $250.00
**   Very good: $200.00**

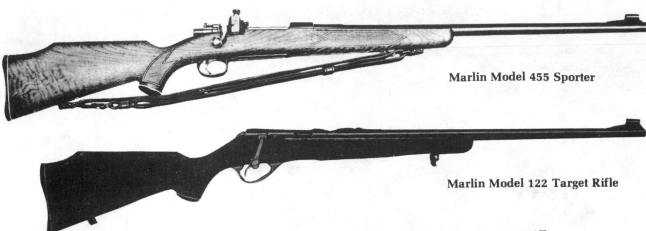

Marlin Model 455 Sporter

Marlin Model 122 Target Rifle

Marlin Model 455 Sporter

Caliber: 270, 30-06, 308
Action: Bolt, FN Mauser action with Sako trigger
Magazine: 5-shot box
Barrel: Stainless steel; 24" round
Sights: Receiver sight-Lyman 48, hooded ramp front
Stock & Forearm: Checkered wood Monte Carlo stock & forearm; cheekpiece
Approximate wt.: 8 ½ lbs.
Comments: Produced from about 1957 until 1959.
Estimated Value: Excellent: $250.00
**   Very good: $220.00**

Marlin Model 122 Target Rifle

Caliber: 22 short, long, long rifle
Action: Bolt action; single shot
Magazine: None
Barrel: 22" round
Sights: Open rear, hooded ramp front
Stock & Forearm: Wood, Monte Carlo pistol grip stock and forearm; swivels
Approximate wt.: 5 lbs.
Comments: This rifle was produced from about 1961 to 1965.
Estimated Value: Excellent: $35.00
**   Very good: $30.00**

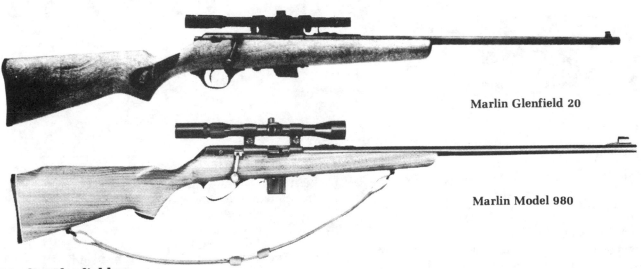

Marlin Glenfield 20

Marlin Model 980

Marlin Glenfield 20

Caliber: 22 short, long, long rifle
Action: Bolt action; thumb safety
Magazine: 7-shot clip
Barrel: 22" round, blued
Sights: Open rear, ramp front; some with scope
Stock & Forearm: Checkered walnut, semi-pistol grip stock and plain forearm
Approximate wt.: 5 ½ lbs.
Comments: Production on this model began about 1966. Price includes scope.
Estimated Value: New (retail): $75.95
**   Excellent: $60.00**
**   Very good: $50.00**

Marlin Model 980

Caliber: 22 Winchester magnum RF
Action: Bolt-action; repeating
Magazine: 8-shot clip
Barrel: 24" round, blued
Sights: Open rear, hooded ramp front
Stock & Forearm: Monte Carlo, one-piece stock & forearm; swivels.
Approximate wt.: 6 lbs.
Comments: Produced from about 1962 until 1970.
Estimated Value: Excellent: $80.00
**   Very good: $65.00**

Marlin Model 780

Marlin Model 781

Marlin Model 782

Marlin Model 783

Marlin Model 780

Caliber: 22 short, long, long rifle
Action: Bolt action; repeating
Magazine: 7-shot clip
Barrel: 22'' blued
Sights: Adjustable rear, ramp front
Stock & Forearm: Checkered walnut, Monte Carlo semi-pistol grip, one piece stock & forearm
Approximate wt.: 6 lbs.
Comments: This rifle is part of 700 series introduced about 1971.
Estimated Value: New (retail): $91.95
     Excellent: **$70.00**
     Very good: **$55.00**

Marlin Model 781

Same as Model 780 except tubular magazine - 25 shorts, 19 longs, 17 long rifles. Weight-5 ½ lbs.
Estimated Value: New (retail): $97.95
     Excellent: **$75.00**
     Very good: **$60.00**

Marlin Model 782

Caliber: 22 magnum Winchester RF
Action: Bolt action; repeating
Magazine: 7-shot clip
Barrel: 22''
Sights: Adjustable rear, ramp front
Stock & Forearm: Monte Carlo semi pistol grip, one piece stock & forearm
Approximate wt.: 6 lbs.
Comments: Introduced as one of the 700 series in 1971.
Estimated Value: New (retail): $102.95
     Excellent: **$ 80.00**
     Very good: **$ 60.00**

Marlin Model 783

Same rifle as Model 782 except magazine is 12-shot tubular.
Estimated Value: New (retail): $105.95
     Excellent: **$ 80.00**
     Very good: **$ 65.00**

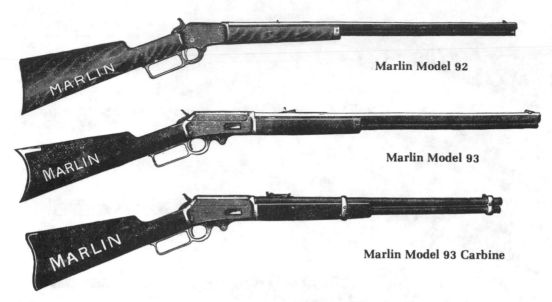

Marlin Model 92

Marlin Model 93

Marlin Model 93 Carbine

Marlin Model 92

Caliber: 22, 32 short or long, rim fire or centerfire
Action: Lever action; exposed hammer
Magazine: 22 caliber: 25 shorts, 20 longs, or 18 long
rifles; 32 caliber: 17 shorts, 14 longs, tubular
under barrel; 16" barrel - 15 shorts, 12 longs
or 10 long rifles
Barrel: 16",' 24", 26", 28" round or octagon, blued
Sights: Open rear, blade front
Stock & Forearm: Plain walnut, straight grip stock &
forearm
Approximate wt.: 5 to 6 lbs.
Comments: This rifle was manufactured from about
1892 to 1916; also known as Model 1892.
Estimated Value: Excellent: $390.00
Very good: $375.00

Marlin Model 93

Caliber: 25-36 Marlin, 30-30, 32 special, 32-40, 38-55
Action: Lever action ; exposed hammer; repeating
Magazine: 10-shot tubular; under barrel
Barrel: 26", 28", 30", or 32" round or octagon
Sights: Open rear, bead front
Stock & Forearm: Plain walnut, straight grip stock and
forearm
Approximate wt.: 7 to 8 lbs.
Comments: This model was manufactured from about
1893 until 1935. It was produced in both
takedown and solid frame models and was
also known as Model 1893.
Estimated Value: Excellent: $500.00
Very good: $450.00

Marlin Model 93 Sporting Carbine

Marlin Model 93 Musket

Marlin Model 93 Sporting Carbine

This is primarily the same gun as the Model 93 Carbine,
except the smaller magazine carries 5 shots.
Estimated Value: Excellent: $500.00
Very good: $450.00

Marlin Model 93 Carbine

Basically the same gun as the Model 93 except: produced in 30-30 and 32 special caliber only; sights are standard carbine sights; 20" round barrel; 7-shot magazine;
weighs between 6 and 7 lbs.
Estimated Value: Excellent: $495.00
Very good: $450.00

Marlin Model 93 Musket

This is the same gun as the Model 93 except: 30" standard barrel; equipped with a musket stock; military
forearm; ramrod; angular bayonet; production stopped
about 1915.
Estimated Value: Excellent: $550.00
Very good: $500.00

Rifles

Marlin Model 1894 (Current)

Marlin Model 1894C

Marlin Model 1895

Marlin Model 1895S

Marlin Model 1897

Marlin Model 1894

Caliber: 25-20, 32-20, 38-40, 44-40; current model 44 magnum.

Action: Lever action; exposed hammer; repeating

Magazine: 10-shot, tubular under barrel

Barrel: Round or octagon, 20'', 24'', 26'', 28'', 30'' or 32''; 20'' on current model

Sights: Open rear, bead front

Stock & Forearm: Plain walnut, straight or pistol grip stock & forearm

Approximate wt: 7 lbs.

Comments: This was called the Model 1894 until the early 1900's; made in both takedown and solid frame models. Produced from about 1894 to 1935. re-introduced in the late 1970's in 44 magnum, with 20'' barrel.

Estimated Value:		Early	Current
	New (retail):		$205.95
	Excellent:	$500.00	$155.00
	Very good:	$450.00	$125.00

Marlin Model 1894C

Similar to the current model 1894 except in 357 caliber; 18½'' barrel; 9 shot magazine. Introduced in 1979.

Estimated Value:	New (retail):	$205.95
	Excellent:	$150.00
	Very good:	$125.00

Marlin Model 1895

Caliber: 33 WCF, 38-56, 40-65, 40-70, 40-82, 45-70

Action: Lever action; exposed hammer; repeating

Magazine: 9-shot tubular, under barrel

Barrel: 24'' octagon or round, blued

Sights: Open rear, bead front

Stock & Forearm: Walnut, straight or pistol grip stock & forearm

Approximate wt.: 8 lbs.

Comments: Made in solid frame and takedown models from about 1895 to 1920.

Estimated Value:	Excellent:	$540.00
	Very good:	$500.00

Marlin Model 1895S

Similar to the Model 1895; introduced in the late 1970's; 45-70 gov't caliber; 22'' barrel; 4 shot magazine; swivels.

Estimated Value:	New (retail):	$282.95
	Excellent:	$215.00
	Very good:	$170.00

Marlin Model 1897

Caliber: 22 short, long, long rifle

Action: Lever action; exposed hammer, repeating

Magazine: 25 shorts, 20 longs, 18 long rifles (full length); 16 shorts, 12 longs and 10 long rifles (half length); tubular blued, under barrel

Barrel: 16'', 24'', 26'', 28''

Sights: Open rear, bead front

Stock & Forearm: Plain walnut straight or pistol grip stock & forearm

Approximate wt.: 6 lbs.

Comments: Produced from about 1897 to 1921.

Estimated Value:	Excellent:	$300.00
	Very good:	$250.00

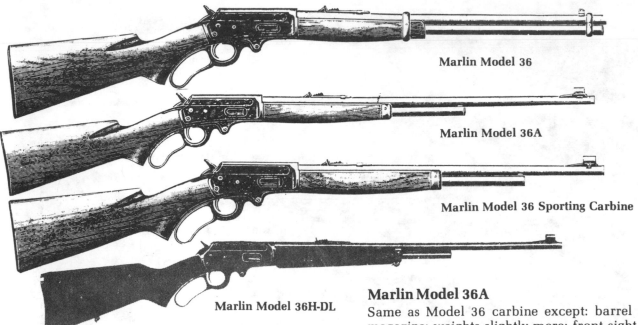

Marlin Model 36

Marlin Model 36A

Marlin Model 36 Sporting Carbine

Marlin Model 36H-DL

Marlin Model 36

Caliber: 30-30, 32 special
Action: Lever action; exposed hammer; repeating
Magazine: 6-shot tubular
Barrel: 20'' round, blued
Sights: Open rear, head front
Stock & Forearm: Pistol grip stock & semi-beavertail forearm; carbine barrel band
Approximate wt.: 6½ lbs.
Comments: Production began about 1936 and continued until 1948.
Estimated Value: Excellent: $190.00
Very good: $150.00

Marlin Model 36A

Same as Model 36 carbine except: barrel is 24''; 2/3 magazine; weights slightly more; front sight is hooded.
Estimated Value: Excellent: $200.00
Very good: $160.00

Marlin Model 36 Sporting Carbine

Same as Model 36A except weight is slightly less and barrel is 20''.
Estimated Value: Excellent: $180.00
Very good: $140.00

Marlin Model 36H-DL

Same rifle as Model 36A except stock and forearm are checkered and have swivels.
Estimated Value: Excellent: $210.00
Very good: $170.00

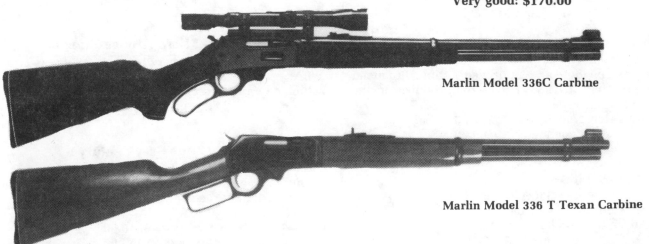

Marlin Model 336C Carbine

Marlin Model 336 T Texan Carbine

Marlin Model 336C Carbine

This is basically the same as the Model 36 Carbine, with a round breech bolt and improved action. 35 caliber Remington was introduced and 32 Special was stopped in 1963. This gun was produced from about 1948 to present.
Estimated Value: New (retail): $198.95
Excellent: $150.00
Very good: $120.00

Marlin Model 336 T Texan Carbine

Same as Model 336C except stock is straight. It was never produced in 32 caliber, but was available from 1963 to 1967 in 44 magnum. It was produced from 1953 to present.
Estimated Value: New (retail): $198.95
Excellent: $150.00
Very good: $120.00

Rifles

Marlin Model 336 Marauder

Marlin Model 336A

Marlin Model 336 A -DL

Marlin Model 336 Sporting Carbine

Marlin Model 336 Micro Groove Zipper

Marlin Model 336 Marauder
Same rifle as Model 336T except weight is slightly less and barrel is only 16¼". It was produced from about 1963 to 1964.
Estimated Value: Excellent: $145.00
                          Very good: $115.00

Marlin Model 336A
This is basically the same rifle as Model 36A with a rounded breech bolt and improved action. Produced from about 1950 to 1963. It was re-introduced in the 1970's and is still being made.
Estimated Value: New (retail): $207.95
                          Excellent: $160.00
                          Very good: $125.00

Marlin Model 336A-DL
Same rifle as Model 336A except it has swivels and checkered stock and forearm.
Estimated Value: Excellent: $170.00
                          Very good: $130.00

Marlin Model 336 Sporting Carbine
Same as Model 336A except weight is slightly less and barrel is 20".
Estimated Value: Excellent: $150.00
                          Very good: $120.00

Marlin Model 336 Micro Groove Zipper
Caliber 219 Zipper, otherwise same rifle as Model 336A.
Estimated Value: Excellent: $200.00
                          Very good: $165.00

Marlin Model 336 Zane Grey Century
Same basic rifle as Model 336A except: barrel is octagonal; 22" barrel; brass fore end cap; brass buttplate and medallion in receiver. Only 10,000 were produced in 1972.
Estimated Value: Excellent: $250.00
                          Very good: $195.00

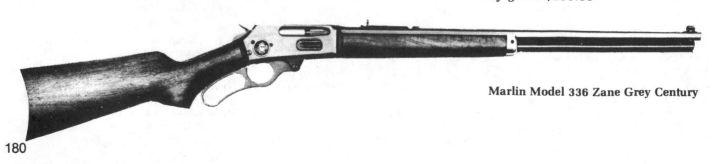

Marlin Model 336 Zane Grey Century

Marlin Model 39

Marlin Model 39A

Marlin Model 39A Mountie

Marlin Model 39M

Marlin Model 39M Golden Mountie

Marlin Model 39

Caliber: 22 short, long, long rifle
Action: Lever action; exposed hammer; repeating; takedown type
Magazine: 25 shorts, 20 longs, 18 long rifles; tubular under barrel
Barrel: 24" octagon
Sights: Bead front, open adjustable rear
Stock & Forearm: Plain pistol grip stock and forearm
Approximate wt.: 6½ lbs.
Comments: Manufactured from about 1938 to 1958.
Estimated Value: Excellent: $225.00
**   Very good: $190.00**

Marlin Model 39A

Same as Model 39 except: round barrel; heavier stock; forearm is semi-beavertail; weight 6½ lbs. Began production about 1938 and was discontinued in 1957. Replaced by Golden 39A.
Estimated Value: Excellent: $135.00
**   Very good: $120.00**

Marlin Model 39M

Similar to 39A with 20" barrel, less capacity in magazine, straight grip stock.
Estimated Value: Excellent: $135.00
**   Very good: $110.00**

Marlin Model 39A Mountie

Same rifle as the Model 39 except: straight grip, lighter stock with trim forearm; weight is 6-6½ lbs. Produced from 1950's to 1960.
Estimated Value: Excellent: $120.00
**   Very good: $100.00**

Marlin Model 39M Golden Mountie

Same gun as Model 39A Mountie except: gold plated trigger; 20" barrel; weight 6 lbs.; magazine capacity 21 shorts, 16 longs, or 15 long rifles. Produced from 1950's to present.
Estimated Value: New (retail) $192.95
**   Excellent: $145.00**
**   Very good: $115.00**

Rifles

Marlin Model Golden 39A

Caliber: 22 short, long, long rifle
Action: Lever-action; exposed hammer; takedown type; gold plated trigger
Magazine: 26 short, 21 long rifles, tubular under barrel
Barrel: 24" micro-groove round barrel
Sights: Bead front with removable hood; adjustable folding semi-buckhorn rear.
Stock & Forearm: Walnut plain pistol grip stock and forearm; steel cap on end.
Approximate wt.: 6¾ lbs.
Comments: Made from about 1960 to date; has gold plated trigger; equipped with sling swivels.
Estimated Value: New (retail): $192.95
     Excellent: $145.00
     Very good: $115.00

Marlin Model 39A Article II

This rifle is a commemorative model of the Model 39A produced for the NRA Centennial in 1971. It has these special features: 24" octagon barrel; walnut pistol grip stock and forearm; brass inlay as in Model 39 Century LTD.
Estimated Value: Excellent: $210.00
     Very good: $170.00

Marlin Model 39M Article II Carbine

Same gun as 39A Article II rifle except: straight grip stock; square lever; 20" octagon barrel; magazine capacity 21 shorts, 16 longs, or 15 long rifles.
Estimated Value: Excellent: $210.00
     Very good: $170.00

Marlin Model 39 Century LTD.

This rifle is a commemorative model based on Model 39A. Made for the Marlin Centennial in 1970, it has these special features: square lever; 20" octagon barrel; brass inlaid receiver; nameplate in stock and brass buttplate; walnut straight stock and forearm.
Estimated Value: Excellent: $225.00
     Very good: $190.00

Marlin Model 444, 444S

Caliber: 444 Marlin
Action: Lever-action; repeating
Magazine: 4-shot, tubular under barrel
Barrel: 22" micro-groove, blued
Sights: Folding open rear, hooded ramp front
Stock & Forearm: Monte Carlo, straight or pistol grip; carbine type forearm; barrel band; swivels.
Approximate wt: 7½ lbs.
Comments: Produced from about 1965 until present. Currently called 444S.
Estimated Value: New (retail): $223.95
     Excellent: $170.00
     Very good: $135.00

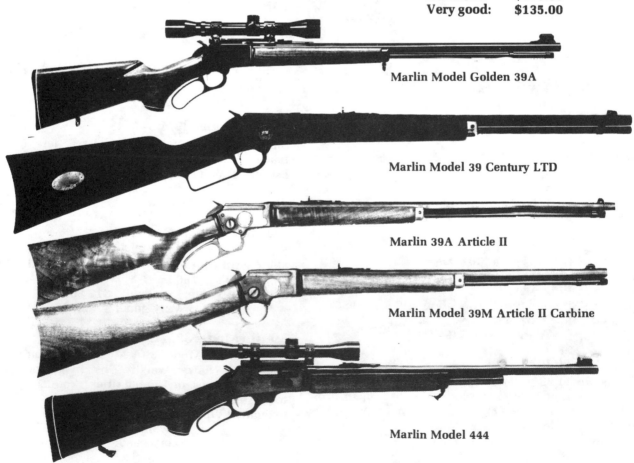

Marlin Model Golden 39A

Marlin Model 39 Century LTD

Marlin 39A Article II

Marlin Model 39M Article II Carbine

Marlin Model 444

Marlin Centennial 1870-1970 Matched Pair
Model 336
Model 39

Marlin Centennial 1870-1970 Matched Pair Models 336 and 39

These are commemoratives rifles in cases with corresponding serial numbers. They have straight grip stock and forearm with brass fore end cap, buttplate and inlaid medallion on engraved receiver. Barrels are 20" octagon and lever is square. Only 1000 sets were produced in 1970 in caliber 30-30 and 22 short, long, long rifle. Price is for set, complete with case in mint unfired condition.

Estimated Value: Excellent: $1,250.00

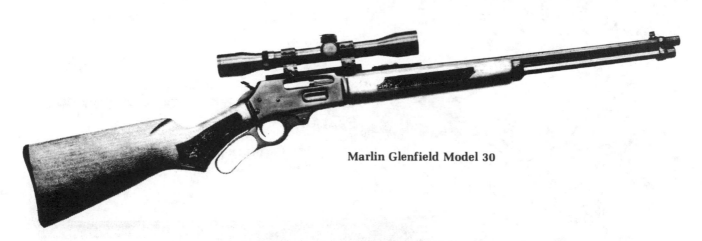

Marlin Glenfield Model 30

Marlin Glenfield Model 30

Caliber: 30-30 Winchester
Action: Lever action; repeating
Magazine: 6-shot tubular
Barrel: 20" round, blued
Sights: Adjustable rear, bead front
Stock & Forearm: Walnut, plain or checkered, semi-pistol grip stock & forearm
Approximate wt: 7 lbs.
Comments: This rifle was manufactured from about 1966 to the late 1970's.
Estimated Value: Excellent: $135.00
                              Very good: $115.00

Marlin Glenfield Model 30GT

Similar to the Glenfield 30 with a straight grip stock and 18½" barrel. Introduced in the late 1970's.
Estimated Value: New (retail): $184.99
                              Excellent: $140.00
                              Very good: $115.00

Marlin Glenfield Model 30A

Similar to the Glenfield 30. Introduced in the late 1970's.
Estimated Value: New (retail): $184.99
                              Excellent: $140.00
                              Very good: $115.00

Marlin Model 375

Caliber: 375 Winchester
Action: Lever action; side ejection; repeating
Magazine: 5 shot tubular
Barrel: 20" round
Sights: Adjustable semi-buckhorn rear, ramp front with brass bead
Stock & Forearm: Plain walnut pistol grip stock & forearm with fluted comb; swivels
Approximate wt: 6¾ lbs.
Comments: Introduced in 1980.
Estimated Value: New (retail): $223.95
                              Excellent: $170.00
                              Very good: $135.00

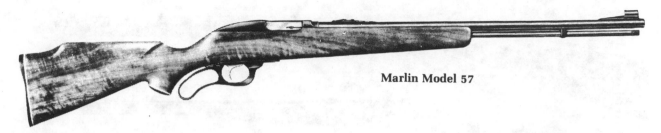

Marlin Model 57

Marlin Model 57

Caliber: 22 short, long, long rifle
Action: Lever action; repeating
Magazine: 19 long rifles, 21 longs, 27 shorts; tubular under barrel
Barrel: 22" round, blued
Sights: Open rear, hooded ramp front
Stock & Forearm: Plain Monte Carlo, pistol grip stock & forearm
Approximate wt.: 6 ¼ lbs.
Comments: This rifle was manufactured from about 1959 to 1965.
Estimated Value: Excellent: $95.00
Very good: $80.00

Marlin Model 57M Levermatic

Caliber: 22 Winchester magnum RF
Action: Lever action; repeating
Magazine: 15-shot tubular, under barrel
Barrel: 24" round
Sights: Open rear, hooded ramp front
Stock & Forearm: Monte Carlo, pistol grip stock & forearm
Approximate wt.: 6 ¼ lbs.
Comments: This rifle is similar to Model 57 and was produced from about 1960 to 1969.
Estimated Value: Excellent: $100.00
Very good: $ 85.00

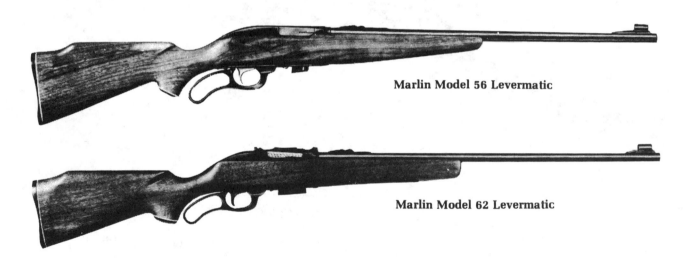

Marlin Model 56 Levermatic

Marlin Model 62 Levermatic

Marlin Model 56 Levermatic

Caliber: 22 short, long, long rifle
Action: Lever action; repeating
Magazine: 8-shot clip
Barrel: 22" round, blued
Sights: Open rear, hooded ramp front
Stock & Forearm: Monte Carlo, pistol grip stock & forearm
Approximate wt.: 5 ¾ lbs.
Comments: This gun, similar to Model 57, was produced from about 1955 to 1965.
Estimated Value: Excellent: $85.00
Very good: $70.00

Marlin Model 62 Levermatic

Caliber: 256 magnum (1963 to 1966), 30 carbine (1966-1969)
Action: Lever-action; repeating
Magazine: 4-shot clip
Barrel: 23" round, blued
Sights: Open rear, hooded ramp front
Stock & Forearm: Monte Carlo, pistol grip stock & forearm; swivels
Approximate wt.: 7 lbs
Comments: This rifle was produced from about 1963-1969.
Estimated Value: Excellent: $140.00
Very good: $120.00

Marlin Model 18 Baby Slide Action

Marlin Model 20

Marlin Model 20 or 20 S

Caliber: 22 short, long, long rifle
Action: Slide action; exposed hammer; repeating
Magazine: 25 short, 20 long, 18 long rifle (full length); 15 shorts, 12 longs, 10 long rifles (half length); tubular, under barrel
Barrel: Octagon; 24" blued
Sights: Open rear, bead front
Stock & Forearm: Plain walnut, straight grip stock and grooved slide handle
Approximate wt.: 5 lbs.
Comments: This model was produced from about 1907 in takedown model and was known as Model 20 S after 1920. Discontinued about 1922.
Estimated Value: Excellent: $225.00
Very good: $195.00

Marlin Model 18 Baby Slide Action

Caliber: 22 short, long, long rifle
Action: Slide action; exposed hammer; repeating
Magazine: 15 shorts, 12 longs or 10 long rifles; tubular, under barrel
Barrel: Round or octagon, 20" blued
Sights: Open rear, bead front
Stock & Forearm: Plain walnut, straight grip stock and slide handle
Approximate wt.: 3 ½ to 4 lbs.
Comments: Production began on this model about 1906, but was discontinued 3 years later.
Estimated Value: Excellent: $220.00
Very good: $190.00

Marlin Model 29

Similar to Model 20 except: round 23" barrel; weighs about 5¾ lbs.; magazine available in half length only; produced from about 1913 to 1916.
Estimated Value: Excellent: $190.00
Very good: $155.00

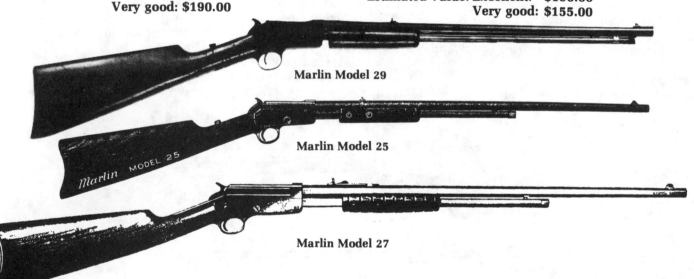

Marlin Model 29

Marlin Model 25

Marlin Model 27

Marlin Model 25

Caliber: 22 short and 22 CB caps only
Action: Slide action; exposed hammer; repeating
Magazine: 15-shot tubular, under barrel
Barrel: 23" octagon barrel
Sights: Open rear, bead front
Stock & Forearm: Plain walnut, straight grip stock and slide handle
Approximate wt.: 4 lbs.
Comments: Production on this takedown model began in 1909 and was stopped 1 year later.
Estimated Value: Excellent: $220.00
Very good: $200.00

Marlin Model 27

Caliber: 25-20, 32-20
Action: Slide action; exposed hammer; repeating
Magazine: 6-shot, 2/3 tubular, under barrel
Barrel: Octagon, 24" blued
Sights: Open rear, bead front
Stock & Forearm: Plain walnut, straight grip stock and grooved slide handle
Approximate wt.: 5¾ lbs.
Comments: This takedown model was produced from about 1910 to 1915.
Estimated Value: Excellent: $225.00
Very good: $200.00

Rifles

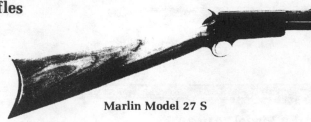

Marlin Model 27 S

Marlin Model 27 S

Same as the Model 27 except: caliber 25 Stevens RF; round barrel; produced from about 1920-1932.
Estimated Value: Excellent: $180.00
Very good: $160.00

Marlin Model 32

Marlin Model 38

Marlin Model 32

Caliber: 22 short, long, long rifle
Action: Slide action; concealed hammer; repeating
Magazine: 25 shorts, 20 longs, 18 long rifles (full length); 15 shorts, 12 longs, 10 long rifles (2/3 length); tubular, under barrel
Barrel: Octagon 24" blued
Sights: Open rear, bead front
Stock & Forearm: Walnut, pistol grip stock and grooved slide handle
Approximate wt.: 5 ½ lbs.
Comments: Takedown model, produced from about 1914 for 1 year.
Estimated Value: Excellent: $240.00
Very good: $220.00

Marlin Model 38

Caliber: 22 short, long, long rifle
Action: Slide action; concealed hammer; repeating
Magazine: 15 shorts, 12 longs, 10 long rifles, 2/3 tubular, under barrel
Barrel: Octagon or round, 24" blued
Sights: Open rear, bead front
Stock & Forearm: Plain pistol grip, stock & grooved slide handle
Approximate wt.: 5 ½ lbs.
Comments: Production began about 1921 on this takedown model and was halted about 1930.
Estimated Value: Excellent: $215.00
Very good: $175.00

Marlin Model 37

Marlin Model 47

Marlin Model 37

Caliber: 22 short, long, long rifle
Action: Slide action, exposed hammer; repeating
Magazine: 25 shorts, 20 longs, or 18 long rifles; tubular, under barrel
Barrel: Round 24"
Sights: Open rear, bead front
Stock & Forearm: Walnut pistol grip stock & forearm
Approximate wt.: 5 lbs.
Comments: This rifle was produced from about 1923 until 1933; takedown model.
Estimated Value: Excellent: $180.00
Very good: $145.00

Marlin Model 47

Same basic rifle as Model 37, used as a bonus giveaway with purchase of Marlin Stocks. Discontinued in 1931 after 6 years production.
Estimated Value: Excellent: $300.00
Very good: $275.00

Marlin Model 50

Marlin Model A-1

Marlin Model A-1E

Marlin Model A-1

Caliber: 22 long rifle
Action: Semi-automatic; repeating
Magazine: 6-shot box (detachable)
Barrel: 24" blued
Sights: Open rear, bead front
Stock & Forearm: Plain pistol grip stock and forearm
Approximate wt.: 6 lbs.
Comments: Produced from about 1935 to 1946, takedown.
Estimated Value: Excellent: $75.00
Very good: $60.00

Marlin Model A-1E

Same rifle as Model A-1 except front sight is hooded and rear sight is peep sight.
Estimated Value: Excellent: $80.00
Very good: $65.00

Model A-1C

This rifle is an improved Model A-1. Forearm is semi-beavertail. It was produced from about 1940 for 6 years.
Estimated Value: Excellent: $75.00
Very good: $60.00

Marlin Model A-1DL

Same rifle as A-1C except: swivels; front sight is hooded; rear sights is peep sight.
Estimated Value: Excellent: $85.00
Very good: $70.00

Marlin Model 50

Caliber: 22 long rifle
Action: Semi-automatic; takedown model; repeating
Magazine: 6-shot box (detachable)
Barrel: 24" round barrel, blued
Sights: Open rear, bead front
Stock & Forearm: Plain, pistol grip stock & grooved forearm
Approximate wt.: 6 lbs.
Comments: Production began about 1931, ended 3 years later.
Estimated Value: Excellent: $75.00
Very good: $60.00

Marlin Model 50 E

Same rifle as Model 50 except front sight is hooded and rear sight is peep sight.
Estimated Value: Excellent: $80.00
Very good: $65.00

Rifles

Marlin Model 88-C

Caliber: 22 long rifle
Action: Semi-automatic
Magazine: 14-shot, tubular in stock
Barrel: 24" round, blued
Sights: Open rear, hooded front
Stock & Forearm: Pistol grip stock and forearm
Approximate wt.: 6¾ lbs.
Comments: A takedown model that was produced from about 1947 to 1956.
Estimated Value: Excellent: $80.00
Very good: $65.00

Marlin Model 88 DL

Same rifle as Model 88-C except stock is checkered and it has swivels and peep sight on receiver. Produced for 3 years beginning about 1953.
Estimated Value: Excellent: $85.00
Very good: $70.00

Marlin Model 89-C

Same rifle as Model 88-C except magazine is 7 or 12 shot clip. It was produced from about 1950 to 1961. It has a tapered forearm.
Estimated Value: Excellent: $75.00
Very good: $60.00

Marlin Model 89-DL

Same rifle as Model 89-C except it has swivels and peep sight on receiver.
Estimated Value: Excellent: $80.00
Very good: $65.00

Marlin Model 98

Caliber: 22 long rifle
Action: Semi-automatic
Magazine: 15-shot tubular
Barrel: 22" round, blued
Sights: Open rear, hooded ramp front
Stock & Forearm: Walnut, Monte Carlo with cheek-piece
Approximate wt.: 6¾ lbs.
Comments: A solid frame rifle produced from about 1950-1959.
Estimated Value: Excellent: $85.00
Very good: $70.00

Marlin Model 99

Caliber: 22 long rifle
Action: Semi-automatic
Magazine: 18-shot tubular
Barrel: 22" round, blued
Sights: Open rear, hooded ramp front
Stock & Forearm: Plain pistol grip stock and forearm
Approximate wt.: 5½ lbs.
Comments: This rifle was produced from about 1959 unti 1961.
Estimated Value: Excellent: $75.00
Very good: $60.00

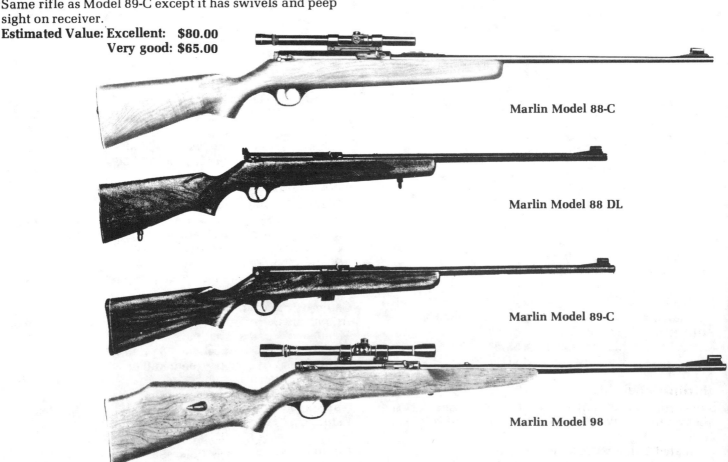

Marlin Model 88-C

Marlin Model 88 DL

Marlin Model 89-C

Marlin Model 98

Marlin Model 99C

Marlin Model 99DL

Marlin Glenfield Model 99G

Marlin Model 989

Marlin Glenfield Model 99G

Basically the same rifle as the Model 99 with a plain stock. Produced from about 1963 to 1965.
Estimated Value: Excellent: $60.00
Very good: $50.00

Marlin Model 99C

Same rifle as Model 99 except stock is Monte Carlo (some are checkered); trigger is gold plated and receiver is grooved. It was produced from 1962 to late 1970's.
Estimated Value: Excellent: $65.00
Very good: $55.00

Marlin Model 989

Caliber: 22 long rifle only
Action: Semi-automatic
Magazine: 7-shot clip
Barrel: 22'' round, blued
Sights: Open rear, hooded ramp front
Stock & Forearm: Monte Carlo pistol grip stock & forearm
Approximate wt.: 5 ½ lbs.
Comments: This rifle was produced for 4 years beginning in 1962.
Estimated Value: Excellent: $60.00
Very good: $50.00

Marlin Model 99DL

Same rifle as Model 99C except it has swivels and jeweled breech bolt. It was made for 5 years beginning about 1960.
Estimated Value: Excellent: $70.00
Very good: $60.00

Rifles

Marlin Glenfield Model 989G

Marlin Model 99 M1

Marlin Model 989 M2

Marlin Glenfield Model 60

Marlin Glenfield Model 989G

This is basically the same rifle as the Marlin Model 989 except stock is plain and front sight is bead. It was produced from about 1962 to 1964.

Estimated Value: Excellent: $50.00
Very good: $40.00

Marlin Model 99 M1

Caliber: 22 long rifle
Action: Semi-automatic
Magazine: 9-shot tubular
Barrel: 18" micro-groove, blued
Sights: Open rear, ramp front (military)
Stock & Forearm: Carbine stock, hand guard and barrel band; swivels
Approximate wt.: 4 ½ lbs.
Comments: This rifle was styled after the U.S. 30 M1 Carbine and was in production from about 1966 to the late 1970's.
Estimated Value: Excellent: $70.00
Very good: $60.00

Marlin Model 989 M2

Same rifle as Model 99 M1 except it has a 7-shot clip magazine.

Estimated Value: Excellent: $75.00
Very good: $65.00

Marlin Glenfield Model 60

Caliber: 22 long rifle
Action: Semi-automatic
Magazine: 18-shot tubular, under barrel
Barrel: 22" round, blued
Sights: Open rear, ramp front. Some with scope
Stock & Forearm: Checkered walnut, semi-pistol grip stock & forearm; or Monte Carlo.
Approximate wt.: 5 ½ lbs.
Comments: This rifle began in production about 1966; still in production. Price includes scope.
Estimated Value: New (retail): $78.95
Excellent: $60.00
Very good: $50.00

Marlin Model 49

Marlin Model 49 DL

Marlin Glenfield Model 70

Marlin Model 49

Caliber: 22 long rifle
Action: Semi-automatic
Magazine: 18-shot tubular
Barrel: 22" round, blued
Sights: Adjustable open rear, ramp front
Stock & Forearm: Pistol grip Monte Carlo stock & forearm
Approximate wt.: 5 ½ lbs.
Comments: This rifle began production in 1968.
Estimated Value: Excellent: $70.00
Very good: $60.00

Marlin Model 49 DL

Same rifle as Model 49 except stock and forearm are checkered; trigger is gold plated. Production began about 1971; ended in late 1970's.
Estimated Value: Excellent: $75.00
Very good: $65.00

Marlin Glenfield Model 70 Carbine

Caliber: 22 long rifle
Action: Semi-automatic
Magazine: 7-shot clip
Barrel: 18" round, blued
Sights: Open rear, ramp front
Stock & Forearm: Checkered walnut, Monte Carlo stock and plain forearm; barrel band; swivels
Approximate wt.: 5 ½ lbs.
Comments: Production from about 1966 to present.
Estimated Value: New (retail): $78.95
Excellent: $60.00
Very good: $50.00

Marlin Glenfield Model 40

Marlin Glenfield Model 40

Caliber: 22 long rifle
Action: Semi-automatic; hammerless; side ejection; repeating
Magazine: 18 shot tubular
Barrel: 22"
Sights: Adjustable open rear, ramp front
Stock & Forearm: Checkered hardwood Monte Carlo, semi-pistol grip stock and forearm
Approximate wt: 5 ½ lbs.
Comments: Produced in the late 1970's.
Estimated Value: Excellent: $70.00
Very good: $55.00

Rifles

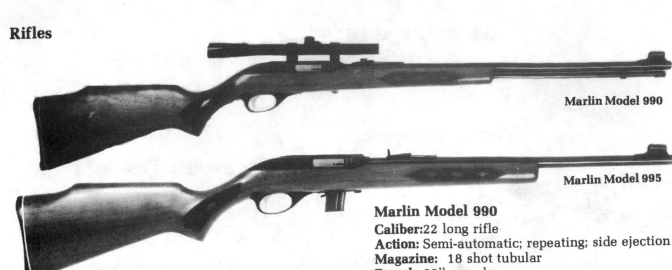

Marlin Model 990

Marlin Model 995

Marlin Model 995

Similar to the Model 990 with a 7 shot clip magazine and 18" barrel.

Estimated Value: New (retail): $92.95
Excellent: $70.00
Very good: $55.00

Marlin Model 990

Caliber: 22 long rifle
Action: Semi-automatic; repeating; side ejection
Magazine: 18 shot tubular
Barrel: 22" round
Sights: Adjustable folding semi-buckhorn rear, ramp front with brass bead
Stock & Forearm: Checkered walnut, Monte Carlo, one piece pistol grip stock & forearm
Approximate wt: 5½ lbs.
Comments: Introduced in the late 1970's.
Estimated Value: New (retail): $99.95
Excellent: $75.00
Very good: $60.00

Mauser

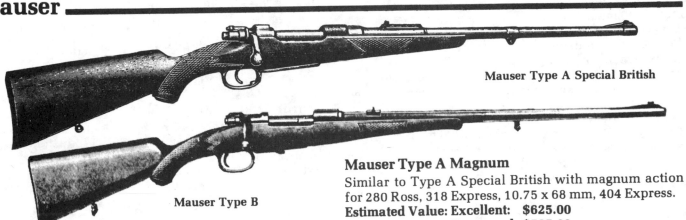

Mauser Type A Special British

Mauser Type B

Mauser Type A Special British

Caliber: 30-06, 7 x 57, 8 x 60, 9 x 57, 9.3 x 62 mm
Action: Bolt action; repeating
Magazine: 5-shot box
Barrel: 23½" blued; octagon or round
Sights: Express rear, hooded ramp front
Stock & Forearm: Checkered walnut, pistol grip, one-piece stock and tapered forearm; swivels
Approximate wt.: 7¼ lbs.
Comments: Made from about 1910 to 1938.
Estimated Value: Excellent: $600.00
Very good: $500.00

Mauser Type A Short Model

Similar to Type A Special British with 21½" barrel and a short action.
Estimated Value: Excellent: $575.00
Very good: $480.00

Mauser Type A Magnum

Similar to Type A Special British with magnum action for 280 Ross, 318 Express, 10.75 x 68 mm, 404 Express.
Estimated Value: Excellent: $625.00
Very good: $525.00

Mauser Type B

Caliber: 30-06, 7x57, 8x57, 8x60, 9.3x62, 10.75x68 mm
Action: Bolt action; repeating
Magazine: 5-shot box
Barrel: 23½" blued
Sights: Leaf rear, ramp front
Stock & Forearm: Checkered walnut, pistol grip, one piece stock and lipped forearm; swivels
Approximate wt.: 7½ lbs.
Comments: Made from about 1910 to 1940.
Estimated Value: Excellent: $525.00
Very good: $425.00

Mauser Type K

Similar to Type B with 21½" barrel and short action.
Estimated Value: Excellent: $500.00
Very good: $410.00

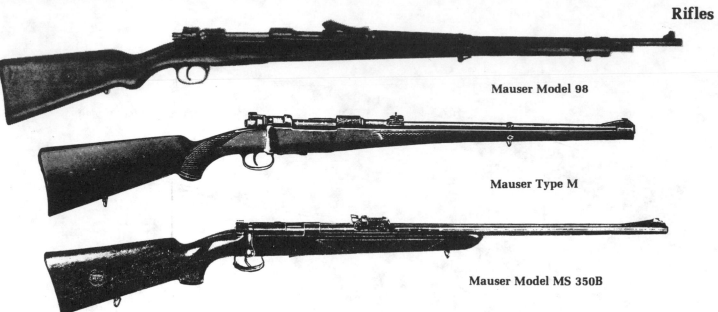

Mauser Model 98

Mauser Type M

Mauser Model MS 350B

Mauser Model 98

Caliber: 7 mm, 7.9 mm
Action: Bolt action; repeating
Magazine: 5-shot box
Barrel: 23½" blued
Sights: Adjustable rear, blade front
Stock & Forearm: Walnut, semi-pistol grip, one piece stock and fluted forearm; barrel band
Approximate wt.: 7½ lbs.
Comments: Made from about 1920 to 1938.
Estimated Value: Excellent: $400.00
Very good: $325.00

Mauser Type M

Caliber: 30-06, 6.5x54, 7x57, 8x52, 8x60, 9x57
Action: Bolt action; repeating
Magazine: 5-shot box
Barrel: 19¾" blued
Sights: 3-leaf rear, ramp front
Stock & Forearm: Checkered walnut, pistol grip, one piece stock and full length forearm; swivels.
Approximate wt.: 6½ lbs.
Comments: Made from about 1910 to 1940.
Estimated Value: Excellent: $600.00
Very good: $490.00

Mauser Type S

Caliber: 6.5x54, 7x57, 8x51, 8x60, 9x57
Action: Bolt action; repeating
Magazine: 5-shot box
Barrel: 19¾" blued
Sights: 3-leaf rear, ramp front
Stock & Forearm: Checkered walnut, pistol grip, one piece stock and lipped full length forearm; swivels
Approximate wt.: 6½ lbs.
Comments: Made from about 1910 to 1940.
Estimated Value: Excellent: $590.00
Very good: $485.00

Mauser Model MS 350B

Caliber: 22 long rifle
Action: Bolt action; repeating
Magazine: 5-shot box
Barrel: 27½" blued
Sights: Micrometer rear, ramp front
Stock & Forearm: Match type; checkered pistol grip; swivels
Approximate wt.: 8 lbs.
Comments: Made from the mid 1920's to mid 1930's.
Estimated Value: Excellent: $390.00
Very good: $320.00

Mauser Model ES 350

Similar to MS 350B with different sights and 26¾" barrel. Made from the mid to late 1930's. Single shot.
Estimated Value: Excellent: $375.00
Very good: $300.00

Mauser Model ES 350B

Similar to MS 350B in single shot.
Estimated Value: Excellent: $300.00
Very good: $225.00

Mauser Model ES 340

Caliber: 22 long rifle
Action: Bolt action; single shot
Magazine: None
Barrel: 25½" blued
Sights: Tangent curve rear, ramp front
Stock & Forearm: Checkered walnut, pistol grip, one piece stock and forearm; swivels
Approximate wt.: 6½ lbs.
Comments: Made from the early 1920's to mid 1930's.
Estimated Value: Excellent: $250.00
Very good: $210.00

Mauser Model ES 340B

Similar to the ES 340 with a 26¾" barrel. Made from the mid to late 1930's.
Estimated Value: Excellent: $260.00
Very good: $215.00

Mauser Model MS 420

Mauser Model MS 420B

Mauser Model MM 410

Mauser Model EL 320

Similar to ES 340 with a 23½" barrel, adjustable rear sight and bead front sight. Made from the late 1920's to mid 1930's.
Estimated Value: Excellent: $225.00
Very good: $175.00

Mauser Model MS 420

Caliber: 22 long rifle
Action: Bolt action; repeating
Magazine: 5-shot detatchable box
Barrel: 25½" blued
Sights: Tangent curve rear, ramp front
Stock & Forearm: Checkered walnut, pistol grip, one-piece stock and forearm; swivels.
Approximate wt.: 6½ lbs.
Comments: Made from the mid 1920's to mid 1930's.
Estimated Value: Excellent: $350.00
Very good: $285.00

Mauser Model MS 420B

Similar to MS 420 with better wood. Made from the mid to late 1930's.
Estimated Value: Excellent: $360.00
Very good: $290.00

Mauser Model MM 410

Caliber: 22 long rifle
Action: Bolt action; repeating
Magazine: 5-shot detatchable box
Barrel: 23½" blued
Sights: Tangent curve rear, ramp front
Stock & Forearm: Checkered, pistol grip, one piece stock and forearm; swivels
Approximate wt.: 6½ lbs.
Comments: Made from mid 1920's to mid 1930's.
Estimated Value: Excellent: $250.00
Very good: $200.00

Mauser Model MM 410 B

Similar to MM 410 except lighter weight model. Made from mid to late 1930's.
Estimated Value: Excellent: $225.00
Very good: $200.00

Mauser Model DSM 34

Similar to the 98 in appearance, in 22 long rifle with a 26" barrel. Made from the mid 1930's to late 1930's. Single Shot.
Estimated Value: Excellent: $250.00
Very good: $225.00

Mauser Model KKW

Similar to DSM 34. Made from the mid 1930's to late 1930's.
Estimated Value: Excellent: $225.00
Very good: $200.00

Mauser Model 2000

Mauser 660 Safari

Mauser 3000

Mauser Varminter 10

Mauser Model 2000

Caliber: 270 Win., 308 Win., 30-06
Action: Bolt action; repeating; adjustable trigger
Magazine: 5 shot box; hinged floor plate
Barrel: 24" Krupp steel
Sights: Folding leaf rear, hooded ramp front
Stock & Forearm: Checkered walnut Monte Carlo pistol grip, one piece stock and forearm; swivels; cheekpiece
Approximate wt: 7 ½ lbs.
Comments: Manufactured in the late 1960's and early 1970's.
Estimated Value: Excellent: $300.00
Very good: $240.00

Mauser Model 660

Caliber: 243, 25-06, 270, 308, 30-06, 7x57, 7mm
Action: Short bolt action; repeating
Magazine: 5-shot box
Barrel: 24" blued
Sights: None
Stock & Forearm: Checkered walnut, Monte Carlo pistol grip, one-piece stock and forearm; swivels; recoil pad
Approximate wt.: 7 lbs.
Comments: Made from the early 1970's to present. No longer available in the United States.
Estimated Value: Excellent: $350.00
Very good: $325.00

Mauser Model 660 Safari

Similar to 660 except: magnum calibers; 28" barrel; express rear sight and ramp front sight; calibers 458 Win., 375 H&H, 338 Win., & 7 mm Rem.
Estimated Value: Excellent: $425.00
Very good: $375.00

Mauser Model 3000

Caliber: 243, 270, 30-06, 308, 375 magnum, 7mm magnum
Action: Bolt action; repeating
Magazine: 5-shot box
Barrel: 22", 26" magnum
Sights: None
Stock & Forearm: Checkered walnut, Monte Carlo pistol grip, one-piece stock and forearm; recoil pad; swivels
Approximate wt.: 7 lbs.
Comments: Made from the early 1970's to present. No longer available in the United States.
Estimated Value: Excellent: $250.00
Very good: $200.00

Mauser Varminter 10

Caliber: 22-250
Action: Bolt action; repeating
Magazine: 5-shot box
Barrel: 24" blued, heavy
Sights: None
Stock & Forearm: Checkered walnut, Monte Carlo pistol grip, one-piece stock and forearm.
Approximate wt.: 8 lbs.
Comments: Made from early 1970's to present. No longer available in the United States.
Estimated Value: Excellent: $250.00
Very good: $200.00

Military, Argentine

Argentine M 1891 Mauser

Argentine M 1891 Carbine

Argentine M 1909 Mauser

Argentine M 1909 Carbine

Argentine Model 1891 Mauser
Caliber: 7.65 mm rimless
Action: Manually operated bolt action; straight bolt handle
Magazine: 5-shot single column box
Barrel: 29" round barrel; cleaning rod in forearm
Sights: Barley corn front; rear adjustable for elevation
Stock & Forearm: Military type, one-piece straight grip stock and full forearm; bayonet lug; two barrel bands
Approximate wt.: 8 ½ lbs.
Comments: Similar to 7.65 mm M1890 Turkish Mauser; obsolete
Estimated Value: Very Good: $100.00
Good: $ 75.00

Argentine Model 1891 Carbine
Similar to Model 1891 Rifle except: 17 ½ " barrel; approximate wt. 6 ½ lbs.; two versions — one with and one without bayonet lug; some still used as police weapon.
Estimated Value: Very Good: $110.00
Good: $ 80.00

Argentine Model 1909 Mauser
Caliber: 7.65 mm rimless
Action: Manually operated bolt with straight handle
Magazine: 5-shot staggered row box magazine
Barrel: 29" round barrel
Sights: Barley corn, tangent leaf rear
Stock & Forearm: Semi-pistol grip military type, one-piece stock and full forearm; two barrel bands; cleaning rod in forearm
Approximate wt.: 9 lbs.
Comments: A slight modification of the German Gewehr 98; obsolete
Estimated Value: Very Good: $110.00
Good: $ 85.00

Argentine Model 1909 Carbine
Similar to Model 1909 Rifle except: 17 ½ " barrel; approximate wt. 6 ½ lbs.; with and without bayonet lugs.
Estimated Value: Excellent: $115.00
Very good: $ 90.00

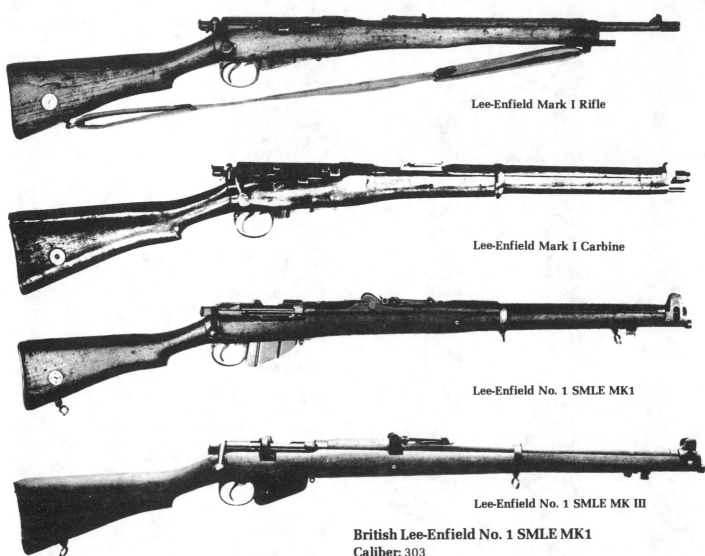

Lee-Enfield Mark I Rifle

Lee-Enfield Mark I Carbine

Lee-Enfield No. 1 SMLE MK1

Lee-Enfield No. 1 SMLE MK III

British Lee-Enfield Mark I
Caliber: 303
Action: Bolt action; repeating; bolt handle curved downward.
Magazine: 10-shot detachable box with cut-off
Barrel: 30''
Sights: Barley corn front, vertical leaf rear
Stock & Forearm: Plain military type stock and forearm
Approximate wt.: 9¼ lbs.
Comments: Adopted by British Army about 1899.
Estimated Value: Very Good: $120.00
Good: $ 90.00

British Lee-Enfield Mark I Carbine
Similar to Lee-Enfield Mark I Rifle except: 21'' barrel.
Estimated Value: Very Good: $125.00
Good: $ 95.00

British Lee-Enfield No. 1 SMLE MK1
Caliber: 303
Action: Bolt action; curved bolt handle
Magazine: 10-shot detachable box with cut-off
Barrel: 25¼''
Sights: Barley corn front with protective ears, tangent leaf rear
Stock & Forearm: Plain wood military stock to the muzzle with full length wood hand guard over barrel
Approximate wt.: 8 lbs.
Comments: Adopted about 1902 by British Army.
Estimated Value: Very Good: $100.00
Good: $ 75.00

British Lee-Enfield No. 1 SMLE MK III
Similar to No. 1 SMLE MKI Except: modified and simplified for mass production; adopted in 1907 and modified again in 1918.
Estimated Value: Very Good: $110.00
Good: $ 90.00

(Pattern 14)
No. 3 MK 1

Lee-Enfield
No. MK 1

Jungle Carbine
No. 5 MK 1

British (Pattern 14) No. 3 MK 1

Caliber: 303
Action: Bolt action; modified Mauser type action; cocked as bolt is moved forward
Magazine: 5-shot non-removable box
Barrel: 26''
Sights: Blade front with protective ears, vertical leaf with aperture rear
Stock & Forearm: Plain military stock with wood hand guard over barrel
Approximate wt.: 9 lbs.
Comments: Made in U.S.A. during World War I for the British Army.
Estimated Value: Very Good:$120.00
Good: $ 95.00

British Lee-Enfield No. 4 MK 1

Caliber: 303
Action: Bolt action
Magazine: 10-shot detachable box
Barrel: 25''
Sights: Blade front with protective ears, vertical leaf with aperture rear
Stock & Forearm: Plain military stock with wood hand guard over barrel
Approximate wt.: 8¾ lbs.
Comments: First produced about 1931 and was redesigned for mass production in 1939 by utilizing stamped parts and other short cuts.
Estimated Value: Very Good:$100.00
Good: $ 75.00

British Jungle Carbine No. 5 MK 1

Caliber: 303
Action: Bolt action
Magazine: 10-shot detachable box
Barrel: 18¾ inches
Sights: Blade front with protective ears; vertical leaf
Stock & Forearm: Military type one-piece stock and forearm; wood hand guard over barrel; one barrel band
Approximate wt.: 7 lbs.
Comments: Made during World War II for jungle fighting.
Estimated Value: Very Good:$125.00
Good: $100.00

Chilean Model 1895

Caliber: 7 mm
Action: Bolt action; straight or turned bolt handle; similar to the Spanish Model 1893 Mauser.
Magazine: 5-shot staggered non-detachable box
Barrel: 29"
Sights: Barley corn front; leaf rear
Stock & Forearm: Plain military type stock with wood hand guard over barrel
Approximate wt.: 9 lbs.
Comments: Since Chile's adoption of the FN rifle, quantities of the Chilean Mausers have to be purchased by U.S.A. Arms dealers.
Estimated Value: Very Good: $90.00
Good: $70.00

Chilean Model 1895 Short

Similar to Model 1895 Rifle except; 22" barrel; approximate wt. 8 ½ lbs.
Estimated Value: Very Good: $95.00
Good: $75.00

Chilean Model 1895 Carbine

Similar to Model 1895 Rifle except: 18¼" barrel; approximate wt. 7 ½ lbs.
Estimated Value: Very Good:$100.00
Good: $ 80.00

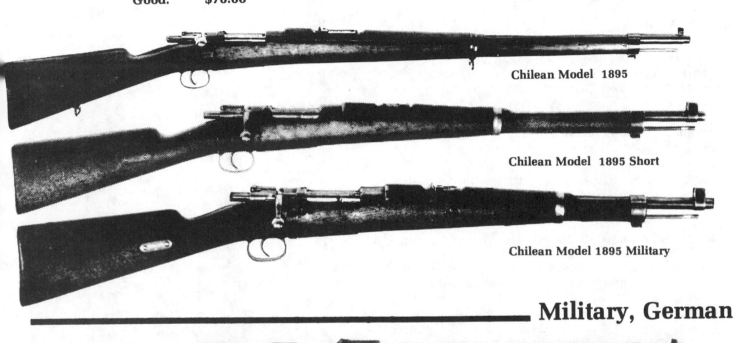

Chilean Model 1895

Chilean Model 1895 Short

Chilean Model 1895 Military

Military, German

German Model 1888 (GEW 88)

German Model 1888 (GEW 88)

Caliber: 7.92 mm
Action: Bolt action; straight bolt handle
Magazine: 5-shot inline non-detachable box
Barrel: 29"
Sights: Barley corn front; leaves with "v" notches rear
Stock & Forearm: Plain, straight grip military stock; no hand guard, but uses a metal barrel jacket that covers barrel to muzzle
Approximate wt.: 8¾ lbs.
Comments: This arm is sometimes called a Mauser or Mannlicher, but actually it is neither; it combines the magazine of the Mannlicher with the bolt features of the Mauser 1871/84; it is unsafe to use with the modern 7.92 mm cartridge.
Estimated Value: Very Good: $85.00
Good: $70.00

German Model 1888 Carbine

German Model 1888 Carbine

Similar to the Model 1888 Rifle except: 18" barrel; approximate wt. 6¾ lbs.; full length stock to muzzle; curved flatten top bolt handle.

Estimated Value: Very Good: $80.00
Good: $65.00

German Model 1891

Similar to Model 1888 Carbine except: stacking hook under forearm and although it is called a rifle, it has an 18" barrel like the carbines.

Estimated Value: Very Good: $85.00
Good: $70.00

German Gewehr 98 (GEW 98)

Caliber: 7.92 mm
Action: Bolt action; straight or curved bolt handle
Magazine: 5-shot staggered non-detachable box; also during World War I, 10 and 25 shot magazines
Barrel: 29"
Sights: Barley corn front, tangent bridge type or tangent leaf "v" rear
Stock & Forearm: Plain, semi-pistol grip military stock and forearm; wood hand guard
Approximate wt.: 9 lbs.
Comments: This was one of the principle rifles of the German Army in World War I; it also appeared in a caliber 22 training rifle in World War I by fitting a liner in the barrel.

Estimated Value: Very Good: $130.00
Good: $110.00

German Model 98 (Kar 98) Carbine

Similar to Model Gewehr 98 Rifle except: 17" barrel; approximate wt. 7½ lbs.; full stock to muzzle; section of forearm from barrel band to muzzle tapered to much smaller size than rest of forearm; curved bolt handle.

Estimated Value: Very Good: $135.00
Good: $115.00

German Model 98a (Kar 98a) Carbine

Similar to Model Gewehr 98 Rifle except: 24" barrel; appeared in 1904 and made in tremendous quantities until 1918; used in World War I and had limited usage in World War II; cut out in stock below bolt handle; curved bolt handle; grip grooves on forearm; stacking hook.

Estimated Value: Very Good: $140.00
Good: $115.00

German Gewehr 98 (GEW 98)   German Model 98 (Kar 98) Carbine   German Model 98 (Kar 98a) Carbine

German Model K 98b (Kar 98b) Carbine

German Mauser Model 98K

German Mauser Model 98K

Caliber: 7.92 mm
Action: Bolt action; turned down bolt handle
Magazine: 5-shot staggered row non-detachable box
Barrel: 24"
Sights: Barley corn open or hooded front, tangent rear with "v" notch
Stock & Forearm: Plain, semi-pistol grip military stock and forearm; wood hand guard; cut out in stock under bolt handle.
Approximate wt.: 8¾ lbs.
Comments: The standard infantry rifle during World War II; widely fluctuating prices on these rifles because some have special unit markings which effect their values.
Estimated Value: Very Good:$150.00 - $500.00
                Good: **$120.00 - $400.00**

German Model K 98b (Kar 98b) Carbine

Although designated as a carbine, it is same length and is similar to Gewehr 98 Rifle except: turned down bolt; grip grooved forearm; these were used in the 1920's and early in World War II.
Estimated Value: Very Good:$125.00
                Good: **$100.00**

Military, Italian

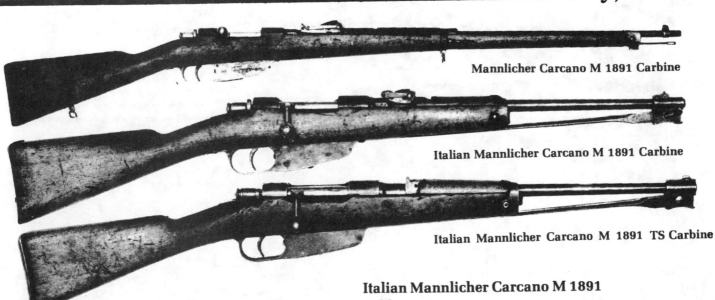

Mannlicher Carcano M 1891 Carbine

Italian Mannlicher Carcano M 1891 Carbine

Italian Mannlicher Carcano M 1891 TS Carbine

Italian Mannlicher Carcano M 1891

Caliber: 6.5 mm
Action: Bolt action; straight bolt handle; a modified Mauser type action
Magazine: 6-shot in line non-detachable box
Barrel: 30½"
Sights: Barley corn front, tangent with "v" notch graduated from 500 to 2000 meters
Stock & Forearm: Plain, straight grip military stock with hand guard (wood) over barrel
Approximate wt.: 8¾ lbs.
Comments: Uses knife type bayonet.
Estimated Value: Very Good: $75.00
                Good: **$55.00**

Italian Mannlicher Carcano M 1891 Carbine

Generally the same specification as M 1891 Military rifle except: 18" barrel; bent bolt handle; folding bayonet permanently attached; approximate wt. 7 lbs.
Estimated Value: Very Good: $70.00
                Good: **$50.00**

Italian Mannlicher Carcano M 1891 TS Carbine

Similar to M 1891 Carbine except: Uses knife type removable bayonet.
Estimated Value: Very Good:$70.00
                Good: **$50.00**

Rifles

Italian Mannlicher Carcano M 1938

Caliber: 7.35 mm; 6.5 mm
Action: Bolt action; bent bolt handle
Magazine: 6-shot incline, non-detachable box
Barrel: 21"
Sights: Barley corn front; adjustable rear
Stock & Forearm: Plain, straight grip military stock; wood hand guard over barrel
Approximate wt.: 7 ½ lbs.
Comments: First of the Italian rifles chambered for the 7.35 mm cartridge; in 1940 the 7.35 mm caliber was dropped; this is the type rifle used to assassinate President John F. Kennedy in 1963; it was a 6.5 mm made in 1940 and sold in U.S.A. as Army surplus.
Estimated Value: Excellent: $85.00
Very good: $65.00

Italian Mannlicher Carcano M 1938 Carbine

Similar to M 1938 Military Rifle except: 18" barrel; folding bayonet permanently attached.
Estimated Value: Excellent: $90.00
Very good: $70.00

Italian Mannlicher Carcano M 1938 TS Carbine

Same as M 1938 Carbine except: detachable knife type bayonet.
Estimated Value: Excellent: $80.00
Very good: $65.00

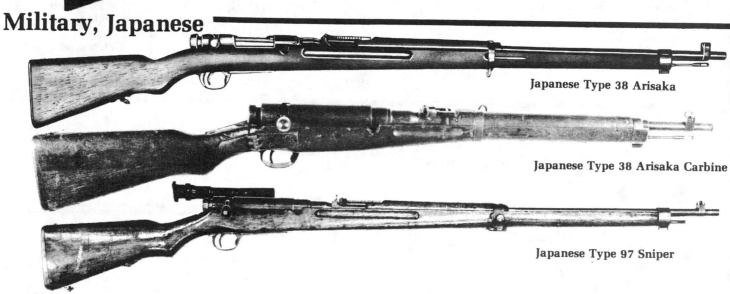

Mannlicher Carcano M 1938

Military, Japanese

Japanese Type 38 Arisaka

Japanese Type 38 Arisaka Carbine

Japanese Type 97 Sniper

Japanese Type 38 Arisaka

Caliber: 6.5 mm Japanese
Action: Bolt action; straight bolt handle
Magazine: 5-shot box magazine with floor plate
Barrel: 31 ½" round barrel
Sights: Barley corn front with protecting ears, rear sight adjustable for elevation
Stock & Forearm: Military finish; plain wood, one-piece full stock; semi-pistol grip; steel butt-plate; cleaning rod under barrel; wood hand guard on top of barrel; two steel barrel bands with bayonet lug on front band
Approximate wt.: 9 ¼ lbs.
Comments: Adopted by Japanese Military in 1905, the 38th year of the Meiji reign.

Estimated Value: Very good: $130.00
Good: $100.00

Japanese Type 38 Arisaka Carbine

Similar to Type 38 Arisaka Rifle except: shorter barrel (20 inch); folding bayonet; approximate wt. about 7 ¼ lbs.; some were converted for paratrooper use by the fitting of a hinged butt stock.,
Estimated Value:

	Carbine	Paratrooper Carbine
Very good:	$120.00	$145.00
Good:	$ 95.00	$115.00

Japanese Type 97 Sniper

Similar to Type 38 Arisaka Rifle except: a snipers version adopted in 1937 with a 2.5 power scope; approximate wt. with scope, 11 lbs.
Estimated Value: Very good: $275.00
Good: $225.00

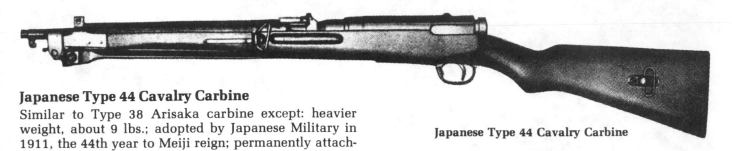

Japanese Type 44 Cavalry Carbine

Similar to Type 38 Arisaka carbine except: heavier weight, about 9 lbs.; adopted by Japanese Military in 1911, the 44th year to Meiji reign; permanently attached folding bayonet.

Japanese Type 44 Cavalry Carbine

Estimated Value: Excellent: $120.00
Very good: $ 90.00

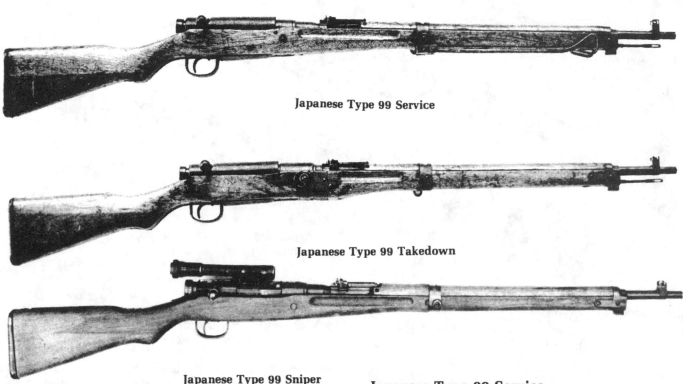

Japanese Type 99 Service

Japanese Type 99 Takedown

Japanese Type 99 Sniper

Japanese Type 99 Takedown

Similar to Type 99 Service Rifle except: 25" barrel only; takedown model (it has a screw-in key that serves as a locking pin. When key is removed, the barrel can be unscrewed from the receiver); the takedown arrangement was unsatisfactory because it weakened the receiver and affected the accuracy.

Estimated Value: **Very good:** **$150.00**
Good: **$115.00**

Japanese Type 99 Sniper

Similar to Type 99 Service Rifle except: adopted in 1942 and equipped with a 4-power scope; 25½" barrel only. Prices include matching number and scope mount.

Estimated Value: **Very good:** **$300.00**
Good: **$250.00**

Japanese Type 99 Service

Caliber: 7.7 mm Japanese
Action: Bolt action
Magazine: 5-shot magazine, non-detachable
Barrel: 25½" or 31½" round barrel
Sights: Fixed front, adjustable or fixed rear
Stock and Forearm: Military finish; plain wood, one-piece full stock; semi-pistol grip; steel buttplate; cleaning rod under barrel; some had bipod attached to under forearm; wood hand guard on top of barrel; two steel bands with bayonet lug on front band
Approximate wt.: 8½ to 9 lbs.
Comments: Some of the last rifles made were of poor quality and unsafe to shoot with heavy load cartridges. Adopted by Japanese Military in 1939, which was Japanese year of 2599.
Estimated Value: **Very good:** **$110.00**
Good: **$ 85.00**

Military, Mexican

Mexican Model 1895 Mauser Military

Mexican Model 1902

Mexican Arisaka (Japanese Type 38 Rifle)

Mexican Model 1936

Mexican Model 1954

Mexican Model 1895 Mauser
Almost identical to the Spanish 1893 Military Rifle in caliber 7 mm. See Spanish Model 1893 Military Rifle for description.

Estimated Value: Very good: $65.00
                   Good: $55.00

Mexican Models 1902 and 1912 Mauser
Almost identical to the Model 1895 Mauser Military Rifle except: Actions were almost the same as Model 98 7.92 mm German Rifle except in caliber 7 mm.

Estimated Value: Very good: $70.00
                   Good: $60.00

Mexican Arisaka (Japanese Type 38 Rifle)
Between 1910 and 1920 Mexico procured arms from many countries. The Arisaka Rifle was purchased from Japan in caliber 7 mm and had the Mexican escutcheon stamped on the receiver. See Japanese Type 38 Arisaka Rifle for general description.

Estimated Value: Very good: $110.00
                   Good: $ 90.00

Mexican Model 1936
Caliber: 7mm
Action: Bolt action; curved bolt handle; Mauser short-type action
Magazine: 5-shot staggered row, non-detachable box
Barrel: 20"
Sights: Hooded barley corn front; tangent rear with "v" notch
Stock & Forearm: Plain semi-pistol grip stock with grip grooves in forearm; wood hand guard
Approximate wt.: 8 ½ lbs.
Comments: A very well made arm of Mexican manufacture; resembles the U.S. Springfield M 1903 - A-1 in appearance.

Estimated Value: Very Good: $145.00
                 Good: $120.00

Mexican Model 1954
Caliber: 30-06
Action: Bolt action; curved bolt handle
Magazine: 5-shot staggered row non-detachable box
Barrel: 24"
Sights: Barley corn hooded front, ramp type aperture rear
Stock & Forearm: Plain semi-pistol grip military stock and wood hand guard; stock is made of laminated plywood.
Approximate wt.: 9 lbs.
Comments: This rifle is patterned after the U.S. Springfield M 1903 - A3 Military Rifle.

Estimated Value: Very Good: $150.00
                 Good: $125.00

Russian Moisin-Nagant M 1891

Caliber: 7.62mm
Action: Bolt action; straight bolt; hexagonal receiver
Magazine: 5-shot box with hinged floor plate
Barrel: 31 ½"
Sights: Blade front, leaf rear
Stock & Forearm: Plain straight grip, military stock and gripped grooved forearm; early models had no hand guard and used swivels for attaching sling; later models used sling slots and had wood hand guard (beginning about 1908)
Approximate wt.: 9 ¾ lbs.
Comments: Adopted in 1891 by Imperial Russia.
Estimated Value: Very Good: $75.00
Good: $60.00

Russian M 1910 Carbine

Caliber: 7.62mm
Action: Bolt action; straight bolt handle; hexagonal receiver
Magazine: 5-shot box with floor plate
Barrel: 20"
Sights: Blade front, leaf type rear adjustable for elevation
Stock & Forearm: Plain straight grip military stock; sling slots in stock and forearm; wood hand guard and grip grooved forearm
Approximate wt.: 7 ½ lbs.
Comments: This carbine does not accept a bayonet.
Estimated Value: Very Good: $90.00
Good: $75.00

Russian Moisin-Nagant M 1891

Russian M-1910 Carbine

Russian M-1938 Carbine

Russian Tokarev M 1938

Russian M 1938 Carbine

This carbine replaced the M1910 and is very similar except: it has a round receiver; hooded front sight and tangent type rear graduated from 100 to 1000 meters; no bayonet attachment.
Estimated Value: Very Good: $80.00
Good: $65.00

Russian Tokarev M 1938

Caliber: 7.62mm
Action: Semi-automatic; gas operated
Magazine: 10-shot removable box
Barrel: 25"
Sights: Hooded post front, tangent rear
Stock & Forearm: Plain semi-pistol grip, two-piece stock and forearm; cleaning rod on right side of forearm; sling swivels
Approximate wt.: 8 ¾ lbs.
Comments: The first of the Tokarev series; wasn't very successful and was replaced by the Tokarev M 1940.
Estimated Value: Very Good: $120.00
Good: $ 95.00

Rifles

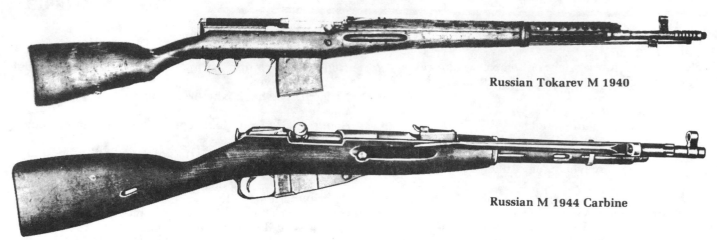

Russian Tokarev M 1940

Russian M 1944 Carbine

Russian Tokarev M 1940
Similar to Tokarev M 1938 except: improved version; cleaning rod in forearm under barrel; 24 ½ " barrel.
Estimated Value: Very Good: $175.00
Good: $150.00

Russian M 1944 Military Carbine
Similar to the M 1938 except: introduced during World War II; permanently fixed bayonet which folds along the right side of the stock; barrel length 20 ½ ".
Estimated Value: Very Good: $120.00
Good: $100.00

Military, Spanish

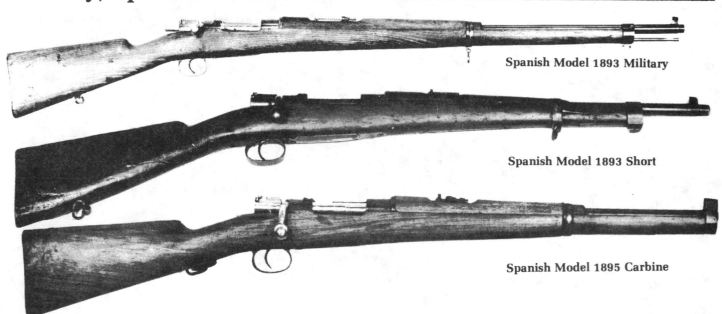

Spanish Model 1893 Military

Spanish Model 1893 Short

Spanish Model 1895 Carbine

Spanish Model 1893
Caliber: 7mm
Action: Bolt action; straight bolt handle
Magazine: 5-shot staggered row non-detachable
Barrel: 30"
Sights: Barley corn front, leaf rear
Stock & Forearm: Plain straight grip military stock with wood hand guard over barrel
Approximate wt.: 9 lbs.
Comments: A number of variations in the Model 1893 were made; it was the principle rifle used in the Spanish-American War.
Estimated Value: Very Good: $65.00
Good: $50.00

Spanish Model 1893 Short
Similar to the M 1893 Rifle except: 22" barrel; approximate wt. 8 ½ lbs.; curved bolt handle.
Estimated Value: Very Good: $60.00
Good: $50.00

Spanish Model 1895 Carbine
Similar to M 1893 Rifle except: 18" barrel; full stock to muzzle; barley corn front sight with protective ears; approximate wt. 7 ½ lbs.
Estimated Value: Very Good: $70.00
Good: $60.00

Spanish Model 1916 Short

Caliber: 7mm
Action: Bolt action; bolt handle curved down
Magazine: 5-shot staggered row non-detachable box
Barrel: 24''
Sights: Barley corn front with ears, tangent rear
Stock & Forearm: Plain military stock and wood hand guard
Approximate wt.: 8 ½ lbs.
Comments: This rifle was made in large quantities during Spanish Civil War; later many were converted to caliber 7.62mm NATO.
Estimated Value: Very Good: $80.00
                             Good: $70.00

Spanish Standard Model Mauser

Caliber: 7.92mm
Action: Bolt action; straight bolt handle
Magazine: 5-shot staggered row, non-detachable box
Barrel: 24''
Sights: Barley corn front, tangent rear
Stock & Forearm: Plain military, semi-pistol grip stock and forearm grooved for finger grip; wood hand guard
Approximate wt.: 9 lbs.
Comments: This rifle was procured in large quantities from other countries during the Spanish Civil War.
Estimated Value: Very Good: $75.00
                             Good: $65.00

Spanish Model 1943

Caliber: 7.92mm
Action: Bolt action; curved bolt handle
Magazine: 5-shot staggered row, non-detachable box
Barrel: 24''
Sights: Barley corn front, tangent rear
Stock & Forearm: Plain military, semi-pistol grip stock and forearm grooved for finger grip; wood hand guard
Approximate wt.: 9 lbs.
Comments: Adopted in 1943 and continued to mid 1950's; this is a modified copy of the German 7.92mm Kar 98K.
Estimated Value: Very Good:$120.00
                             Good: $100.00

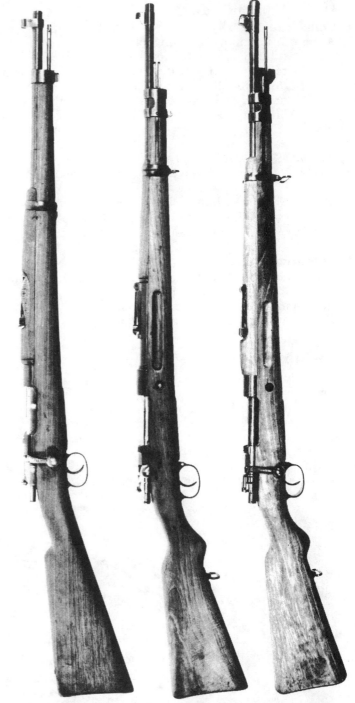

Spanish Model   Spanish Standard   Spanish Model
1916 Short   1943

Military, U.S.

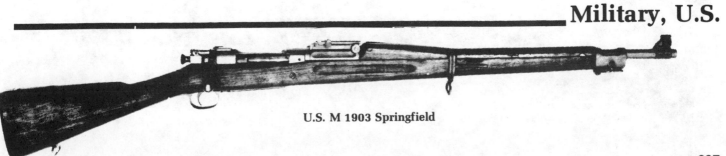

U.S. M 1903 Springfield

Rifles

U.S. M 1903 Springfield
Caliber: 30-06
Action: Bolt action; repeating; cocked as bolt handle is rotated clockwise to close and lock; knob at rear protrudes when piece is cocked; manual thumb safety at rear of bolt; turned down bolt handle; action is basically a modification of the Mauser Model 98
Magazine: 5-shot staggered row, non-removable box magazine
Barrel: 24"
Sights: Blade front, leaf with aperture and notched battle rear
Stock & Forearm: Plain straight, one-piece stock and forearm; wood hand guard over barrel; a cleaning rod type bayonet contained in the forearm under barrel
Approximate wt.: 8¾ lbs.
Comments: Adopted by U.S. 1903; made by Springfield and Rock Island.
Estimated Value: Very Good: $240.00
Good: $180.00

U.S. M 1903 - A1 Springfield
Basically the same as M 1903 Military rifle except: pistol grip stock with grasping grooves in forearm; checkered buttplate and serrated trigger; adopted in 1929, and made until 1939 by Springfield Armory - last serial number was about 1,532,878; in 1942 Remington Arms Co. made about 348,000 with a few minor modifications before the M 1903 A 3 was adopted; serial numbers from 3,000,001 to 3,348,085.
Estimated Value: Very Good: $210.00
Good: $160.00

U.S. M 1903 - A3 Springfield
Generally the same as the U.S. M 1903 - A1 except: many parts are stamped sheet metal and other modifications to lower cost and increase production; straight or pistol grip stocks; made during World War II under emergency conditions.
Estimated Value: Very Good: $180.00
Good: $150.00

U.S. M 1917 Enfield
Caliber: 30-06
Action: Bolt action; repeating; cocked as bolt is moved forward; bolt handle is crooked rear-ward; modified Mauser type action
Magazine: 5-shot staggered row, non-removable box type
Barrel: 26"
Sights: Blade front with protecting ears, leaf with aperture rear
Stock & Forearm: Plain one-piece, semi-pistol grip stock and forearm; wood hand guard over barrel
Approximate wt.: 8¼ lbs.
Comments: This gun was developed from the British P-13 and P-14 system as an emergency arm for U.S. in World War I. Made from about 1917 to 1918. Also manufactured in the U.S. for Great Britain in caliber 303 in 1917.
Estimated Value: Very Good: $150.00
Good: $120.00

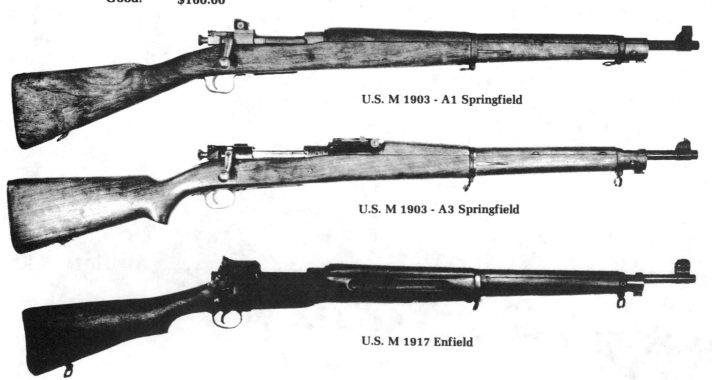

U.S. M 1903 - A1 Springfield

U.S. M 1903 - A3 Springfield

U.S. M 1917 Enfield

U.S. 30 caliber M1

U.S. Garand 30 caliber M1

Johnson M 1941

U.S. Garand

Caliber: 30-06
Action: Semi-automatic; gas operated
Magazine: 8-shot staggered row, non-detachable box
Barrel: 24"
Sights: Blade front with protective ears, aperture rear or flip over type rear.
Stock & Forearm: One-piece stock and forearm; wood hand guard over top of barrel
Approximate wt.: 9 ½ lbs.
Comments: Produced by Winchester and Springfield during World War II. Additional M1's produced after World War II by International Harvester and Harrington & Richardson. Add $150.00 for Winchester.
Estimated Value: Very Good: $550.00
                Good: **$425.00**

U.S. M1 Carbine

Caliber: 30 M1 Carbine
Action: Semi-automatic; gas operated
Magazine: 15 or 30-shot staggered row, detachable box
Barrel: 18"
Sights: Blade front with protective ears; aperture rear or flip down rear
Stock & Forearm: One-piece wood stock and forearm; wood hand guard on top of barrel
Approximate wt.: 5 ½ lbs.
Comments: Developed during World War II to replace the sidearms used by non-commissioned officers, special troops, and company grade officers.
Estimated Value: Very Good: $300.00
                Good: **$225.00**

U.S. M1 A1 30 Carbine

Same general specifications as U.S. M1 30 caliber Military Carbine except: folding metal stock; 25" overall length when folded; approximate wt. 6 ¼ lbs.
Estimated Value: Very Good: $450.00
                Good: **$375.00**

Johnson M 1941

Caliber: 30-06
Action: Semi-automatic; recoil action; hesitation-locked breech; barrel partially recoils to begin unlocking phase; manual safety in front of trigger guard
Magazine: 10-shot rotary type; a vertical feed magazine was also made
Barrel: 22"
Sights: Post front with protective ears, aperture rear
Stock & Forearm: Plain wood, semi-pistol grip stock and forearm; metal hand guard over barrel above forearm
Approximate wt.: 9 ½ lbs.
Comments: The Johnson was thought to be superior to the M1 but a series of tests and demonstrations in 1939 and 1940 indicated that it wasn't superior; used by U.S. Marines for a limited period in World War II; also used by the Dutch in the East Indies; many rebarreled in other calibers after World War II.
Estimated Value: Very Good: $775.00
                Good: **$650.00**

Mossberg

Mossberg Model B
Caliber: 22 short, long, long rifle
Action: Bolt action; single shot
Magazine: None
Barrel: 22" blued
Sights: Open rear, bead front
Stock & Forearm: Plain wood, semi-pistol grip stock & forearm
Approximate wt.: 5 lbs.
Comments: Manufactured in the early 1930's.
Estimated Value: Excellent: $50.00
      Very good: $40.00

Mossberg Model R
Caliber: 22 short, long, long rifle
Action: Bolt action; repeating
Magazine: Tubular, 14 long rifles, 16 longs, 20 shorts
Barrel: 24" blued
Sights: Open rear, bead front
Stock & Forearm: Walnut, semi-pistol grip stock & forearm
Approximate wt.: 5 lbs.
Comments: Made in the early 1930's.
Estimated Value: Excellent: $60.00
      Very good: $50.00

Mossberg Model 10
Caliber: 22 short, long, long rifle
Action: Bolt action; single shot
Magazine: None
Barrel: 22" blued
Sights: Open rear, bead front
Stock & Forearm: Walnut, semi-pistol grip stock & forearm; swivels
Approximate wt.: 4 lbs.
Comments: Manufactured from the early to mid 1930's. Takedown type.
Estimated Value: Excellent: $50.00
      Very good: $40.00

Mossberg Model 20
Similar to the Model 10 with a 24" barrel and grooved forearm.
Estimated Value: Excellent: $50.00
      Very good: $40.00

Mossberg Model 30
Similar to the Model 20 with peep rear sight and hooded ramp front sight.
Estimated Value: Excellent: $50.00
      Very good: $40.00

Mossberg Model 40
Similar to the Model 30 with: tubular magazine that holds 16 long rifle, 18 longs, 22 shorts; bolt action; repeating.
Estimated Value: Excellent: $65.00
      Very good: $55.00

Mossberg Model 35

Mossberg Model M
Caliber: 22
Action: Bolt action; single shot; cocking piece
Magazine: None; single shot
Barrel: 20" round
Sights: Open rear, blade front
Stock & Forearm: Plain one piece, semi-pistol grip stock and tapered forearm
Approximate wt.: 4½ lbs.
Comments: A smal boys rifle made in the early 1930's.
Estimated Value: Excellent: $65.00
      Very good: $55.00

Mossberg Model 14
Caliber: 22 short, long, long rifle
Action: Bolt action; single shot
Magazine: None
Barrel: 24" blued
Sights: Peep rear, hooded ramp front
Stock & Forearm: Plain, semi-pistol grip, one-piece stock & forearm; swivels
Approximate wt.: 5½ lbs.
Comments: Made in the mid 1930's.
Estimated Value: Excellent: $55.00
      Very good: $45.00

Mossberg Model 34
Similar to the Model 14. Made in the mid 1930's.
Estimated Value: Excellent: $50.00
      Very good: $40.00

Mossberg Model 35
Caliber: 22 long rifle
Action: Bolt action; single shot
Magazine: None
Barrel: 26" blued, heavy
Sights: Micrometer rear, hooded ramp front
Stock & Forearm: Plain walnut, semi-pistol grip, one-piece stock & forearm; cheekpiece; swivels
Approximate wt.: 8¼ lbs.
Comments: Made in the Mid 1930's.
Estimated Value: Excellent: $75.00
      Very good: $65.00

Mossberg Model 35A
Similar to the Model 35. Made in the late 1930's; target stock & sights.
Estimated Value: Excellent: $80.00
      Very good: $65.00

Mossberg Model 35A-LS
Similar to the 35A with special Lyman sights
Estimated Value: Excellent: $85.00
      Very good: $70.00

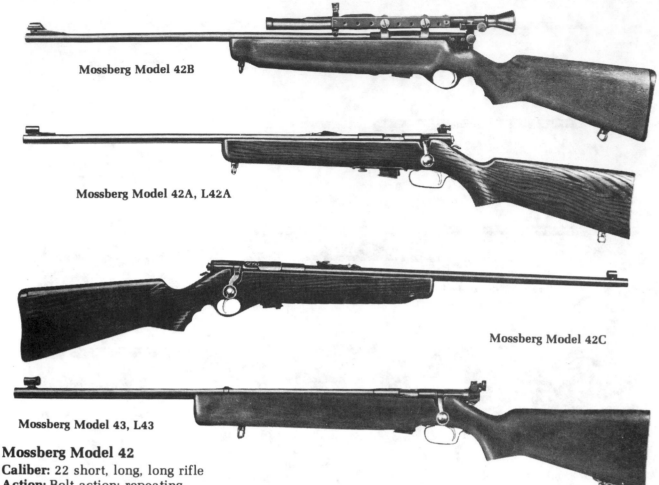

Mossberg Model 42B

Mossberg Model 42A, L42A

Mossberg Model 42C

Mossberg Model 43, L43

Mossberg Model 42

Caliber: 22 short, long, long rifle
Action: Bolt action; repeating
Magazine: 7-shot detachable box
Barrel: 24" blued
Sights: Open rear, receiver peep, hooded ramp front
Stock & Forearm: Plain walnut, semi-pistol grip, one-piece stock & forearm; swivels
Approximate wt.: 5 lbs.
Comments: Made in the mid 1930's; takedown type.
Estimated Value: Excellent: $60.00
Very good: $50.00

Mossberg Model 42A, L42A

Similar to the Model 42 but higher quality. L42A is left hand action. Made in the late 1930's.
Estimated Value: Excellent: $65.00
Very good: $55.00

Mossberg Model 42B

An improved version of the Model 42A with micrometer peep sight and 5-shot magazine. Manufactured from the late 1930's to early 1940's.
Estimated Value: Excellent: $70.00
Very good: $60.00

Mossberg Model 42C

Similar to the Model 42B without the peep sight.
Estimated Value: Excellent: $65.00
Very good: $55.00

Mossberg Model 42M

More modern version of the Model 42 with a 23" barrel; full length, 2 piece stock & forearm; cheekpiece; 7-shot magazine. Made from the early 1940's to early 1950's.
Estimated Value: Excellent: $65.00
Very good: $55.00

Mossberg Model 42MB

Similar to the Model 42. Used as military training rifle in Great Britain in World War II; full stock.
Estimated Value: Excellent: $100.00
Very good: $ 85.00

Mossberg Model 43, L43

Caliber: 22 long rifle
Action: Bolt action; repeating
Magazine: 7-shot detachable
Barrel: 26" blued
Sights: Special Lyman sights
Stock & Forearm: Walnut, semi-pistol grip, one piece stock & forearm; cheekpiece; swivels
Approximate wt.: 8¼ lbs.
Comments: Made in the late 1930's. L43 is left hand action.
Estimated Value: Excellent: $95.00
Very good: $75.00

Rifles

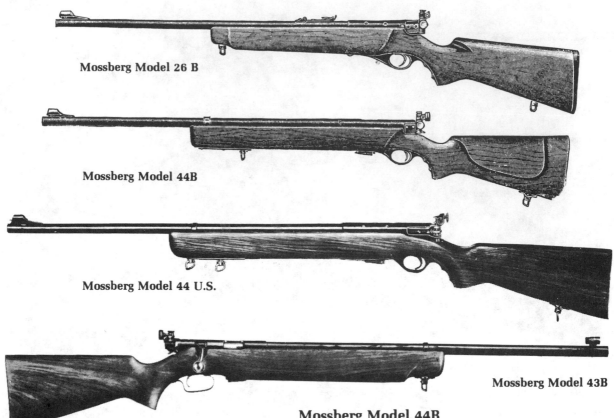

Mossberg Model 26 B

Mossberg Model 44B

Mossberg Model 44 U.S.

Mossberg Model 43B

Mossberg Model 26 B
Caliber: 22 short, long, long rifle
Action: Bolt action; single shot
Magazine: None
Barrel: 26" blued
Sights: Micrometer rear, hooded ramp front
Stock & Forearm: Plain, semi-pistol grip, one-piece stock & forearm; swivels
Approximate wt.: 5 ½ lbs.
Comments: Made in the late 1930's.
Estimated Value: Excellent: $55.00
Very good: $45.00

Mossberg Model 26C
Similar to the 26B without swivels or peep sight.
Estimated Value: Excellent: $50.00
Very good: $40.00

Mossberg Model 44
Caliber: 22 short, long, long rifle
Action: Bolt action; repeating
Magazine: Tubular, 16 long rifles, 18 longs, 22 shorts
Barrel: 24" blued
Sights: Peep rear, hooded ramp front
Stock & Forearm: Plain walnut, semi-pistol grip, one-piece stock & forearm; swivels
Approximate wt.: 6 lbs.
Comments: Made in the mid 1930's.
Estimated Value: Excellent: $60.00
Very good: $50.00

Mossberg Model 44B
Caliber: 22 long rifle
Action: Bolt action; repeating
Magazine: 7-shot detatchable box
Barrel: 26" heavy barrel
Sights: Micrometer receiver, hooded front
Stock & Forearm: Plain semi-pistol grip, one-piece stock & forearm; swivels; cheekpiece
Approximate wt.: 8 lbs.
Comments: Made in the late 1930's and early 1940's.
Estimated Value: Excellent: $65.00
Very good: $50.00

Mossberg Model 43B
Similar to the 44B with special Lyman sights.
Estimated Value: Excellent: $70.00
Very good: $55.00

Mossberg Model 44 U.S.
Improved version of the Model 44B. Made in the late 1930's.
Estimated Value: Excellent: $90.00
Very good: $75.00

Mossberg Model 35B
Single shot version of the Model 44B. Made in the late 1930's.
Estimated Value: Excellent: $50.00
Very good: $40.00

Mossberg Model 45

Mossberg Model 45A, L45A

Mossberg Model 45B

Mossberg Model 46

Mossberg Model 25

Caliber: 22 short, long, long rifle
Action: Bolt action; single shot
Magazine: None
Barrel: 24" blued
Sights: Peep rear, hooded ramp front
Stock & Forearm: Plain walnut, pistol grip, one-piece stock & forearm; swivels
Approximate wt.: 5 lbs.
Comments: Made in the mid 1930's.
Estimated Value: Excellent: $50.00
Very good: $40.00

Mossberg Model 25A

Similar to the Model 25 with higher quality finish and better wood. Made in the late 1930's.
Estimated Value: Excellent: $55.00
Very good: $45.00

Mossberg Model 45

Caliber: 22 short, long, long rifle
Action: Bolt action; repeating
Magazine: Tubular, 15 long rifles, 18 longs, 22 shorts
Barrel: 24" blued
Sights: Peep rear, hooded ramp front
Stock & Forearm: Plain, semi-pistol grip, one-piece stock & forearm; swivels
Approximate wt.: 6¾ lbs.
Comments: Made in the mid 1930's.
Estimated Value: Excellent: $60.00
Very good: $50.00

Mossberg Model 45C

Similar to the Model 45 without sights.
Estimated Value: Excellent: $50.00
Very good: $40.00

Mossberg Model 45A, L45A

Improved version of the Model 45, made in the late 1930's. L45A is left hand action.
Estimated Value: Excellent: $65.00
Very good: $55.00

Mossberg Model 45AC

Similar to the Model 45A without open sight.
Estimated Value: Excellent: $55.00
Very good: $45.00

Mossberg Model 45B

Similar to the Model 45A with open rear sight. Made in the late 1930's.
Estimated Value: Excellent: $50.00
Very good: $40.00

Mossberg Model 46

Caliber: 22 short, long, long rifle
Action: Bolt action; repeating
Magazine: Tubular, 15 long rifles, 18 longs, 22 shorts
Barrel: 26" blued
Sights: Micrometer rear, hooded ramp front
Stock & Forearm: Plain, semi-pistol grip, one piece stock & forearm; cheekpiece; swivels
Approximate wt.: 7½ lbs.
Comments: Made in the mid 1930's.
Estimated Value: Excellent: $60.00
Very good: $50.00

Rifles

Mossberg Model 46C

A heavy barrel version of the Model 46.
Estimated Value: Excellent: $65.00
Very good: $55.00

Mossberg Model 46A

An improved version of the Model 46 made in the late 1930's.
Estimated Value: Excellent: $70.00
Very good: $60.00

Mossberg Model 46 AC

Similar to the 46A with open rear sight.
Estimated Value: Excellent: $60.00
Very good: $50.00

Mossberg Model 46A-LS, L46A-LS

Similar to the Model 46A with special Lyman sights. L46A-LS is left hand action.
Estimated Value: Excellent: $75.00
Very good: $65.00

Mossberg Model 46B

Similar to the Model 46A with open rear sight and receiver peep sight. Made in the late 1930's.
Estimated Value: Excellent: $65.00
Very good: $50.00

Mossberg Model 46BT

A heavy barrel version of the Model 46B
Estimated Value: Excellent: $70.00
Very good: $60.00

Mossberg Model 46M

Similar to the Model 46 with full length, 2 piece forearm. Made about 1940 to the early 1950s.
Estimated Value: Excellent: $75.00
Very good: $60.00

Mossberg Model 346K

Caliber: 22 short, long, long rifle
Action: Bolt action; repeating
Magazine: Tubular, 20 long rifles, 23 longs, 30 shorts
Barrel: 26'' blued
Sights: Micrometer rear, hooded front
Stock & Forearm: Plain, Monte Carlo pistol grip, one-piece stock & lipped forearm; cheekpiece; swivels
Approximate wt.: 7 lbs.
Comments: Made from the late 1940's to mid 1950's.
Estimated Value: Excellent: $60.00
Very good: $50.00

Mossberg Model L46A-LS

Mossberg Model 46B

Mossberg Model 46 BT

Mossberg Model 46M

Mossberg Model 346K

Mossberg Model 346 B

Mossberg Model 320K

Mossberg Model 340K

Mossberg Model 340B

Mossberg Model 320 B

Mossberg Model 340M Carbine

Mossberg Model 346 B
Similar to the Model 346K with peep rear sight and hooded ramp front sight.
Estimated Value: Excellent: $65.00
Very good: $55.00

Mossberg Model 320K
Single shot version of the Model 36K. Weighs about 5¾ lbs. Discontinued about 1960.
Estimated Value: Excellent: $50.00
Very good: $40.00

Mossberg Model 340K
Similar to the Model 346K with 7-shot clip magazine.
Estimated Value: Excellent: $55.00
Very good: $45.00

Mossberg Model 340B
Similar to the 346B with 7-shot clip magazine. Currently manufactured.
Estimated Value: New (retail): $96.50
Excellent: $70.00
Very good: $60.00

Mossberg Model 320 B
Similar to the 340K in single shot. Made from about 1960 for 11 years.
Estimated Value: Excellent: $45.00
Very good: $35.00

Mossberg Model 340M Carbine
Similar to the Model 340K with full length forearm & 18'' barrel. Made in the early 1970's.
Estimated Value: Excellent: $70.00
Very good: $55.00

Rifles

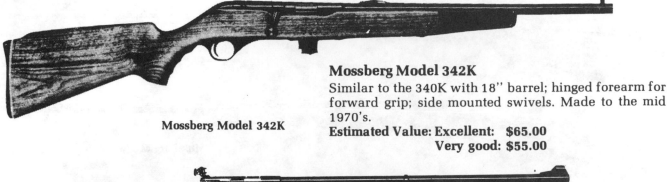

Mossberg Model 342K

Mossberg Model 342K

Similar to the 340K with 18" barrel; hinged forearm for forward grip; side mounted swivels. Made to the mid 1970's.

Estimated Value: Excellent: $65.00
Very good: $55.00

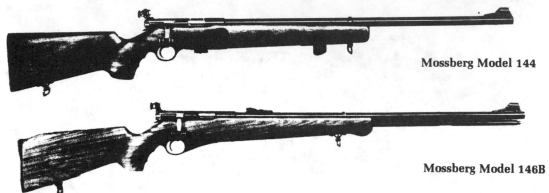

Mossberg Model 144

Mossberg Model 146B

Mossberg Model 144

Caliber: 22 long rifle
Action: Bolt action; repeating
Magazine: 7-shot detatchable box
Barrel: 26" blued, heavy
Sights: Micrometer receiver, hooded front
Stock & Forearm: Walnut, semi-pistol grip, one-piece stock & forearm; hand rest; swivels
Approximate wt.: 8 lbs.
Comments: Made from the late 1940's to present.
Estimated Value: New (retail): $138.95
Excellent: $100.00
Very good: $ 80.00

Mossberg Model 146B

Caliber: 22 short, long, long rifle
Action: Bolt action; repeating
Magazine: Tubular, 20 long rifles, 23 long, 30 shorts
Barrel: 26" blued
Sights: Micrometer rear, hooded front
Stock & Forearm: Plain, Monte Carlo pistol grip, one piece stock and lipped forearm; cheekpiece; swivels
Approximate wt.: 7 lbs.
Comments: Made from the late 1940's to mid 1950's.
Estimated Value: Excellent: $75.00
Very good: $65.00

Mossberg Model 140K

Mossberg Model 140B

Mossberg Model 140K

Caliber: 22 short, long, long rifle
Action: Bolt action; repeating
Magazine: 7-shot clip
Barrel: 24½" blued
Sights: Open rear, bead front
Stock & Forearm: Walnut, Monte Carlo pistol grip, one-piece stock & forearm; cheekpiece; swivels
Approximate wt.: 5¾ lbs.
Comments: Made in the mid 1950's.
Estimated Value: Excellent: $60.00
Very good: $50.00

Mossberg Model 140B

Similar to the 140K with hooded ramp front sight, peep rear sight.
Estimated Value: Excellent: $65.00
Very good: $55.00

Mossberg Model 640k Chuckster

Mossberg Model 620K

Mossberg Model 321K

Mossberg Model 341

Mossberg Model 353

Mossberg Model 640K Chuckster

Caliber: 22 magnum
Action: Bolt action; repeating
Magazine: 5-shot clip
Barrel: 24" blued
Sights: Open rear, bead front
Stock & Forearm: Checkered walnut, Monte Carlo pistol grip, one-piece stock & forearm; swivels
Approximate wt.: 6 lbs.
Comments: Made from about 1960 to present.
Estimated Value: New (retail): $101.50
              Excellent: $ 75.00
              Very good: $ 65.00

Mossberg Model 620K

Similar to the 640K in single shot. Discontinued in mid 1970's.
Estimated Value: Excellent: $50.00
                Very good: $40.00

Mossberg Model 321K

Caliber: 22 short, long, long rifle
Action: Bolt action; single shot
Magazine: None
Barrel: 24" blued
Sights: Open rear, ramp front
Stock & Forearm: Checkered, Monte Carlo pistol grip, one-piece stock & forearm
Approximate wt.: 6 ½ lbs.
Comments: Made from the early 1970's to present.
Estimated Value: New (retail): $78.95
              Excellent: $60.00
              Very good: $50.00

Mossberg Model 341

Similar to the 321K with: 7-shot clip magazine; swivels; bolt action; repeating.
Estimated Value: New (retail): $89.95
              Excellent: $65.00
              Very good: $55.00

Mossberg Model 353K

Similar to the 321K except: semi-automatic; hinged grip forearm (tenite); 18" barrel; 7-shot clip magazine; 22 long rifle only.
Estimated Value: New (retail): $99.95
              Excellent: $75.00
              Very good: $60.00

Mossberg Model 800 A

Mossberg Model 800 Varmint

Mossberg Model 810

Mossberg Model 810

Caliber: 30-06, 7mm Remington magnum, 270
Action: Bolt action; repeating
Magazine: Detatchable 4-shot box
Barrel: 22" blued
Sights: Leaf rear, ramp front
Stock & Forearm: Checkered, Monte Carlo pistol grip, one-piece stock & forearm; swivels; recoil pad.
Approximate wt.: 7½-8 lbs.
Comments: Add $15.00 for 7 mm Rem. magnum caliber. Discontinued in the late 1970's.
Estimated Value: Excellent: $200.00
Very good: $165.00

Mossberg Model RM-7A

Caliber: 30-06
Action: Bolt action; hammerless; repeating
Magazine: 4 shot rotary
Barrel: 22" round
Sights: Adjustable folding leaf rear, ramp front
Stock & Forearm: Checkered walnut, one piece pistol grip stock and forearm; fluted comb; recoil pad
Approximate wt: 7½ lbs.
Comments: Introduced in the late 1970's.
Estimated Value: New (retail): $286.95
Excellent: $215.00
Very good: $175.00

Mossberg Model 800 A

Caliber: 308, 243, 22-250
Action: Bolt action; repeating
Magazine: 4-shot box
Barrel: 22" blued
Sights: Leaf rear, ramp front
Stock & Forearm: Checkered wood, Monte Carlo pistol grip, one-piece stock & forearm; swivels
Approximate wt.: 6½ lbs.
Comments: Discontinued in the late 1970's.
Estimated Value: Excellent: $175.00
Very good: $145.00

Mossberg Model 800 Varmint

Similar to the 800A with a 24" barrel and scope mounts. In 243, 22-250 calibers.
Estimated Value: Excellent: $180.00
Very good: $150.00

Mossberg Model 800 Target

Similar to the 800A with scope mounts & scope in 308, 243, 22-250 calibers.
Estimated Value: Excellent: $225.00
Very good: $180.00

Mossberg Model RM-7B

Similar to the Model RM-7A; 7mm Rem. magnum caliber; 3 shot magazine; 24" barrel.
Estimated Value: New (retail): $285.95
Excellent: $215.00
Very good: $175.00

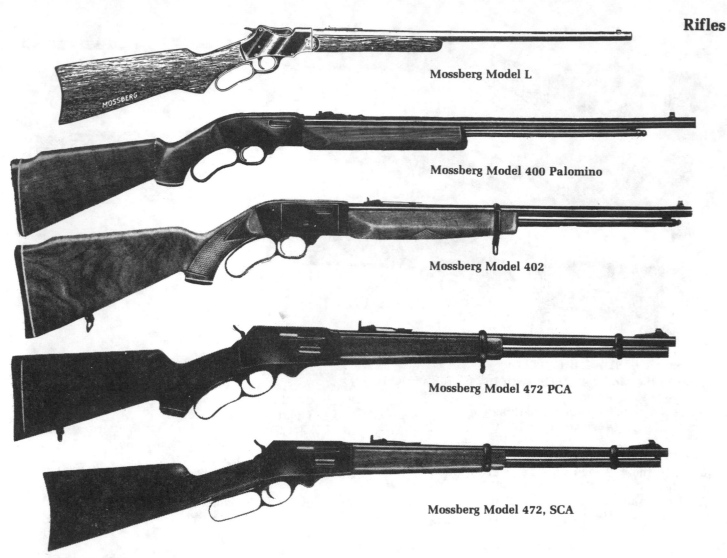

Mossberg Model L

Mossberg Model 400 Palomino

Mossberg Model 402

Mossberg Model 472 PCA

Mossberg Model 472, SCA

Mossberg Model L
Caliber: 22
Action: Falling block; lever action; single shot
Magazine: None
Barrel: 24" blued
Sights: Open rear, bead front
Stock & Forearm: Plain walnut, semi-pistol grip & small forearm
Approximate wt.: 5 lbs.
Comments: Made from the late 1920's to early 1930's.
Estimated Value: Excellent: $190.00
Very good: $160.00

Mossberg Model 400 Palomino
Caliber: 22 short, long, long rifle
Action: Lever action; hammerless; repeating
Magazine: Tubular, 15 long rifles, 17 longs, 20 shorts
Barrel: 24" blued
Sights: Adjustable open rear, bead front
Stock & Forearm: Checkered walnut, Monte Carlo pistol grip, stock & forearm; barrel band; swivels
Approximate wt.: 4¾ lbs.
Comments: Made in the early 1960's.
Estimated Value: Excellent: $80.00
Very good: $65.00

Mossberg Model 402
Similar to the Model 400 with smaller capacity magazine. Discontinued in the early 1970's.
Estimated Value: Excellent: $75.00
Very good: $60.00

Mossberg Model 472 PCA, SCA, 479 PCA, SCA
Caliber: 30-30 35 Remington
Action: Lever action; exposed hammer; repeating
Magazine: 6-shot tubular
Barrel: 20" blued
Sights: Adjustable rear, ramp front
Stock & Forearm: Plain pistol grip stock & forearm; barrel band; swivels; or straight grip stock (SCA).
Approximate wt.: 7½ lbs.
Comments: Currently sold as 479 series.
Estimated Value: New (retail): $186.95
Excellent: $140.00
Very good: $110.00

Rifles

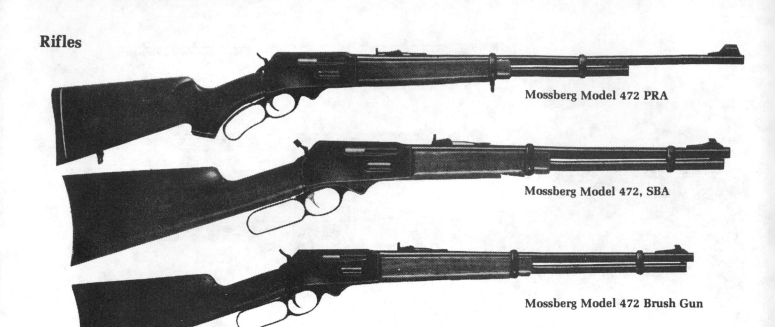

Mossberg Model 472 PRA

Mossberg Model 472, SBA

Mossberg Model 472 Brush Gun

Mossberg Model 472 Brush Gun

Similar to the Model 472 PCA with 18" barrel; straight stock; 5-shot magazine.
Estimated Value: Excellent: **$125.00**
                        Very good: **$100.00**

Mossberg Model 472 PRA, SBA

Similar to the 472 PCA with 24" barrel, hooded front sight. Discontinued in the late 1970's.
Estimated Value: Excellent: **$130.00**
                        Very good: **$100.00**

Mossberg Model K

Caliber: 22 short, long, long rifle
Action: Slide action; hammerless; repeating
Magazine: Tubular, 14 long rifles, 16 longs, 20 shorts
Barrel: 22" blued
Sights: Open rear, bead front
Stock & Forearm: Plain walnut, straight grip stock and
                        grooved slide handle
Approximate wt.: 5 lbs.
Comments: Made from the early 1920's to early 1930's.
                        Takedown type.
Estimated Value: Excellent: **$90.00**
                        Very good: $75.00

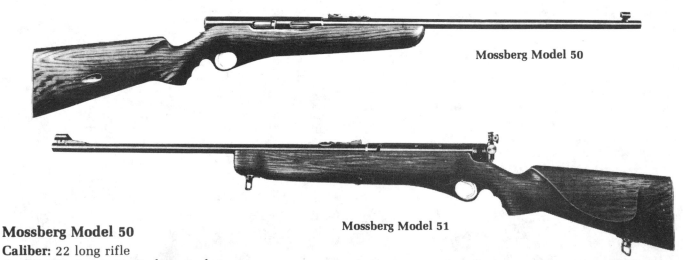

Mossberg Model 50

Mossberg Model 51

Mossberg Model 50

Caliber: 22 long rifle
Action: Semi-automatic; hammerless
Magazine: 15-shot tubular in stock
Barrel: 24" blued
Sights: Open rear, hooded ramp front
Stock & Forearm: Walnut, semi-pistol grip, one piece
                        stock & forearm
Approximate wt.: 7 lbs.
Comments: Made from the late 1930's to early 1940's.
Estimated Value: Excellent: **$65.00**
                        Very good: **$55.00**

Mossberg Model 51

Similar to the Model 50 with: receiver peep sight; swivels; cheekpiece. Made in the late 1930's.
Estimated Value: Excellent: **$75.00**
                        Very good: **$65.00**

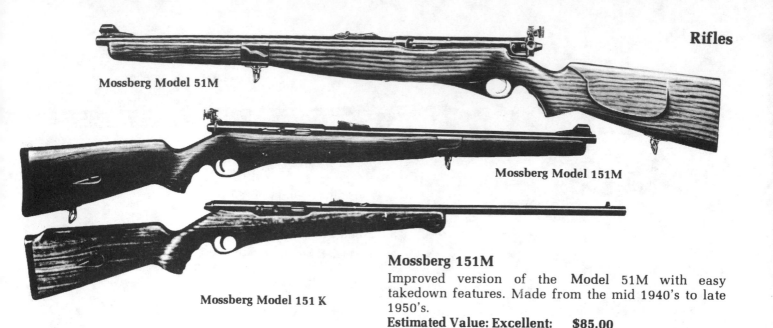

Mossberg Model 51M

Mossberg Model 151M

Mossberg Model 151 K

Mossberg 151M

Improved version of the Model 51M with easy takedown features. Made from the mid 1940's to late 1950's.

Estimated Value: Excellent: $85.00
Very good: $75.00

Mossberg Model 51M

Similar to the Model 51 with full length, 2 piece forearm, and a 20'' barrel. Made from the late 1930's to mid 1940's.

Estimated Value: Excellent: $80.00
Very good: $70.00

Mossberg Model 151K

Similar to the 151M with: Monte Carlo stock; standard length, lipped forearm; 24'' barrel; no peep sight or swivels.

Estimated Value: Excellent: $75.00
Very good: $60.00

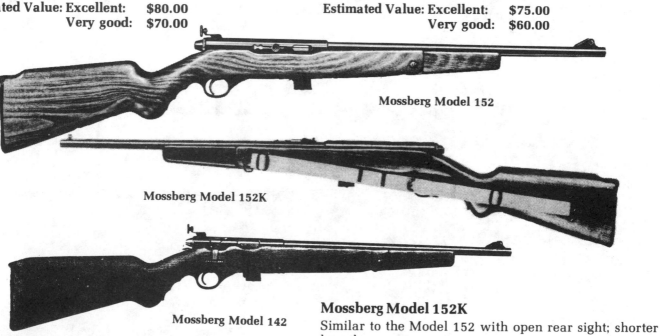

Mossberg Model 152

Mossberg Model 152K

Mossberg Model 142

Mossberg Model 152K

Similar to the Model 152 with open rear sight; shorter barrel.

Estimated Value: Excellent: $65.00
Very good: $55.00

Mossberg Model 142

Similar to the Model 152 in bolt action; available in long, short or long rifle.

Estimated Value: Excellent: $60.00
Very good: $50.00

Mossberg Model 152

Caliber: 22 long rifle
Action: Semi-automatic
Magazine: 7-shot detatchable box
Barrel: 18'' blued
Sights: Peep rear, military front
Stock & Forearm: Plain, semi-pistol grip, one piece stock and hinged forearm for forward grip; side mounted swivels
Approximate wt.: 5 lbs.
Comments: Made from the alte 1940's to late 1950's.
Estimated Value: Excellent: $70.00
Very good: $60.00

Mossberg Model 142K

Similar to the Model 142 with open rear sight.
Estimated Value: Excellent: $50.00
Very good: $40.00

Rifles

Mossberg Model 430

Mossberg Model 432

Mossberg Model 430

Caliber: 22 long rifle
Action: Semi-automatic
Magazine: 18-shot tubular
Barrel: 24" blued
Sights: Open rear, bead front
Stock & Forearm: Checkered walnut, Monte Carlo pistol grip stock & forearm
Approximate wt.: 6 ¼ lbs.
Comments: Made in the early 1970's.
Estimated Value: Excellent: $75.00
Very good: $60.00

Mossberg Model 432

Similar to the 430 with straight grip stock; barrel band; smaller capacity magazine:
Estimated Value: Excellent: $65.00
Very good: $55.00

Mossberg Model 351 C (Carbine)

Mossberg Model 351K

Mossberg Model 350K

Mossberg Model 351 C (Carbine)

Similar to the 351K with 18½" barrel; barrel bands; swivels.
Estimated Value: Excellent: $65.00
Very good: $55.00

Mossberg Model 351K

Caliber: 22 long rifle
Action: Semi-automatic
Magazine: 15-shot tubular, in stock
Barrel: 24" blued
Sights: Open rear, bead front
Stock & Forearm: Walnut, Monte Carlo semi-pistol grip, one-piece stock & forearm
Approximate wt.: 6 lbs.
Comments: Made from about 1960 to 1970.
Estimated Value: Excellent: $70.00
Very good: $60.00

Mossberg Model 350K

Caliber: 22 long rifle
Action: Semi-automatic
Magazine: 7-shot clip
Barrel: 23½" blued
Sights: Open rear, bead front
Stock & Forearm: Walnut, Monte Carlo semi-pistol grip, one-piece stock & forearm
Approximate wt.: 6 lbs.
Comments: Made from the late 1950's to early 1970's.
Estimated Value: Excellent: $65.00
Very good: $55.00

Mossberg Model 352K Carbine

Mossberg Model 352K Carbine
Caliber: 22 long rifle
Action: Semi-automatic
Magazine: 7-shot clip
Barrel: 18½" blued
Sights: Open rear, bead front
Stock & Forearm: Walnut, Monte Carlo semi-pistol grip, one piece stock & forearm; swivels; hinged forearm for forward grip
Approximate wt.: 5 lbs.
Comments: Made from the late 1950's to early 1970's.
Estimated Value: Excellent: $60.00
              Very good: $50.00

Mossberg Model 377 Plinkster
Caliber: 22 long rifle
Action: Semi-automatic; hammerless
Magazine: 15 shot tubular; stock load
Barrel: 20" round
Sights: None; 4X scope standard
Stock & Forearm: Molded structural foam, one piece Monte Carlo pistol grip stock and forearm; thumb hole; cheekpiece
Approximate wt: 6¼ lbs.
Comments: Introduced in the late 1970's.
Estimated Value: New (retail): $90.95
                 Excellent: $70.00
                 Very good: $55.00

Musketeer

Musketeer Mauser

Musketeer Carbine
Same as Musketeer Mauser except shorter barrel.
Estimated Value: Excellent: $245.00
              Very good: $200.00

Musketeer Mauser
Caliber: 243, 25-06, 270, 264 magnum, 308, 30-06, 7mm magnum, 300 magnum
Action: FN Mauser bolt action
Magazine: 5-shot (3-shot magnum)
Barrel: 24" blued
Sights: Hooded ramp front, leaf rear
Stock & Forearm: Checkered walnut, Monte Carlo pistol grip, one-piece stock & forearm
Approximate wt.: 7¼ lbs.
Comments: Made from the early 1960's to the early 1970's.
Estimated Value: Excellent: $270.00
              Very good: $220.00

New Haven

New Haven Model 453 T

New Haven Model 453 TS
Similar to the Model 453 T with a 4X scope.
Estimated Value: New (retail): $96.13
                 Excellent: $70.00
                 Very good: $55.00

New Haven Model 453 T
Caliber: 22 short, long or long rifle
Action: Semi-automatic hammerless
Magazine: 7 shot clip
Barrel: 18" blued
Sights: Open rear, blade front
Stock & Forearm: Plain one piece Monte Carlo, pistol grip stock and forearm
Approximate wt: 5½ lbs.
Comments: Introduced in the late 1970's.
Estimated Value: New (retail): $79.13
                 Excellent: $60.00
                 Very good: $45.00

Rifles

New Haven Model 740 T

Caliber: 22 Win. magnum
Action: Bolt action; hammerless; repeating
Magazine: 5 shot clip
Barrel: 26" blued
Sights: Open rear, blade front
Stock & Forearm: Plain birch, one piece Monte Carlo pistol grip stock and forearm
Approximate wt: 6½ lbs.
Comments: Introduced in the late 1970's.
Estimated Value: New (retail): $84.49
Excellent: $65.00
Very good: $50.00

New Haven Model 679

Caliber: 30-30 Win.
Action: Lever action; exposed hammer; repeating
Magazine: 6 shot tubular
Barrel: 20" blued
Sights: Open rear, ramp front
Stock & Forearm: Plain birch, semi-pistol grip stock and forearm; barrel band
Approximate wt: 6¾ lbs.
Comments: Introduced in the late 1970's.
Estimated Value: New (retail): $165.00
Excellent: $120.00
Very good: $ 95.00

New Haven Model 740TS

Similar to the Model 740T with 4X scope.
Estimated Value: New (retail): $101.48
Excellent: $ 75.00
Very good: $ 60.00

Newton

Newton Standard, 1st Model

Newton Standard, 2nd Model

Newton, Buffalo Newton

Newton Mauser

Newton Standard, 1st Model

Caliber: 22, 256, 280, 30-06, 30, 35
Action: Bolt action; double set trigger
Magazine: 5-shot box
Barrel: 24" blued
Sights: Open rear, ramp front
Stock & Forearm: Checkered wood, pistol grip stock and forearm
Approximate wt.: 7½ lbs.
Comments: Made before World War I.
Estimated Value: Excellent: $500.00
Very good: $400.00

Newton Standard, 2nd Model

Very similar to 1st Model with improved action. Made to the early 1920's.
Estimated Value: Excellent: $550.00
Very good: $450.00

Newton, Buffalo

Similar to the 2nd Model, made from the early 1920's to the early 1930's.
Estimated Value: Excellent: $525.00
Very good: $430.00

Newton Mauser

Caliber: 256
Action: Mauser type bolt action; set trigger
Magazine: 5-shot box
Barrel: 24" blued
Sights: Open rear, ramp front
Stock & Forearm: Checkered wood, pistol grip stock and forearm
Approximate wt.: 7 lbs.
Comments: Made before World War I.
Estimated Value: Excellent: $420.00
Very good: $340.00

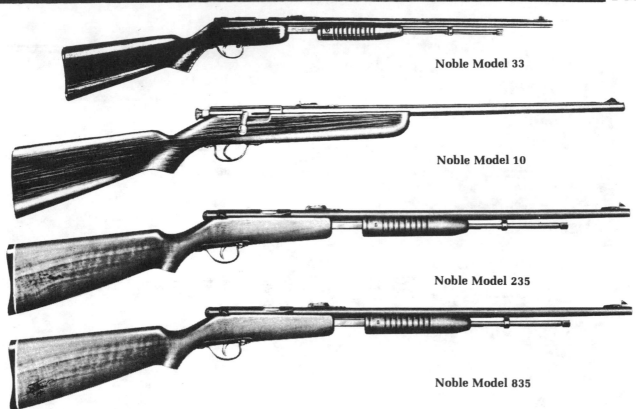

Noble Model 33

Noble Model 10

Noble Model 235

Noble Model 835

Noble Model 33

Caliber: 22 short, long, long rifle
Action: Slide action; hammerless; repeating
Magazine: Tubular, 15 long rifles, 17 longs, 21 shorts
Barrel: 24" blued
Sights: Open rear, blade front
Stock & Forearm: Semi-pistol grip, tenite stock and slide handle
Approximate wt.: 6 lbs.
Comments: Made from the late 1940's to the early 1950's
Estimated Value: Excellent: $75.00
Very good: $60.00

Noble Model 33A

Similar to the Model 33 with a wood stock and grooved slide handle. Made until the mid 1950's.
Estimated Value: Excellent: $80.00
Very good: $65.00

Noble Model 10

Caliber: 22 short, long, long rifle
Action: Bolt action; single shot
Magazine: None
Barrel: 24" blued
Sights: Open rear, bead front
Stock & Forearm: Walnut, semi-pistol grip, one-piece stock and forearm
Approximate wt.: 4 lbs.
Comments: Made from the middle 1950's to the late 1950's.
Estimated Value: Excellent: $40.00
Very good: $30.00

Noble Model 20

Similar to the Model 10 with: 22" barrel; slightly curved buttplate; manual cocking device. Made from the late 1950's to the early 1960's.
Estimated Value: Excellent: $45.00
Very good: $35.00

Noble Model 235

Caliber: 22 short, long, long rifle
Action: Slide action, hammerless repeater
Magazine: Tubular, 15 long rifles, 17 longs, 21 shorts
Barrel: 24" blued
Sights: Open rear, ramp front
Stock & Forearm: Wood, semi-pistol grip stock and grooved slide handle
Approximate wt.: 5½ lbs.
Comments: Manufactured from the early 1950's to the early 1970's.
Estimated Value: Excellent: $75.00
Very good: $60.00

Noble Model 835

Very similar to the Model 235. Made in the early 1970's.
Estimated Value: Excellent: $70.00
Very good: $60.00

Noble Model 222

Noble Model 275

Noble Model 875

Noble Model 285

Noble Model 222

Caliber: 22 short, long, long rifle
Action: Bolt action; single shot; manual cock
Magazine: None
Barrel: 22" blued
Sights: Peep or V notch rear, ramp front
Stock & Forearm: Wood, semi-pistol grip, one piece
  stock & forearm
Approximate wt.: 5 lbs.
Comments: Manufactured from the late 1950's to the
  early 1970's.
Estimated Value: Excellent: $50.00
            Very good: $40.00

Noble Model 275

Caliber: 22 short, long, long rifle
Action: Lever action; hammerless; repeating
Magazine: Tubular, 15 long rifles, 17 longs, 21 shorts
Barrel: 24" blued
Sights: Open rear, ramp front
Stock & Forearm: Wood, semi-pistol grip, one-piece
  stock & forearm
Approximate wt.: 5 ½ lbs.
Comments: Manufactured from the late 1950's to the
  early 1970's.
Estimated Value: Excellent: $75.00
            Very good: $65.00

Noble Model 285 or 885

Caliber: 22 long rifle
Action: Semi-automatic
Magazine: 15-shot tubular
Barrel: 22" blued
Sights: Open adjustable rear, blade front
Stock & Forearm: Wood, semi-pistol grip, one-piece
  stock and forearm
Approximate wt.: 5 ½ lbs.
Comments: Made from the early to mid 1970's.
Estimated Value: Excellent: $80.00
            Very good: $70.00

Noble Model 875

Similar to the Model 275. Made from the early to mid
1970's.
Estimated Value: Excellent: $80.00
            Very good: $70.00

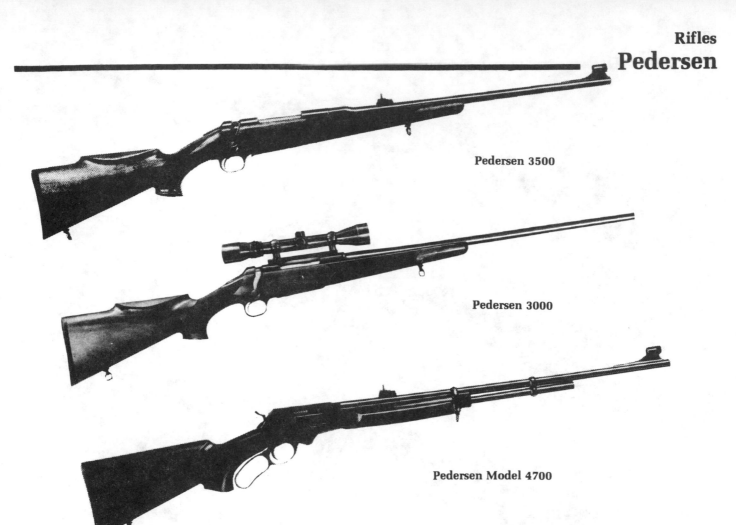

Pedersen 3500

Pedersen 3000

Pedersen Model 4700

Pedersen Model 3000

Caliber: 270, 30-06, 7 mm magnum
Action: Mossberg type, bolt action; adjustable trigger
Magazine: 3-shot box
Barrel: 22", 24" blued
Sights: None
Stock & Forearm: Checkered walnut, pistol grip, one piece stock & forearm; cheekpiece; swivels
Approximate wt.: 6¾ lbs.
Comments: Made in 3 grades during the 1970's.

Estimated Value:	Grade I	Grade II
Excellent:	$800.00	$650.00
Very good:	$675.00	$530.00

Pedersen Model 3500

Caliber: 7 mm magnum, 270, 30-06
Action: Bolt action; adjustable trigger
Magazine: 3-shot box
Barrel: 22", 24" blued
Sights: None
Stock & Forearm: Checkered walnut, pistol grip stock & forearm
Approximate wt.: 6¾ lbs.
Comments: Made during the 1970's.
Estimated Value: Excellent: $225.00
Very good: $175.00

Pedersen Model 3500 A

Same as the 3500 with a better finish and select walnut.
Estimated Value: Excellent: $300.00
Very good: $240.00

Pedersen Model 4700

Caliber: 30-30, 35 Rem.
Action: Lever action; exposed hammer; repeating
Magazine: 5-shot tubular
Barrel: 24" blued
Sights: Open rear, hooded ramp front
Stock & Forearm: Walnut pistol grip, stock & short tapered forearm; cheekpiece; swivels
Approximate wt.: 7½ lbs.
Comments: Manufactured during the 1970's.
Estimated Value: Excellent: $220.00
Very good: $175.00

Plainfield Model M1 Carbine

Plainfield Model M1 Sporter

Plainfield Deluxe Sporter or Plainfielder

Plainfield Commando or Paratrooper

Plainfield Model M1 Carbine

Caliber: 30 M1 or 5.7 mm (.223)
Action: Gas operated, semi-automatic
Magazine: 15-shot detachable clip
Barrel: 18'' blued
Sights: Open adjustable rear, gold beaded ramp front
Stock & Forearm: Wood, semi-pistol grip one-piece stock & forearm; slot in stock; metal ventilated hand guard
Approximate wt.: 6 lbs.
Comments: Made from about 1960 to present.
Estimated Value: New (retail): $160.00
Excellent: $120.00
Very good: $100.00

Plainfield Model M1 Sporter

Similar to the M1 Carbine with a wood hand guard and no slot in the stock.
Estimated Value: Excellent: $125.00
Very good: $105.00

Plainfield Deluxe Sporter or Plainfielder

Similar to the Sporter with a checkered walnut, Monte Carlo pistol grip stock & forearm.
Estimated Value: Excellent: $150.00
Very good: $120.00

Plainfield Commando or Paratrooper

Similar to the M1 Carbine with pistol grip at rear and at forearm; telescoping wire shoulder stock.
Estimated Value: New (retail): $193.00
Excellent: $145.00
Very good: $120.00

Remington No. 5 1897 Model Military

Remington Military Breech-Loading

Remington No. 1 Light Baby

Remington No. 1 Sporting

Remington No. 5 1897 Model Military

Caliber: 7 mm or 30 Government
Action: Single-shot; rolling block; smokeless powder action with case hardened frame; visible hammer
Magazine: None
Barrel: 30" light round tapered barrel
Sights: Post front, folding leaf rear
Stock & Forearm: Plain straight grip, oiled walnut, two-piece, full stock with steel buttplate and capped forearm; ram-rod under forearm; two barrel bands and hand guard on top of barrel
Approximate wt.: 8½ lbs.
Comments: Produced from about 1897 to 1906.
Estimated Value: Excellent: $225.00
**   Very good: $200.00**

Remington Military Breech-Loading

Caliber: C.F. 43 Spanish, 43 Egyptian, 50-70 Government, 58 Berdan. Early models used rim fire cartridges. Models for Center fire cartridges produced after 1872.
Action: Single-shot; rolling block with single trigger; visible hammer
Magazine: None
Barrel: 30" to 36" round barrel
Sights: Military (post front and folding leaf rear)
Stock & Forearm: Plain walnut, straight stock and forearm; long forearm with ram rod; steel buttplate on stock
Approximate wt.: 8 to 11 lbs.
Comments: Made from about 1867 to 1902 (large number sold to Egypt, France and Spain) and sold commercially in U.S.A. Some are unmarked; some have Arabic marked barrels, and some marked Remington's, caliber not marked.
Estimated Value: Excellent: $120.00
**   Very good: $100.00**

Remington No. 1 Light Baby Carbine

Caliber: 44-40
Action: Single-shot; rolling block with single trigger; visible hammer
Magazine: None
Barrel: 20", light round
Sights: Pointed post front, military folding leaf rear
Stock & Forearm: Plain oiled walnut, straight stock with metal buttplate and short forearm; barrel band
Approximate wt.: 5¾ lbs.
Comments: Made from about 1892 to 1902.
Estimated Value: Excellent: $300.00
**   Very good: $275.00**

Remington No. 1 Sporting

Caliber: Early guns for rim fire 50-70, 44 long & extra long, or 46 long & extra long. After 1872 made for Centerfire 40-50, 40-70, 44-77, 45-70, or 45 sporting cartridge
Action: Single shot; rolling block, with single trigger; visible hammer
Magazine: None
Barrel: 28" or 30" tapered octagon
Sights: Sporting front, folding leaf rear
Stock & Forearm: Plain walnut, straight grip stock with flanged-top steel buttplate and short plain walnut forearm with thin round front
Approximate wt.: 8½ to 12 lbs.
Comments: Produced from about 1868 to 1902. Caliber marked on barrel.
Estimated Value: Excellent: $250.00
**   Very good: $220.00**

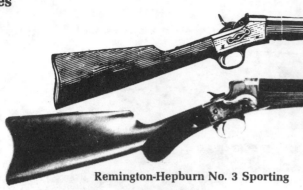

Remington No. 1 ½ Sporting

Remington-Hepburn No. 3 Sporting

Remington No. 5 1897 Carbine

Caliber: 7 mm
Action: Single-shot; rolling-block; ordnance steel; smokeless powderaction with case hardened steel frame; visible hammer
Magazine: None
Barrel: 20" round, smokeless steel barrel
Sights: Post front, military rear
Stock & Forearm: Plain, straight grip, oiled walnut, two-piece stock and forearm; steel buttplate; short forearm; barrel band; hand guard on top of barrel.
Approximate wt.: 5 lbs.
Comments: Made from about 1897 to 1906.
Estimated Value: Excellent: $160.00
Very good: $140.00

Remington No. 1 ½ Sporting

Similar to No. 1 Sporting Rifle except: lighter action, stocks and smaller caliber barrels; approximate wt. 5 ½ to 7 lbs.; made in following pistol calibers - Rim fire 22 S, L, and extra long; 25 Stevens and 25 longs; 32 or 38 long and extra long; Center fire Winchester 32-20; 38-40; or 44-40; barrel lengths 24, 26, 28, or 30 inches. Made from the 1869 to 1902.
Estimated Value: Excellent: $250.00
Very good: $225.00

Remington No. 2 Sporting

Caliber: Early models were for rim fire 22, 25, 32, or 38. Later models for center fire 22, 25-21, 25-25, 25-20, 32 long, 38 long, or 38-40
Action: Single-shot; rolling block; single trigger
Magazine: None
Barrel: 24 to 30" light weight, octagon
Sights: Bead front, sporting rear with elevation adjustment
Stock & Forearm: Plain oiled finish walnut, straight stock and forearm with lip at front.
Approximate wt.: 5 to 6 lbs.
Comments: Produced from about 1873 to 1902; caliber stamped under barrel at forearm.
Estimated Value: Excellent: $270.00
Very good: $250.00

Remington No. 2 Sporting

Remington-Hepburn No. 3 Sporting

Caliber: Center fire 22, 25-20, 25-25, 32, 32-10, 32-20, 32-40, 38, 38-40, 38-50, 38-55, 40-60, 40-65, 40-82, 45-70 government, or 45-90. Also made by order for 40-50, 40-70, 40-90, or 44-77 bottle neck Remington, 45-90, 45-105, or 50-90 Sharps and 50-70 Government.
Action: Hepburn drop block; side-lever opens and closes action; single-shot with low visible hammer; early models with single trigger; later models with single or double set triggers
Magazine: None
Barrel: 28" to 32" round, octagon or half octagon
Sights: Blade front; sporting rear adjustable for elevation; other optional sights on order.
Stock & Forearm: Plain straight grip or checkered pistol grip, oiled wood stock, with steel buttplate and matching short forearm with lipped front
Approximate wt.: 8 to 12 lbs.
Comments: Produced from about 1880 to 1906.
Estimated Value: Excellent: $275.00
Very good: $250.00

Remington No. 4 New Model

Remington No. 4 New Model

Caliber: Rim fire only in 22 short, long, and long rifle, 25 Stevens, or 32 long
Action: Single-shot; rolling block; light short action with automatic shell ejector; visible hammer
Magazine: None
Barrel: 22 ½" light octagon in 22 & 25 caliber; 24" in 32 caliber; round barrel after 1941.
Sights: Bead front, plain "v" notch rear.
Stock & Forearm: Plain varnished, straight grip two-piece stock and forearm; short round front forearm
Approximate wt.: 4 ¼ lbs.
Comments: Produced from about 1891 to 1934.
Estimated Value: Excellent: $270.00
Very good: $245.00

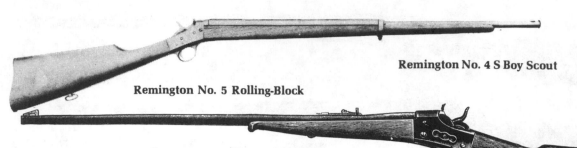

Remington No. 4 S Boy Scout

Remington No. 5 Rolling-Block

Remington No. 4 S Boy Scout or Military Model
Caliber: 22 short only until 1915, then chambered for 22 short or 22 long
Action: Single-shot; case hardened No. 4 rolling-block action; visible hammer
Magazine: None
Barrel: 28" medium, round barrel
Sights: Blade front, open "v" notch rear adjustable for elevation
Stock & Forearm: Musket style, oiled walnut, one-piece, full-length stock and forearm with steel buttplate and one barrel band; bayonet lug below barrel near muzzle; hand guard on top of barrel.
Approximate wt.: 5 lbs.
Comments: Called Boy Scout model from 1913 to 1915 then renamed Military Model. Produced from about 1913 to 1932.
Estimated Value: Excellent: $300.00
　　　　　　　　Very good: $250.00

Remington No. 5 Rolling-Block
Caliber: 7 mm Mauser, 30-30, or 30-40 Krag
Action: New Ordnance steel; single-shot; rolling-block; smokeless powder action with case hardened frame
Magazine: None
Barrel: 28"-30" light steel round barrel
Sights: Blade front, Rocky Mountain rear
Stock & Forearm: Plain varnished, straight grip, walnut two-piece stock and forearm; steel buttplate on stock and forearm lipped at front.
Approximate wt.: 7¼ lbs.
Comments: Made from about 1896 to 1906.
Estimated Value: Excellent: $235.00
　　　　　　　　Very good: $200.00

Remington No. 6

Remington No. 7 Target

Remington No. 6
Caliber: 22 short, long, long rifle, 32 short & long RF
Action: Single-shot; rolling-block; visible hammer; takedown model
Magazine: None
Barrel: 20" round tapered barrel
Sights: Bead front; open rear; also tang peep sight available
Stock & Forearm: Plain varnished walnut, straight grip stock and short forearm; steel buttplate
Approximate wt.: 4 lbs.
Comments: Produced from about 1902 to 1934.
Estimated Value: Excellent: $150.00
　　　　　　　　Very good: $135.00

Remington No. 7 Target
Caliber: 22 long rifle, 22 WRF, or 25 Stevens
Action: Single-shot; rolling block; visible hammer;
Magazine: None
Barrel: 24", 26", or 28"; half-octagon barrel
Sights: Bead front, adjustable dovetail rear
Stock & Forearm: Varnished checkered walnut pistol grip stock and forearm; capped pistol grip; rubber buttplate; lipped forearm
Approximate wt.: 7 lbs.
Comments: Manufactured from about 1904 to 1906.
Estimated Value: Excellent: $540.00
　　　　　　　　Very good: $500.00

Remington-Lee Sporting

Remington-Lee Military

Remington-Lee Military Carbine

Remington-Lee Sporting

Caliber: 6 mm U.S. Navy, 30-30 Sporting, 30-40 U.S. Government, 7 mm Mauser, or 7.65 mm Mauser

Action: Improved smokeless powder, bolt action; repeating

Magazine: 5-shot removable box

Barrel: 24" to 28" round smokeless steel barrel

Sights: Bead or blade front, open rear adjustable for elevation

Stock & Forearm: Checkered walnut half pistol grip, one-piece stock and forearm; forearm grooved on each side with lip at front

Approximate wt.: 6¾ lbs.

Comments: Some were produced with deluxe grand walnut stock, half-octagon barrel, and Lyman sights. Made from about 1897 to 1906. Prices are for standard grade.

Estimated Value: Excellent: $360.00
Very good: $310.00

Remington-Lee Military

Caliber: 30-40 Krag, 303 British, 6 mm Lee Navy, 7 mm Mauser, or 7.65 mm Mauser

Action: Improved smokeless powder bolt action; repeating; rimless cartridges

Magazine: 5-shot removable box

Barrel: 29" round smokeless steel barrel

Sights: Post front; folding leaf rear

Stock & Forearm: Plain walnut, straight grip, one-piece stock and long forearm; cleaning rod; barrel bands; wood hand guard on top of barrel.

Approximate wt.: 8½ lbs.

Comments: Produced from about 1897 to 1902.

Estimated Value: Excellent: $250.00
Very good: $210.00

Remington-Lee Military Carbine

Similar to Remington-Lee rifle except: 20" barrel; approximate wt. 6½ lbs.; one barrel band.

Estimated Value: Excellent: $275.00
Very good: $235.00

Remington Model 1907-15

Caliber: 8 mm Lebel

Action: Smokeless powder bolt action; repeating; self-cocking striker with knurled top for uncocking and manual cocking

Magazine: 5-shot box magazine

Barrel: 26" to 31" round barrel with 4 groove rifling

Sights: Ivory bead dovetail front, folding leaf rear

Stock & Forearm: Plain varnished walnut, one-piece stock and long forearm; barrel bands; cleaning rod in forearm under barrel

Approximate wt.: 8 to 9 lbs.

Comments: Made from about 1907 to 1915; left side of action marked "Remington MLE 1907-15"; right side of barrel near action marked "RAC 1907-15".

Estimated Value: Excellent: $240.00
Very good: $200.00

Remington Model 1907-15 Carbine

Same as Remington Model 1907-15 repeating rifle except: 22" barrel; no barrel bands; short forearm; approximate wt. 6½ lbs.

Estimated Value: Excellent: $210.00
Very good: $180.00

Remington, Enfield Pattern, 1914 Military

Caliber: 303 British (rimmed).

Action: British smokeless powder bolt action; repeating; self-cocking on down stroke of bolt handle

Magazine: 5-shot box magazine

Barrel: 26" round tapered barrel

Sights: Protected post front, protected folding leaf rear

Stock & Forearm: Oil finished walnut, one-piece stock and forearm; wood hand guard on top of barrel; modified pistol grip stock; full length forearm with two barrel bands

Approximate wt.: 10 lbs.

Comments: Manufactured from about 1915 to 1916 for the British Army; Serial No. on action and bolt, "R" preceeding action serial no.; approximately 600,000 produced.

Estimated Value: Excellent: $220.00
Very good: $190.00

Remington, Enfield U S Model 1917 Military

Caliber: 30-06 Government, rimless

Action: Smokeless powder bolt action; repeating; self-cocking on down stroke of bolt handle; actions made with interchangeable parts

Magazine: 5-shot box magazine

Barrel: 26" round tapered barrel

Sights: Protected post front, protected folding leaf rear

Stock & Forearm: Plain one-piece walnut, stock and forearm; wood hand guard over barrel; modified pistol grip stock; full length forearm with finger grooves and two barrel bands; equipped with sling loops and bayonet lug.

Approximate wt.: 10 lbs.

Comments: Made from about 1917 to 1918. Marked "Model of 1917", Remington and serial No. on bridge.

Estimated Value: Excellent: $225.00
Very good: $200.00

Remington, Enfield Pattern, 1914 Military

Remington, Enfield U S Model 1917 Military

Remington Model 30 (Early Variety)

Remington Model 30 (Intermediate Variety)

Remington Model 30 (Early Variety)

Caliber: 30-06 Government

Action: Improved 1917 Enfield bolt action; repeating; self-cocking when bolt is closed; hinged floor plate; side-safety

Magazine: 5-shot box magazine

Barrel: 24" light round barrel

Sights: Slip on band front sight, adjustable rear sight

Stock & Forearm: Plain varnished walnut, one-piece pistol grip stock and forearm; steel buttplate; grooved forearm with lipped front tip.

Approximate wt.: 8 lbs.

Comments: Made from about 1921 to 1926; approximately 8,500 produced; marked "Remington Arms Co. Inc., Remington Ilion Works, Ilion, N.Y. Made in U.S.A.".

Estimated Value: Excellent: $250.00
Very good: $200.00

Remington Model 30 (Intermediate Variety)

Same as Model 30 (Early Variety) rifle except: calibers -30-06 Government, 25, 30, 32, and 35 Remington and 7 mm Mauser; 22" barrel length; also made in 20" barrel carbine; made from about 1926 to 1930; approxiate wt. 7 lbs.

Estimated Value: Excellent: $240.00
Very good: $200.00

Remington Model 30 Express

Remington Model 33

Remington Model 34

Remington Model 30 Express

Caliber: 25, 30, 32, or 35 Remington, 30-06 Government, 7mm Mauser until 1936. After 1936 calibers 257 Roberts and 30-06 Government only

Action: Bolt action; repeating; self-cocking; thumb safety

Magazine: 5-shot box magazine

Barrel: 22" or 24" round barrel

Sights: Bead front, adjustable open rear

Stock & Forearm: Plain or checkered walnut pistol grip, one-piece stock and forearm; early models have grooved forearm with lipped tip

Approximate wt.: 7 ½ lbs.

Comments: Produced from about 1921 to 1940.

Estimated Value: Excellent: $240.00
Very good: $200.00

Remington Model 30R Carbine

Same as Model 30 Express Rifle except: 20" barrel; plain walnut one-piece stock and forearm; approximate wt. 7 lbs.

Estimated Value: Excellent: $230.00
Very good: $180.00

Remington Model 30S Sporting

Similar to Model 30 Express Rifle except: caliber 257 Roberts, 7 mm Mauser, or 30-06; approximate wt. 8 lbs.; rear peep sight; special grade high comb stock; produced from about 1930 to 1940; 24" barrel.

Estimated Value: Excellent: $275.00
Very good: $225.00

Remington Model 33

Caliber: 22 short, long, & long rifle

Action: Single-shot; bolt action; takedown model; exposed knurled cocking-piece

Magazine: None

Barrel: 24" round barrel

Sights: Bead front, open rear adjustable for elevation

Stock & Forearm: Plain varnished walnut, pistol grip, one-piece stock and forearm

Approximate wt.: 4 lbs.

Comments: Produced from about 1931 to 1936; finger grooves added to forearm in 1934.

Estimated Value: Excellent: $60.00
Very good: $50.00

Remington Model 33 NRA Junior Target

Same as Model 33 except: post front sight; peep rear sight; equipped with 1" leather sling; swivels; approximate wt. 4 ½ lbs.

Estimated Value: Excellent: $70.00
Very good: $60.00

Remington Model 34

Caliber: 22 short, long, long rifle

Action: Bolt action; repeating; takedown model; self-cocking; thumb safety

Magazine: Tubular magazine under barrel holds 22 shorts, 17 longs, or 15 long rifles

Barrel: 24" round barrel

Sights: Bead front, adjustable open rear

Stock & Forearm: Plain wood, one-piece pistol grip stock and grooved forearm

Approximate wt.: 5 ½ lbs.

Comments: Manufactured from about 1933 to 1935; also produced in Model 34 NRA target model with peep rear sight and sling swivels.

Estimated Value: Excellent: $105.00
Very good: $ 95.00

Remington Model 41

Caliber: 22 short, long, long rifle, 22 WFR
Action: Bolt action; single-shot; takedown model; exposed knurled cocking-piece
Magazine: None
Barrel: 27" round barrel
Sights: Bead or hooded ramp front sight, open rear adjustable for elevation or peep rear sight
Stock & Forearm: Plain pistol grip one-piece stock and forearm; hard rubber buttplate
Approximate wt.: 5 lbs.
Comments: Produced from about 1936 to 1940 in following models:

    41 A - "Standard" model with open sights.
    41 P - "Target" model with target sights.
    41 AS - "Special" model chambered for 22 WFR.
    41 SB - "Smoothbore" model - no rifling chambered for 22 LR shot shell only.

Estimated Value: Excellent: $75.00
Very good: $65.00

Remington Model 341 Sportsmaster

Caliber: 22 short, long, long rifle
Action: Bolt action; repeating; takedown model; self-cocking; thumb safety
Magazine: Tubular magazine under barrel holds 22 shorts, 17 longs, or 15 long rifles
Barrel: 27" round barrel
Sights: Bead front, open rear adjustable for elevation
Stock & Forearm: Plain wood, pistol grip one-piece stock and forearm
Approximate wt.: 6 lbs.
Comments: Produced from about 1935 to 1940. Also made in Model 341 P, which had hooded front sight and peep rear sight.
Estimated Value: Excellent: $80.00
Very good: $70.00

Remington Model 341 S Sportmaster

Same as Model 341 except: smooth bore for 22 shot cartridges.
Estimated Value: Excellent: $65.00
Very good: $55.00

Remington Model 37 Rangemaster

Caliber: 22 long rifle
Action: Bolt action; repeating self-cocking; thumb safety; adjustable trigger
Magazine: 5-shot clip and single-shot adaptor
Barrel: 28" heavy, semi-floating target barrel
Sights: Target sights; drilled for scope mount
Stock & Forearm: Lacquer finished heavy target, one-piece walnut stock and forearm; high flute comb stock, with plain pistol grip and steel buttplate; early models had rounded beaver tail forearm with one barrel band; barrel band dropped in 1938 and forearm modified
Approximate wt.: 12 lbs.
Comments: Manufactured from about 1937 to 1940.
Estimated Value: Excellent: $325.00
Very good: $290.00

Remington Model 37 (1940 Model)

Similar to Model 37 rifle except: improved trigger mechanism; re-designed stock; wide beavertail forearm; produced from about 1940 to 1955.
Estimated Value: Excellent: $335.00
Very good: $300.00

Remington Model 41

Remington Model 341

Remington Model 37

Remington Model 37 (1940 Model)

Remington Model 510 Targetmaster

Remington Model 510 C Carbine

Remington Model 510 Targetmaster

Caliber: 22 short, long, & long rifle
Action: Bolt action; single-shot; takedown model; self-cocking with thumb safety and cocking indicator
Magazine: None
Barrel: 25" light round barrel
Sights: Sporting or target sights
Stock & Forearm: Plain walnut, one piece pistol grip stock and forearm
Approximate wt.: 5 lbs.
Comments: Manufactured from about 1939 to 1962 in 3 models: 510 A standard model; 510 P with peep sights; 510 SB was smooth-bore chambered for 22 shot shells; minor changes in manufacture, in markings, and in stocks for the pre-World War II and post World War II models.
Estimated Value: Excellent: $60.00
Very good: $50.00

Remington Model 510 C Carbine

Same as Model 510 A single shot rifle except: 21" barrel and approximate wt. 5 ½ lbs.; produced from about 1961 to 1962.
Estimated Value: Excellent: $60.00
Very good: $50.00

Remington Model 511 Scoremaster

Remington Model 511 SB

Remington Model 511 Scoremaster

Caliber: 22 short, long, long rifle
Action: Bolt action; repeating; self-cocking; thumb safety; cocking indicator; takedown model
Magazine: 6-shot clip; also 10-shot clip after 1952
Barrel: 25" light round barrel
Sights: Open sporting sights
Stock & Forearm: Plain wood pistol grip, one-piece stock and forearm
Approximate wt.: 5 ¾ lbs.
Comments: Made from about 1939 to 1962 with production stopped during World War II; made in pre-war and post-war models.
Estimated Value: Excellent: $85.00
Very good: $70.00

Remington Model 511 SB

Same as Model 511 Scoremaster Rifle except: smooth bore for using 22 shot cartridges.
Estimated Value: Excellent: $70.00
Very good: $60.00

Remington Model 512 Sportmaster

Caliber: 22 short, long, long rifle
Action: Bolt action; repeating; self-cocking; thumb safety; cocking indicator
Magazine: Tubular magazine under barrel holds 22 shorts, 17 longs, and 15 long rifles
Barrel: 25" light round barrel
Sights: Bead front, open rear adjustable for elevation
Stock & Forearm: Plain walnut, pistol grip, one-piece stock and forearm; composition buttplate
Approximate wt.: 5 ½ lbs.
Comments: Manufactured from about 1940 to 1942 and from 1946 to 1962; the pre-war and post-war models may have minor changes in manufacture, markings, and stocks.
Estimated Value: Excellent: $80.00
Very good: $70.00

Remington Model 512 SB

Same as model 512 Sportmaster except: smooth bore for 22 shot cartridges.
Estimated Value: Excellent: $70.00
Very good: $60.00

Remington Model 513 T Matchmaster

Caliber: 22 long rifle
Action: Bolt action; repeating; self-cocking; side safety; cocking indicator; adjustable trigger
Magazine: 6-shot clip
Barrel: 27" medium round barrel; semi-floating type
Sights: Target sights; top of receiver grooved for scope mount after 1954.
Stock & Forearm: Plain, heavy, high fluted comb; lacquered walnut, pistol grip, one-piece stock and beavertail forearm
Approximate wt.: 9 lbs.
Comments: Produced from about 1940 to 1942 and from 1945 to 1968.
Estimated Value: Excellent: $165.00
Very good: $135.00

Remington Model 513 S Sporter Rifle

Similar to Model 513 T Matchmaster except; lighter sporting checkered walnut, one-piece stock and forearm; approximate wt. 6 ¾ lbs.; ramp front sight and adjustable open rear sight; produced from about 1940 to 1958.
Estimated Value: Excellent: $150.00
Very good: $120.00

Remington Model 512 Sportmaster

Remington Model 512 SB Rifle

Remington Model 513 T Matchmaster

Remington Model 514

Remington Model 514

Caliber: 22 short, long, long rifle
Action: Bolt action; single-shot; takedown model; self-cocking
Magazine: None
Barrel: 21" (514 BR) or 24" light round
Sights: Sporting or target sights
Stock & Forearm: Plain walnut, one-piece pistol grip stock and forearm
Approximate wt.: 4 ¼ lbs.
Comments: Produced from about 1948 to 1972 in three models: 514 Standard Model; 514 P had target sights (peep rear sight); 514 BR Boys Rifle with 1" shorter stock and 21" barrel.
Estimated Value: Excellent: $55.00
Very good: $45.00

Remington Model 720

Remington Model 721

Remington Model 720

Caliber: 257 Roberts, 270 Winchester, 30-06 Government

Action: Bolt action; repeating; self-cocking; side-safety; removable floor plate

Magazine: 5-shot box magazine; removable floor plate

Barrel: 20, 22, or 24 inch round barrel

Sights: Ramp front sight, adjustable open rear sight

Stock & Forearm: Checkered walnut, pistol grip, one-piece stock and forearm

Approximate wt.: 8 lbs.

Comments: Manufactured from about 1941 to 1946.

Estimated Value: Excellent: $240.00
Very good: $195.00

Remington Model 721

Caliber: 270, 30-06, or 300 magnum. After 1959, 280 Remington

Action: Bolt action; repeating; self-cocking; side-safety; adjustable trigger

Magazine: 4-shot box magazine with fixed floor plate; 3-shot in 300 magnum

Barrel: 24" or 26" round barrel

Sights: Ramp front, sporting rear with step elevator

Stock & Forearm: Plain or checkered walnut, pistol grip, one-piece stock and forearm; aluminum shotgun buttplate

Approximate wt.: 8 lbs.

Comments: Made from about 1948 to 1958 in six grades; standard grade made from 1948 to 1961. Prices are for standard grade.

Estimated Value: Excellent: $165.00
Very good: $130.00

Remington Model 521

Remington Model 722

Remington Model 521 TL Target

Caliber: 22 long rifle

Action: Bolt action; repeating; self-cocking; thumb safety; cocking indicator

Magazine: 5-shot or 10-shot clip

Barrel: 25" medium weight round barrel

Sights: Post front sight, Lyman #57 receiver sight (peep sight)

Stock & Forearm: Heavy target, one-piece pistol grip stock and semi-beavertail forearm; varnished or oil finished; rubber buttplate

Approximate wt.: 6½ lbs.

Comments: Manufactured from about 1948 to 1968; a low cost rifle intended for junior target shooters.

Estimated Value: Excellent: $75.00
Very good: $65.00

Remington Model 722

Caliber: 257 Roberts or 300 Savage; in 1950 222 Remington; in 1956 308 Winchester and 244 Remington; in 1958 222 Remington magnum; and 243 Winchester in 1960

Action: Bolt action; repeating; self-cocking; side-safety; fixed floor plate; adjustable trigger

Magazine: 4-shot box magazine; 5-shot in 222 magnum caliber

Barrel: 22" or 24" round barrel

Sights: Ramp bead front, open adjustable rear

Stock & Forearm: Plain or checkered; varnished, walnut pistol-grip, one-piece stock and forearm; after 1950 option of high-comb stock and tapered forearm

Approximate wt.: 7 to 8½ lbs.

Comments: Produced from about 1948 to 1958 in seven grades; standard grade made from about 1948 to 1961.

Estimated Value: Excellent: $180.00
Very good: $145.00

Remington Model 725 (Early)

Caliber: 270, 280, 30-06
Action: Bolt action; repeating; self-cocking; thumb safety
Magazine: 4-shot box
Barrel: 22" round barrel
Sights: Hooded ramp front; adjustable open rear
Stock & Forearm: Checkered walnut, Monte Carlo pistol grip one-piece, stock and forearm; capped grip stock with shot gun buttplate and sling loops
Approximate wt.: 7 ½ lbs.
Comments: Produced from about 1958 to 1959.
Estimated Value: Excellent: $270.00
Very good: $215.00

Remington Model 725 (Late)

Same as Model 725 (Early) Rifle except: also in calibers 243 Winchester; 244 Remington; or 222 Remington. 24" barrel in 222 Remington and aluminum buttplate on all calibers. Made from about 1960 to 1961 in three grades. Prices are for standard grade.
Estimated Value: Excellent: $275.00
Very good: $220.00

Remington Model 725 Magnum

Caliber: 375 Holland & Holland or 458 Winchester magnum
Action: Bolt action; magnum repeating; self-cocking; thumb safety
Magazine: 3-shot box magazine
Barrel: 26" heavy round barrel with muzzle brake
Sights: Ramp front, deluxe adjustable rear
Stock & Forearm: Fancy reinforced, checkered walnut, Monte Carlo pistol grip one-piece stock and forearm; stock with cap and rubber recoil pad; black forearm tip; quick detachable leather sling
Approximate wt.: 9 lbs.
Comments: Manufactured from about 1960 to 1961 in three grades. Prices are for ADL grade.
Estimated Value: Excellent: $475.00
Very good: $380.00

Remington Model 725 (Early)

Remington Model 725 (Late)

Remington Model 725 Magnum

Remington Model 10 Nylon

Remington Model 10 Nylon Carbine

Caliber: 22 short, long, long rifle
Action: Bolt action; single-shot; self-cocking striker with indicator; slide safety
Magazine: None
Barrel: 19 ½" round barrel
Sights: Ramp front; adjustable open rear
Stock & Forearm: Nylon checkered, pistol grip, one-piece, stock and forearm; shotgun buttplate
Approximate wt.: 4 lbs.
Comments: Produced from about 1963 to 1964.
Estimated Value: Excellent: $60.00
Very good: $50.00

Remington Model 10 SB

Same as Model 10 except: smooth bore; chambered for 22 shotshell.
Estimated Value: Excellent: $50.00
Very good: $40.00

Remington Nylon 11

Remington Nylon 12

Remington Nylon 11

Caliber: 22 short, long, long rifle
Action: Bolt action; repeating; self-cocking; cocking indicator
Magazine: 6-shot or 10-shot clip
Barrel: 19½" round barrel
Sights: Ramp front, adjustable open rear
Stock & Forearm: Polished brown nylon one-piece stock, forearm and hand guard (over barrel); checkered, capped, pistol grip stock with shot gun buttplate; checkered forearm with blunt reversed cap; white liners and two white diamond inlays on each side
Approximate wt.: 4½ lbs.
Comments: Produced from about 1962 to 1964.
Estimated Value: Excellent: $75.00
Very good: $65.00

Remington Nylon 12

Similar to Remington Nylon 11 Rifle except: tubular magazine under barrel holds 14 to 21 shots.
Estimated Value: Excellent: $85.00
Very good: $75.00

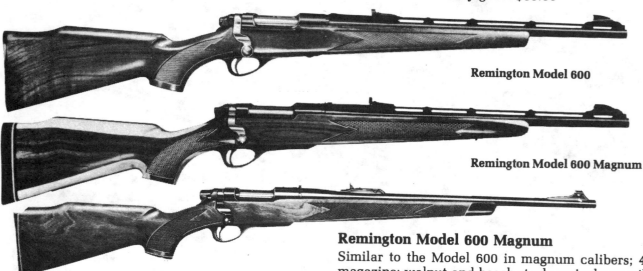

Remington Model 600

Remington Model 600 Magnum

Remington Model 660

Remington Model 600

Caliber: 6mm Rem., 222 Rem., 243 Win., 308 Win., 35 Rem.
Action: Bolt action; repeating
Magazine: 5 shot box
Barrel: 18½"; ventilated rib
Sights: Open rear; blade front
Stock & Forearm: Checkred walnut, Monte Carlo one piece pistol grip stock and forearm.
Approximate wt: 6 lbs.
Comments: A carbine style rifle made in the mid 1960's.
Estimated Value: Excellent: $150.00
Very good: $120.00

Remington Model 600 Magnum

Similar to the Model 600 in magnum calibers; 4 shot magazine; walnut and beech stock; swivels; recoil pad.
Estimated Value: Excellent: $170.00
Very good: $135.00

Remington Model 660

Similar to the Model 600; 20" barrel without rib; beaded front sight; made in the late 1960's and early 1970's.
Estimated Value: Excellent: $140.00
Very good: $115.00

Remington Model 660 Magnum

Similar to the Model 600 Magnum; 20" barrel without rib; beaded front sight; made in the late 1960's to early 1970's.
Estimated Value: Excellent: $160.00
Very good: $130.00

Remington Model 580

Caliber: 22 short, long, long rifle
Action: Bolt action; single-shot; self-cocking striker
Magazine: None
Barrel: 24" round barrel
Sights: Bead front; adjustable open rear
Stock & Forearm: Plain wood Monte Carlo pistol grip, one-piece stock and forearm; plastic shotgun buttplate
Approximate wt.: 5 lbs.
Comments: Manufactured from about 1967 to late 1970's; also available in Boys model (stock is shorter for young shooters).
Estimated Value: Excellent: $60.00
            Very good: $50.00

Remington Model 580 SB

Same as Model 580 except: smooth bore for 22 long rifle shotshell only.
Estimated Value: Excellent: $60.00
            Very good: $50.00

Remington Model 581

Caliber: 22 short, long, long rifle
Action: Bolt action; repeating; self-cocking; thumb safety
Magazine: 5-shot clip; single shot adaptor
Barrel: 24" round
Sights: Bead front, adjustable open rear sight
Stock & Forearm: Plain wood; Monte Carlo pistol grip one-piece stock and forearm
Approximate wt.: 5 ¼ lbs.
Comments: Made from about 1967 to present. Add $5.00 for left hand action.
Estimated Value: New (retail): $115.95
            Excellent: $ 90.00
            Very good: $ 70.00

Remington Model 582

Same as Model 581 except: 14 to 20 shot tubular magazine under barrel.
Estimated Value: New (retail): $134.95
            Excellent: $105.00
            Very good: $ 80.00

Remington Model 580

Remington Model 580 SB

Remington Model 581

Remington Model 582

Remington Model 788

Remington Model 788

Caliber: 222, 22-250, 223 Remington, 6mm Remington, 243 Winchester, and 308 Winchester, 7mm-08 Remington added 1980.
Action: Bolt action; repeating; self-cocking; thumb safety
Magazine: 5-shot clip in 222 caliber and 4-shot clip in other calibers
Barrel: 24" round tapered barrel in calibers 222, 22-250 and 223 Remington. 22" barrel in other calibers. 18 ½" barrel available 1980.
Sights: Blade front, adjustable rear
Stock & Forearm: Monte Carlo pistol grip, one-piece stock & forearm; current model has fluted comb and wider pistol grip and forearm, swivels available.
Approximate wt: 7 ½ lbs.
Comments: Made from about 1967 to present. Add $5.00 for left hand action, $25.00 for scope.
Estimated Value: New (retail): $209.95
            Excellent: $160.00
            Very good: $125.00

Rifles

Remington Model 591

Remington Model 592

Remington Model 591

Caliber: 5mm Remington rim-fire
Action: Bolt action; repeating; self-cocking; thumb safety
Magazine: 4-shot clip
Barrel: 24'' round barrel
Sights: Bead post front; adjustable open rear
Stock & Forearm: One-piece plain hardwood stock and forearm with Monte Carlo comb and pistol grip
Approximate wt.: 5 lbs.
Comments: Manufactured from about 1970 to 1974.
Estimated Value: Excellent: $150.00
                  Very good: $135.00

Remington Model 592

Same as Model 591 except: 10-shot tubular magazine under barrel.
Estimated Value: Excellent: $160.00
                  Very good: $145.00

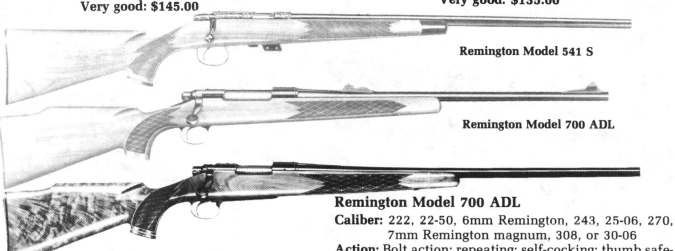

Remington Model 541 S

Remington Model 700 ADL

Remington Model 700 BDL Custom

Remington Model 541 S

Caliber: 22 long rifle
Action: Bolt action; repeating; self-cocking; thumb safety
Magazine: 5-shot clip
Barrel: 24''
Sights: None; barrel and receiver are drilled for a wide variety of optional scopes or sights
Stock & Forearm: One-piece checkered pistol grip stock and forearm
Approximate wt.: 5 ½ lbs.
Comments: Designed after the Remington Model 540 X Target Rifle; engraved receiver and trigger guard; made from about 1972 to date.
Estimated Value: New (retail): $294.95
                  Excellent: $225.00
                  Very good: $175.00

Remington Model 700 ADL

Caliber: 222, 22-50, 6mm Remington, 243, 25-06, 270, 7mm Remington magnum, 308, or 30-06
Action: Bolt action; repeating; self-cocking; thumb safety; checkered bolt handle
Magazine: 4 to 6 shot box magazine (depending on caliber)
Barrel: 22'' or 24'' round tapered barrel
Sights: Ramp front, adjustable, notched, removable rear
Stock & Forearm: Checkered walnut Monte Carlo pistol grip, one-piece stock and forearm; shot gun buttplate
Approximate wt.: 7 ½ lbs.
Comments: Production started about 1962; still being produced. Add $15.00 for magnum.
Estimated Value: New (retail): $297.95
                  Excellent: $225.00
                  Very good: $180.00

Remington Model 700 BDL Custom

Same as Model 700 ADL except: custom deluxe grade with black forearm end on early models; sling strap; additional calibers as follows: .17 Remington, .264 Winchester magnum, .300 Winchester magnum. Add $15.00 for magnum.
Estimated Value: New (retail): $357.95
                  Excellent: $270.00
                  Very good: $215.00

Remington Model 700 Safari

Remington Model 700 BDL Classic

Similar to 700 BDL with stock styling changes. Add $15.00 for magnum.

Estimated Value:	New (retail):	$327.95
	Excellent:	$250.00
	Very good:	$200.00

Remington Model 700 BDL Varmint Special

Similar to 700 BDL with heavy barrel in 222 Remington, 22-250 Remington, 223 Remington, 6mm Remington, 243 Winchester, 25-06 Remington. 7mm-08 added 1980.

Estimated Value:	New (retail):	$377.95
	Excellent:	$285.00
	Very good:	$230.00

Remington Model 700 BDL Safari

Similar to 700 BDL in 375 H & H magnum and 458 Winchester magnum. Recoil pad.

Estimated Value:	New (retail):	$579.95
	Excellent:	$440.00
	Very good:	$350.00

Remington Model 40 X Target

Remington Model 40XR

Remington Model 40XB

Remington Model 40XBBR

Remington Model 40 X Target

Caliber: 22 long rifle 1960; in 1961 also 222 Remington; 308, 20-06, or others on special order

Action: Bolt action; single-shot; self-cocking; thumb safety; adjustable trigger

Magazine: None

Barrel: 28" standard or heavy round barrel with bedding device in forearm

Sights: Removable target sights, scope block on barrel

Stock & Forearm: Oiled, plain, heavy target, pistol grip, one-piece stock and beavertail forearm; rubber shot gun buttplate; high fluted comb stock.

Approximate wt.: 11 to 12 lbs.

Comments: Manufactured from about 1956 to 1963. Replaced by Model 40 XB match rifle in 1964 to 1975.

Estimated Value:	22 LR	Other Calibers
Excellent:	$210.00	$240.00
Very good:	$190.00	$200.00

Remington Model 40XR

A target rifle similar to the Model 40 with widened stock and forearm; adjustable buttplate; hand stop; introduced in the late 1970's.

Estimated Value:	New (retail):	$499.95
	Excellent:	$390.00
	Very good:	$310.00

Remington Model 40XB Rangemaster

Similar to the Model 40X target with a stainless steel barrel. Currently produced.

Estimated Value:	New (retail):	$634.95
	Excellent:	$480.00
	Very good:	$390.00

Remington Model 40XBBR

Similar to the Model 40XB Rangemaster with a 20" or 24" barrel. Currently produced.

Estimated Value:	New (retail):	$669.95
	Excellent:	$525.00
	Very good:	$420.00

Remington Model 540-X

Remington Model 540XR

Remington Nylon 76

Remington Model 540-X, 540 XR

Caliber: 22 long rifle
Action: Bolt action; single-shot; self-cocking striker; slide safety adjustable match trigger
Magazine: None
Barrel: 26" heavy target barrel
Sights: Receiver drilled and tapped for scope mount; sights optional equipment
Stock & Forearm: Full pistol grip heavy wood one-piece stock and forearm; thumb-grooved stock with 4-way adjustable buttplate rail.
Approximate wt.: 8¾ lbs.
Comments: Made from about 1970 to present. A heavy rifle designed for bench shooting.
Estimated Value: New (retail): $264.95
               Excellent: $200.00
               Very good: $160.00

Remington Nylon 76

Caliber: 22 long rifle
Action: Lever-action; repeating; side ejection; lever under stock operates sliding bolt which ejects empty case, chambers cartridge from magazine, and cocks concealed striker; safety located on top of stock behind receiver
Magazine: 14-shot tubular magazine located in stock
Barrel: 19½" round barrel
Sights: Blade front, open rear sight
Stock & Forearm: Checkered nylon, 2-piece stock and forearm; pistol grip stock; forearm lipped at tip with nylon hand guard over barrel
Approximate wt.: 4½ lbs.
Comments: Manufactured from about 1962 to 1964; the only lever action repeater made by Remington Arms Co.
Estimated Value: Excellent: $125.00
                   Very good: $110.00

Remington Model No. 12

Remington Model 14

Remington Model 14

Caliber: 25, 30, 32, 35, Remington
Action: Slide-action; hammerless; takedown model
Magazine: 5-shot tubular magazine under barrel
Barrel: 22" round
Sights: Bead front, adjustable rear
Stock & Forearm: Plain or checkered walnut, pistol grip stock and grooved or checkered forearm
Approximate wt.: 7 lbs.
Comments: Manufactured from about 1912 to 1935 in 4 grades. Higher grades had checkering and engraving. Prices are for standard grade (plain).
Estimated Value: Excellent: $250.00
                   Very good: $200.00

Remington Model No. 12

Caliber: 22 short, long, long rifle
Action: Slide-action; hammerless; takedown model
Magazine: Tubular, 10 to 15 shot located under barrel
Barrel: 22" or 24" round or octagon barrel
Sights: Bead front, rear adjustable for elevation
Stock & Forearm: Plain or engraved; varnished plain or checkered, straight or pistol grip, walnut stock with rubber or steel buttplate; forearm grooved or checkered walnut
Approximate wt.: 5½ lbs.
Comments: Produced from about 1909 to 1936 in 4 grades. Higher grades had checkering and engraving. Prices are for standard grade (plain).
Estimated Value: Excellent: $180.00
                   Very good: $150.00

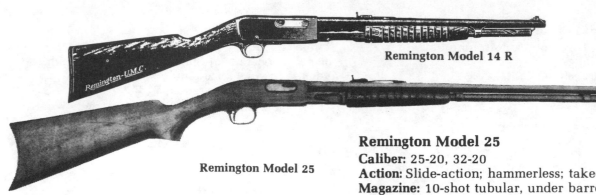

Remington Model 14 R

Remington Model 25

Remington Model 14 R Carbine

Same as Model 14 rifle except: 18½" barrel; straight grip stock; approximate wt. 6 lbs.; standard grade only.
Estimated Value: Excellent: $260.00
　　　　　　　Very good: $220.00

Remington Model 14½

Similar to the Model 14 rifle except: caliber 38-40 and 44-40, only; 22½ barrel; 11-shot magazine; discontinued about 1925; standard grade only.
Estimated Value: Excellent: $260.00
　　　　　　　　Very good: $220.00

Remington Model 14½ Carbine

Same as Model 14½ rifle except: 18½" barrel; 9-shot magazine.
Estimated Value: Excellent: $250.00
　　　　　　　　Very good: $210.00

Remington Model 25

Caliber: 25-20, 32-20
Action: Slide-action; hammerless; takedown model
Magazine: 10-shot tubular, under barrel
Barrel: 24"
Sights: Bead front, open rear
Stock & Forearm: Plain or checkered walnut, pistol grip stock and grooved or checkered forearm
Approximate wt.: 6 lbs.
Comments: Manufactured from about 1923 to 1936 in 4 grades. Higher grades had checkering and engraving. Prices are for standard grade (plain).
Estimated Value: Excellent: $240.00
　　　　　　　　Very good: $200.00

Remington Model 25 R Carbine

Same as Model 25 Rifle except: 18½" barrel; straight grip stock; 6-shot magazine; approximate wt. 4½ lbs.; standard grade only.
Estimated Value: Excellent: $225.00
　　　　　　　　Very good: $185.00

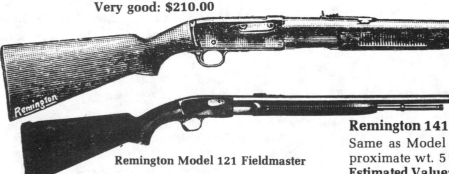

Remington Model 141 Gamemaster

Remington Model 121 Fieldmaster

Remington 141 R Carbine

Same as Model 141 A rifle except: 18½" barrel; approximate wt. 5½ lbs.; standard grade only.
Estimated Value: Excellent: $225.00
　　　　　　　　Very good: $190.00

Remington Model 141 Gamemaster

Caliber: 30, 32, and 35 Remington
Action: Slide-action; hammerless; takedown model
Magazine: 5-shot tubular under barrel
Barrel: 24" round barrel
Sights: Ramp front, adjustable rear
Stock & Forearm: Plain or checkered walnut, pistol grip stock and grooved or checkered semi-beavertail forearm
Approximate wt.: 7 lbs.
Comments: Produced from about 1936 to 1942 and from 1946 to 1950 in 4 grades. Higher grade rifles had checkered pistol grip stock and forearm and engraving. Prices are for standard grade (plain).
Estimated Value: Excellent: $250.00
　　　　　　　　Very good: $200.00

Remington Model 121 Fieldmaster

Caliber: 22 short, long, long rifle
Action: Slide action; hammerless; takedown model
Magazine: 20 shorts, 15 longs, or 14 long rifles; tubular magazine under barrel.
Barrel: 24" round barrel
Sights: Bead front, adjustable rear
Stock & Forearm: Plain or checkered, walnut pistol grip stock and grooved or checkered semi-beavertail forearm
Approximate wt.: 6 lbs.
Comments: Produced from about 1936 to 1942 and from 1946 to 1955 in 4 grades. Higher grades checkered and engraved. Prices are for standard grade (plain).
Estimated Value: Excellent: $220.00
　　　　　　　　Very good: $185.00

Rifles

Remington Model 121 SB

Same as Model 121 except: smooth bore barrel for 22 shot cartridges.
**Estimated Value: Excellent: $200.00
Very good: $175.00**

Remington Model 121 S

Similar to Model 121 except: Caliber 22 Remington special, only; 12-shot magazine; standard grade.
**Estimated Value: Excellent: $210.00
Very good: $185.00**

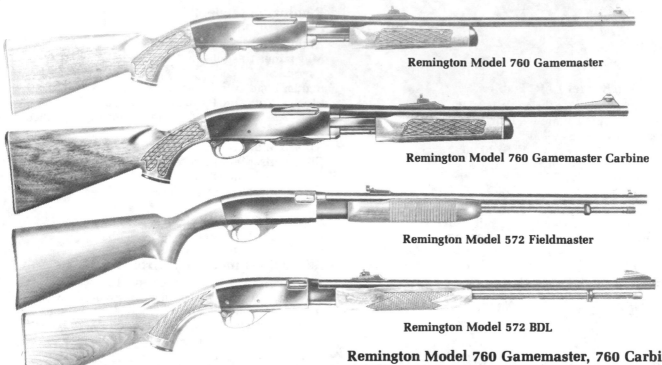

Remington Model 760 Gamemaster

Remington Model 760 Gamemaster Carbine

Remington Model 572 Fieldmaster

Remington Model 572 BDL

Remington Model 572 A Fieldmaster

Caliber: 22 short, long, long rifle
Action: Slide-action; hammerless solid frame; side-ejection
Magazine: 14 to 20 shot tubular under barrel
Barrel: 21" and 24" round tapered
Sights: Bead front, adjustable open rear
Stock & Forearm: Plain or checkered walnut, pistol grip stock and grooved or checkered forearm
Approximate wt: 5 ½ lbs.
Comments: Manufactured from about 1955 to present
**Estimated Value: New (retail): $134.95
Excellent: $105.00
Very good: $ 85.00**

Remington Model 572 SB

Same as Model 572 rifle except: smooth bore, for 22 shot cartridges; standard grade only.
**Estimated Value: Excellent: $100.00
Very good: $ 80.00**

Remington 572 BDL Fieldmaster

Deluxe version of 572A Fieldmaster. Currently produced.
**Estimated Value: New (retail): $149.95
Excellent: $115.00
Very good: $ 90.00**

Remington Model 760 Gamemaster, 760 Carbine

Caliber: 30-06, 308, 300 Savage, 35 Remington, 280, 270 Winchester, 257 Roberts, 244 Remington, 243 Winchester, 6mm Remington, 223, and 222. Presently being made in calibers: 30-06, 308 Winchester, 270 Remington, 243 Winchester, and 6 mm Remington.
Action: Slide action; hammerless; side ejection; solid-frame; cross-bolt safety
Magazine: 4-shot box
Barrel: 22" round tapered; 18½" on Carbine
Sights: Ramp bead front, adjustable open rear
Stock & Forearm: Plain or checkered walnut, pistol grip stock and grooved checkered semi-beavertail forearm
Approximate wt.: 7 ½ lbs.
Comments: Manufactured from about 1952 to present. Carbine made from 1960 to 1969 in 270, 280; 1962 to present in 30-06 and 308 Winchester.
**Estimated Value: New (retail): $309.95
Excellent: $235.00
Very good: $190.00**

Remington Model 760 BDL Gamemaster

Similar to Model 760 with basketweave checkering, Monte Carlo stock, available in 30-06, 270, 308.
**Estimated Value: New (retail): $339.95
Excellent: $255.00
Very good: $205.00**

Remington Model No. 8

Remington Model No. 16

Remington Model No. 8

Caliber: 25, 30, 32, or 35 Remington
Action: Semi-automatic; top ejection; for smokeless powder; takedown model; solid-breech and sliding barrel type
Magazine: 5-shot detachable box
Barrel: 22'' round barrel
Sights: Bead front, open rear
Stock & Forearm: Plain or engraved; varnished, plain or checkered, straight grip, two-piece walnut stock and forearm; rubber or steel buttplate and lipped forearm
Approximate wt.: 7¾ lbs.
Comments: Manufactured from about 1906 to 1936 in 5 grades - A, C, D, E, & F; jacket marked "Manufactured by the Remington Arms Co, Ilion, N.Y., U.S.A." Browning's Patent's Oct. 8, 1900. Oct. 15, 1900. July 2, 1902. Prices for standard grade.
Estimated Value: Excellent: $240.00
Very good: $200.00

Remington Model No. 16

Caliber: 22 Remington automatic
Action: Semi-automatic; hammerless; solid breech; sliding bolt; side ejection; takedown model
Magazine: 15-shot tubular located in stock
Barrel: 22'' round
Sights: Bead front, adjustable notch sporting rear
Stock & Forearm: Plain or engraved; varnished, plain or checkered, straight grip, two-piece walnut stock & forearm; steel buttplate and blunt lip on forearm
Approximate wt.: 5¾ lbs.
Comments: Manufactured from about 1914 to 1928 in 4 grades (A, C, D, & F). Prices for standard grade.
Estimated Value: Excellent: $225.00
Very good: $200.00

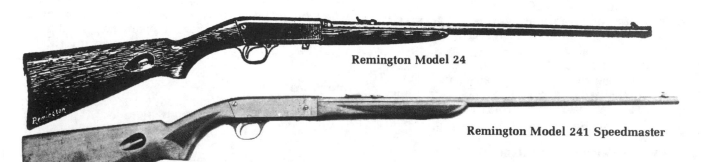

Remington Model 24

Remington Model 241 Speedmaster

Remington Model 24

Caliber: 22 short only or 22 long rifle only
Action: Semi-automatic; hammerless; solid breech; sliding bolt; bottom ejection
Magazine: 15-shot stock tube in 22 short and 10-shot in 22 long rifle
Barrel: 19'' round barrel
Sights: Bead front, adjustable rear
Stock & Forearm: Plain or engraved; varnished, plain or checkered, one-half pistol grip, two-piece walnut stock and forearm; steel buttplate with lipped forearm
Approximate wt.: 4¾ lbs.
Comments: Manufactured from about 1922 to 1935 in 5 grades (A, C, D, E, & F). Prices for standard grade.
Estimated Value: Excellent: $150.00
Very good: $130.00

Remington Model 241 Speedmaster

Caliber: 22 short only or 22 long rifle only
Action: Semi-automatic; hammerless; solid breech; bottom ejection; takedown type; sliding bolt action; thumb safety.
Magazine: 15-shot in 22 short and 10-shot in 22 long rifle; tubular magazine in stock
Barrel: 24'' round barrel
Sights: Bead front, notched rear adjustable for elevation
Stock & Forearm: Plain or engraved; varnished walnut palin or checkered, pistol grip two-piece stock and forearm; semi-beavertail
Approximate wt: 6 lbs.
Comments: Improved version of Model 24; produced from about 1935 to 1951 in 5 grades (A, B, D, E, & F). Prices for standard grade.
Estimated Value: Excellent: $175.00
Very good: $145.00

Rifles

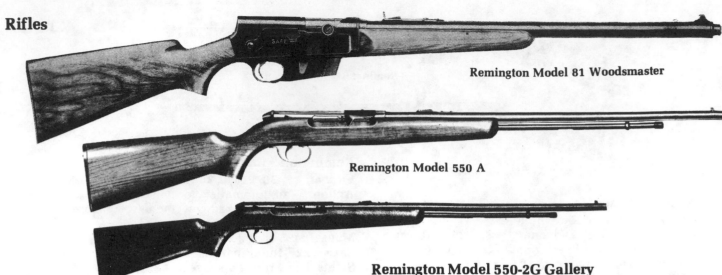

Remington Model 81 Woodsmaster

Remington Model 550 A

Remington Model 550-2G Gallery

Remington Model 550 A

Caliber: 22 short, long, long rifle
Action: Semi-automatic; hammerless; side ejection; solid breech; sliding bolt; floating power piston which permits using 22 short, long, or long rifle interchangeably and still function as semi-automatic; takedown type with thumb safety
Magazine: 20-shot 22 short and 15-shot 22 long rifle
Barrel: 24" round barrel
Sights: Dovetail bead front and notched rear adjustable for elevation
Stock & Forearm: One-piece plain varnished stock and forearm with pistol grip and hard rubber buttplate
Approximate wt.: 6½ lbs.
Comments: Replaced the Model 241 because it was less expensive to produce. Made from about 1941 to 1942 and from 1946 to 1970. Receiver top grooved for telescope sight mounts.
Estimated Value: Excellent: $110.00
Very good: $ 90.00

Remington Model 550-2G Gallery

Similar to Model 550 A except: chambered for 22 short caliber only.
Estimated Value: Excellent: $105.00
Very good: $ 85.00

Remington Model 81 Woodsmaster

Caliber: From 1936 to 1942 in 25, 30, 32, or 35 Remington, from 1946 to 1950 in 30, 32, 35, or 300 Savage
Action: Semi-automatic; top ejection; takedown model; solid breech; sliding barrel type
Magazine: 5-shot detachable box
Barrel: 22" round
Sights: Bead front, sporting rear with notched elevator
Stock & Forearm: Plain or engraved; varnished, plain or checkered, pistol grip, two-piece walnut stock and forearm; rubber buttplate and semi-beavertail style forearm
Approximate wt.: 7¾ lbs.
Comments: Produced from about 1936 to 1942 and from 1946 to 1950 in 5 grades (A, B, D, E, & F). An improved version of the Model No. 8. Prices are for standard grade.
Estimated Value: Excellent: $250.00
Very good: $210.00

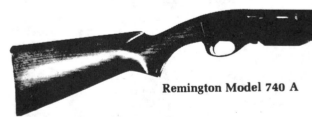

Remington Model 740 A

Remington Model 740 ADL Deluxe Grade

Same as Model 740 A except: deluxe checkered stock and forearm; also grip cap and sling swivels.
Estimated Value: Excellent: $220.00
Very good: $185.00

Remington Model 740 BDL Special Grade

Same as Model 740 ADL Deluxe Grade except: stock and forearm have deluxe finish on select wood.
Estimated Value: Excellent: $250.00
Very good: $210.00

Remington Model 740 A Woodsmaster

Caliber: 30-06 or 308
Action: Semi-automatic; gas operated; side ejection; hammerless
Magazine: 4-shot detachable box
Barrel: 22" round
Sights: Ramp front, open rear adjustable for elevation
Stock & Forearm: Plain pistol grip stock and forearm; semi-beavertail forearm with finger grooves
Approximate wt.: 7½ lbs.
Comments: Produced from about 1950 to 1960.
Estimated Value: Excellent: $210.00
Very good: $175.00

Remington Model 552 A Speedmaster

Remington Model 552 BDL Deluxe

Remington Model 552 BDL Deluxe Speedmaster

Same as Model 552 Speedmaster except: high quality finish checkered stock and forearm; ramp front sight and adjustable rear (elevation and windage); made from about 1961 to present.

Estimated Value: New (retail): $145.95
           Excellent: $110.00
           Very good: $ 90.00

Remington Model 552 GS Gallery Special

Same as Model 552 Speedmaster except: caliber 22 short only.

Estimated Value: Excellent: $100.00
           Very good: $ 80.00

Remington Model 552 A Speedmaster

Caliber: 22 short, long, and long rifle interchangeably

Action: Semi-automatic; hammerless; side ejection; solid breech; sliding bolt; floating power piston which permits using 22 short, long and long rifle cartridges interchangeably

Magazine: 20-shot 22 short; and 15-shot 22 long rifle tubular under barrel

Barrel: 21'' and 23'' round tapered

Sights: Bead front, notched rear adjustable for elevation

Stock & Forearm: Pistol grip one-piece plain stock and semi-beavertail forearm; hard composition checkered buttplate

Approximate wt: 5 ¾ lbs.

Comments: Produced from about 1958 to present

Estimated Value: New (retail): $129.95
           Excellent: $100.00
           Very good: $ 80.00

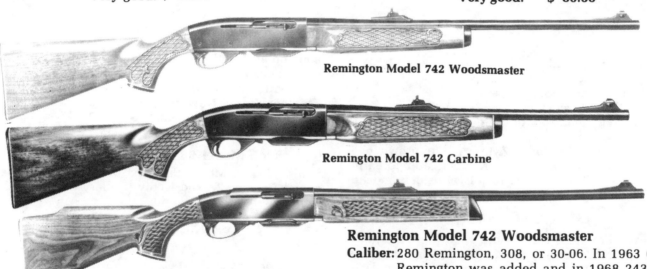

Remington Model 742 Woodsmaster

Remington Model 742 Carbine

Remington Model 742 BDL

Remington Model 742 Woodsmaster Carbine

Same as Model 742 Woodmaster Rifle except: barrel length 18½''; approximate wt. 6½ lbs.; calibers 280, 30-06 or 308 only.

Estimated Value: New (retail): $352.95
           Excellent: $265.00
           Very good: $215.00

Remington Model 742 BDL Woodsmaster

Same as Model 742 Woodmaster Rifle except: calibers 30-06 or 308 only; left or right hand models; checkered Monte Carlo stock; black tipped forearm.

Estimated Value: New (retail): $382.95
           Excellent: $290.00
           Very good: $230.00

Remington Model 742 Woodsmaster

Caliber: 280 Remington, 308, or 30-06. In 1963 6 mm Remington was added and in 1968 243 Winchester

Action: Semi-automatic; side ejection; hammerless; gas operated sliding bolt

Magazine: 4-shot detachable box

Barrel: 22'' round tapered barrel

Sights: Gold bead front, step adjustable rear with windage adjustment

Stock & Forearm: Plain, engraved and gold inlaid; plain or checked and standard or deluxe finish two-piece walnut stock and semi-beavertail forearm; aluminum buttplate on stock

Approximate wt.: 7 ½ lbs.

Comments: Manufactured from about 1960 to present; in 1969 Remington advertised many fancy grades. Prices are for standard grade.

Estimated Value: New (retail): $352.95
           Excellent: $265.00
           Very good: $215.00

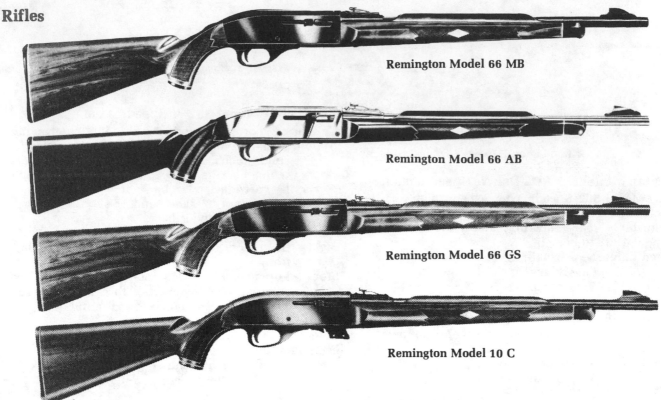

Remington Model 66 MB

Remington Model 66 AB

Remington Model 66 GS

Remington Model 10 C

Remington Model 66 MB and 66SG

Caliber: 22 long rifle
Action: Semi-automatic; side ejection; solid breech; sliding bolt
Magazine: 14-shot tubular in stock
Barrel: 20" round steel
Sights: Blade front; rear sight adjustable for windage and elevation
Stock & Forearm: Du-Pont "Zytel" nylon brown one-piece receiver, stock and forearm; checkered pistol grip stock and lipped forearm which covers top of barrel.
Approximate wt: 4 lbs.
Comments: Produced from about 1959 to present; based on a new design concept in which the stock, receiver, and forearm are made in one piece; also Model 66 SG - Seneca Green instead of brown. (Discontinued)
Estimated Value: New (retail):　$99.95
　　　　　　　　　 Excellent:　　$75.00
　　　　　　　　　 Very good:　　$60.00

Remington Model 66 AB, 66 BD

Same as Remington Model 66 MB except: Black stock and forearm with chrome plated barrel and receiver covers; made from about 1962 to present; BD has black receiver (deduct $5.00)
Estimated Value: New (retail): $105.95
　　　　　　　　　 Excellent:　　$ 80.00
　　　　　　　　　 Very good:　　$ 65.00

Remington Model 66 GS

Similar to the Model Same as Model 66 MB except: chambered for 22 short only (Gallery Special). Made from about 1963 to present.
Estimated Value:　New (retail):　$115.95
　　　　　　　　　 Excellent:　　$ 90.00
　　　　　　　　　 Very good:　　$ 70.00

Remington Model 10 C

Same as Remington Model 66 MB except: 10-shot removable box magazine. Produced from about 1970 to late 1970's.
Estimated Value: Excellent:　　$70.00
　　　　　　　　　 Very good:　　$55.00

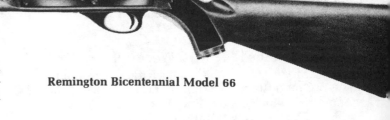

Remington Bicentennial Model 66

Same as Remington Model 66 MB except: limited number of selected rifles produced in 1976 to commemorate 200 years of nation's history; eagle inscribed on left side of receiver.
Estimated Value: Excellent:　　$110.00
　　　　　　　　　 Very good:　　$100.00

Remington Bicentennial Model 66

Ruger No. 1

Ruger No. 1 Light Sporter

Ruger No. 1 Medium Sporter

Ruger No. 1 Tropical

Ruger No. 1 Special Varminter

Ruger No. 1

Caliber: 22-250, 243, 25-06, 6mm Rem., 270, 30-06, 7mm Rem. magn., 300 Win., 458, 45-70, 375 H&H

Action: Falling block; under lever; single shot; hammerless

Magazine: None

Barrel: 26'' tapered

Sights: Open

Stock & Forearm: Checkered walnut, pistol grip stock and forearm; swivels

Approximate wt.: 8 lbs.

Comments: Manufactured from the late 1960's to present.

Estimated Value: New (retail): $348.00
           Excellent: $260.00
           Very good: $210.00

Ruger No. 1 Light Sporter

Similar to No. 1 in 243, 270 or 30-06 only; 22'' barrel.

Estimated Value: New (retail): $348.00
           Excellent: $260.00
           Very good: $210.00

Ruger No. 1 Medium Sporter

Similar to No. 1 Light Sporter in heavier calibers and with a 22'' of 26'' barrel.

Estimated Value: New (retail): $348.00
           Excellent: $260.00
           Very good: $210.00

Ruger No. Tropical

A 24'' barrel version of No. 1 in 375 H&H magnum, and 458 magnum only.

Estimated Value: New (retail): $348.00
           Excellent: $260.00
           Very good: $210.00

Ruger No. 1 Special Varminter

Similar to No. 1 in 22-250, 25-06, 7mm, and 300 magnum; heavy 24'' barrel.

Estimated Value: New (retail): $348.00
           Excellent: $260.00
           Very good: $210.00

Rifles

Ruger Model 77 **Ruger 77 Round Top** **Ruger 77 Varmint**

Ruger No. 3

Caliber: 22 Hornet, 30-40 Krag, 45-70, 223, 375 Win.
Action: Falling block; under lever; hammerless; single shot
Magazine: None
Barrel: 22'' blued
Sights: Folding leaf rear, bead front
Stock & Forearm: Plain walnut, straight grip stock an forearm; barrel band
Approximate wt.: 6 lbs.
Comments: Made from the late 1960's to present.
Estimated Value: New (retail): **$225.00**
  Excellent: **$170.00**
  Very good: **$135.00**

Ruger Model 77

Caliber: 220, 22-250, 25-06, 243 Winchester, 250-3000, 257, 6mm, 270 Winchester, 7mm Remington magnum, 7 x 57mm, 300 magnum, 30-06, 338 magnum, 458 magnum
Action: Bolt action; repeating; either short or magnum action
Magazine: 5-shot box with hinged floor plate; 4-shot in magnum calibers
Barrel: 22' blued
Sights: Adjustable leaf rear, beaded ramp front
Stock & Forearm: Checkered walnut, pistol grip, one piece stock and tapered forearm; recoil pad; swivels
Approximate wt: 6¾ lbs.
Comments: Made from the late 1960's to preent; Add $100.0 for 458 magnum
Estimated Value: New (retail): **$297.50**
  Excellent: **$225.00**
  Very good: **$180.00**

Ruger 77 Round Top

Similar to Model 77 with round top receiver and open sights. Made from early 1970's to present.
Estimated Value: New (retail): **$297.50**
  Excellent: **$225.00**
  Very good: **$180.00**

Ruger 77 Varmint

Similar to Model 77 in 22-250, 220, 243, 6mm, 308 or 25-06 calibers; 24'' or 26'' tapered barrel; no sights. Made from early 1970's to present.
Estimated Value: New (retail): **$297.50**
  Excellent: **$225.00**
  Very good: **$180.00**

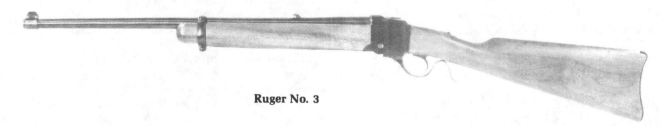

Ruger No. 3

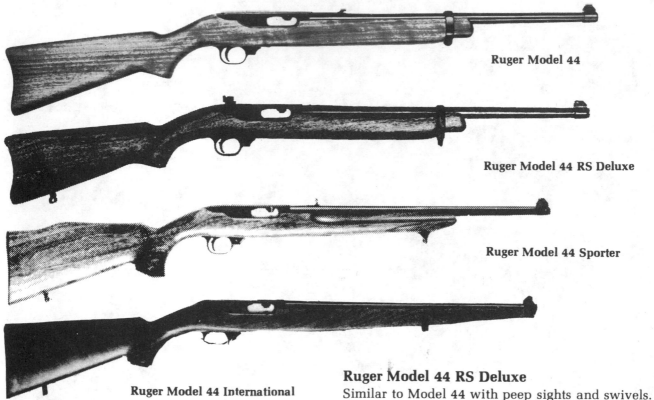

Ruger Model 44

Ruger Model 44 RS Deluxe

Ruger Model 44 Sporter

Ruger Model 44 International

Ruger Model 44

Caliber: 44 magnum
Action: Gas operated semi-automatic
Magazine: 4-shot tubular
Barrel: 18½" blued
Sights: Leaf rear, bead front
Stock & Forearm: Plain walnut, semi-pistol grip, one piece stock and forearm; barrel band
Approximate wt.: 5¾ lbs.
Comments: Made from about 1960 to present
Estimated Value: New (retail): $240.00
           Excellent: **$180.00**
           Very good: **$145.00**

Ruger Model 44 RS Deluxe
Similar to Model 44 with peep sights and swivels.
Estimated Value: Excellent: **$200.00**
           Very good: **$160.00**

Ruger Model 44 Sporter
Similar to Model 44 with Monte Carlo stock, fluted forearm and swivels. Made to early 1970's.
Estimated Value: Excellent: **$210.00**
           Very good: **$165.00**

Ruger Model 44 International
Similar to Model 44 with a full length stock and swivels. Made to early 1970's.
Estimated Value: Excellent: **$220.00**
           Very good: **$175.00**

Ruger Mini 14

Ruger Mini 14
Caliber: 223 Commercial or Military
Action: Gas operated semi-automatic
Magazine: 5-shot detachable box; 10- and 20-shot available
Barrel: 18½" blued
Sights: Adjustable rear, bead front
Stock & Forearm: Plain walnut, semi-pistol grip, one piece stock and forearm; handguard over barrel
Approximate wt.: 6½ lbs.
Comments: Made from the early 1970's to present. Add $50.00 for Stainless Steel finish.
Estimated Value: New (retail): $227.50
           Excellent: **$170.00**
           Very good: **$140.00**

Rifles

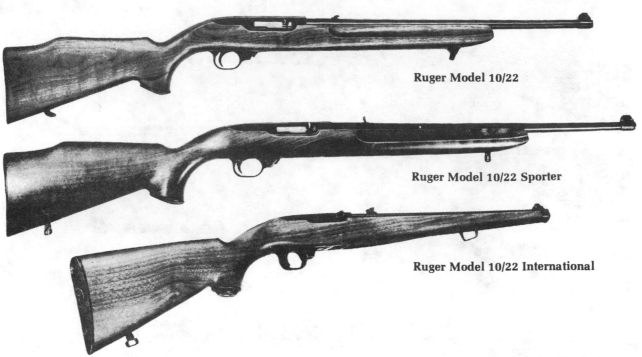

Ruger Model 10/22

Ruger Model 10/22 Sporter

Ruger Model 10/22 International

Ruger Model 10/22
Caliber: 22 long rifle
Action: Semi-automatic
Magazine: 10-shot detachable rotary
Barrel: 18½" blued
Sights: Adjustable leaf rear, bead front
Stock & Forearm: Plain walnut, semi-pistol grip, one piece stock & forearm; barrel band
Approximate wt.: 5 lbs.
Comments: Manufactured from about 1964 to present.
Estimated Value: New (retail): $107.50
        Excellent: $ 80.00
        Very good: $ 65.00

Ruger Model 10/22 Sporter
Similar to Model 10/22 with: Monte Carlo stock; fluted bandless forearm; swivels.
Estimated Value: New (retail): $128.50
        Excellent: $ 95.00
        Very good: $ 85.00

Ruger Model 10/22 International
Similar to Model 10/22 with full length stock and swivels. Made to early 1970's.
Estimated Value: Excellent: **$100.00**
        Very good: $ 85.00

Sako

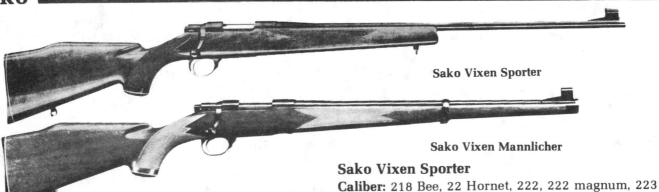

Sako Vixen Sporter

Sako Vixen Mannlicher

Sako Vixen Mannlicher
Similar to Sporter with a full length stock; 20" barrel; barrel band.
Estimated Value: Excellent: **$375.00**
        Very good: **$300.00**

Sako Vixen Sporter
Caliber: 218 Bee, 22 Hornet, 222, 222 magnum, 223
Action: Short stroke bolt action, Mauser type
Magazine: 5-shot
Barrel: 23½" blued
Sights: Open rear, hooded ramp front
Approximate wt.: 6½ lbs.
Comments: Made from World War II to the early 1970's. Vixen, Forester and Finnbear became M74 Short, Meduim, Long actions.
Estimated Value: Excellent: **$350.00**
        Very good: **$280.00**

Sako Vixen Heavy Barrel

Sako Forester Sporter

Sako Forester Mannlicher

Sako Forester Heavy Barrel

Sako Finnbear

Sako Finnbear Mannlicher

Sako Vixen Heavy Barrel

Similar to Sporter with heavy barrel and in larger calibers only.

Estimated Value: Excellent: $390.00
Very good: $310.00

Sako Forester Sporter

Similar to Vixen Sporter with medium action and in 22-250, 243, and 308 calibers. Made from the late 1950's to early 1970's.

Estimated Value: Excellent: $350.00
Very good: $280.00

Sako Forester Mannlicher

Similar to Forester Sporter with full length stock; 20'' barrel; barrel band.

Estimated Value: Excellent: $390.00
Very good: $310.00

Sako Forester Heavy Barrel

Similar to Forester with a heavy 24'' barrel.

Estimated Value: Excellent: $400.00
Very good: $320.00

Sako Finnbear

Similar to Vixen with: long action; recoil pad; 25-06, 264 magnum, 270, 30-06, 300 magnum, 7mm magnum, 3785 H&H. Made from the early 1960's to the early 1970's.

Estimated Value: Excellent: $425.00
Very good: $340.00

Sako Finnbear Mannlicher

Similar to Finnbear with: full length stock; 20'' barrel; barrel band.

Estimated Value: Excellent: $450.00
Very good: $360.00

Rifles

Sako Model 74 Super Sporter

Sako Model 74 Super Sporter Heavy Barrel

Sako Model 74 Deluxe Sporter

Sako Model 74 Super Sporter Heavy Barrel

Similar to Model 74 Super Sporter in short, medium, or long action and heavy barrel.

Estimated Value: Excellent: $375.00
Very good: $200.00

Sako Model 74 Deluxe Sporter

Similar to Model 74 Super Sporter with recoil pad, select wood and high quality finish. Add $25.00 for magnum.

Estimated Value: Excellent: $450.00
Very good: $360.00

Sako Model 74 Super Sporter

Similar to Vixen, Forester, a nd Finnbear, in short action medium action, and long action; 23 or 24'' barrel; Made in 1970's.

Estimated Value: Excellent: $350.00
Very good: $280.00

Sako Mauser

Sako Model A11 Standard

Sako Mauser

Caliber: 270, 30-06
Action: FN Mauser bolt action; repeating
Magazine: 5-shot box
Barrel: 24'' blued
Sights: Leaf rear, hooded ramp front
Stock & Forearm: Checkered walnut, Monte Carlo pistol grip, one piece stock and tapered forearm; swivels
Approximate wt.: 7 ½ lbs.
Comments: Manufactured from World War II to about 1960.
Estimated Value: Excellent: $400.00
Very good: $320.00

Sako Mauser Magnum

Similar to Sako Mauser in magnum calibers 300 H&H, 375 H&H and recoil pad.
Estimated Value: Excellent: $425.00
Very good: $350.00

Sako Model A1 Standard

Caliber: 17 Rem., 222 Rem., 223 Rem.
Action: Short throw bolt action; repeating
Magazine: 5 shot
Barrel: 23½''
Sights: None
Stock & Forearm: Checkered walnut pistol grip Monte Carlo, one piece stock and forearm; swivels
Approximate wt: 6 ½ lbs.
Comments: Currently available. Add $50.00 for 17 Rem. caliber
Estimated Value: New (retail): $499.95
Excellent: $375.00
Very good: $300.00

Sako Model A11 Standard

Similar to the A1 Standard with a medium throw action and in 220 Swift, 22-250 Rem., 243 Win., 308 Win. calibers.
Estimated Value: New (retail): $499.95
Excellent: $375.00
Very good: $300.00

Sako Model A1 Deluxe

Sako Varmint

Sako Carbine

Sako Model A111 Standard

Similar to the Model A1 Standard with a long throw action; 25-06 Rem., 270 Win., 30-06, 7mm Rem. magnum, 300 Win. magnum, 338 Win. magnum, 375 H & H magnum; recoil pad. Add $50.00 for magnum.

Estimated Value: New (retail): $499.95
Excellent: $375.00
Very good: $300.00

Sako Model A1 Deluxe

A deluxe version of the A1; recoil pad.

Estimated Value: New (retail): $716.00
Excellent: $540.00
Very good: $435.00

Sako Model A11 Deluxe

Similar to the Model A11 with deluxe features; recoil pad.

Estimated Value: New (retail): $716.00
Excellent: $540.00
Very good: $435.00

Sako Model A111 Deluxe

Similar to the Model A111 with deluxe features. Add $53.00 for magnum.

Estimated Value: New (retail): $716.00
Excellent: $540.00
Very good: $435.00

Sako Varmint

Similar to the Models A1, A11, & A111 with heavy varmint barrel.

Estimated Value: New (retail): $584.95
Excellent: $440.00
Very good: $350.00

Sako Carbine

Similar to the Models A1, A11, & A111 with a 20" barrel and full length forearm.

Estimated Value: New (retail): $599.95
Excellent: $450.00
Very good: $360.00

Sako Finnwolf Sporter

Sako Model 78

Caliber: 22 long rifle; 22 Win. magnum; 22 Hornet
Action: Bolt action; repeating
Magazine: 5 shot; 4 shot in magnum
Barrel: 22½"; heavy barrel available
Sights: Folding leaf rear, hooded ramp front
Stock & Forearm: Checkered walnut pistol grip Monte Carlo, one piece stock and forearm; swivels
Approximate wt: 6¾ lbs.
Comments: Currently available. Add $40.00 for magnum or heavy barrel, $67.00 for Hornet.

Estimated Value: New (retail): $324.95
Excellent: $245.00
Very good: $195.00

Sako Finnwolf Sporter

Caliber: 243, 308
Action: Lever action; hammerless; repeating
Magazine: 4-shot clip
Barrel: 23" blued
Sights: No rear, hooded ramp front
Stock & Forearm: Checkered walnut, Monte Carlo pistol grip, one piece stock and tapered forearm; swivels
Approximate wt.: 7 lbs.
Comments: Made from the mid 1960's to early 1970's.

Estimated Value: Excellent: $350.00
Very good: $280.00

Sako Finnwolf Deluxe Sporter

Same as Finnwolf with select wood.

Estimated Value: Excellent: $375.00
Very good: $300.00

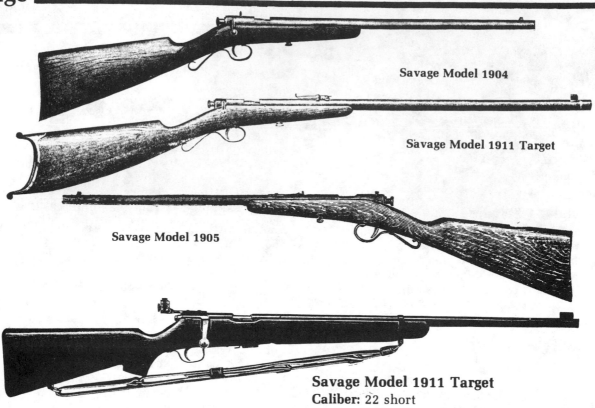

Savage Model 1904

Savage Model 1911 Target

Savage Model 1905

Savage Model 19

Savage Model 1904

Caliber: 22 short, long, long rifle
Action: Bolt action; single shot
Magazine: None; single shot
Barrel: 18''
Sights: Open rear, bead front
Stock & Forearm: Straight wood, one-piece stock and forearm
Approximate wt.: 3 lbs.
Comments: This is a boy's lightweight takedown rifle produced from 1904 until 1917.
Estimated Value: Excellent: $75.00
Very good: $65.00

Savage Model 1905

Caliber: 22 short, long, long rifle
Action: Bolt action; single shot
Magazine: None; single shot
Barrel: 22''
Sights: Open rear, bead front
Stock & Forearm: Plain straight grip one-piece stock & forearm
Approximate wt.: 5 lbs.
Comments: This is a lightweight takedown boy's rifle that was produced until about 1917.
Estimated Value: Excellent: $85.00
Very good: $75.00

Savage Model 1911 Target

Caliber: 22 short
Action: Bolt action; single shot
Magazine: None
Barrel: 20''
Sights: Adjustable rear, bead front
Stock & Forearm: Walnut straight grip one-piece stock and forearm
Approximate wt.: 4 lbs.
Comments: Patterned after a military rifle, this gun was made from 1911 to 1916.
Estimated Value: Excellent: $80.00
Very good: $70.00

Savage Model 19 & 19L Target

Caliber: 22 long rifle
Action: Bolt action; speed lock; repeating
Magazine: 5-shot detachable box
Barrel: 25''
Sights: Extension rear, hooded front
Stock & Forearm: Walnut, full pistol grip target stock and beavertail forearm; swivels
Approximate wt.: 7 ½ lbs.
Comments: Produced from 1933 until the mid 1940's. The model 19L had special Lyman receiver and front sights. Add $10-$15 for Model 19L.
Estimated Value: Excellent: $150.00
Very good: $125.00

Savage Model 19M

This is the same rifle as the Model 19 except it has a heavier 28'' barrel. Approximate wt. is 9 ¼ lbs.
Estimated Value: Excellent: $160.00
Very good: $135.00

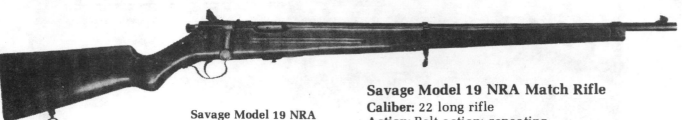

Savage Model 19 NRA

Savage Model 19 NRA Match Rifle

Caliber: 22 long rifle
Action: Bolt action; repeating
Magazine: 5-shot detachable box
Barrel: 25"
Sights: Adjustable peep rear, blade front
Stock & Forearm: Wood pistol grip full military stock and forearm
Approximate wt.: 7 lbs.
Comments: Produced from 1919 until 1932.
Estimated Value: Excellent: $150.00
Very good: $130.00

Savage Model 19H Hornet

Same rifle as Model 19 except loading port, bolt mechanism and magazine are like Model 23-D.
Estimated Value: Excellent: $225.00
Very good: $200.00

Savage Model 20

Savage Model 23A Sporter

Savage Model 23 AA

Savage Model 23 B,

Savage Model 20

Caliber: 300 Savage, 250-3000
Action: Bolt action; repeating
Magazine: 5-shot
Barrel: 22" (250 caliber), 24" (300 caliber)
Sights: Open rear, bead front. (In 1926 rear peep sight)
Stock & Forearm: Checkered walnut, full pistol grip stock and forearm. (In 1926 cut to semi-pistol grip)
Approximate wt.: 5¾ to 7 lbs.
Comments: This rifle was produced from 1920 through 1929.
Estimated Value: Excellent: $270.00
Very good: $225.00

Savage Model 23A Sporter, 23 AA, 23 B, 23 C, 23 D

Caliber: 22 long rifle (Model 23A, 23AA); from 1933 to 1947 in 22 Hornet (Model 23D); 25-20 (Model 23B) 32-20 (Model 23C).
Action: Bolt action; from 1933-1942 (Model 23AA) speed lock
Magazine: 5-shot detachable box
Barrel: 23", 25" from 1933 till 1942 on Model 23B
Sights: Open rear, blade or bead front
Stock & Forearm: Plain walnut, semi-pistol grip stock and forearm
Approximate wt.: 6 to 6½ lbs.
Comments: Produced: 23A from 1923-1933; Model 23AA with improved lock - 1933-1942; Model 23B , 1933-1942; Model 23C, 23D - 1933-1947.
Estimated Value:

	23A	23AA	23B	23C	23D
Excellent:	$135.00	$145.00	$160.00	$155.00	$210.00
Very good:	$115.00	$125.00	$140.00	$135.00	$180.00

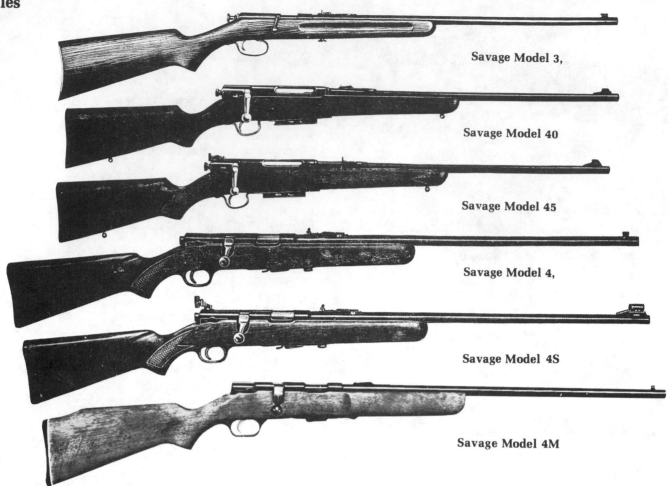

Savage Model 3,

Savage Model 40

Savage Model 45

Savage Model 4,

Savage Model 4S

Savage Model 4M

Savage Model 3, 3S, 3ST

Caliber: 22 short, long, long rifle
Action: Bolt action; single shot
Magazine: None
Barrel: 26'' before World War II, 24'' after
Sights: Open rear, bead front; 3S and 3ST have peep rear and hooded front
Stock & Forearm: Walnut, semi-pistol grip; 3ST has swivels
Approximate wt.: 4 to 5 lbs.
Comments: This is a takedown model produced from 1933 until the early 1950's. The 3 ST was discontinued before World War II.
Estimated Value: Excellent: $60.00
      Very good: $50.00

Savage Model 40

Caliber: 250-3000, 300 Savage, 30-30, 30-06
Action: Bolt action; repeating
Magazine: 4 shot-detachable box
Barrel: 22'' for caliber 250-3000 and 30-30; 24'' for other models
Sights: Open rear, ramp front
Stock & Forearm: Plain walnut, pistol grip, stock and lipped forearm after 1936; checkered stock after 1940.
Approximate wt.: 7 ½ lbs.
Comments: Made from 1928 until World War II.
Estimated Value: Excellent: $240.00
      Very good: $200.00

Savage Model 45

This is a special grade version of the Model 40. It has a checkered stock and forearm and a special receiver sight. Discontinued in 1940.
Estimated Value: Excellent: $270.00
      Very good: $230.00

Savage Model 4, 4S, 4M

Caliber: 22 short, long, long rifle; 4M chambered for 22 Rimfire magnum
Action: Bolt action; repeating
Magazine: 5-shot detachable box
Barrel: 24''
Sights: Open rear, bead front; 4S has peep rear and hooded front.
Stock & Forearm: Checkered walnut, pistol grip stock and grooved forearm on pre-World War II models; plain on post-World War II models.
Approximate wt.: 5 ½ lbs.
Comments: The Model 4 and 4S were produced from 1933 until the mid 1960's. 4M was made during the early to mid 1960's. Add $10.00 for model 4M.
Estimated Value: Excellent: $75.00
      Very good: $65.00

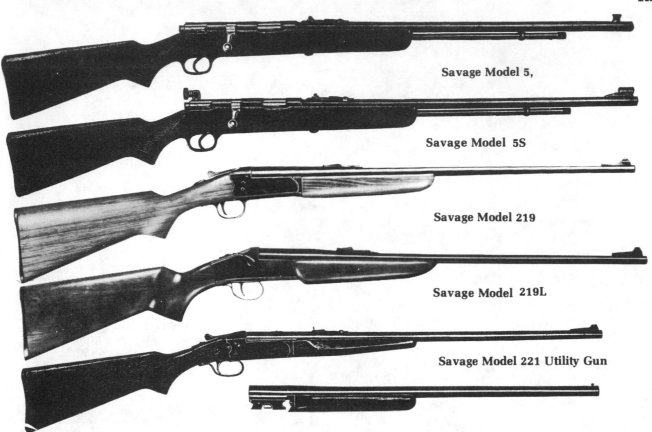

Savage Model 5,

Savage Model 5S

Savage Model 219

Savage Model 219L

Savage Model 221 Utility Gun

Savage Model 5, 5S

Model 5 is similar to the Model 4 except the magazine is tubular and the gun weighs about 6 lbs. The Model 5S has peep rear and hooded front sight. They were produced from the mid 1930's until 1961; caliber 22 short, long, long rifle.
Estimated Value: Excellent: $80.00
Very good: $70.00

Savage Model 219, 219L

Caliber: 22 Hornet, 25-20, 32-20, 30-30
Action: Hammerless; single shot; automatic ejector; shotgun style, top break lever; 219L has side lever.
Magazine: Single shot
Barrel: 26''
Sights: Open rear, bead front
Stock & Forearm: Plain walnut, pistol grip stock & forearm
Approximate wt.: 6 lbs.
Comments: This takedown model was made from 1938 to 1965 as Model 219. From 1965 for 2 years with side lever, as 219L.
Estimated Value: Excellent: $75.00
Very good: $60.00

Savage Model 221 Utility Gun

This is basically the same rifle as the Model 219 except it was offered in 30-30 only with an interchangeable 12 gauge 30'' shotgun barrel. Prices include the 12 gauge interchangeable shotgun barrel.
Estimated Value: Excellent: $120.00
Very good: $100.00

Savage Model 222

This is the same gun as Model 221 except shotgun barrel is 16 gauge, 28''.
Estimated Value: Excellent: $120.00
Very good: $100.00

Savage Model 223

This is the same gun as Model 221 except shotgun barrel is 20 gauge, 28''.
Estimated Value: Excellent: $130.00
Very good: $110.00

Savage Model 227

This is the same gun as Model 221 except it is 22 Hornet and the shotgun barrel is 12 gauge, 30''.
Estimated Value: Excellent: $120.00
Very good: $100.00

Savage Model 228

This is the same gun as Model 227 except shotgun barrel is 16 gauge, 28''.
Estimated Value: Excellent: $120.00
Very good: $100.00

Savage Model 229

Basically the same gun as Model 227 except shotgun barrel is 20 gauge, 28''.
Estimated Value: Excellent: $130.00
Very good: $110.00

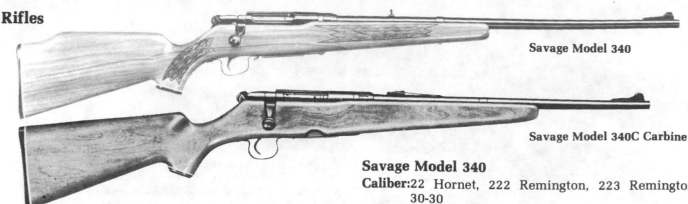

Savage Model 340

Savage Model 340C Carbine

Savage Model 340

Caliber: 22 Hornet, 222 Remington, 223 Remington, 30-30
Action: Bolt action; repeating
Magazine: 4-shot clip in 22 Hornet and 222 Remington; 3-shot clip in 30-30
Barrel: 20", 22", 24"
Sights: Open rear, ramp front; hooded ramp after 1980
Stock & Forearm: Plain walnut pistol grip stock & forearm; after 1965, checkered
Approximate wt: 6 to 7 lbs.
Comments: Produced from 1950 to present. Before 1950 this model was manufactured as a Stevens.
Estimated Value: New (retail): $176.60
Excellent: $135.00
Very good: $110.00

Savage Model 340S

This is the same rifle as Model 340 except sights are peep rear, hooded front. It was produced from about 1955 to 1960.
Estimated Value: Excellent: $135.00
Very good: $110.00

Savage Model 340C Carbine

This is basically the same as Model 340 in caliber 30-30. The barrel is slightly over 18". Produced in the mid 1960's.
Estimated Value: Excellent: $130.00
Very good: $105.00

Savage Model 110 Sporter

Savage Model 110 S

Savage Model 110 MCL

Savage Model 110 S

Similar to the Model 110 with heavy barrel; no sights; stippled checkering; recoil pad; introduced in the late 1970's.
Estimated Value: New (retail): $274.75
Excellent: $210.00
Very good: $170.00

Savage Model 110 Sporter

Caliber: 243, 270, 308, 30-06
Action: Bolt action; repeating
Magazine: 4-shot staggered box
Barrel: 22"
Sights: Open rear, ramp front
Stock & Forearm: Sporter, checkered walnut pistol grip stock & forearm
Approximate wt.: 6¾ lbs.
Comments: This gun was produced from 1958 until the early 1960's when it was replaced by 110E.
Estimated Value: Excellent: $170.00
Very good: $135.00

Savage Model 110 MC and MCL

The same rifle as 110 Sporter except in additional 22-250 caliber & 24" barrel. A Monte Carlo stock was also included. The MCL is the same in left-hand action. (add about $5-$10). Made from late 1950's to about 1969.
Estimated Value: Excellent: $175.00
Very good: $140.00

Savage Model 110C

Savage Model 110E

Savage Model 110 CL

Savage Model 112-R

A varmint rifle similar to the Model 110; plain walnut semi-pistol grip one piece stock and forearm; swivels; recoil pad; no sights; 22-250, 25-06 calibers; introduced in 1979.

Estimated Value: New (retail): $299.00
Excellent: $225.00
Very good: $185.00

Savage Model 110C, 110CL

Caliber: 22-250, 243, 25-06, 270, 308, 30-06, 7mm Remington magnum, 300 Winchester magnum
Action: Bolt action; repeating
Magazine: 4-shot clip, 3 in magnum calibers
Barrel: 22" and 24"
Sights: Open rear, ramp front
Stock & Forearm: Checkered walnut, Monte Carlo stock & forearm; magnum has recoil pad
Approximate wt.: 6 ¾ to 8 lbs.
Comments: This rifle has been in production since 1966. Add $20.00 for magnum. 110CL is left hand model (add $10.00)
Estimated Value: New (retail): $273.15
Excellent: $210.00
Very good: $170.00

Savage Model 110E

Caliber: 243 Winchester, 7mm Remington magnum, 30-06
Action: Bolt action; repeating
Magazine: 4-shot staggered box; 3-shot staggered box in magnum
Barrel: 20" blue; 24" stainless steel in magnum
Sights: Open rear, ramp front
Stock & Forearm: Walnut Monte Carlo, plain or checkered; magnum has recoil pad
Approximate wt.: 6 ¾ to 7 ¾ lbs.
Comments: This gun was produced from 1963 to late 1970's. Add $25 for magnum.
Estimated Value: Excellent: $160.00
Very good: $130.00

Savage Model 110EL

This is the left-hand action version of 110E in either 7mm Remington magnum or 30-06. Add $25.00 for magnum.
Estimated Value: Excellent: $180.00
Very good: $145.00

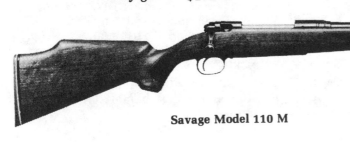

Savage Model 110 M

Savage Model 110 M and 110 ML

Caliber: 7mm Remington magnum, 264, 300, 338 Winchester
Action: Bolt action; repeating
Magazine: 4-shot staggered box
Barrel: 24"
Sights: Open rear, ramp front
Stock & Forearm: Walnut pistol grip, Monte Carlo stock & forearm; recoil pad
Approximate wt.: 7 ½ to 8 lbs.
Comments: Produced from 1963 to 1969. 110 ML is the same in left-hand action. (Add $5 to $10).
Estimated Value: Excellent: $210.00
Very good: $170.00

Rifles

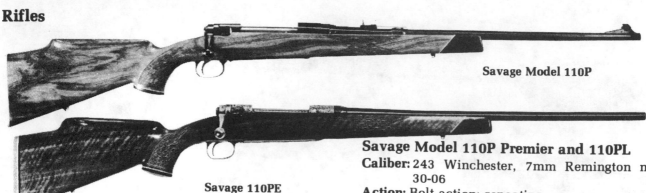

Savage Model 110P

Savage 110PE

Savage Model 110P Premier and 110PL
Caliber: 243 Winchester, 7mm Remington magnum, 30-06
Action: Bolt action; repeating
Magazine: 4-shot staggered box, 3 in magnum
Barrel: 22" blue; 24" stainless steel in magnum
Sights: Open rear folding leaf, ramp front
Stock & Forearm: Walnut and rosewood Monte Carlo stock & forearm swivels; magnum has recoil pad
Approximate wt.: 7 to 8 lbs.
Comments: Made from mid 1960's until 1970. 110PL is left hand action. Add $10-$15 for magnum.
Estimated Value: Excellent: $300.00
Very good: $240.00

Savage 110PE Presentation and 110PEL
Same rifle as Models 110P and 110PL except receiver, floorplate and trigger guard are engraved. It was produced for 2 years beginning in 1968. Add $10-$15 for magnum.
Estimated Value: Excellent: $510.00
Very good: $410.00

Savage Model 111

Savage Model 112V

Savage Model 111
Caliber: 7mm (7x57), 243, 270, 30-06, 7mm magnum
Action: Bolt action; hammerless; repeating
Magazine: 4 shot box; 3 shot in magnum
Barrel: 24"
Sights: Adjustable removable rear, removable hooded ramp front
Stock & Forearm: Checkered walnut Monte Carlo, one piece pistol grip stock and forearm; swivels
Approximate wt: 6¾ lbs.
Comments: A deluxe high powered rifle made from the mid to late 1970's. Add $10.00 for magnum.
Estimated Value: Excellent: $220.00
Very good: $175.00

Savage Model 840
Caliber: 222 Rem.
Action: Bolt action; bolt cocks on opening stroke; repeating
Magazine: 4 shot detachable clip
Barrel: 24" tapered medium weight steel barrel
Sights: Ramp front with gold bead; sporting rear with step elevator
Stock & Forearm: Plain one piece hardwood stock and forearm, pistol grip; fluted comb
Approximate wt: 6¾ lbs.
Comments: Made in the mid 1970's.
Estimated Value: Excellent: $120.00
Very good: $100.00

Savage Model 840-T
Same as the Model 840 with a 4X scope.
Estimated Value: Excellent: $135.00
Very good: $115.00

Savage Model 112V
Caliber: 222, 223, 22-250, 220 Swift, 25-06, 243
Action: Bolt action single shot; hammerless
Magazine: None
Barrel: 26" chrome-molly steel; tapered
Sights: None
Stock & Forearm: Checkered walnut, one piece pistol grip stock and forearm; fluted comb; swivels
Approximate wt: 9¼ lbs.
Comments: A varmint rifle made in the mid to late 1970's.
Estimated Value: Excellent: $225.00
Very good: $180.00

Savage Model 65-M

Savage Model 1899 (99)

Savage Model 65-M
Caliber: 22 magnum
Action: Bolt action; repeating
Magazine: 5 shot clip
Barrel: 22" blued
Sights: Open rear, ramp front
Stock & Forearm: Checkered walnut, one piece semi-
pistol grip stock and forearm
Approximate wt: 5¾ lbs.
Comments: Introduced in the late 1970's.
Estimated Value: New (retail): $94.05
                    Excellent: $70.00
                    Very good: $55.00

Savage Model 1899 (99)
Caliber: 303 Savage, 25-35, 32-40, and 38-55
Action: Hammerless; lever action
Magazine: 5-shot rotary
Barrel: Round, half octagon or octagon - 20", 22", 26"
Sights: Adjustable rear, dovetail, open sporting front
Stock & Forearm: Walnut straight grip stock, tapered
forearm
Approximate wt.: 7½ lbs.
Comments: This is the backbone of the Savage line and
has been manufactured in many variations
over the years. It was first produced in
1899.
Estimated Value: Excellent: $210.00
                        Very good: $175.00

Savage Model 1899 Military

Savage Model 99 A

Savage Model 99H Carbine

Savage Model 1899 Military
This is the same rifle as the Model 99 except: barrel is
28"; bayonet; stock is musket style; sights are military.
It was produced from about 1899-1907; caliber 30-30
Winchester.
Estimated Value: Excellent: $325.00
                     Very good: $290.00

Savage Model 99A
Basically the same as Model 1899 in solid frame and in
calibers 300 Savage, 303 Savage and 30-30. It was produced from 1922 to present. Later models in calibers
243, 308, 250.
Estimated Value: New (retail): $284.00
                     Excellent: $215.00
                     Very good: $175.00

Savage Model 99 B
Takedown version of Model 99A; produced from about
1922 to 1937.
Estimated Value: Excellent: $230.00
                     Very good: $195.00

Savage Model 99H Carbine
Basically the same as 99A with: addition of 250-3000
caliber; short barrel; carbine stock and forearm; barrel
bands. Produced until 1940
Estimated Value: Excellent: $225.00
                     Very good: $190.00

Rifles

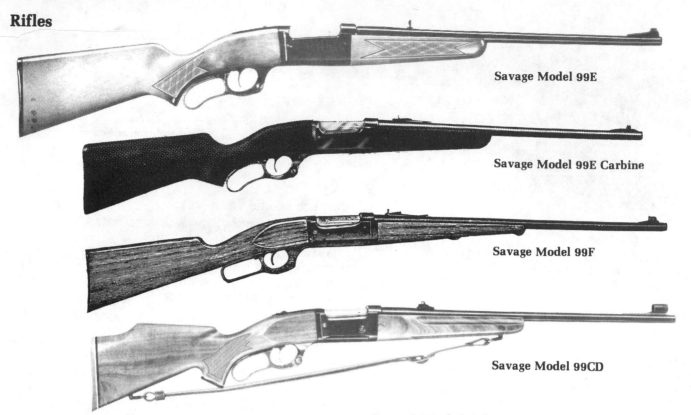

Savage Model 99E

Savage Model 99E Carbine

Savage Model 99F

Savage Model 99CD

Savage Model 99E

This is similar to the Model 99A in 22 Hi Power, 250/3000, 30-30, 300 Savage, 303 Savage. 22" or 24" barrel. It was produced into the 1930's.
Estimated Value: Excellent: $210.00
Very good: $180.00

Savage Model 99E Carbine

Similar to Model 99H in 243 Winchester, 300 Savage, 308 Winchester calibers only. Stock and forearm are checkered walnut pistol grip. Production began in 1961.
Estimated Value: New (retail): $251.35
Excellent: $190.00
Very good: $155.00

Savage Model 99F

This is a lightweight takedown version of the Model 99E, produced until about 1940. Production resumed about 1955 to 1972 in caliber 243, 300 & 308.
Estimated Value: Excellent: $240.00
Very good: $185.00

Savage Model 99 CD

This is a solid frame version of Model 99F with a checkered pistol grip stock and forearm. It has been in production since 1955; 4-shot detachable box magazine.
Estimated Value: New (retail): $322.95
Excellent: $245.00
Very good: $195.00

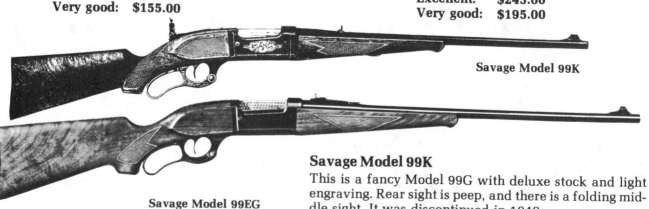

Savage Model 99K

Savage Model 99EG

Savage Model 99G

This is a takedown version of the Model 99E with a checkered walnut pistol grip stock and forearm. Discontinued in 1940.
Estimated Value: Excellent: $230.00
Very good: $195.00

Savage Model 99K

This is a fancy Model 99G with deluxe stock and light engraving. Rear sight is peep, and there is a folding middle sight. It was discontinued in 1940.
Estimated Value: Excellent: $650.00
Very good: $575.00

Savage Model 99EG

This is the Model G produced after World War II, from 1955 to 1961.
Estimated Value: Excellent: $180.00
Very good: $145.00

Savage Model 99R

Savage Model 99RS

Savage Model 99DL

Savage Model 99C

Savage Model 99 PE Presentation

Savage Model 99 DE Citation

Savage Model 99R

Similar to other Model 99's. Production stopped in 1940. It was resumed from 1955 to 1961 in 24" barrel only with swivel attachments in a variety of calibers. Add $50.00 for pre-World War II models.

Estimated Value: Excellent: $215.00
Very good: $175.00

Savage Model 99 RS

The same rifle as Model 99 except those before World War II have rear peep sight and folding middle sight. Those made after the war have a special receiver sight. Discontinued in 1961; solid frame. Add $50.00 for pre-World War II models.

Estimated Value: Excellent: $240.00
Very good: $200.00

Savage Model 99 DL

This is a late Model 99, in production from about 1960 to mid 1970's. Basically the same as Model 99F with a Monte Carlo stock and swivels.

Estimated Value: Excellent: $210.00
Very good: $170.00

Savage Model 99C

This model is currently in production. It is much like the Model 99F except it has a 3 or 4-shot detachable clip magazine. It has been in production since 1965; calibers: 22-250, 243, 308.

Estimated Value: New (retail): $291.75
Excellent: $220.00
Very good: $175.00

Savage Model 99 PE Presentation

This rifle is much like the Model 99 DL except receiver is engraved, stock and forearm are hand checkered Monte Carlo. It was produced from 1968 until 1970.

Estimated Value: Excellent: $450.00
Very good: $375.00

Savage Model 99 DE Citation

A less elaborate example of the Model 99 PE. Produced from 1968 to 1970.

Estimated Value: Excellent: $330.00
Very good: $275.00

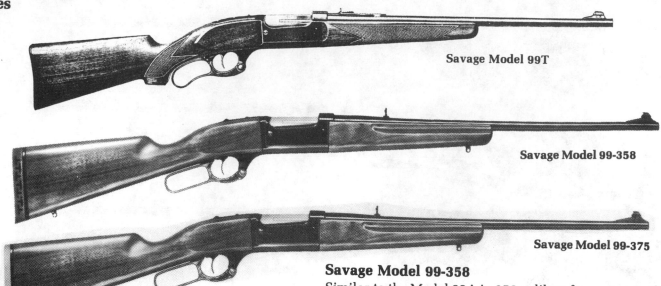

Savage Model 99T

Savage Model 99-358

Savage Model 99-375

Savage Model 99T

This rifle has the same basic specifications as the other Model 99's. It is a solid frame with a checkered walnut pistol grip stock and forearm. It was produced until 1940.

Estimated Value: Excellent: $270.00
Very good: $220.00

Savage Model 99-358

Similar to the Model 99A in 358 caliber; forearm rounded; swivels; recoil pad; introduced in 1979.

Estimated Value: **New (retail):** $299.00
Excellent: $230.00
Very good: $190.00

Savage Model 99-375

Similar to the Model 99-358 in 375 Winchester caliber. Introduced in 1980.

Estimated Value: **New (retail):** $299.00
Excellent: $230.00
Very good: $190.00

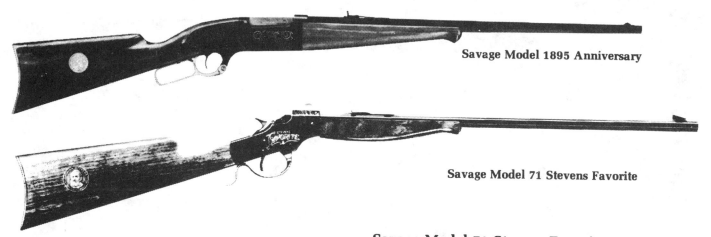

Savage Model 1895 Anniversary

Savage Model 71 Stevens Favorite

Savage Model 1895 Anniversary

Caliber: 308 Winchester
Action: Lever action; hammerless
Magazine: 5-shot rotary
Barrel: 24" octagon
Sights: Open rear, blade front (brass)
Stock & Forearm: Walnut straight grip with brass medallion inlaid and brass buttplate.
Approximate wt.: 7½ lbs.
Comments: Less than 10,000 of this limited commemorative were produced in 1970 on the 75th anniversary of the rifle.
Estimated Value: Mint: $550.00
Excellent: $325.00
Very good: $285.00

Savage Model 71 Stevens Favorite

Caliber: 22 long rifle
Action: Lever action; exposed hammer; falling block
Magazine: Single shot
Barrel: 22" octagon
Sights: Open rear, blade front
Stock & Forearm: Plain walnut, straight grip stock with lipped forearm; brass medallion in stock
Approximate wt.: 4½ lbs.
Comments: This commemorative is a replica of the Stevens Favorite issued to honor Joshua Stevens. 15,000 produced in 1971.
Estimated Value: **Mint:** $175.00
Excellent: $120.00
Very good: $100.00

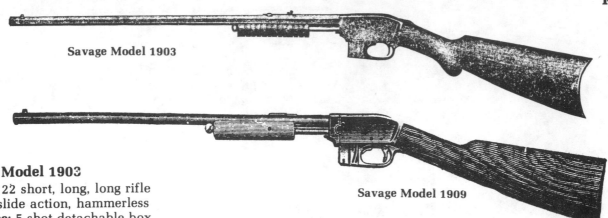

Savage Model 1903

Savage Model 1909

Savage Model 1903

Caliber: 22 short, long, long rifle
Action: slide action, hammerless
Magazine: 5-shot detachable box
Barrel: 24" octagon
Sights: Open rear, bead front
Stock & Forearm: Checkered walnut, pistol grip stock and grooved slide handle
Approximate wt.: 5 lbs.
Comments: This takedown model was produced from 1903 until 1922.
Estimated Value: Excellent: $200.00
Very good: $175.00

Savage Model 1909

This is a lighter version of the Model 1903 with a straight stock and forearm and a round 20" barrel. Discontinued about 1915.
Estimated Value: Excellent: $220.00
Very good: $190.00

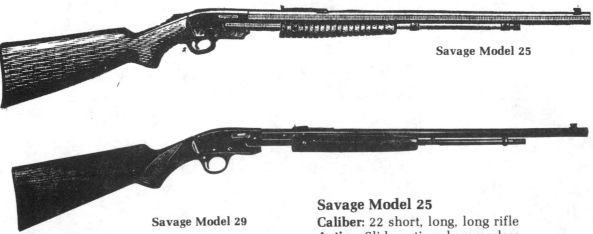

Savage Model 25

Savage Model 29

Savage Model 25

Caliber: 22 short, long, long rifle
Action: Slide action; hammerless
Magazine: 20 shorts, 17 longs, 15 long rifles tubular
Barrel: 24" octagon
Sights: Open rear, blade front
Stock & Forearm: Walnut, pistol grip stock & grooved slide handle
Approximate wt.: 5 ¾ lbs.
Comments: This takedown model was produced from the mid 1920's until 1929.
Estimated Value: Excellent: $150.00
Very good: $125.00

Savage Model 29

This rifle is very similar to the Model 25 except pre-war models are checkered; barrel is round on post-war models. Made from 1929 until the late 1960's. Add $50.00 for pre-World War II models (octagon barrel).
Estimated Value: Excellent: $125.00
Very good: $100.00

Savage Model 1914

Caliber: 22 short, long, long rifle
Action: Slide action; hammerless
Magazine: 20 shorts, 17 longs, 15 long rifles, tubular
Barrel: 24" octagon or half octagon
Sights: Open rear, bead front
Stock & Forearm: Plain wood, pistol grip stock & grooved slide handle
Approximate wt.: 5 ¾ lbs.
Comments: This takedown rifle was produced until 1924.
Estimated Value: Excellent: $175.00
Very good: $150.00

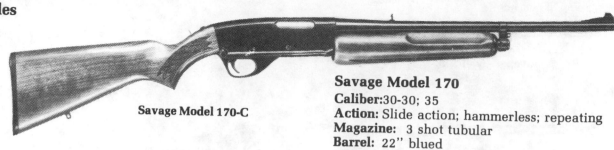

Savage Model 170-C

Savage Model 170

Caliber: 30-30; 35
Action: Slide action; hammerless; repeating
Magazine: 3 shot tubular
Barrel: 22" blued
Sights: Ramp front, folding leaf rear; hooded ramp after 1980
Stock & Forearm: Checkered walnut Monte Carlo semi-pistol grip stock & fluted slide handle; swivels
Approximate wt: 6¾ lbs.
Comments: Introduced in the late 1970's.
Estimated Value: New (retail): $188.75
                 Excellent: $145.00
                 Very good: $115.00

Savage Model 170-C

A carbine version of the Model 170; not available with a Monte Carlo stock; 18½" barrel; not available in 35 caliber.
Estimated Value: Excellent: $150.00
                 Very good: $115.00

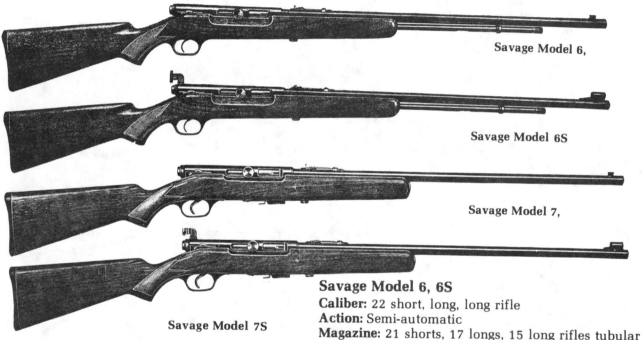

Savage Model 6,

Savage Model 6S

Savage Model 7,

Savage Model 7S

Savage Model 6, 6S

Caliber: 22 short, long, long rifle
Action: Semi-automatic
Magazine: 21 shorts, 17 longs, 15 long rifles tubular
Barrel: 24"
Sights: Open rear, bead front; 6S has peep rear, hooded front
Stock & Forearm: Checkered walnut, pistol grip before World War II; plain walnut pistol grip after the war.
Approximate wt.: 6 lbs.
Comments: This takedown model was manufactured from 1938 until late 1960's.
Estimated Value: Excellent: $90.00
                 Very good: $70.00

Savage Model 7, 7S

Basically the same as Model 6 and 6S except they are equipped with a 5-shot detachable box magazine. Produced from the late 1930's until the early 1950's.
Estimated Value: Excellent: $80.00
                 Very good: $65.00

Savage Model 1912

Caliber: 22 long rifle
Action: Semi-automatic, hammerless
Magazine: 7-shot detachable box
Barrel: 20" half-octagon
Sights: Open rear, bead front
Stock & Forearm: Plain wood, straight grip stock and forearm
Approximate wt.: 4½ lbs.
Comments: This takedown was Savage's first semi-automatic and was discontinued in 1916.
Estimated Value: Excellent: $150.00
                 Very good: $125.00

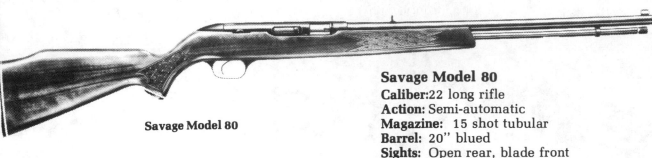

Savage Model 80

Savage Model 80

Caliber: 22 long rifle
Action: Semi-automatic
Magazine: 15 shot tubular
Barrel: 20" blued
Sights: Open rear, blade front
Stock & Forearm: Checkered walnut one piece Monte Carlo pistol grip stock and forearm.
Approximate wt: 6 lbs.
Comments: Introduced in the mid 1970's.
Estimated Value: New (retail): $104.35
Excellent: $ 80.00
Very good: $ 65.00

Sears

Sears Model 53

Caliber: 243, 30-06
Action: Bolt action; hammerless; repeating
Magazine: 5-shot tubular
Barrel: 24" blued
Sights: Folding rear, ramp front
Stock & Forearm: Checkered walnut, Monte Carlo pistol grip one-piece stock and tapered forearm; swivels
Approximate wt.: 6¾ lbs.
Comments: Made until mid 1970's.
Estimated Value: Excellent: $160.00
Very good: $130.00

Sears Ted Williams Model 53 A

Same as Model 53 in 30-06 caliber only; 22" barrel; Presently manufactured.
Estimated Value: New (retail): $189.99
Excellent: $150.00
Very good: $120.00

Sears Ted Williams Model 73

Same as Ted Williams 53 with select wood and fancy finish.
Estimated Value: New (retail): $229.99
Excellent: $185.00
Very good: $150.00

Sears Model 2200 Semi-automatic

Caliber: 22 long rifle
Action: Semi-automatic; hammerless; side ejection
Magazine: 15 shot tubular
Barrel: 20" round; blued
Sights: Sporting front, rear adjustable for elevation; receiver grooved for scope
Stock & Forearm: Checkered pistol grip one piece walnut finish hardwood stock and forearm
Approximate wt: 5½ lbs.
Comments: Manufactured at present.
Estimated Value: New (retail): $69.99
Excellent: $50.00
Very good: $45.00

Sears Model 2200 Bolt Action

Same as the Model 2200 Semi-automatic except: bolt action repeater; 5 shot box magazine; 22 short, long, or long rifle caliber.
Estimated Value: New (retail): $69.99
Excellent: $50.00
Very good: $45.00

Sears Model 2200 Lever Action

Caliber: 22 short, long or long rifle
Action: Lever action; single shot; exposed hammer
Magazine: None; single shot
Barrel: 18½" round; blued
Sights: Sporting front, rear adjustable for elevation
Stock & Forearm: Smooth, straight grip, two piece hardwood stock and forearm
Approximate wt: 5½ lbs.
Comments: Presently manufactured
Estimated Value: New (retail): $54.99
Excellent: $40.00
Very good: $30.00

Rifles

Sears Model 1

Sears Model 2

Sears Model 1
Similar to Model 2 but single shot version, no Monte Carlo stock.
Estimated Value: Excellent: $40.00
Very good: $30.00

Sears Model 2
Caliber: 22 short, long, long rifle
Action: Bolt action; hammerless; repeating
Magazine: 6 shot clip
Barrel: 20'' blued
Sights: Open rear, bead front
Stock & Forearm: Wood, Monte Carlo semi-pistol grip, one-piece stock and tapered forearm
Approximate wt.: 5 lbs.
Comments: Manufactured in the 1970's.
Estimated Value: Excellent: $55.00
Very good: $45.00

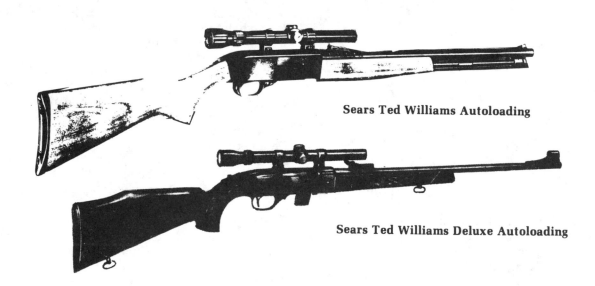

Sears Ted Williams Autoloading

Sears Ted Williams Deluxe Autoloading

Sears Ted Williams Autoloading
Caliber: 22 short, long, long rifle
Action: Semi-automatic; hammerless; side ejection
Magazine: Tubular 15 long rifles 17 longs, 21 shorts
Barrel: 20½'' blued
Sights: None, scope
Stock & Forearm: Wood, semi-pistol grip stock & forearm
Approximate wt.: 5 lbs.
Comments: Manufactured in the 1970's.
Estimated Value: Excellent: $55.00
Very good: $45.00

Sears Ted Williams Deluxe Autoloading
Caliber: 22
Action: Semi-automatic; hammerles; side ejection
Magazine: 5-shot clip
Barrel: 20'' blued
Sights: Rear tangent, hooded ramp front
Stock & Forearm: Checkered walnut, Monte Carl pistol grip one-piece stock and tapered forearm; swivels
Approximate wt.: 6 lbs.
Comments: Manufactured in the 1970's.
Estimated Value: Excellent: $60.00
Very good: $50.00

Sears Ted Williams Model 100

Sears Ted Williams Model 100
Caliber: 30-30 Winchester
Action: Lever action; exposed hammer; repeating
Magazine: 6-shot tubular
Barrel: 20'' blued
Sights: Open rear, blade front
Stock & Forearm: Walnut straight grip stock and forearm
Approximate wt.: 6 ½ lbs.
Comments: Made for Sears by Winchester.
Estimated Value: New (retail): $139.99
                  Excellent: $110.00
                  Very good: $ 90.00

Sedgley

Sedgley Springfield Sporter
Caliber: 218 Bee, 220 Swift, 22 Hornet, 22-4000, 25-35, 250-3000, 257 Roberts, 270 Winchester, 7mm, 30-06
Action: Bolt action; Springfield type (1903)
Magazine: 5-shot box
Barrel: 24''
Sights: Lyman rear, hooded ramp front
Stock & Forearm: Checkered walnut, pistol grip, one piece stock & lipped forearm; swivels
Approximate wt.: 7 ½ lbs.
Comments: Maufactured in right and left hand action from the late 1920's to World War II.
Estimated Value: Excellent: $480.00
                  Very good: $400.00

Sedgley Springfield Sporter

Sedgley Mannlicher
Similar to the Sporter with a full length forearm; 20'' barrel.
Estimated Value: Excellent: $525.00
                  Very good: $435.00

Smith & Wesson

Smith & Wesson Model A

Smith & Wesson Model A
Caliber: 22-250, 243, 270, 308, 30-06, 7mm magnum, 300 magnum
Action: Bolt action; repeating adjustable trigger
Magazine: 5-shot box
Barrel: Blued, 23 ¾''; tapered
Sights: Folding rear, hooded ramp front with silver bead
Stock & Forearm: Checkered walnut, Monte Carlo pistol grip, one-piece stock and tapered forearm; Add $15.00 for magnum.
Approximate wt: 7 lbs.
Comments: Made only in the early 1970's.
Estimated Value: Excellent: $275.00
                  Very good: $220.00

Smith & Wesson Model B
A 20'' barrel version of the Model A; not available in 22-250 or magnum; Monte Carlo stock.
Estimated Value: Excellent: $250.00
                  Very good: $200.00

Rifles

Smith & Wesson Model C
Same as Model B without Monte Carlo stock; has straight grip stock.
Estimated Value: Excellent: $225.00
Very good: $180.00

Smith & Wesson Model D
Same as Model C with full length forearm.
Estimated Value: Excellent: $260.00
Very good: $210.00

Smith & Wesson Model E
Same as Model B with full length forearm.
Estimated Value: Excellent: $275.00
Very good: $220.00

Smith & Wesson Model 1500
Caliber: 30-06, 270 Win., 243 Win., 25-06 Rem., 7mm Rem. magnum, 300 Win. magnum
Action: Bolt action; hammerless; repeating
Magazine: 5 shot box
Barrel: 23½"
Sights: Folding leaf rear, hooded ramp front
Stock & Forearm: Checkered walnut pistol grip, one piece stock and forearm; swivels
Approximate wt: 7 lbs.
Comments: Currently available. Add $15.00 for magnum, $35.00 for Deluxe Model
Estimated Value: New (retail): $297.95
Excellent: $225.00
Very good: $175.00

Smith & Wesson Model B

Smith & Wesson Model E

Standard

Standard Model M
A slide action only version of the Standard G with no gas operation feature.
Estimated Value: Excellent: $225.00
Very good: $175.00

Standard Model G
Caliber: 25-35, 30-30, 25 Remington, 30 Remington, 35 Remington
Action: Gas operated, semi-automatic; hammerless; can also be operated as slide action
Magazine: 4 or 5-shot tubular
Barrel: 22' blued
Sights: Bead front, open rear
Stock & Forearm: Wood, straight grip stock & slide handle
Approximate wt: 7¾ lbs.
Comments: Made in the early part of this century, the Standard G was one of the first gas operated autploaders available.
Estimated Value: Excellent: $325.00
Very good: $250.00

Stevens

Stevens Model No. 14 Little Scout
Caliber: 22 long rifle
Action: Pivoted block; exposed hammer; single shot
Magazine: None; single shot
Barrel: Round, 18"
Sights: Flat front, open rear
Stock & Forearm: Plain walnut, straight grip, one-piece stock and forearm
Approximate wt.: 2½ lbs.
Comments: Produced from 1904 to about 1912 when it was replaced by Model 14½.
Estimated Value: Excellent: $120.00
Very good: $100.00

Stevens Model No. 14½ Little Scout

Stevens Model No. 14½ Little Scout
This rifle is very similar to Model No. 14, except rolling block action and separated, short forearm. Produced from 1912 to World War II.
Estimated Value: Excellent: $125.00
Very good: $110.00

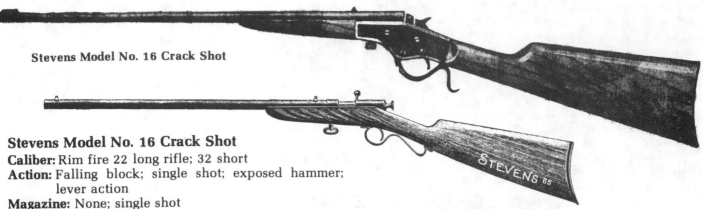

Stevens Model No. 16 Crack Shot

Stevens Model No. 65 Little Krag

Stevens Model No. 16 Crack Shot

Caliber: Rim fire 22 long rifle; 32 short
Action: Falling block; single shot; exposed hammer; lever action
Magazine: None; single shot
Barrel: Round, 20"
Sights: Blade front, open rear
Stock & Forearm: Plain, walnut, straight grip stock with slightly lipped forearm
Approximate wt.: 3¾ lbs.
Comments: This rifle was produced from the turn of the Century until 1912, when it was replaced by the Model No. 26.
Estimated Value: Excellent: $240.00
Very good: $200.00

Stevens Model No. 16½ Crack Shot

The same as No. 16 except it is smoothbore for shot cartridges. Produced from 1907 to 1912.
Estimated Value: Excellent: $220.00
Very good: $180.00

Stevens Model No. 65 Little Krag

Caliber: 22 automatic
Action: Bolt action; single shot
Magazine: None; single shot
Barrel: Round, 20"
Sights: Bead front, fixed peep or open rear
Stock & Forearm: Plain walnut straight grip, one-piece stock and forearm
Approximate wt.: 3¼ lbs.
Comments: This small 22 rifle was produced from 1903 until about 1910.
Estimated Value: Excellent: $90.00
Very good: $75.00

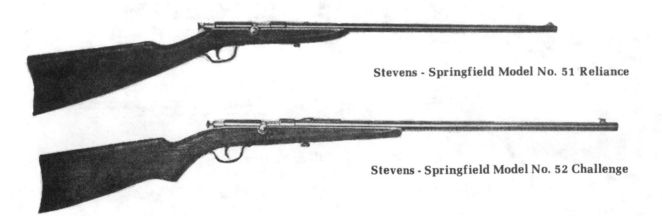

Stevens - Springfield Model No. 51 Reliance

Stevens - Springfield Model No. 52 Challenge

Stevens - Springfield Model No. 51 Reliance

Caliber: 22 short, long, long rifle
Action: Bolt action; single shot
Magazine: None; single shot
Barrel: 20", round
Sights: Blade front, open rear
Stock & Forearm: Plain walnut, straight grip, one-piece stock and forearm
Approximate wt.: 3 lbs.
Comments: Takedown. Made from 1930 for about 5 years.
Estimated Value: Excellent: $55.00
Very good: $45.00

Stevens - Springfield Model No. 52 Challenge

Caliber: 22 long rifle
Action: Bolt action; single shot
Magazine: None; single shot
Barrel: 22", round
Sights: Bead front, adjustable sporting rear
Stock & Forearm: Plain walnut, pistol grip, one-piece stock and forearm
Approximate wt.: 3½ lbs.
Comments: Takedown, produced from early 1930's to just before World War II.
Estimated Value: Excellent: $50.00
Very good: $40.00

Rifles

Stevens - Springfield Model No. 53 Springfield Jr.
Caliber: 22 long rifle
Action: Bolt action; single shot
Magazine: None; single shot
Barrel: 24''
Sights: Bead front, adjustable sporting rear
Stock & Forearm: Plain walnut, semi-pistol grip stock and forearm
Approximate wt.: 4 ½ lbs.
Comments: Takedown. Produced from 1930 until shortly after World War II.
Estimated Value: Excellent: $55.00
Very good: $45.00

Stevens Model No. 419 Junior Target
Caliber: 22 short, long, long rifle
Action: Bolt action; single shot
Magazine: None; single shot
Barrel: 26''
Sights: Blade front, peep rear
Stock & Forearm: Plain walnut, pistol grip stock with grooved forearm; swivels
Approximate wt.: 5 ½ lbs.
Comments: Produced from 1932 until 1936.
Estimated Value: Excellent: $75.00
Very good: $65.00

Stevens - Springfield Model No. 53 Springfield Jr.

Stevens Model No. 419 Junior Target

Stevens Models No. 053 Buckhorn

Stevens Model No. 66 Buckhorn

Stevens Model No. 066 Buckhorn

Stevens Models No. 53 & 053 Buckhorn
Caliber: 22 short, long, long rifle
Action: Bolt action; single shot
Magazine: None, single shot
Barrel: 24''
Sights: 053: hooded ramp front, open middle peep receiver. 53: open rear, bead front
Stock & Forearm: Plain walnut pistol grip stock and forearm
Approximate wt.: 5 ½ lbs.
Comments: This takedown rifle was manufactured from the mid 1930's until the late 1940's.
Estimated Value: Excellent: $60.00
Very good: $50.00

Stevens Model No. 66 Buckhorn
Caliber: 22 short, long, long rifle
Action: Bolt action; repeating
Magazine: Tubular, 19 shorts, 15 longs, 13 long rifles
Barrel: 24''
Sights: Bead front, open rear
Stock & Forearm: Plain walnut, semi-pistol grip stock and forearm
Approximate wt.: 5 lbs.
Comments: This takedown rifle was made from the late 1920's until after World War II.
Estimated Value: Excellent: $70.00
Very good: $60.00

Stevens Model No. 066 Buckhorn
This is the same rifle as the Model No. 66 except: hooded ramp front sight; open middle sight; receiver peep sight. Manufactured from mid 1930's until late 1940's.
Estimated Value: Excellent: $75.00
Very good: $65.00

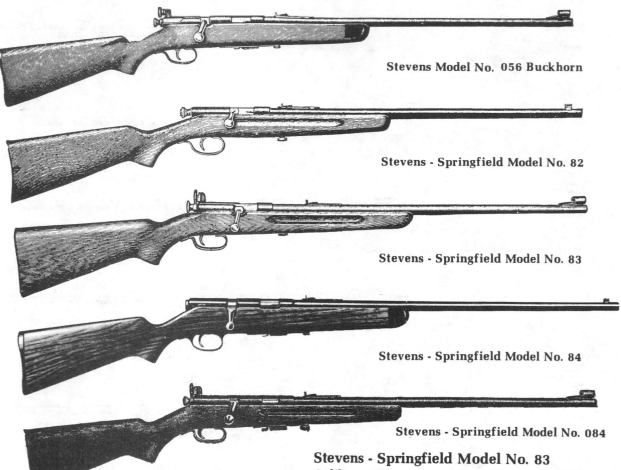

Stevens Model No. 056 Buckhorn

Stevens - Springfield Model No. 82

Stevens - Springfield Model No. 83

Stevens - Springfield Model No. 84

Stevens - Springfield Model No. 084

Stevens Model No. 56 & 056 Buckhorn

Caliber: 22 short, long, long rifle
Action: Bolt action; repeating
Magazine: 5-shot clip
Barrel: 24"
Sights: 56: bead front, open rear; 056: hooded ramp front, open middle receiver peep
Stock & Forearm: Plain walnut, pistol grip stock and black tipped forearm
Approximate wt.: 6 lbs.
Comments: This takedown model was made from the mid 1930's until late 1940's.
Estimated Value: Excellent: $70.00
Very good: $60.00

Stevens - Springfield Model No. 82

Caliber: 22
Action: Bolt action; single shot
Magazine: None; single shot
Barrel: 22"
Sights: Bead front, open rear
Stock & Forearm: Plain walnut, pistol grip stock; groove in forearm
Approximate wt.: 4 lbs.
Comments: Manufactured from middle 1930's until 1940. Takedown.
Estimated Value: Excellent: $50.00
Very good: $40.00

Stevens - Springfield Model No. 83

Caliber: 22 short, long, long rifles, 22 WRF, 25 Stevens RF
Action: Bolt action; single shot
Magazine: None; single shot
Barrel: 24"
Sights: Hooded ramp front, open middle, peep rear
Stock & Forearm: Plain walnut, pistol grip with groove in forearm.
Approximate wt.: 4½ lbs.
Comments: This takedown rifle was made from the middle 1930's until 1940.
Estimated Value: Excellent: $55.00
Very good: $45.00

Stevens - Springfield Models No. 84 & 084
(Stevens Model No. 84 after 1948)

Caliber: 22 short, long, long rifle
Action: Bolt action; repeating
Magazine: 5-shot clip
Barrel: 24"
Sights: Bead front, open rear on 84; hooded ramp, peep rear on 84 Stevens or 084.
Stock & Forearm: Plain walnut, pistol grip stock and forearm; black tip on forearm of Model 84.
Approximate wt.: 6 lbs.
Comments: This takedown was made from early 1940 until the mid 1960's.
Estimated Value: Excellent: $70.00
Very good: $60.00

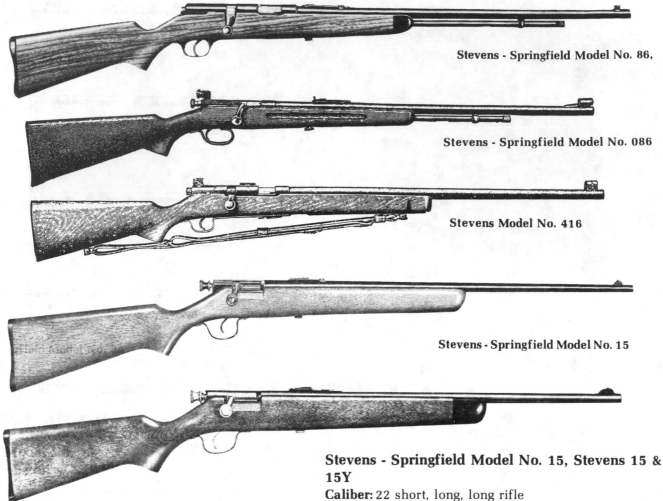

Stevens - Springfield Model No. 86,

Stevens - Springfield Model No. 086

Stevens Model No. 416

Stevens - Springfield Model No. 15

Stevens - Springfield Model No. 15Y

Stevens - Springfield Model No. 86, 086
(Stevens Model No. 86 after 1948)

Model 86 is same as Model 84 except it has a tubular magazine that holds 21 shorts, 17 longs, 15 long rifles. Made from mid 1930's until mid 1960's. Model 86 Stevens or 086 Stevens is same as 084 or 84 Stevens except it has tubular magazine.

Estimated Value: Excellent: $80.00
**   Very good: $70.00**

Stevens Model No. 416

Caliber: 22 long rifle
Action: Bolt action; repeating
Magazine: 5-shot clip
Barrel: 26'' heavy
Sights: Hooded ramp front, receiver peep
Stock & Forearm: Plain walnut, pistol grip stock & forearm
Approximate wt.: 9½ lbs.
Comments: Manufactured from late 1930's to late 1940's.
Estimated Value: Excellent: $115.00
**   Very good: $100.00**

Stevens - Springfield Model No. 15, Stevens 15 & 15Y

Caliber: 22 short, long, long rifle
Action: Bolt action; single shot
Magazine: None; single shot
Barrel: Stevens-Springfield: 22''; Stevens 15 - 24''; Stevens 15Y - 21''
Sights: Bead front, open rear
Stock & Forearm: Plain walnut pistol grip, 15Y: short butt stock, black tipped forearm
Approximate wt.: 4 to 5 lbs.
Comments: Manufactured: Stevens-Springfield 15 - late 1930's to late 1940's. Stevens 15 - late 1940's to mid 1960's. Stevens 15Y - late 1950's to mid 1960's.
Estimated Value: Excellent: $45.00
**   Very good: $35.00**

Stevens Model No. 325, 325 S

Caliber: 30-30
Action: Bolt action; repeating
Magazine: 3-shot clip
Barrel: 21''
Sights: Bead front, open rear; 325 S peep rear
Stock & Forearm: Plain walnut, pistol grip stock & forearm
Approximate wt.: 6¾ lbs.
Comments: Made from late 1940's to early 1950's.
Estimated Value: Excellent: $55.00
**   Very good: $45.00**

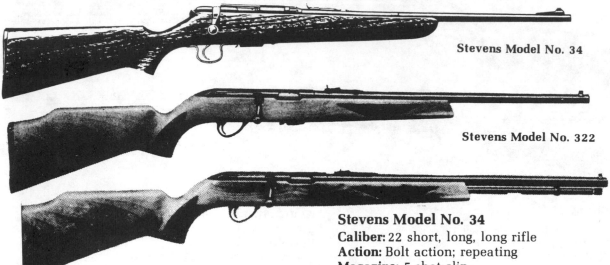

Stevens Model No. 34

Stevens Model No. 322

Stevens Model No. 46

Stevens Model No. 322, 322S

Caliber: 22 Hornet
Action: Bolt action; repeating
Magazine: 5-shot clip
Barrel: 21"
Sights: Ramp front, open rear; 322 S has peep rear
Stock & Forearm: Plain walnut, pistol grip stock & forearm
Approximate wt.: 6¾ lbs.
Comments: Made from late 1940's to early 1950's.
Estimated Value: Excellent: $120.00
Very good: $100.00

Stevens Model No. 34

Caliber: 22 short, long, long rifle
Action: Bolt action; repeating
Magazine: 5-shot clip
Barrel: 20"
Sights: Sporting front, open rear
Stock & Forearm: Plain walnut, pistol grip, before 1969; checkered Monte Carlo after 1969.
Approximate wt.: 5 ½ lbs.
Comments: Made from mid 1960's to present.
Estimated Value: New (retail): $73.90
Excellent: $60.00
Very good: $50.00

Stevens Model No. 46

Similar to Model 34 except with tubular magazine. Discontinued in late 1960's.
Estimated Value: Excellent: $65.00
Very good: $55.00

Stevens Model No. 73

Stevens Model 120

Stevens Model 120

Caliber: 22 short, long, or long rifle
Action: Bolt action; single shot; cocking piece
Magazine: None
Barrel: 24" blued
Sights: Blade front, elevator open rear
Stock & Forearm: Plain hardwood, semi-pistol grip one piece stock and forearm
Approximate wt: 5 lbs.
Comments: Produced in the late 1970's.
Estimated Value: Excellent: $45.00
Very good: $35.00

Stevens Model No. 73, 73 Y

Caliber: 22 short, long, long rifle
Action: Bolt action; single shot
Magazine: None; single shot
Barrel: 20" on 73; 18" in 73Y
Sights: Sporting front, open rear
Stock & Forearm: Plain walnut pistol grip; short stock on 73Y (Youth Model)
Approximate wt: 73 - 4¾ lbs; 73Y - 4 ½ lbs.
Comments: Made from 1965 to late 1970's.
Estimated Value: Excellent: $40.00
Very good: $35.00

Rifles

Stevens Model 246

Stevens Model 110 E

Stevens Model 246

Caliber: 22 short, long, or long rifle
Action: Bolt action; repeating
Magazine: Tubular, 22 shorts, 17 longs, 15 long rifles
Magazine: 20" blued
Sights: Blade front, elevator open rear
Stock & Forearm: Checkered hardwood, one piece, semi-pistol grip stock and forearm
Approximate wt: 5 lbs.
Comments: Produced in the late 1970's.
Estimated Value: Excellent: $65.00
Very good: $55.00

Stevens Model 110 E

Caliber: 243; 30-06
Action: Bolt action; repeating
Magazine: 4 shot
Barrel: 22" blued
Sights: Ramp front, open rear
Stock & Forearm: Checkered hardwood, one piece Monte Carlo, semi-pistol grip stock and forearm
Approximate wt: 7 lbs.
Comments: Produced in the late 1970's to present.
Estimated Value: New (retail): $203.25
Excellent: $155.00
Very good: $125.00

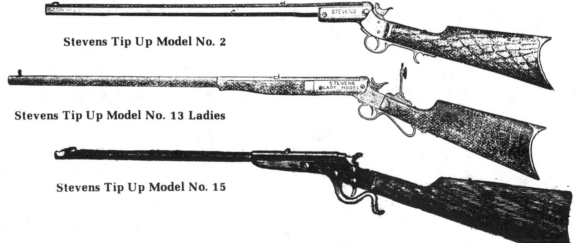

Stevens Tip Up Model No. 2

Stevens Tip Up Model No. 13 Ladies

Stevens Tip Up Model No. 15

Stevens Tip Up Models No. 2, 5, 6, 7, 8, 9, 11 Ladies & 13 Ladies

Caliber: RF 22 long rifle, 25 Stevens and 32 long (in #11)
Action: Single shot, tip up; exposed hammer
Magazine: None; single shot
Barrel: Octagon 24" for #2; 28" half octagon optional on #7; all others 24" half octagon
Sights: Beach combination front, open rear; peep on #5 and #7 and #13; Blade front, open rear on #2; Open on #11.
Stock & Forearm: Walnut straight stock and forearm; no forearm on #2 & #5
Approximate wt.: 5½ to 6½ lbs.
Comments: This series replaced the 1888 and was produced until it was replaced in 1902 by a line of Falling block rifles.
Estimated Value: Excellent: $230.00
Very good: $210.00

Stevens Model No. 15 Maynard Jr.

Caliber: 22 long rifle or short
Action: Lever action; tip up; exposed hammer
Magazine: None; single shot
Barrel: 18" part octagon
Sights: Open rear, blade front
Stock & Forearm: Plain walnut, straight stock and short forearm
Approximate wt.: 2¾ lbs.
Comments: This small rifle was made to compete with cheap imports. Produced from 1901 - 1910.
Estimated Value: Excellent: $120.00
Very good: $100.00

Stevens Model No. 15½ Maynard Jr.

This is the same gun as the No. 15 except it is smoothbore for 22 long rifle shot cartridges.
Estimated Value: Excellent: $125.00
Very good: $105.00

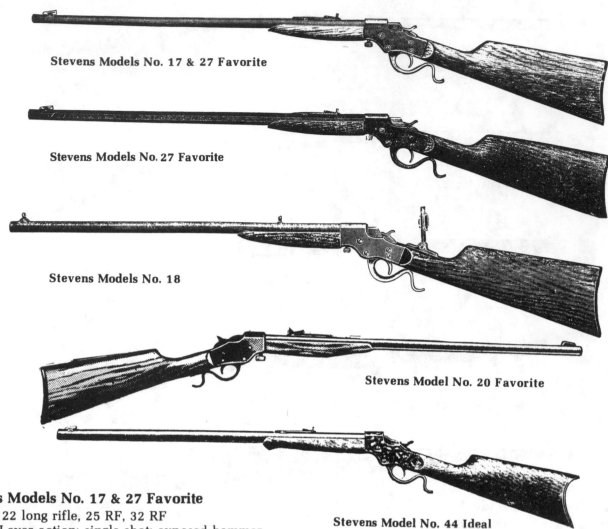

Stevens Models No. 17 & 27 Favorite

Stevens Models No. 27 Favorite

Stevens Models No. 18

Stevens Model No. 20 Favorite

Stevens Model No. 44 Ideal

Stevens Models No. 17 & 27 Favorite

Caliber: 22 long rifle, 25 RF, 32 RF
Action: Lever action; single shot; exposed hammer
Magazine: None; single shot
Barrel: 24" round (octagon barrel on Model 27); other lengths available as option
Sights: Open rear, Rocky Mountain front
Stock & Forearm: Plain walnut, straight grip, short tapered forearm
Approximate wt.: 4 to 5 lbs.
Comments: This takedown model was produced from the 1890's until the mid 1930's.
Estimated Value: Excellent: $135.00
Very good: $110.00

Stevens Models No. 18 & 28 Favorite

This is the same rifle as the Model No. 17 except it has a Beach combination front sight, Vernier peep rear sight and leaf middle sight. Model 28 has octagon barrel.
Estimated Value: Excellent: $145.00
Very good: $120.00

Stevens Models No. 19 & 29 Favorite

This is the same rifle as the Model No. 17 except it has Lyman front sight, leaf middle sight and Lyman combination rear sight. Model 29 has octagon barrel.
Estimated Value: Excellent: $150.00
Very good: $125.00

Stevens Model No. 20 Favorite

This is the same rifle as the Model No. 17 except the barrel is smoothbore for 22 RF and 32 RF shot cartridges.
Estimated Value: Excellent: $140.00
Very good: $125.00

Stevens Model No. 44 Ideal

Caliber: 22 long rifle; 25 RF, 25-20 SS, 32-20, 32-40, 38-55, 44-40
Action: Lever action; rolling block; exposed hammer; single shot
Magazine: None; single shot
Barrel: 24" or 26" round, octagon or half octagon
Sights: Open rear, Rocky Mountain front
Stock & Forearm: Plain walnut, straight grip
Approximate wt.: 7 lbs.
Comments: This rifle was produced from the late 1890's until the early 1930's and is a takedown model.
Estimated Value: Excellent: $275.00
Very good: $250.00

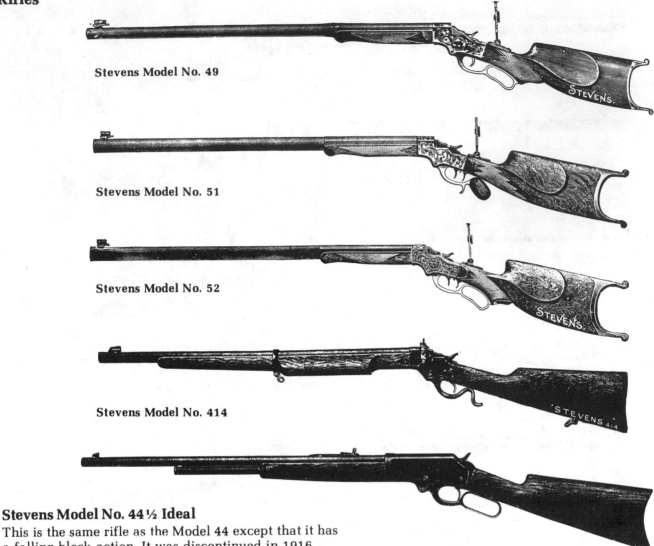

Stevens Model No. 49

Stevens Model No. 51

Stevens Model No. 52

Stevens Model No. 414

Stevens Model No. 425 High Power

Stevens Model No. 44½ Ideal

This is the same rifle as the Model 44 except that it has a falling block action. It was discontinued in 1916.
Estimated Value: Excellent: $350.00
Very good: $300.00

Stevens Models No. 45 to 54

These rifles are structurally the same as the Model 44. They differ in engraving and finishes and are generally fancy models that bring extremely high prices. They were produced until World War I; target sights and stocks.
Estimated Value: Excellent: $480.00 - $1,000.00
Very good: $250.00 - $ 700.00

Stevens Model No. 414 Armory

Caliber: 22 long rifle only or 22 short only
Action: Lever action; exposed hammer; rolling block
Magazine: None; single shot
Barrel: 26" heavy round
Sights: Rocky Mountain front, adjustable receiver rear
Stock & Forearm: Plain walnut straight grip, military stock and forearm; bands; swivels
Approximate wt.: 8 lbs.
Comments: Produced from 1912 until just before World War I.
Estimated Value: Excellent: $290.00
Very good: $250.00

Stevens Model No. 425 High Power

Caliber: Rimless Remington 25, 30, 32, 35; smokeless flatnose
Action: Lever action; exposed hammer; single extractor
Magazine: 5-shot tubular under barrel
Barrel: 22" round
Sights: Post front, adjustable sporting rear
Stock & Forearm: Plain walnut, straight grip stock and forearm
Approximate wt.: 7 lbs.
Comments: Produced for about 5 years beginning in 1911.
Estimated Value: Excellent: $160.00
Very good: $140.00

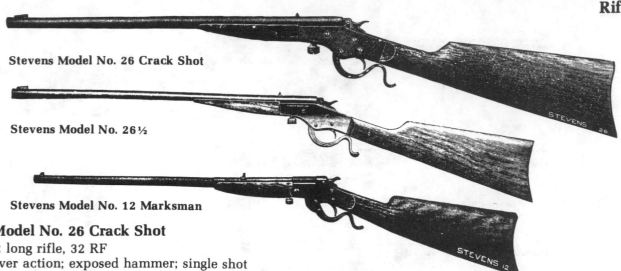

Stevens Model No. 26 Crack Shot

Stevens Model No. 26½

Stevens Model No. 12 Marksman

Stevens Model No. 26 Crack Shot
Caliber: 22 long rifle, 32 RF
Action: Lever action; exposed hammer; single shot
Magazine: None; single shot
Barrel: 18", 22"
Sights: Blade front, open rear
Stock & Forearm: Plain walnut, straight grip stock and tapered forearm
Approximate wt.: 3¼ to 3½ lbs.
Comments: This takedown rifle was produced from 1913 until just prior to World War II.
Estimated Value: Excellent: $135.00
Very good: $110.00

Stevens Model No. 26½
The same gun as No. 26 except smoothbore for shot cartridges.
Estimated Value: Excellent: $130.00
Very good: $110.00

Stevens Model No. 12 Marksman
Caliber: 22 long rifle, 25 RF, 32 RF
Action: Lever action; tip up; exposed hammer; single shot
Magazine: None; single shot
Barrel: 20", round
Sights: Bead front, open rear
Stock & Forearm: Plain walnut, straight grip stock and short tapered forearm
Approximate wt.: 4 lbs.
Comments: Replaced the Little Maynard. Made from 1912 until just before World War II.
Estimated Value: Excellent: $100.00
Very good: $85.00

Stevens Model No. 72 Crackshot

Stevens Model No. 89

Stevens Model No. 72 Crackshot
Caliber: 22 short, long, long rifle
Action: Falling block; single shot
Magazine: None; single shot
Barrel: 22" octagon
Sights: Sporting front, open rear
Stock & Forearm: Plain walnut, straight grip stock and tapered forearm
Approximate wt.: 4½ lbs.
Comments: Made from early 1970's to present.
Estimated Value: New (retail): $94.50
Excellent: $75.00
Very good: $60.00

Stevens Model No. 89
Caliber: 22 short, long, long rifle
Action: Lever action; automatic ejection; exposed hammer
Magazine: None; single shot
Barrel: 18½"
Sights: Sporting front, open rear
Stock & Forearm: Straight walnut stock and forearm with carbine band
Approximate wt.: 5 lbs.
Comments: Production began mid 1970's.
Estimated Value: New (retail): $66.80
Excellent: $50.00
Very good: $40.00

Rifles

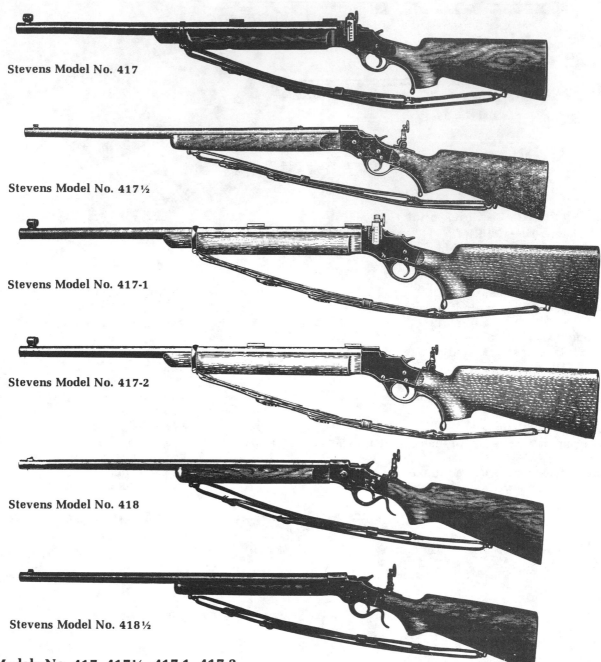

Stevens Model No. 417

Stevens Model No. 417½

Stevens Model No. 417-1

Stevens Model No. 417-2

Stevens Model No. 418

Stevens Model No. 418½

Stevens Models No. 417, 417½, 417-1, 417-2, 417-3, Walnut Hill

Caliber: 22 long rifle, 22 WRF, 25 Stevens
Action: Lever action; exposed hammer; single shot
Magazine: None, single shot
Barrel: 28" or 29" heavy
Sights: 417: Lyman 52L extension rear; 417½: Lyman 144 tang peep and folding center; 417-1: Lyman 48L rear; 417-2: 144 rear; 417-3: no sights.
Stock & Forearm: Plain walnut, pistol grip stock and forearm; bands; swivels
Approximate wt.: 8¼ to 10½ lbs.
Comments: These rifles were produced from the early 1930's until the late 1940's. Models differ only in sights.
Estimated Value: Excellent: $450.00
**   Very good: $375.00**

Stevens Models No. 418, 418½ Walnut Hill

Caliber: 418 22 long rifle, 22 short only; 418½: 22 WRF or 25 Stevens RF only.
Action: Lever action; exposed hammer; single shot
Magazine: None; single shot
Barrel: 26"
Sights: Lyman 144 Tang peep, blade front. 418½: Lyman 2 A tang peep, bead front
Stock & Forearm: Plain walnut pistol grip stock and forearm; swivels
Approximate wt.: 6½ lbs.
Comments: This rifle was manufactured from the early 1930's to just before World War II.
Estimated Value: Excellent: $275.00
**   Very good: $225.00**

Stevens Model No. 80 Repeating Gallery

Stevens Model No. 70 Visible Loading

Stevens Model No. 75 Hammerless

Stevens Model No. 71 Visible Loading

Stevens Model No. 80 Repeating Gallery
Caliber: 22 short
Action: Slide action; hammerless
Magazine: 16 shot, tubular
Barrel: 24" round
Sights: Bead front, open rear
Stock & Forearm: Plain walnut, straight grip stock and grooved forearm
Approximate wt.: 5 ¼ lbs.
Comments: This takedown was made for about 5 years beginning in 1906.
Estimated Value: Excellent: $200.00
       Very good: $175.00

Stevens Model No. 70 Visible Loading
Caliber: 22 short, long, long rifle
Action: Slide action; exposed hammer
Magazine: Tubular 11 long rifles, 13 longs, 15 shorts
Barrel: Round 20", 22"
Sights: Bead front, open rear
Stock & Forearm: Plain walnut, straight grip stock and grooved slide handle
Approximate wt.: 4 ½ lbs.
Comments: Produced from 1907 until the early 1930's.
Estimated Value: Excellent: $175.00
       Very good: $150.00

Stevens Model No. 75 Hammerless
Caliber: 22 short, long, long rifle
Action: Slide action; hammerless; side ejection
Magazine: Tubular, 20 shorts, 17 longs, 15 long rifles
Barrel: 24"
Sights: Bead front, adjustable rear
Stock & Forearm: Plain walnut, straight grip stock and grooved slide handle
Approximate wt.: 5 ¼ lbs.
Comments: Made from the early 1930's until World War II.
Estimated Value: Excellent: $170.00
       Very good: $145.00

Stevens Model No. 71 Visible Loading
Caliber: 22 short, long, long rifle
Action: Slide action; exposed hammer
Magazine: Tubular, 15 shorts, 13 longs, 11 long rifles
Barrel: 24" octagon
Sights: Bead front, adjustable flat top sporting rear
Stock & Forearm: Plain walnut, pistol grip stock and grooved slide handle
Approximate wt.: 5 lbs.
Comments: This replaced the No. 70, and was discontinued prior to World War II.
Estimated Value: Excellent: $165.00
       Very good: $145.00

Stevens - Springfield Model No. 85

Stevens - Springfield Model No. 87

Stevens Model No. 57

Stevens Model No. 76

Stevens Model 887-T

Stevens - Springfield Model No. 85, 085 (Stevens Model No. 85 after 1948)

Caliber: 22 long rifle
Action: Semi-automatic; repeating
Magazine: 5-shot clip
Barrel: 24"
Sights: Bead front, open rear on 85. Hooded ramp front and peep rear on 085, 85 Stevens
Stock & Forearm: Plain walnut pistol grip stock and forearm. 85 has black tipped forearm
Approximate wt.: 6 lbs.
Comments: Made from late 1930's until after World War II
Estimated Value: Excellent: $80.00
Very good: $70.00

Stevens - Springfield Model No. 87, & 087 (Stevens Model 87 after 1948)

This is the same as the No. 85, 085 except it has tubular magazine that holds 15 shots.
Estimated Value: Excellent: $85.00
Very good: $75.00

Stevens Model No. 87 K Scout

Carbine version of Model No. 87, 20" barrel; produced until 1969.
Estimated Value: Excellent: $75.00
Very good: $60.00

Stevens Model No. 57 & 057

Caliber: 22 long rifle
Action: Semi-automatic; repeating
Magazine: 5-shot clip
Barrel: 24"
Sights: 57: bead front, open rear; 057: hooded ramp front, open middle, receiver peep
Stock & Forearm: Plain walnut pistol grip stock and forearm; black tipped forearm on 57
Approximate wt.: 6 lbs.
Comments: Manufactured from late 1930's to late 1940's.
Estimated Value: Excellent: $80.00
Very good: $70.00

Stevens Model No. 76 & 076

Same as 057 & 57 except with 15-shot tubular magazine.
Estimated Value: Excellent: $85.00
Very good: $75.00

Stevens Model 887

Caliber: 22 long rifle
Action: Semi-automatic
Magazine: 15 shot tubular
Barrel: 20" blued
Sights: Blade front, elevator open rear
Stock & Forearm: Checkered hardwood semi-pistol grip, one piece stock and forearm
Approximate wt: 6 lbs.
Comments: Produced in the late 1970's.
Estimated Value: Excellent: $60.00
Very good: $50.00

Stevens Model 887-T

Similar to the Model 887 with a 4x scope.
Estimated Value: New (retail): $85.50
Excellent: $65.00
Very good: $55.00

Universal Model 440 Vulcan

Universal M1 or 1000

Universal M1 or 1000 Deluxe

Universal 1020

Universal Ferret

Universal 440 Vulcan

Caliber: 44 magnum
Action: Slide action; hammerless; repeating
Magazine: 5-shot clip
Barrel: 18¼'' carbine
Sights: Adjustable rear, ramp front with gold bead
Stock & Forearm: Walnut, semi pistol grip stock and slide handle
Approximate wt.: 6 lbs.
Comments: Made from the mid 1960's to early 70's
Estimated Value: Excellent: $210.00
Very good: $170.00

Universal M1 or 1000, 1003

Similar to the U.S. M1 Carbine with a 5-shot detachable clip. Made in 30 caliber from the mid 1960's to present. Currently sold as 1003.
Estimated Value: New (retail): $175.00
Excellent: $130.00
Very good: $105.00

Universal Ferret

Similar to the M1 with a Monte Carlo stock, no sights, and in 256 caliber.
Estimated Value: New (retail): $208.95
Excellent: $160.00
Very good: $125.00

Universal M1 or 1000 Deluxe, 1005 SB, 1010N, 1015G

This is the same as the 1000 with a Monte Carlo stock and also available in nickel or gold plate.

Estimated Value:	1005 SB Blue	1010N Nickel	1015G Gold
New (retail):	$211.95	$224.95	$273.95
Excellent:	$160.00	$170.00	$210.00
Very good:	$125.00	$140.00	$175.00

Universal 1020, 1020 TB, 1025 TCO

Similar to the 1000 with a Monte Carlo stock and a water resistant teflon finish in green, blue, tan or black. Currently produced as 1020 TB (black) and 1025 TCO (green).
Estimated Value: New (retail): $242.95
Excellent: $180.00
Very good: $140.00

Universal Model 5000 PT

Caliber: 30 M1
Action: Gas operated semi-automatic; convertible to single shot
Magazine: 5 shot clip; 15 or 30 shot available
Barrel: 18''
Sights: Adjustable peep rear, blade front with wings
Stock & Forearm: Metal folding shoulder extension stock; walnut pistol grip forearm; metal handguard
Approximate wt: 6 lbs.
Comments: A paratrooper type carbine with folding stock.
Estimated Value: New (retail): $218.60
Excellent: $165.00
Very good: $135.00

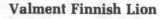

Valmet Finnish Lion

Valment Finnish Lion

Caliber:22 long rifle
Action: Bolt action; single shot
Magazine: None
Barrel: 29" blued, heavy
Sights: Extended peep rear, changeable front
Stock & Forearm: Free-rifle, pistol grip, with thumb hole, one piece stock & forearm; palm rest; swivels; Swiss butt plate
Approximate wt: 15 lbs.
Comments: International Match type rifle. Discontinued in late 1970's.
Estimated Value: Excellent: $425.00
                    Very good: $350.00

Valmet Model M-72S

Valmet Model M-62/S

Valmet Model M-72S, M-715S, M-71S

Caliber:223, 5.56mm
Action: Gas operated, semi-automatic
Magazine: 15 or 30 shot, curved detachable box
Barrel: 16½"
Sights: Open tangent rear, hooded post front; both adjustable
Stock & Forearm: Wood or reinforced resin stock; pistol grip; swivels; wood stock and forearm and plastic pistol grip on current model (M-71S).
Approximate wt: 8¾ lbs.
Comments: Similar to the M-62/S. Still in production.
Estimated Value: New (retail): $695.00
                    Excellent: $520.00
                    Very good: $415.00

Valmet Model M-62/S

Caliber:7.62 x 39mm Russian
Action: Gas piston, rotating bolt; semi-automatic
Magazine: 15 or 30 shot, curved detachable box
Barrel: 16½"
Sights: Adjustable tangent peep rear, adjustable hooded post front
Stock & Forearm: Fixed metal tube stock or walnut; pistol grip; ventilated forearm
Approximate wt: 8¾ lbs.
Comments: A powerful semi-automatic, made from the mid 1970's to present. Add $15.00 for wood stock version.
Estimated Value: New (retail): $695.00
                    Excellent: $525.00
                    Very good: $425.00

Valmet Model M-76 FS

Similar to the Model M-62 S in 223 caliber.
Estimated Value: New (retail): $695.00
                    Excellent: $525.00
                    Very good: $420.00

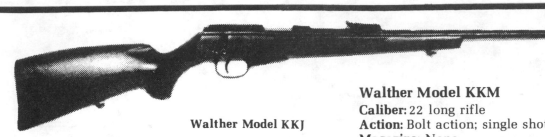

Walther Model KKJ

Walther Model KKJ

Caliber: 22 Hornet, 22 long rifle, 22 WRM
Action: Bolt action; repeating; double set trigger available
Barrel: 22½'' blued
Magazine: 5-shot detachable clip
Sights: Adjustable rear, hooded ramp front
Stock & Forearm: Checkered walnut, pistol grip stock & forearm; cheekpiece; swivels
Approximate wt.: 5½ lbs.
Comments: Made from about 1957 to late 1970's. Add $20.00 for double set trigger.
Estimated Value: Excellent: **$360.00**
                    Very good: **$285.00**

Walther Model KKM

Caliber: 22 long rifle
Action: Bolt action; single shot
Magazine: None
Barrel: 28'' tapered barrel; blued
Sights: Olympic front, changeable micro adjustable rear
Stock & Forearm: Walnut match style with thumbhole; adjustable butt plate; heavy forearm with hand shelf; cheekpiece
Approximate wt.: 15 lbs.
Comments: A match rifle made from the late 1950's to late 1970's.
Estimated Value: Excellent: **$500.00**
                    Very good: **$400.00**

Walther Model KKM

Walther Model UIT

Walther Moving Taget

Caliber: 22 long rifle
Action: Bolt action; single shot
Magazine: None
Barrel: 23½'' blued
Sights: Micro adjustable rear, globe front
Stock & Forearm: Walnut, pistol grip, thumb hole match type with adjustable cheekpiece and butt plate
Approximate wt: 8¼ lbs.
Comments: A match rifle made in 1970's.
Estimated Value: Excellent: **$475.00**
                    Very good: **$380.00**

Walther Model UIT

Caliber: 22 long rifle
Action: Bolt action, single shot
Magazine: None
Barrel: 25½''
Sights: Changeable front, micro adjustable rear
Stock & Forearm: Match style, walnut pistol grip stock & wide forearm
Approximate wt: 10¼ lbs.
Comments: A match rifle made from the mid 1960's.
Estimated Value: Excellent: **$475.00**
                    Very good: **$380.00**

Walther Prone 400

Similar to the UIT with split stock and adjustable cheekpiece.
Estimated Value: Excellent: **$490.00**
                    Very good: **$390.00**

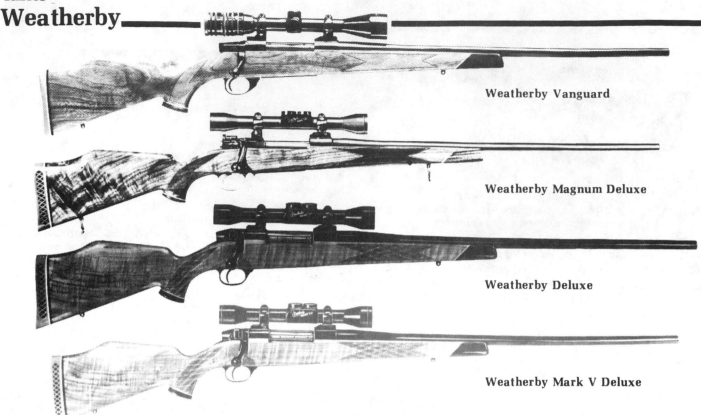

Weatherby Vanguard

Weatherby Magnum Deluxe

Weatherby Deluxe

Weatherby Mark V Deluxe

Weatherby Vanguard

Caliber: 25-06, 243, 270, 30-06, 308, 7mm Rem. magnum, 300 Win. magnum
Action: Bolt action; repeating
Magazine: 5-shot, (3-shot magnum) box with hinged floor plate.
Barrel: 24'' blued
Sights: None
Stock & Forearm: Checkered walnut, Monte Carlo, pistol grip, one-piece stock & forearm; recoil pad; swivels
Approximate wt.: 8 lbs.
Comments: Made from the early 1970's to present.
Estimated Value: New (retail): $439.95
             Excellent: $330.00
             Very good: $270.00

Weatherby Magnum Deluxe

Caliber: 378 magnum, 300 magnum, 375 magnum, 7mm magnum, 270 magnum, 275 magnum, and 220 rocket
Action: Bolt action; Mauser type
Magazine: 3-shot
Barrel: 24'' blued; 26'' available on some calibers
Sights: None
Stock & Forearm: Checkered wood, Monte Carlo pistol grip, one-piece stock and tapered forearm; recoil pad; swivels; cheekpiece
Approximate wt.: 7-8 lbs.
Comments: Made from the late 1940's to the late 1950's.
Estimated Value: Excellent: $350.00
             Very good: $280.00

Weatherby Deluxe

Similar to the Magnum Deluxe but in 270 Winchester caliber.
Estimated Value: Excellent: $325.00
             Very good: $260.00

Weatherby Mark V Deluxe

Caliber: 22-250, 30-06, 240, 257, 270, 7mm, 300 Win., 340, 378, 460
Action: Bolt action; repeating
Magazine: 3 or 4 shot, depending on caliber
Barrel: 24'' or 26'' blued
Sights: None
Stock & Forearm: Checkered walnut, Monte Carlo pistol grip, one piece stock & tapered forearm; cheekpiece; recoil pad; swivels.
Approximate wt.: 7-10 lbs.
Comments: Made from the late 1950's to present.
Estimated Value: New (retail): $639.00 - 919.00
             Excellent: $480.00 - $690.00
             Very good: $385.00 - $550.00
(Depending on Caliber)

Weatherby Model Varmintmaster

A scaled down version of the Mark V Deluxe in 22-250 or 224 Weatherby magnum; 26'' barrel
Estimated Value: New (retail): $639.95
               Excellent: $480.00
               Very good: $385.00

Weatherby Mark XXII (Clip)

Weatherby Mark XXII Deluxe

Caliber: 22 long rifle
Action: Semi-automatic; hammerless
Magazine: 5 or 10 shot clip or 15-shot tubular
Barrel: 24" blued
Sights: Open rear, ramp front
Stock & Forearm: Checkered walnut, Monte Carlo pistol grip, one-piece stock & tapered forearm; swivels
Approximate wt.: 6 lbs.
Comments: Made from the mid 1960's to date. Add $10.00 for tubular magazine.
Estimated Value: New (retail): $279.95
            Excellent: $210.00
            Very good: $170.00

Weatherby Mark XXII (Tubular)

Western Field

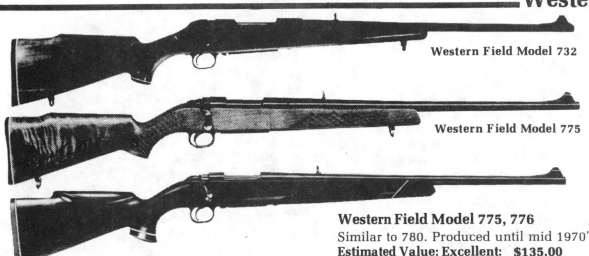

Western Field Model 732

Western Field Model 775

Western Field Model 730

Western Field Model 775, 776

Similar to 780. Produced until mid 1970's.
Estimated Value: Excellent: $135.00
            Very good: $110.00

Western Field Model 730

Similar to 732. Produced until mid 1970's.
Estimated Value: Excellent: $170.00
            Very good: $135.00

Western Field Model 732

Caliber: 7 mm, 30-06
Action: Bolt action; hammerless; repeating
Magazine: 4 or 5 shot tubular, depending on caliber
Barrel: 22" blued
Sights: Leaf rear, bead front
Stock & Forearm: Checkered walnut, Monte Carlo pistol grip, one-piece stock and forearm; swivels
Approximate wt.: 8 lbs.
Comments: Manufactured into the late 1970's..
Estimated Value: Excellent: $175.00
            Very good: $140.00

Western Field Model 815

Caliber: 22 short, long, long rifle
Action: Bolt action; single shot; hammerless
Magazine: None
Barrel: 24" blued
Sights: Adjustable rear, bead front
Stock & Forearm: Wood, Monte Carlo pistol grip, one-piece stock and tapered forearm
Approximate wt.: 8 lbs.
Comments: Made until the mid 1970's.
Estimated Value: Excellent: $40.00
            Very good: $35.00

Rifles

Western Field Bolt Action Repeater

Western Field Model 830

Western Field Model 780

Western Field Model 842

Western Field Bolt Action Repeater

Caliber:22 short, long, long rifle; 22 WRM
Action: Bolt action; hammerless; repeating
Magazine: 7-shot clip in 22; 5 shot in 22 WRM
Barrel: 24" blued
Sights: Adjustable rear, ramp front
Stock & Forearm: Walnut, pistol grip, one-piece stock and forearm.
Approximate wt: 6 lbs.
Comments: Add $5.00 for 22 WRM
Estimated Value: New (retail): $69.99
Excellent: $55.00
Very good: $45.00

Western Field Model 830

Similar to Model 832. Made until mid 1970's.
Estimated Value: Excellent: $50.00
Very good: $40.00

Western Field Model 780

Caliber: 243, 308
Action: Bolt action; hammerless; repeating
Magazine: 5-shot tubular
Barrel: 22" blued
Sights: Adjustable rear, bead front
Stock & Forearm: Checkered walnut, Monte Carlo pistol grip, one piece stock and forearm
Approximate wt.: 6 ½ lbs.
Comments: Manufactured to the late 1970's.
Estimated Value: Excellent: $150.00
Very good: $120.00

Western Field Model 842

Caliber: 22 short, long, long rifle
Action: Bolt action; hammerless; repeating
Magazine: Tubular, 18 long rifles, 20 longs, 22 shorts
Barrel: 24" blued
Sights: Adjustable rear, bead front
Stock & Forearm: Walnut, Monte Carlo pistol grip, one-piece stock and forearm
Approximate wt.: 6 ¼ lbs.
Comments: Manufactured until the mid 1970's.
Estimated Value: Excellent: $55.00
Very good: $45.00

Western Field Bolt Action

Caliber:30-06
Action: Bolt action; repeating
Magazine: 4 shot, hinged floorplate
Barrel: 22" round, blued
Sights: Bead front, adjustable rear
Stock & Forearm: Smooth hardwood pistol grip, one piece stock and forearm with sling swivels
Approximate wt: 7 ¾ lbs.
Comments: Currently manufactured.
Estimated Value: New (retail): $199.99
Excellent: $150.00
Very good: $120.00

Western Field Model 78 Deluxe

Caliber:7mm magnum, 30-06
Action: Bolt action
Magazine: 3 shot rotary magazine in 7mm and 4 shot in 30-06
Barrel: 24" in 7mm and 22" in 30-06
Sights: Bead front, adjustable rear
Stock & Forearm: Checkered walnut pistol grip stock and forearm; swivels
Approximate wt: 8 ¾ lbs., 7mm; 7 ½ lbs. 30-06
Comments: Currently manufactured.
Estimated Value: New (retail): $249.99
Excellent: $190.00
Very good: $150.00

Western Field Model 72

Caliber: 30-30
Action: Lever action; exposed hammer; repeating; side ejection
Magazine: 6-shot tubular
Barrel: 18", 20" blued
Sights: Adjustable open rear, ramp front
Stock & Forearm: Walnut, pistol grip; two piece stock and forearm; barrel band; fluted comb
Approximate wt: 7 ½ lbs.
Comments: Manufactured into the late 1970's.
Estimated Value: Excellent: $110.00
Very good: $ 90.00

Western Field Model 740

Similar to Model 72 with: recoil pad; 20" barrel. Produced until mid 1970's.
Estimated Value: Excellent: $100.00
Very good: $ 80.00

Western Field Model 865

Caliber: 22 short, long, long rifle
Action: Lever action; hammerless; repeating
Magazine: Tubular, 13 long rifles, 15 longs, 20 shorts
Barrel: 20" blue
Sights: Adjustable rear, bead front
Stock & Forearm: Wood, Monte Carlo pistol grip stock and forearm; barrel band; swivels
Approximate wt.: 7 lbs.
Comments: Manufactured until the mid 1970's.
Estimated Value: Excellent: $75.00
Very good: $65.00

Western Field Model 79

Caliber: 30-30
Action: Lever action; exposed hammer; repeating; side ejection
Magazine: 6 shot tubular, side load
Barrel: 20" round blued
Sights: Bead front, rear adjustable for elevation
Stock & Forearm: Smooth, hardwood pistol grip stock and forearm
Approximate wt: 7 lbs.
Comments: Manufactured at present.
Estimated Value: New (retail): $159.99
Excellent: $120.00
Very good: $100.00

Western Field Model 892

Caliber: 22 long rifle
Action: Semi-automatic; hammerless
Magazine: 18-shot tubular
Barrel: 24" blued
Sights: Open rear, bead front
Stock & Forearm: Checkered walnut, Monte Carlo pistol grip stock and forearm
Approximate wt.: 7 lbs.
Comments: Made until mid 1970's.
Estimated Value: Excellent: $70.00
Very good: $60.00

Western Field Semi-automatic

Caliber: 22 long rifle
Action: Semi-automatic; hammerless
Magazine: 15 shot tubular in butt stock
Barrel: 21"
Sights: Blade front, rear adjustable for elevation
Stock & Forearm: Smooth hardwood one piece grip stock and forearm
Approximate wt: 5 ½ lbs.
Comments: Presently being produced.
Estimated Value: New (retail): $74.99
Excellent: $55.00
Very good: $45.00

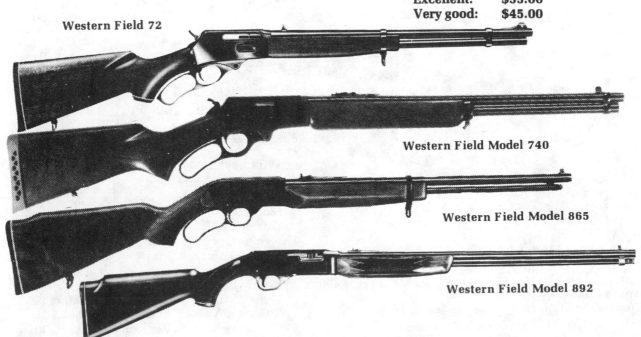

Western Field 72
Western Field Model 740
Western Field Model 865
Western Field Model 892

Rifles

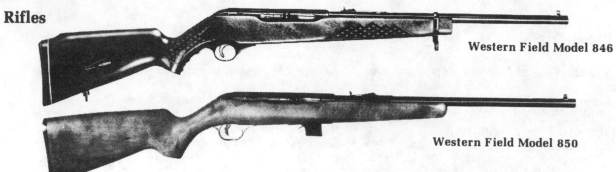

Western Field Model 846

Western Field Model 850

Western Field Model 850

Caliber: 22 long rifle
Action: Semi-automatic; hammerless
Magazine: 7-shot clip
Barrel: 18½" blued
Sights: Adjustable rear, bead front
Stock & Forearm: Wood, semi-pistol grip, one piece stock and tapered forearm
Approximate wt.: 5½ lbs.
Comments: Made to the mid 1970's.
Estimated Value: Excellent: $50.00
Very good: $40.00

Western Field Model 846

Caliber: 22 long rifle
Action: Semi-automatic; hammerless
Magazine: 15-shot tubular, stock load
Barrel: 18½" blued
Sights: Adjustable rear, bead front
Stock & Forearm: Checkered wood, pistol grip, one-piece stock and forearm; barrel band; swivels
Approximate wt.: 5¼ lbs.
Comments: Made until mid 1970's.
Estimated Value: Excellent: $60.00
Very good: $50.00

Winchester

Winchester Lee

Winchester Lee Musket

Similar to the Winchester Lee, with military sights, full length, musket forearm; 28" barrel; swivels
Estimated Value: Excellent: $750.00
Very good: $600.00

Winchester Lee

Caliber: 6mm, 236
Action: Bolt action; repeating
Magazine: 5-shot non-detachable box
Barrel: 24", round; nickel steel
Sights: Open rear, bead front
Stock & Forearm: Semi-pistol grip, one-piece stock & fluted, lipped forearm.
Approximate wt: 7½ lbs.
Comments: Made from the late 1890's to early 1900's.
Estimated Value: Excellent: $775.00
Very good: $625.00

Winchester Model 1900

Winchester Model 02

Winchester Model 02

Similar to the Model 1900 with extended trigger guard; addition of 22 long rifle & extra long. Made from about 1920 to the early 1930's.
Estimated Value: Excellent: $150.00
Very good: $135.00

Winchester Model 1900

Caliber: 22 short, long
Action: Single shot; bolt action; cocking piece
Magazine: None
Barrel: 18" blued, round
Sights: Open rear, blade front
Stock & Forearm: Plain, straight grip, one-piece gum stock & forearm
Approximate wt: 3 lbs.
Comments: Made from about 1900 to 1902.
Estimated Value: Excellent: $145.00
Very good: $130.00

Winchester Thumb Trigger

Winchester Model 04

Winchester Model 04

Similar to the Model 02 with a 21'' barrel. Made from 1904 to the early 1930's.
Estimated Value: Excellent: $160.00
Very good: $145.00

Winchester Thumb Trigger

Similar to the Model 02 with no trigger. The gun is discharged by pushing a button behind the cocking piece. Made to the early 1920's.
Estimated Value: Excellent: $190.00
Very good: $175.00

Winchester Model 52

Winchester Model 52 Sporting

Winchester Model 52 Heavy Barrel

Winchester Model 52-B

Winchester Model 52

Caliber: 22 long rifle
Action: Bolt action; repeating
Magazine: 5-shot detachable box
Barrel: 28'' blued
Sights: Peep rear, blade front
Stock & Forearm: Plain walnut, pistol grip, one-piece stock & forearm
Approximate wt: 8½ lbs.
Comments: Manufactured from about 1920 to the late 1930's.
Estimated Value: Excellent: $300.00
Very good: $270.00

Winchester Model 52 Heavy Barrel

Similar to the Model 52 but with a heavy barrel and special Lyman sights.
Estimated Value: Excellent: $310.00
Very good: $275.00

Winchester Model 52 Sporting

Similar to the Model 52 except: 24'' barrel; special Lyman sights; checkering; cheekpiece. Manufactured to the late 1950's.
Estimated Value: Excellent: $650.00
Very good: $575.00

Winchester Model 52-B

Similar to the Model 52 with improved action; high comb stock available. Manufactured from the mid 1930's to late 1940's.
Estimated Value: Excellent: $240.00
Very good: $200.00

Winchester Model 52-B Heavy Barrel

Winchester Model 52-B Bull Gun

Winchester Model 52-B Sporting

Winchester Model 52-C Bull Gun

Winchester Model 52-C Target

Winchester Model 52-D Target

Winchester Model 52-C

Winchester Model 52-B Heavy barrel
Similar to the Model 52-B with a heavy barrel.
Estimated Value: Excellent: $290.00
Very good: $265.00

Winchester Model 52-B Bull Gun
Similar to the Model 52-B Heavy Barrel with still heavier barrel. Weighs about 12 lbs.
Estimated Value: Excellent: $325.00
Very good: $290.00

Winchester Model 52-B Sporting
Similar to the Model 52 Sporting with a 52-B action. Made to the early 1960's.
Estimated Value: Excellent: $650.00
Very good: $600.00

Winchester Model 52-C Target
Similar to the 52-B with more improvements on the action; high comb stock. Made from the late 1940's to early 1960's.
Estimated Value: Excellent: $275.00
Very good: $220.00

Winchester Model 52-C
Similar to the Model 52 Heavy Barrel with a 52-C action.
Estimated Value: Excellent: $300.00
Very good: $250.00

Winchester Model 52-C Bull Gun
Similar to the Model 52-B Bull Gun with a 52-C action.
Estimated Value: Excellent: $300.00
Very good: $250.00

Winchester Model 52-D Target
Similar to the 52-C; single shot; hand stop on forearm. Made from the early 1960's to late 1970's; 22 long rifle caliber; approx. wt. 11 lbs.
Estimated Value: Excellent: $350.00
Very good: $285.00

Winchester Model 54

Winchester Model 54 Sporting (Improved)

Winchester Model 54 Super

Winchester Model 54 Sniper

Winchester Model 54 National Match

Winchester Model 54

Caliber: 270, 7x57, 30-30, 30-06, 7.65x53mm, 9x57mm; 7mm, 250-3000, 22 Hornet, 220 Swift; 257 Roberts
Action: Bolt action; repeating
Magazine: 5-shot non-detachable box
Barrel: 24'' blued
Sights: Open rear, bead front
Stock & Forearm: Checkered walnut, pistol grip, one-piece stock & forearm
Approximate wt: 7 ½ lbs.
Comments: Manufactured from the mid 1920's to the mid 1930's.
Estimated Value: Excellent: $475.00
Very good: $400.00

Winchester Model 54 Carbine

Similar to the Model 54 with a 20'' barrel, no checkering in stock.
Estimated Value: Excellent: $450.00
Very good: $375.00

Winchester Model 54 Sporting (Improved)

Similar to the Model 54 with an improved action; 26'' barrel; additional calibers. Manufactured from about 1930 for 6 years.
Estimated Value: Excellent: $480.00
Very good: $405.00

Winchester Model 54 Carbine (Improved)

Similar to the Model 54 Carbine with improved action. Made from 1930 to the mid 1930's.
Estimated Value: Excellent: $485.00
Very good: $410.00

Winchester Model 54 Super

Similar to the Model 54 with cheekpiece; select wood; deluxe finish; swivels.
Estimated Value: Excellent: $500.00
Very good: $425.00

Winchester Model 54 Sniper

Similar to the Model 54 with a 26'' heavy barrel; special Lyman sights; 30-06 caliber only.
Estimated Value: Excellent: $550.00
Very good: $475.00

Winchester Model 54 Sniper Match

Deluxe version of the Model 54 Sniper, with high quality finish.
Estimated Value: Excellent: $560.00
Very good: $485.00

Winchester Model 54 National Match

Similar to the Model 54 with special Lyman sights and marksman stock.
Estimated Value: Excellent: $475.00
Very good: $400.00

Winchester Model 54 Target

Similar to the Model 54 with a 24'' barrel and special Lyman sights.
Estimated Value: Excellent: $515.00
Very good: $445.00

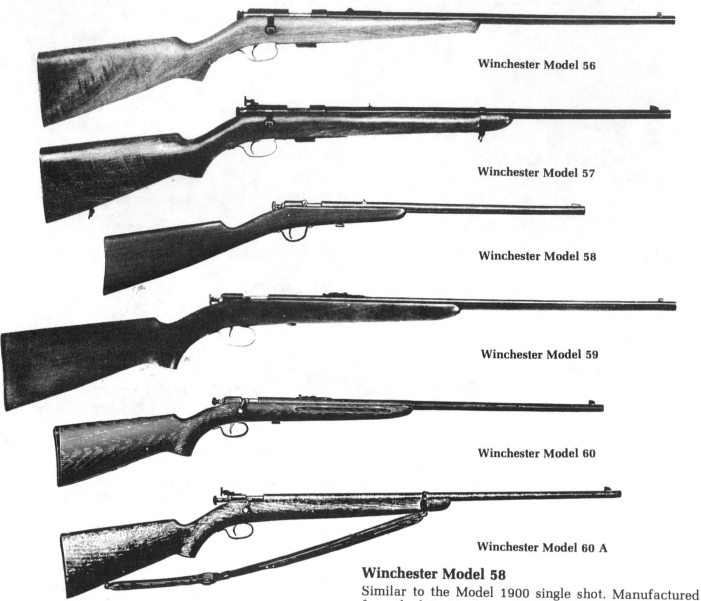

Winchester Model 56

Winchester Model 57

Winchester Model 58

Winchester Model 59

Winchester Model 60

Winchester Model 60 A

Winchester Model 56

Caliber:22 short or long rifle only
Action: Bolt action; repeating
Magazine: 5 or 10 shot detachable box
Barrel: 22'' blued
Sights: Open rear, bead front
Stock & Forearm: Plain walnut, semi-pistol grip, one-piece stock & lipped forearm
Approximate wt: 5 lbs.
Comments: Made from the mid to the late 1920's. A fancy version was available with checkered walnut stock & forearm.
Estimated Value: Excellent: $150.00
Very good: $125.00

Winchester Model 57

Similar to the Model 56 with longer, unlipped forearm; barrel band; swivels; special Lyman sights; target model. Made from the mid 1920's to mid 1930's.
Estimated Value: Excellent: $200.00
Very good: $175.00

Winchester Model 58

Similar to the Model 1900 single shot. Manufactured from the late 1920's to early 1930's.
Estimated Value: Excellent: $110.00
Very good: $ 90.00

Winchester Model 59

Similar to the Model 58 with a 23'' barrel. Weight about 4 ½ lbs. made from about 1930 to 1931.
Estimated Value: Excellent: $100.00
Very good: $ 80.00

Winchester Model 60

Similar to the Model 59 with 23'' or 27'' barrel. Made from the early to mid 1930's.
Estimated Value: Excellent: $110.00
Very good: $ 90.00

Winchester Model 60 A

Similar to the Model 60 with special Lyman sights; swivels; Made to about 1940.
Estimated Value: Excellent: $90.00
Very good: $80.00

Winchester Model 67

Winchester Model 67 Boy's

Winchester Model 68

Winchester Model 677

Winchester Model 69

Winchester Model 67

Caliber: 22 short, long, long rifle
Action: Bolt action; single shot; cocking piece
Magazine: None
Barrel: 27'' blued
Sights: Oepn rear, bead front
Stock & Forearm: Plain wood, semi-pistol grip, one-piece stock & fluted forearm
Approximate wt: 5 lbs.
Comments: Manufactured from the mid 1930's to the early 1960's.
Estimated Value: **Excellent:** $75.00
Very good: $60.00

Winchester Model 67 Boy's

Similar to the Model 67 with a 20'' barrel and youth stock.
Estimated Value: Excellent: $75.00
Very good: $60.00

Winchester Model 68

Similar to the Model 67 with peep rear sight. Made from the mid 1930's to mid 1940's.
Estimated Value: **Excellent:** $80.00
Very good: $70.00

Winchester Model 677

Similar to the Model 67 with no sights. Made only in the late 1930's.
Estimated Value: Excellent: $85.00
Very good: $75.00

Winchester Model 69

Caliber: 22 short, long, long rifle
Action: Bolt action; repeating
Magazine: 5 or 10 shot detachable box
Barrel: 25'' blued
Sights: Peep or open rear, ramp front
Stock & Forearm: Plain walnut, semi-pistol grip, one-piece stock & forearm
Approximate wt: 5 ½ lbs.
Comments: Manufactured from the mid 1930's to the early 1960's.
Estimated Value: **Excellent:** $75.00
Very good: $65.00

Winchester Model 69 Target

Winchester Model 697

Winchester Model 69 Match

Similar to the Model 69 Target with special Lyman sights.
Estimated Value: Excellent: $125.00
Very good: $105.00

Winchester Model 69 Target

Similar to the Model 69 with peep sight only; swivels.
Estimated Value: Excellent: $120.00
Very good: $ 95.00

Winchester Model 697

Similar to the Model 69 with no sights. Made from the late 1930's to early 1940's.
Estimated Value: Excellent: $110.00
Very good: $ 90.00

Winchester Model 70 (1937)

Winchester Model 70 (1964)

Winchester Model 70 (1971)

Winchester Model 70 XTR

Winchester Model 70 (1937)

Caliber: 375 H&H magnum, 300 H&H magnum, 308 Win., 30-06, 7x57mm, 270 Win., 257 Roberts, 250-3000, 243, 220, 22 Hornet
Action: Bolt action; repeating
Magazine: 5-shot box, 4-shot box in magnum
Barrel: 24'', 26'' blued
Sights: Open rear, hooded ramp front
Stock & Forearm: Checkered walnut, one-piece pistol grip stock & forearm
Approximate wt.: 7¾ lbs.
Comments: Made from about 1937 to 1963. Add $150.00 for mint unfired condition.
Estimated Value: Excellent: $570.00
Very good: $465.00

Winchester Model 70 (1964)

Similar to the Model 70 (1937) with improvements; Monte Carlo stock; swivels. Made from about 1964 until 1970; calibers 22-250, 222 Rem., 225, 243, 270, 308, 30-06.
Estimated Value: Excellent: $270.00
Very good: $220.00

Winchester Model 70 (1971), 70 XTR

Similar to the Model 70 (1964) with improvements. Made from 1971 to present.
Estimated Value: New (retail): $354.00
Excellent: $265.00
Very good: $210.00

Winchester Model 70A, 70A XTR

Similar to the Model 70 (1971) with a special steel barrel; adjustable sights. Made from the early 1970's to present; 4-shot or 3-shot (mag.) box magazine. Add $20.00 for 264 Win. mag., 7mm Rem. mag., or 300 Win. magnum. Police Model $10.00 less.

Estimated Value: New (retail): $313.00
Excellent: $235.00
Very good: $190.00

Winchester Model 70 Super (1937)

Similar to the Model 70 (1937) with swivels; deluxe finish; cheekpiece. Made to early 1960s.

Estimated Value: Excellent: $690.00
Very good: $575.00

Winchester Model 70 Super

Similar to the Model 70 Super (1937) with recoil pad; select wood. Produced from mid 1960's to mid 1970's.

Estimated Value: Excellent: $390.00
Very good: $320.00

Winchester Model 70 Target (1937)

Similar to the Model 70 (1937) with 24" barrel and improved stock. Made until about 1963. Add $10.00 for mint unfired condition.

Estimated Value: Excellent: $750.00
Very good: $600.00

Winchester Model 70 Target (1964) & (1971)

Similar to the Model 70 Target (1937) with aluminum hand stop. Model (1971) has minor improvements; calibers 30-06, 308 Win., or 308 Int'l Army. Add $132.00 for Int'l Army.

Estimated Value: Excellent: $425.00
Very good: $350.00

Winchester Model 70 National Match

Similar to the Model 70 (1937) with marksman stock in 30-06 caliber. Made to the early 1960's.

Estimated Value: Excellent: $625.00
Very good: $525.00

Winchester Model 70A

Winchester Model 70 Super (1937)

Winchester Model 70 Super

Winchester Model 70 Target (1937)

Winchester Model 70 Target (1964)

Winchester Model 70 National Match

Rifles

Winchester Model 70 Mannlicher

Winchester Model 70 Varmint (1956) &1964) (1971)

Winchester Model 70 Featherweight Sporter

Winchester Model 70 Featherweight Super

Winchester Model 70 African (1956)

Winchester Model 70 Mannlicher

Similar to the Model 70 (1964) with full length forearm. Made to the early 1970's; 19-inch barrel; calibers 243, 270, 308, 30-06.

Estimated Value: Excellent: $300.00
Very good: $250.00

Winchester Model 70 Varmint (1956) (1964) (1971) 70 XTR Varmint

Similar to the Model 70 (1937) with heavy 26" barrel. Improvements made along wth other Model 70's. Calibers 222 Rem., 22-250, or 243 Win. Add $100.00 for pre-1964 models.

Estimated Value: New (retail): $373.00
Excellent: $280.00
Very good: $225.00

Winchester Model 70 Featherweight Sporter

Similar to the Model 70 (1937) with improved stock and lightweight. Made from the early 1950's to 1960's.

Estimated Value: Excellent: $575.00
Very good: $470.00

Winchester Model 70 Featherweight Super

Similar to the Featherweight Sporter with deluxe finish; cheekpiece; swivels.

Estimated Value: Excellent: $450.00
Very good: $375.00

Winchester Model 70 African (1956)

Similar to the Model 70 (1937) Super Grade with recoil pad; Monte Carlo stock; 3-shot magazine; 24" barrel. Available only in 458 caliber. Made to 1963.

Estimated Value: Excellent: $850.00
Very good: $725.00

Winchester Model 70 Westerner

Similar to the Model 70 Alaskan. Made in the early 1960's.
Estimated Value: Excellent: $550.00
Very good: $475.00

Winchester Model 70 Magnum

Similar to the Model 70 (1964) with Monte Carlo stock; recoil pad; swivels; 3-shot magazine. Made to the early 1970's.
Estimated Value: Excellent: $300.00
Very good: $250.00

Winchester Model 70 Deluxe

Similar to the Model 70 (1964) with Monte Carlo stock; recoil pad; deluxe features. Made to the early 1970's.
Estimated Value: Excellent: $325.00
Very good: $275.00

Winchester Model 70 African (1964)

Similar to the Model 70 African (1956) with improvements. Made to 1970.
Estimated Value: Excellent: $450.00
Very good: $375.00

Winchester Model 70 African (1971)

Similar to the Model 70 African (1964) with floating barrel; caliber 458 Win. mag.
Estimated Value: New (retail): $607.00
Excellent: $460.00
Very good: $365.00

Winchester Model 70 Alaskan

Similar to the Model 70 (1937) with 24'' or 26'' barrel. Made in the early 1960's.
Estimated Value: Excellent: $575.00
Very good: $500.00

Winchester Model 70 African (1964)

Winchester Model 70 African (1971)

Winchester Model 70 Alaskan

Winchester Model 70 Magnum

Winchester Model 70 Deluxe

Rifles

Winchester Model 72

Winchester Model 75 Target

Winchester Model 75 Sporter

Winchester Model 43

Winchester Model 43 Special

Winchester Model 47

Winchester Model 72

Caliber: 22 short, long, long rifle
Action: Bolt action; repeating
Magazine: Tubular, 15 long rifles, 16 longs, 20 shorts
Barrel: 25" blued
Sights: Peep or open rear, bead front
Stock & Forearm: Plain walnut, semi-pistol grip, one-piece stock & forearm
Approximate wt: 5¾ lbs.
Comments: Made from the late 1930's to late 1950's.
Estimated Value: Excellent: $100.00
Very good: $ 80.00

Winchester Model 75 Target

Caliber: 22 long rifle
Action: Bolt action; repeating
Magazine: 5 or 10 shot detachable box
Barrel: 28", blued
Sights: Special target sights
Stock & Forearm: Plain walnut, one-piece pistol grip stock & forearm
Approximate wt: 8¾ lbs.
Comments: Made from the late 1930's to late 1950's.
Estimated Value: Excellent: $240.00
Very good: $195.00

Winchester Model 75 Sporter

Similar to the Model 75 with: checkering; 24" barrel; hooded ramp front sight; weighs 5¾ lbs.
Estimated Value: Excellent: $270.00
Very good: $230.00

Winchester Model 43

Caliber: 218 Bee, 22 Hornet, 25-20, 32-30 (25-20 and 32-30 dropped in 1950).
Action: Bolt action; repeating
Magazine: 3 shot detachable box
Barrel: 24" blued
Sights: Open rear, hooded ramp front
Stock & Forearm: Plain wood, one-piece semi-pistol grip stock & forearm; swivels
Approximate wt: 6 lbs.
Comments: Made from the late 1940's to late 1950's.
Estimated Value: Excellent: $330.00
Very good: $280.00

Winchester Model 43 Special

Similar to the Model 43 with checkering and choice of open rear sight or micrometer.
Estimated Value: Excellent: $335.00
Very good: $285.00

Winchester Model 47

Similar to the Model 43 in 22 short, long, or long rifle single shot; 25" barrel. Made from the late 1940's to mid 1950's.
Estimated Value: Excellent: $100.00
Very good: $ 85.00

Winchester Model 670

Winchester Model 770

Winchester Model 770 Magnum

Winchester Model 670

Caliber: 243, 270, 30-06, 225, 243, 270, 308, 30-06 magnum, 300 Win. magnum, 264 Win. magnum.
Action: Bolt action; repeating
Magazine: 4-shot box, 3-shot box in magnum
Barrel: 19", 22", 24", blued
Sights: Open rear, ramp front
Stock & Forearm: Checkered walnut, Monte Carlo pistol grip, one-piece stock & forearm
Approximate wt: 7 lbs.
Comments: Made from the mid 1960's to the late 1970's.
Estimated Value: Excellent: $210.00
                   Very good: $175.00

Winchester Model 770

Caliber: 22-250, 222, 243, 270, 30-06, 308
Action: Bolt action; repeating
Magazine: 4-shot box
Barrel: 22" blued
Sights: Open rear, hooded ramp front
Stock & Forearm: Checkered walnut, Monte Carlo pistol grip, one-piece stock & forearm; swivels
Approximate wt: 7 lbs.
Comments: Made from the late 1960's to early 1970's.
Estimated Value: Excellent: $225.00
                   Very good: $180.00

Winchester Model 770 Magnum

Similar to the Model 770 in magnum, with recoil pad and 24" barrel, 3 shot magazine.
Estimated Value: Excellent: $225.00
                   Very good: $175.00

Winchester Model 310

Winchester Model 320

Winchester Model 310

Caliber: 22 short, long, long rifle
Action: Bolt action; single shot
Magazine: None
Barrel: 22" blued
Sights: Adjustable rear, ramp front
Stock & Forearm: Checkered walnut Monte Carlo, pistol grip, one piece stock & forearm; swivels
Approximate wt: 6 lbs.
Comments: Made from the early to mid 1970's.
Estimated Value: Excellent: $60.00
                   Very good: $50.00

Winchester Model 320

Similar to the Model 310 in repeating action with a 5-shot clip magazine.
Estimated Value: Excellent: $75.00
                   Very good: $65.00

Rifles

Winchester Model 121

Winchester Model 131

Winchester Model 121

Caliber: 22 short, long, long rifle
Action: Bolt action; single shot
Magazine: None
Barrel: 20½" blued
Sights: Open rear, bead post front
Stock & Forearm: Plain, semi-pistol grip, one-piece stock & forearm
Approximate wt: 5 lbs.
Comments: Made from the late 1960's to early 1970's.
Estimated Value: Excellent: $50.00
Very good: $40.00

Winchester Model 121 Deluxe

Similar to the Model 121 with Monte Carlo stock; swivels; slightly different sights.
Estimated Value: Excellent: $55.00
Very good: $45.00

Winchester Model 121 Youth

Similar to the Model 121 with shorter barrel & youth stock.
Estimated Value: Excellent: $40.00
Very good: $30.00

Winchester Model 131

Similar to the Model 121 with semi-Monte Carlo stock; 7-shot clip magazine.
Estimated Value: Excellent: $60.00
Very good: $50.00

Winchester Model 141

Similar to the 131 with tubular magazine.
Estimated Value: Excellent: $70.00
Very good: $60.00

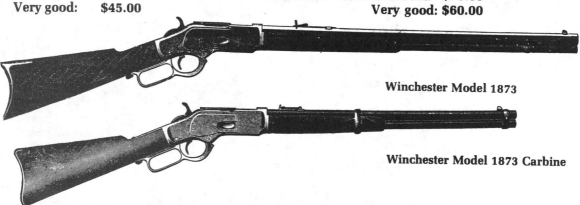

Winchester Model 1873

Winchester Model 1873 Carbine

Winchester Model 1873

Caliber: 32-20, 38-40, 44-40, 22
Action: Lever action; exposed hammer; repeating
Magazine: 6 or 15 shot tubular
Barrel: 24" or 26" round, octagon or half-octagon
Sights: Open rear, blade front
Stock & Forearm: Straight grip stock & forearm
Approximate wt: 8½-9 lbs.
Comments: Thousands of this model were sold by Winchester until the mid 1920's. Add $200.00 to $300.00 for Deluxe engraved models
Estimated Value: Excellent: $600.00 - $1,600.00
Very good: $500.00 - $1,350.00

Winchester Model 1873 Carbine

Similar to the Model 1873 with a 20" barrel and 12 shot magazine.
Estimated Value: Excellent: $600.00 - $1,600.00
Very good: $450.00 - $1,200.00

Winchester Model 1873 Musket

Similar to the Model 1873 with a 30" round barrel, full length forearm and 17 shot magazine.
Estimated Value: Excellent: $650.00 - $1,500.00
Very good: $500.00 - $1,200.00

Winchester Model 1886

Winchester Model 1886 Carbine

Winchester Model 92

Winchester Model 92 Carbine

Winchester Model 53

Winchester Model 65

Winchester Model 92

Caliber:25-20, 32-30, 38-40, 44-40
Action: Lever action; exposed hammer; repeating
Magazine: 7 or 13 shot, tubular
Barrel: 24'' round, half octagon or octagon
Sights: Open rear, bead front
Stock & Forearm: Plain wood, straight grip stock & forearm
Approximate wt: 7 lbs.
Comments: Manufactured from about 1892 until early 1930's.
Estimated Value: Excellent: $500.00 - $650.00
Very good: $400.00 - $500.00

Winchester Model 92 Carbine

Similar to the Model 92 with a 20'' barrel; barrel band; and 5 or 11 shot magazine. Discontinued in the early 1940's.
Estimated Value: Excellent: $475.00 - $550.00
Very good: $425.00 - $500.00

Winchester Model 53

Similar to the Model 92 with a 6 or 7 shot magazine; 22'' nickel steel barrel; choice of straight or pistol grip stock. Made from the mid 1920's to the early 1930's.
Estimated Value: Excellent: $395.00
Very good: $350.00

Winchester Model 65

Similar to the Model 53 in 25-20 & 32-20 caliber; semi-pistol grip stock; other minor improvements. Made from the early 1930's to late 1940's.
Estimated Value: Excellent: $420.00
Very good: $340.00

Winchester Model 65, 218 Bee

Similar to the Model 65 with peep sight and 24'' barrel. Made from the late 1930's to late 1940's.
Estimated Value: Excellent: $825.00
Very good: $690.00

Winchester Model 1886

Caliber: 45-70, 33 Win. (Also others on early models)
Action: Lever action; exposed hammer; repeating
Magazine: 4 or 8 shot tubular
Barrel: 26'', round, half octagon or octagon
Sights: Open rear, blade front
Stock & Forearm: Plain wood, straight grip stock & forearm
Approximate wt.: 7 ½ lbs.
Comments: Manufactured from the mid 1880's to the mid 1930's.
Estimated Value: Excellent: $500.00 - $1,500.00
Very good: $360.00 - $1,200.00

Winchester Model 1886 Carbine

Similar to the Model 1886 with a 22'' barrel.
Estimated Value: Excellent: $450.00 - $1,400.00
Very good: $350.00 - $1,200.00

Rifles

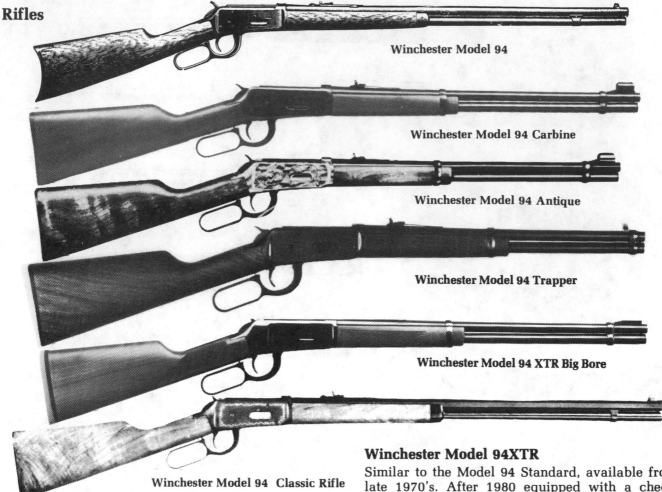

Winchester Model 94

Winchester Model 94 Carbine

Winchester Model 94 Antique

Winchester Model 94 Trapper

Winchester Model 94 XTR Big Bore

Winchester Model 94 Classic Rifle

Winchester Model 94

Caliber: 25-35, 30-30, 32 Special, 32-40, 38-55
Action: Lever action; exposed hammer; repeating
Magazine: 4 or 7 shot, tubular
Barrel: 22", 26", round, half octagon or octagon
Sights: Open rear, bead front
Stock & Forearm: Straight stock & forearm; saddle ring on some models
Approximate wt: 6¾ lbs.
Comments: Manufactured from 1894 to the late 1930's. Sometimes referred to as the "Klondike" model.
Estimated Value: Excellent: $450.00 - $650.00
               Very good: $300.00 - $500.00

Winchester Model 94 Carbine

Similar to the Model 94 with a 20" barrel; barrel band; saddle ring. Still sold; 6-shot magazine; presently sold in 30-30 caliber. Add $300.00 for pre-World War II models.
Estimated Value: New (retail): $176.00
               Excellent: $135.00
               Very good: $110.00

Winchester Model 94 Antique

Similar to the Model 94 with case hardened, scroll design frame. Made from the late 1960's to present
Estimated Value: New (retail): $188.00
               Excellent: $140.00
               Very good: $115.00

Winchester Model 94XTR

Similar to the Model 94 Standard, available from the late 1970's. After 1980 equipped with a checkered walnut straight grip stock.
Estimated Value: New (retail): $198.00
               Excellent: $150.00
               Very good: $120.00

Winchester Model 94 Trapper

Similar to the Model 94 with a 16" barrel. Introduced in 1980.
Estimated Value: New (retail): $176.00
               Excellent: $135.00
               Very good: $110.00

Winchester Model 94 Standard

This is an improved version of the Model 94 available from the late 1970's.
Estimated Value: New (retail): $176.00
               Excellent: $135.00
               Very good: $110.00

Winchester Model 94 XTR Big Bore

Similar to the Model 94XTR in 375 caliber; recoil pad.
Estimated Value: New (retail): $253.00
               Excellent: $195.00
               Very good: $155.00

Winchester Model 94 Classic Rifle or Carbine

Similar to the Model 94 with select walnut stock; scroll engraving. Made from the late 1960's to early 1970's.
Estimated Value: Excellent: $150.00
               Very good: $125.00

Winchester Model 55

Winchester Model 64

Winchester Model 64 Zipper

Winchester Model 64 Deer

Winchester Model 64

Similar to the Model 94 & 55 with improvements; available in 25-35, 30-30, 32 calibers (219 Zipper from 1938-41) Made from the early 1930's to the late 1950's. Reissued in the early 1970's in 30-30 caliber. Add $200.00 for 219 Zipper caliber, $100.00 for pre-1960 models.
Estimated Value: Excellent: $225.00
Very good: $175.00

Winchester Model 64 Deer

Similar to the Model 64 in 32 and 30-30 caliber; swivels; checkered pistol grip stock. Manufactured from the mid 1930's to mid 1950's.
Estimated Value: Excellent: $380.00
Very good: $325.00

Winchester Model 55

Similar to the Model 94 with a 24" nickel steel barrel. Made from the mid 1920's to the early 1930's.
Estimated Value: Excellent: $425.00
Very good: $375.00

Winchester Model 95 Carbine

Winchester Model 95

Winchester Model 95

Caliber: 30-40 Krag, 30-06, 30-30, 303, 35, 405
Action: Lever action; exposed hammer; repeating
Magazine: 4-shot box
Barrel: 24", 26", 28", octagon, round or half octagon
Sights: Open rear, bead front
Stock & Forearm: Plain wood, straight stock and tapered lipped forearm. A limited number were available with a pistol grip.
Approximate wt: 8 ½ lbs.
Comments: Made from about 1895 to the early 1930's. A few thousand early models were built with a flat receiver.
Estimated Value: Excellent: $300.00 - $600.00
Very good: $250.00 - $475.00

Winchester Model 95 Carbine

Similar to the Model 95 with a 22" barrel.
Estimated Value: Excellent: $375.00 - $800.00
Very good: $300.00 - $675.00

Winchester Model 1895 Musket

Similar to the Model 1895 with a 28" or 30" round nickel steel barrel; full length forearm; barrel bands; 30 gov't caliber.
Estimated Value: Excellent: $550.00 - $1,200.00
Very good: $450.00 - $1,000.00

Winchester Model 1895 NRA Musket

Similar to the Model 1895 Musket with a 24" barrel.
Estimated Value: Excellent: $700.00 - $1,000.00
Very good: $600.00 - $ 850.00

Rifles

Winchester Model 71

Winchester Model 88

Winchester Model 71

Caliber: 348 Win.
Action: Lever action; exposed hammer; repeating
Magazine: 4-shot tubular
Barrel: 20" or 24" blued
Sights: Open rear, hooded ramp front; peepsights available
Stock & Forearm: Plain or checckered walnut pistol grip stock & forearm; swivels available
Approximate wt: 8 lbs.
Comments: Made from the mid 1930's to the late 1950's
Estimated Value: **Excellent:**   **$500.00**
                          Very good: **$425.00**

Winchester Model 71 Special

Similar to the Model 71 with checkering & swivels.
Estimated Value: Excellent: $510.00
                    Very good: $435.00

Winchester Model 88

Caliber: 243, 284, 308, 358
Action: Lever action; hammerless; repeating
Magazine: 4-shot box on late models; 5 shot on early models, 3 shot in 284 caliber
Barrel: 22"
Sights: Folding leaf rear, hooded ramp front
Stock & Forearm: Checkered walnut, semi-pistol grip, one-piece stock & forearm; barrel band
Approximate wt: 7¼ lbs.
Comments: Manufactured from the mid 1950's to mid 1970's.
Estimated Value: **Excellent:**   **$240.00**
                          Very good: **$190.00**

Winchester Model 88 Carbine

Similar to the Model 88 with a palin stock and forearm and 19" barrel. Made from the late 1960's to early 1970's.
Estimated Value: **Excellent:**   **$250.00**
                          Very good: **$200.00**

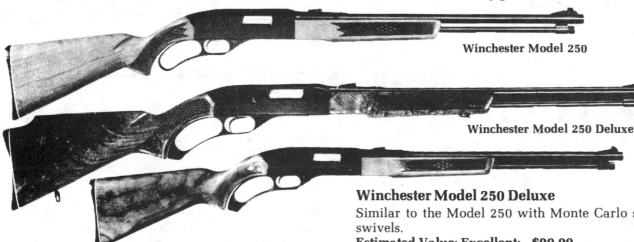

Winchester Model 250

Winchester Model 250 Deluxe

Winchester Model 255

Winchester Model 250

Caliber: 22 short, long, long rifle
Action: Lever action; hammerless; repeating
Magazine: Tubular, 15 long rifles, 17 longs, 21 shorts
Barrel: 20½" blued
Sights: Open rear, ramp front
Stock & Forearm: Plain walnut, or checkered, semi-pistol grip stock & forearm
Approximate wt.: 5 lbs.
Comments: Made from the early 1960's to mid 1970's.
Estimated Value: Excellent: $75.00
                    Very good: $65.00

Winchester Model 250 Deluxe

Similar to the Model 250 with Monte Carlo stock and swivels.
Estimated Value: Excellent: $90.00
                    Very good: $75.00

Winchester Model 255

Similar to the Model 250 in 22 magnum caliber; 11 shot magazine. Made from the mid 1960's to early 1970's.
Estimated Value: Excellent: $100.00
                    Very good: $ 80.00

Winchester Model 255 Deluxe

Similar to the Model 250 Deluxe in 22 magnum caliber; 11 shot magazine.
Estimated Value: Excellent: $120.00
                    Very good: $ 95.00

Winchester Model 150

Winchester Model 9422

Winchester 9422 Magnum

Winchester Model 150

Caliber: 22 short, long, long rifle
Action: Lever action; hammerless; repeating
Magazine: Tubular, 15 long rifles, 17 longs, 21 shorts
Barrel: 20½" blued
Sights: Open adjustable rear, blade front
Stock & Forearm: Straight stock & forearm; barrel band; alloy receiver
Approximate wt: 5 lbs.
Comments: Made from the late 1960's to mid 1970's.
Estimated Value: Excellent: $100.00
                    Very good: $ 80.00

Winchester Model 9422, 9422 XTR

Caliber: 22 short, long, long rifle; 22 magnum
Action: Lever action; exposed hammer; repeating
Magazine: Tubular, 15 long rifles, 17 longs, 21 shorts
Barrel: 20½"
Sights: Adjustable rear, hooded ramp front
Stock & Forearm: Plain wood, straight grip stock & forearm; barrel band
Approximate wt: 6¼ lbs.
Comments: Made from about 1972 to present. Checkered stock after 1980.
Estimated Value: New (retail): $230.00
                    Excellent: $150.00
                    Very good: $120.00

Winchester 9422 XTR Magnum

Similar to the Model 9422 in 22 magnum, 11 shot magazine. Checkered stock after 1980.
Estimated Value: New (retail): $236.00
                    Excellent: $175.00
                    Very good: $140.00

Nebraska Centennial

Centennial '66

Winchester Commemoratives

Lever action. Rifles and carbines in 30-30 calibers. Prices for mint unfired condition in original box or carton.

Model	Date	Approx # made	Issue cost	Est. value
Wyo. Dia. Jub.	1964	1500	100.00	900.00
Neb. Cent.	1966	2500	125.00	900.00
Centennial '66	1966	102,000	125.00	350.00
Canadian Centennial	1967	90,400	125.00	400.00
Ala. Purchase	1967	1500	125.00	900.00
Buffalo Bill	1968	113,000	129.95	200.00
Ill. Sesqui.	1968	37,000	110.00	250.00
Golden Spike	1969	70,000	119.95	250.00
T. Roosevelt	1969	52,000	125.00	275.00
Cowboy	1969	27,000	125.00	300.00
Lone Star	1970	38,000	140.00	300.00
NRA	1971-72	47,000	149.95	225.00
Texas Ranger	1973	4850	134.95	450.00
Bicentennial	1976	20,000	325.00	550.00
Wells Fargo	1977	20,000	395.00	525.00
Antlered Game	1978	19,999	374.95	400.00
Legendary Frontiersmen	1979	19,999	425.00	450.00
Oliver Winchester	1980	19,999	500.00	500.00

Rifles

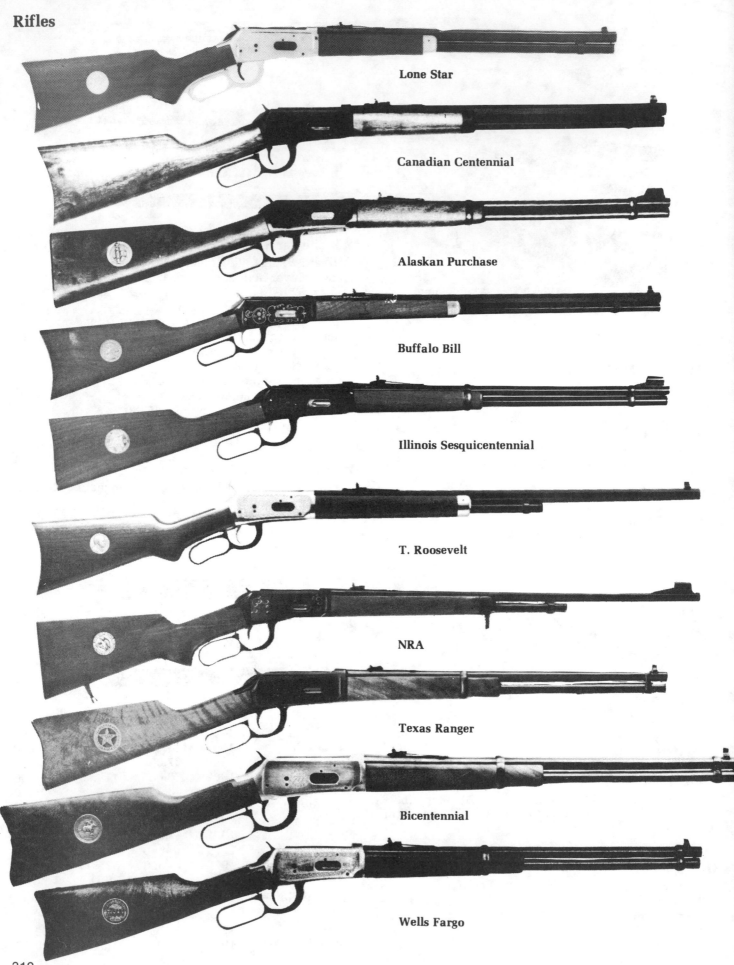

Lone Star

Canadian Centennial

Alaskan Purchase

Buffalo Bill

Illinois Sesquicentennial

T. Roosevelt

NRA

Texas Ranger

Bicentennial

Wells Fargo

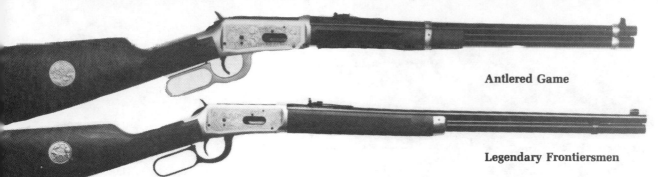

Antlered Game

Legendary Frontiersmen

Winchester Model 1890

Caliber: 22 short, long, long rifle
Action: Slide action; exposed hammer; repeating
Magazine: Tubular, 11 long rifles, 12 longs, 15 shorts
Barrel: 24" octagon
Sights: Open rear, bead front
Stock & Forearm: Plain wood, straight grip stock & grooved slide handle
Approximate wt.: 5¾ lbs.
Comments: Manufactured from 1890 to the early 1930's.
Estimated Value: Excellent: $300.00
Very good: $250.00

Winchester Model 06

Caliber: 22 short, long, long rifle
Action: Slide action; exposed hammer; repeating
Magazine: Tubular, 11 long rifles, 12 longs, 15 shorts
Barrel: 20" blued
Sights: Open rear, bead front
Stock & Forearm: Plain wood, straight stock, grooved or plain slide handle; Nickel trimmed receiver and pistol grip stock available.
Approximate wt.: 5 lbs.
Comments: Made from 1906 until the early 1930's.
Estimated Value: Excellent: $300.00
Very good: $250.00

Winchester Model 1890

Winchester Model 06

Winchester Model 61

Winchester Model 62

Winchester Model 61

Caliber: 22 short, long, long rifle
Action: Slide action; hammerless; repeating
Magazine: Tubular; 14 long rifles, 16 longs, 20 shorts
Barrel: 24" blued; round or octagon
Sights: Open rear, bead front
Stock & Forearm: Plain wood, semi-pistol grip stock and grooved slide handle
Approximate wt.: 5½ lbs.
Comments: Made from the early 1930's to the early 1960's.
Estimated Value: Excellent: $250.00
Very good: $220.00

Winchester Model 61 Magnum

Similar to the Model 61 in 22 magnum. Made in the early 1960's.
Estimated Value: Excellent: $275.00
Very good: $235.00

Winchester Model 62, 62A

Caliber: 22 short, long, long rifle
Action: Slide action; exposed hammer; repeating
Magazine: Tubular, 14 long rifles, 16 longs, 20 shorts.
Barrel: 23", blued
Sights: Open rear, blade front
Stock & Forearm: Walnut straight grip stock, grooved slide handle
Approximate wt: 5½ lbs.
Comments: Made from the early 1930's to the late 1950's. A gallery model was available chambered for 22 short only. It became 62A in the 1940's with internal improvements.
Estimated Value: Excellent: $260.00
Very good: $220.00

Rifles

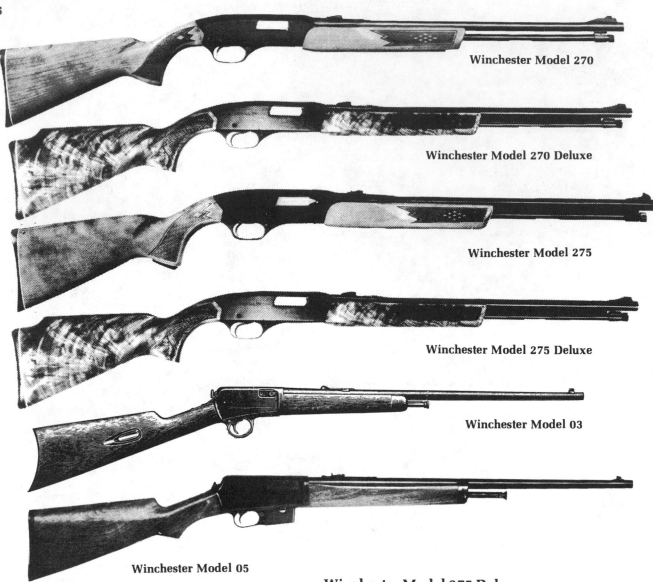

Winchester Model 270

Winchester Model 270 Deluxe

Winchester Model 275

Winchester Model 275 Deluxe

Winchester Model 03

Winchester Model 05

Winchester Model 270

Caliber: 22 short, long, long rifle
Action: Slide action; hammerless; repeating
Magazine: Tubular, 15 long rifles, 17 longs, 21 shorts
Barrel: 20½''
Sights: Open rear, ramp front
Stock & Forearm: Walnut pistol grip stock & slide handle; plastic available; later models checkered
Approximate wt.: 5 lbs.
Comments: Made from the mid 1960's to mid 1970's.
Estimated Value: Excellent: $85.00
Very good: $75.00

Winchester Model 270 Deluxe

Similar to the Model 270 with Monte Carlo stock.
Estimated Value: Excellent: $95.00
Very good: $85.00

Winchester Model 275

Similar to the Model 270 in 22 magnum caliber.
Estimated Value: Excellent: $90.00
Very good: $80.00

Winchester Model 275 Deluxe

Similar to the Model 270 Deluxe in 22 magnum caliber.
Estimated Value: Excellent: $135.00
Very good: $110.00

Winchester Model 03

Caliber: 22 short, long, long rifle
Action: Semi-automatic; hammerless
Magazine: 10-shot tubular, loaded in stock
Barrel: 20'' blued
Sights: Open rear, bead front
Stock & Forearm: Plain wood, semi-pistol grip or straight stock; checkering on some models
Approximate wt: 6 lbs.
Comments: Made from 1903 to the mid 1930's.
Estimated Value: Excellent: $200.00
Very good: $160.00

Winchester Model 05

Similar to the Model 03, with a 5 or 10 shot detachable box magazine; 22'' barrel. Made to about 1920.
Estimated Value: Excellent: $100.00
Very good: $ 80.00

Winchester Model 07

Winchester Model 10

Winchester Model 74

Winchester Model 07
Caliber: 351
Action: Semi-automatic; hammerless
Magazine: 5 or 10 shot detachable box
Barrel: 20'' blued
Sights: Open rear, bead front
Stock & Forearm: Semi-pistol grip stock & forearm; plain wood
Approximate wt: 7 ½ lbs.
Comments: Manufactured from 1907 to the late 1950's.
Estimated Value: Excellent: $350.00
                      Very good: $280.00

Winchester Model 10
Similar to the Model 07 except: 401 caliber; 4-shot magazine. Made until the mid 1930's.
Estimated Value: Excellent: $400.00
                  Very good: $325.00

Winchester Model 77

Winchester Model 55

Winchester Model 63

Winchester Model 63
Caliber: 22 long rifle, high speed; 22 long rifle Super X
Action: Semi-automatic; hammerless
Magazine: 10-shot tubular, load in stock
Barrel: 20'', 23'' blued
Sights: Open rear, bead front
Stock & Forearm: Plain walnut, pistol grip stock & forearm
Approximate wt: 5 ½ lbs.
Comments: Manufactured from the early 1930's to the late 1950's.
Estimated Value: Excellent: $275.00
                    Very good: $245.00

Winchester Model 74
Caliber: 22 long rifle only or short only.
Action: Semi-automatic
Magazine: 14 long rifles, 20 shorts, tubular in stock
Barrel: 24'' blued
Sights: Open rear, bead front
Stock & Forearm: Plain walnut, one-piece semi-pistol grip stock & forearm
Approximate wt: 6 ¼ lbs.
Comments: Manufactured from the late 1930's to the mid 1950's.
Estimated Value: Excellent: $160.00
                    Very good: $130.00

Winchester Model 55
Caliber: 22 short, long, long rifle
Action: Single shot; hammerless
Magazine: None
Barrel: 22''
Sights: Open rear, bead front
Stock & Forearm: Plain wood, semi-pistol grip, one-piece stock & forearm
Approximate wt: 5 ½ lbs.
Comments: Made from the late 1950's to the early 1960's.
Estimated Value: Excellent: $80.00
                    Very good: $70.00

Winchester Model 77
Caliber: 22 long rifle
Action: Semi-automatic
Magazine: 8-shot detachable box
Barrel: 22'' blued
Sights: Open rear, bead front
Stock & Forearm: Plain walnut, semi-pistol grip, one piece stock & forearm
Approximate wt: 5 ½ lbs.
Comments: Made from the mid 1950's to early 1960's.
Estimated Value: Excellent: $110.00
                    Very good: $ 90.00

Rifles

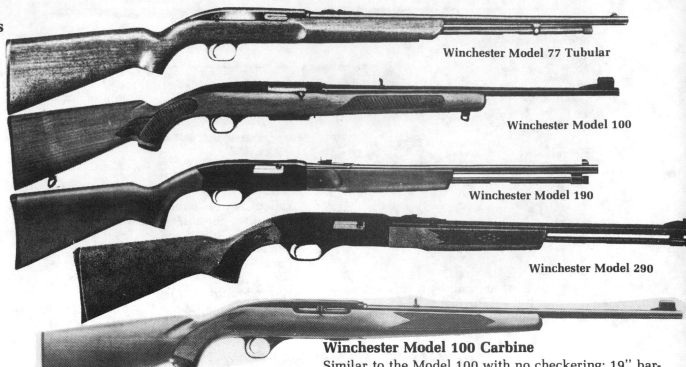

Winchester Model 77 Tubular

Winchester Model 100

Winchester Model 190

Winchester Model 290

Winchester Model 490

Winchester Model 77 Tubular
Similar to the Model 77 with a 15-shot tubular magazine.
Estimated Value: Excellent: $120.00
Very good: $100.00

Winchester Model 190
Caliber:22 long, short, or long rifle
Action: Semi-automatic; hammerless
Magazine: Tubular, 15 long rifles, 17 longs, 21 shorts
Barrel: 20½", 22"
Sights: Open rear, blade front
Stock & Forearm: Plain, walnut semi-pistol grip stock & forearm
Approximate wt: 5 lbs.
Comments: 22 short dropped in the early 1970's. Made from the mid 1960's to the late 1970's.
Estimated Value: Excellent: $80.00
Very good: $65.00

Winchester Model 100
Caliber:243, 248, 308
Action: Gas operated, semi-automatic; hammerless
Magazine: 4-shot clip, 3-shot in 284
Barrel: 19", 22" blued
Sights: Open rear, hooded ramp front
Stock & Forearm: Checkered walnut, one-piece stock & forearm; swivels
Approximate wt: 7 lbs.
Comments: Made from the early 1960's to mid 1970's.
Estimated Value: Excellent: $240.00
Very good: $200.00

Winchester Model 100 Carbine
Similar to the Model 100 with no checkering; 19" barrel; barrel bands.
Estimated Value: Excellent: $235.00
Very good: $190.00

Winchester Model 190 Carbine
Similar to the Model 190 with a 20½" barrel; barrel band & swivels; discontinued in the early 1970's.
Estimated Value: Excellent: $85.00
Very good: $70.00

Winchester Model 290
Caliber:22, short, long, long rifle
Action: Semi-automatic; hammerless
Magazine: Tubular, 15 longs, 17 long rifles, 21 shorts
Barrel: 20½"
Sights: Open rear, ramp front
Stock & Forearm: Checkered walnut pistol grip stock and forearm.
Approximate wt: 5 lbs.
Comments: Made from the mid 1960's to mid 1970's.
Estimated Value: Excellent: $85.00
Very good: $70.00

Winchester Model 290 Deluxe
Similar to the Model 290 with Monte Carlo stock. Discontinued in the mid 1970's.
Estimated Value: Excellent: $85.00
Very good: $70.00

Winchester Model 490
Caliber:22 long rifle
Action: Semi-automatic
Magazine: 5, 10, or 15 shot clip
Barrel: 22" blued
Sights: Folding leaf rear, hooded ramp front
Stock & Forearm: Checkered walnut one piece pistol grip stock and forearm
Approximate wt: 6 lbs.
Comments: Made in the mid 1970's.
Estimated Value: Excellent: $80.00
Very good: $65.00

Handguns

AMT

AMT 380 Backup

Caliber: 380 ACP
Action: Semi-automatic; concealed hammer; manual and grip safeties
Magazine: 5-shot clip
Barrel: 2½"
Sights: Fixed
Finish: Smooth wood grips; all stainless steel construction
Length overall: 5"
Approximate wt.: 17 oz.
Comments: Made from the 1970's to present.
Estimated Value: New (retail): $250.00
Excellent: $190.00
Very good: $150.00

AMT 380 Backup

AMT Combat Government

Caliber: 45 ACP
Action: Semi-automatic; exposed hammer; loaded chamber indicator; manual and grip safeties; adjustable target type trigger
Magazine: 7 shot clip
Barrel: 5"
Sights: Fixed
Finish: Checkered walnut grip; all stainless steel construction
Length overall: 8½"
Approximate wt.: 39 oz.
Comments: Made from the 1970's to present.
Estimated Value: New (retail): $400.00
Excellent: $300.00
Very good: $250.00

AMT Hardballer

AMT Combat Government

AMT Hardballer

Same as the AMT Combat Government except: adjustable combat type sights; serrated matte slide rib; grooved front and backstraps
Estimated Value: New (retail): $450.00
Excellent: $340.00
Very good: $275.00

AMT Skipper

Same as the AMT Hardballer except 4" barrel and 7½" overall.
Estimated Value: New (retail): $450.00
Excellent: $340.00
Very good: $275.00

AMT Hardballer Long Slide

Same as the AMT Hardballer except: 7" barrel and 10½" overall length.
Estimated Value: New (retail): $595.00
Excellent: $450.00
Very good: $360.00

American

American 25 Automatic

Caliber: 25 ACP
Action: Semi-automatic; concealed hammer
Magazine: 8-shot clip
Barrel: 2"
Sights: Fixed
Finish: Blue or stainless steel; smooth walnut grips
Length overall: 4½"
Approximate wt.: 15 ounces
Comments: Made from about 1969 to 1974.

Estimated Value:	Blue	Stainless Steel
Excellent:	$70.00	$100.00
Very good:	$60.00	$ 80.00

American 25 Automatic

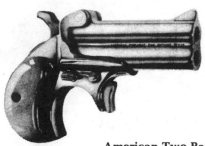

American Two Barrel Derringer

American Two Barrel Derringer

Caliber: 22 short, long, long rifle; 22 WRM, 38 Special
Action: Single action; exposed hammer; spur trigger; tip up barrels
Cylinder: None; cartridges chamber in barrels; 2-shot capacity
Barrel: 3" double barrel (superposed)
Sights: Fixed
Finish: Stainless steel; checkered plastic grips
Length overall: 5"
Approximate wt.: 12 oz.
Comments: Made from about 1972 to 1974. All stainless steel construction.
Estimated Value: Excellent: $70.00
Very good: $50.00

Astra

Astra 1911 Model - Patent

Astra 1915 Model - Patent

Astra 1924 Hope

Astra 1911 Model - Patent

Caliber: 32 ACP (7.65mm)
Action: Semi-automatic; concealed hammer
Magazine: 7-shot clip
Barrel: 3¼"
Sights: Fixed
Finish: Blued; checkered hard rubber grips
Length overall: 5¾"
Approximate wt.: 29 oz.
Comments: A Spanish copy of the Browning blowback action, probably made of trade parts. Not made by Unceta y Compania.
Estimated Value: Excellent: $85.00
Very good: $75.00

Astra 1915 Model - Patent

Caliber: 32 ACP (7.65mm)
Action: Semi-automatic; concealed hammer
Magazine: 9-shot clip
Barrel: 3¼"
Sights: Fixed
Finish: Blued; checkered hard rubber grips
Length overall: 5¾"
Approximate wt.: 29 oz.
Comments: A Spanish copy of the Browning blowback action, probably made of trade parts. Not made by Unceta y Compania.
Estimated Value: Excellent: $90.00
Very good: $75.00

Astra 1924 Hope

Caliber: 25 ACP (6.35mm)
Action: Semi-automatic; concealed hammer
Magazine: 6-shot clip
Barrel: 2"
Sights: Fixed
Finish: Blued; checkered rubber grips
Length overall: 4 1/3"
Approximate wt.: 12 oz.
Comments: Some of these pistols do not have "HOPE" designation on barrel.
Estimated Value: Excellent: $70.00
Very good: $60.00

Astra 1916 Model - Patent

Caliber: 32 ACP (7.65mm)
Action: Semi-automatic; concealed hammer
Magazine: 9-shot clip
Barrel: 4"
Sights: Fixed
Finish: Blued; checkered hard rubber grips
Length overall: 6½"
Approximate wt.: 32 oz.
Comments: A Spanish copy of the Browning blowback action, made under several trade names, probably of trade parts. Many were sold in the United States, Central America and South America. Not made by Unceta y Compania.
Estimated Value: Excellent: $100.00
Very good: $ 80.00

Handguns

Astra Model 2000 Cub Pocket

Caliber: 22 short, 25 ACP (6.35mm)
Action: Semi-automatic; exposed hammer
Magazine: 6-shot clip
Barrel: 2 1/8"
Sights: Fixed
Finish: Blued; chrome and/or engraved; checkered grips
Length overall: 4½"
Approximate wt.: 13-14 oz.
Comments: A well-made pistol of the post-World War II period. Importation was discontinued to the United States in 1968.

Estimated Value:	Blue	Chrome
Excellent:	$125.00	$140.00
Very good:	$100.00	$110.00

Astra Model 2000 Cub Pocket

Astra Camper Pocket

Same as ASTRA CUB (Model 2000) except: 22 caliber short only; 4-inch barrel which extends beyond front of slide; laterally adjustable rear sight. Discontinued in 1966.

Estimated Value:	Blue	Chrome
Excellent:	$100.00	$110.00
Very good:	$ 80.00	$ 90.00

Astra Camper Pocket

Astra Model 300

Caliber: 380 ACP (9mm Kurz)
Action: Semi-automatic; concealed hammer
Magazine: 7-shot clip
Barrel: 4¼"
Sights: Fixed
Finish: Blued; checkered rubber grips
Length overall: 6½"
Approximate wt.: 21 oz.
Comments: This pistol was a shorter version of the Model 400 and production was started in 1922.

Estimated Value:	Excellent:	$145.00
	Very good:	$115.00

Astra Model 300

Astra Model 400

Astra Model 600

Astra Model 600

Caliber: 32 ACP (7.65mm) 9mm Luger
Action: Semi-automatic; concealed hammer
Magazine: 10-shot clip in 32 caliber; 8-shot clip in 9mm.
Barrel: 5¼"
Sights: Fixed
Finish: Blued; checkered rubber grips
Length overall: 8½"
Approximate wt.: 35 oz.
Comments: Made from 1944 to 1945 for military and police use. The 9mm was used as a substitute pistol in German military service, so some will have German acceptance marks.

Estimated Value:	Excellent:	$140.00
	Very good:	$110.00

Astra Model 400

Caliber: 9mm Bayard long; 38 ACP, 9mm Steyr, 9mm Glisenti, 9mm Luger, 9mm Browning long cartridges can be used due to chamber design.
Action: Semi-automatic; concealed hammer
Magazine: 9-shot clip
Barrel: 6"
Sights: Fixed
Finish: Blued; checkered rubber grips
Length overall: 9"
Approximate wt.: 36 oz.
Comments: Made from 1921 until 1945 for both commercial and military use.

Estimated Value:	Excellent:	$175.00
	Very good:	$140.00

Astra Model 800 Condor

Caliber: 9mm Parabellum
Action: Semi-automatic; exposed hammer
Magazine: 8-shot clip
Barrel: 5¼"
Sights: Fixed
Finish: Blued; checkered grips
Length overall: 8¼"
Approximate wt.: 32 oz.
Comments: A post-war version of the Model 600 military pistol. It has a loaded chamber indicator.
Estimated Value: Excellent: $375.00
Very good: $300.00

Astra Model 800 Condor

Astra Model 200 Firecat

Astra Model 200 Firecat

Caliber: 25 ACP (6.35mm)
Action: Semi-automatic; concealed hammer; grip safety
Magazine: 6-shot clip
Barrel: 2¼"
Sights: Fixed
Finish: Blued or chrome; plastic grips
Length overall: 4½"
Approximate wt.: 13 oz.
Comments: A well-machined pistol made from early 1920 to date. It was imported to the United States from World War II until 1968.

Estimated Value:	Blue	Chrome
Excellent:	$110.00	$125.00
Very good:	$ 90.00	$100.00

Astra Model 3000

Astra Model 3000

Caliber: 22 long rifle, 32 ACP, 380 ACP (9mm short).
Action: Semi-automatic; concealed hammer
Magazine: 10-shot in 22 caliber; 7-shot in 32 caliber; 6-shot in 380; clip
Barrel: 4"
Sights: Fixed
Finish: Blued; checkered grips
Length overall: 6 3/8"
Approximate wt.: 23 oz.
Comments: Made from about 1947 to 1956. Well-machined and well-finished commercially produced pistol. The 380 caliber has loaded chamber indicator.
Estimated Value: Excellent: $150.00
Very good: $125.00

Astra Model 4000 Falcon

Caliber: 22 long rifle, 32 ACP (7.65mm) 380 ACP (9mm short)
Action: Semi-automatic; exposed hammer
Magazine: 10-shot in 22 caliber; 8-shot in 32 caliber; 7-shot in 380 caliber
Barrel: 4¼"
Sights: Fixed
Finish: Blued; checkered grips
Length overall: 6½"
Approximate wt.: 20 to 24 oz.
Comments: A conversion unit was available to fit the 32 caliber and 380 caliber pistols, so that 22 caliber long rifle ammunition could be used.
Estimated Value: Excellent: $140.00
Very good: $110.00

Astra Model 5000 Constable

Caliber: 22 long rifle, 32 ACP (7.65mm), 380 ACP
Action: Double action; semi-automatic; exposed hammer with round spur
Magazine: 10-shot in .22 caliber long rifle; 8-shot in 32 ACP; 7-shot in 380 ACP; clip
Barrel: 3½"
Sights: Fixed
Finish: Blued or chrome; grooved grips
Length overall: 6 5/8"
Approximate wt: 24 to 26 oz.
Comments: The barrel is rigidly mounted in the frame, all steel construction with hammer block safety. Add $100.00 for fatory engraving. Add $15.00 for chrome finish.
Estimated Value: New (retail): $245.00
Excellent: $185.00
Very good: $150.00

Astra Model 4000 Falcon

Astra Model 5000 Constable

Handguns

Astra 357 Magnum Revolver

Astra Cadix

Caliber: 22 short, long, and long rifle, 38 Special
Action: Double action
Cylinder: Swing out 9-shot in 22 cal.; 5-shot in 38 Special
Barrel: 2'', 4'', and 6''
Sights: Adjustable rear on 4'' and 6'' barrel
Finish: Blued; checkered grips
Length overall: 6½'', 9'', 11''
Approximate wt.: 25 to 27 oz.
Comments: Made from about 1960 to the late 1960's.
Estimated Value: Excellent: $90.00
              Very good: $70.00

Astra 357 Magnum Revolver

Caliber: 357 magnum, 38 Special
Action: Double action
Cylinder: 6-shot, swing out
Barrel: 3'', 4'', 6'', 8¾'' heavy weight with rib
Sights: Adjustable rear, fixed front
Finish: Blued; wood grips
Length overall: 8¼'', 9¼''
Approximate wt.: 38 to 42 oz.
Comments: All steel construction with wide spur hammer and grooved trigger. Currently made. Add $10.00 for 8¾'' barrel.
Estimated Value: New (retail): $275.00
              Excellent: $200.00
              Very good: $160.00

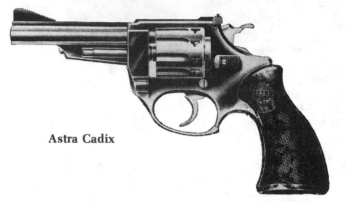

Astra Cadix

Auto Mag

Auto Mag.

Caliber: 357 auto magnum or 44 auto magnum custom loaded or hand loaded cartridges (no commercial ammo available). All of the auto magnum cartridges are based on the 308 Winchester or the 7.26 NATO cases
Action: Semi-automatic; exposed hammer; adjustable trigger
Magazine: 7-shot clip
Barrel: 6½'' ventilated rib
Sights: Ramp front sight and adjustable rear sight
Finish: Stainless steel; checkered plastic grips
Length overall: 11½''
Approximate wt.: 60 oz.
Comments: The most potent autoloader made. Requires special ammunition made from the 308 Winchester or 7.62 NATO cases. Made from about 1970 to late 1970's. All stainless steel construction.
Estimated Value: Excellent: $550.00 - $700.00
              Very good: $475.00 - $625.00

Auto Mag. M. 180

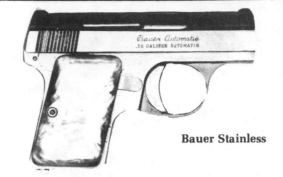

Bauer Stainless

Caliber: 25 ACP, 22 long rifle
Action: Semi-automatic; concealed hammer
Magazine: 6-shot clip
Barrel: 2 1/8"
Sights: Fixed
Finish: Heat treated stainless steel; plastic grips
Length overall: 4"
Approximate wt.: 10 oz.
Comments: Manufactured completely in the United States from about 1972 to present.
Estimated Value: New (retail): **$117.00**
                    Excellent: **$ 90.00**
                    Very good: **$ 75.00**

Bauer Stainless

Bayard

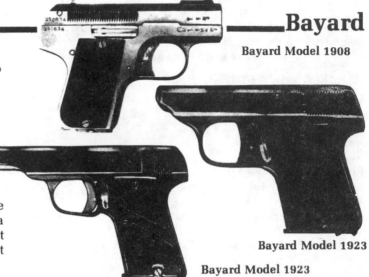

Bayard Model 1908

Bayard Model 1923

Bayard Model 1923

Bayard Model 1908

Caliber: 25 ACP (6.35mm), 32 ACP (7.65mm), 380 ACP (9mm short)
Action: Semi-automatic; concealed hammer
Magazine: 6-shot clip
Barrel: 2 ¼"
Sights: Fixed
Finish: Blued; checkered grips
Length overall: 5"
Approximate wt.: 15 to 17 oz.
Comments: Made from basic Pieper patents of the 1900's. All calibers appear the same from a side view. Commercially sold throughout the world and one of the most compact pistols made.
Estimated Value: Excellent: **$120.00**
                    Very good: **$100.00**

Bayard Model 1923 (25 ACP)

Caliber: 25 ACP
Action: Semi-automatic; concealed hammer
Magazine: 6-shot clip
Barrel: 2 1/8"
Sights: Fixed
Finish: Blued; checkered grips
Length overall: 4 1/3"
Approximate wt.: 12 oz.
Comments: A Belgian variation of the Browning. This model has better construction than the model 1908.
Estimated Value: Excellent: **$130.00**
                    Very good: **$110.00**

Bayard Model 1923 (32, 380)

Caliber: 32 ACP (7.65mm), 380 ACP (9mm short)
Action: Semi-automatic; concealed hammer
Magazine: 6-shot clip
Barrel: 3 3/8"
Sights: Fixed
Finish: Blued; checkered grips
Length overall: 5 ¾"
Approximate wt.: 18 to 19 oz.
Comments: A Belgian variation of the Browning. Better construction than the 1908.
Estimated Value: Excellent: **$150.00**
                    Very good: **$125.00**

Bayard Model 1930

Caliber: 25 ACP (6.35mm)
Action: Semi-automatic; concealed hammer
Magazine: 6-shot clip
Barrel: 2"
Sights: Fixed
Finish: Blued; checkered grips
Length overall: 4 3/8"
Approximate wt.: 12 oz.
Comments: A modification of the Model 1923.
Estimated Value: Excellent: **$160.00**
                    Very good: **$130.00**

Bayard Model 1930

Beretta Model 1915

Caliber: 32 ACP (7.65mm)
Action: Semi-automatic; concealed hammer
Magazine: 8-shot clip
Barrel: 3 ¼"
Sights: Fixed
Finish: Blued; wood or metal grips
Length overall: 5 7/8"
Approximate wt.: 20 oz.
Comments: The earliest of the Beretta series used for military service during World War I, as well as being sold commercially. Has rigid lanyard loop on left side. Grip safety was added in 1919. Made from about 1915 to 1924.
Estimated Value: Excellent: **$175.00**
                         Very good: **$140.00**

Beretta Model 1915

Beretta Model 1919 "Bantam"

Caliber: 25 ACP (6.35mm)
Action: Semi-automatic; concealed hammer
Magazine: 7-shot clip
Barrel: 2 ½"
Sights: Fixed
Finish: Blued; wood grips
Length overall: 4 ½"
Approximate wt.: 14 oz.
Comments: Basic Beretta patent with addition of a grip safety. The front sight contour was changed prior to World War II. Importation to the United States was discontinued in 1956.
Estimated Value: Excellent: **$150.00**
                         Very good: **$120.00**

Beretta Model 1919 "Bantam"

Beretta Model 1923

Caliber: 9mm Luger
Action: Semi-automatic; exposed hammer
Magazine: 9-shot clip
Barrel: 4"
Sights: Fixed
Finish: Blued; wood grips
Length overall: 6 ½"
Approximate wt.: 30 oz.
Comments: Basically an Italian service pistol, but also was sold commercially. A modified version of the 1915 and 1919 patents. This was the first model produced with exposed hammer. Lanyard loop on left side.
Estimated Value: Excellent: $200.00
                         Very good: $150.00

Beretta Model 1923

Beretta Model 1931

Beretta Model 1931

Caliber: 32 ACP (7.65mm)
Action: Semi-automatic; concealed hammer
Magazine: 7-shot clip
Barrel: 3 5/16"
Sights: Fixed
Finish: Blued; wood grips
Length overall: 5 ¾"
Approximate wt.: 22 oz.
Comments: A modified version of the Model 1923.
Estimated Value: Excellent: $180.00
                         Very good: $150.00

Beretta Model 934 (1934) 380 and 935 (1935) 32

Caliber: 32 ACP (7.65mm), 380 ACP (9mm short)
Action: Semi-automatic; exposed hammer
Magazine: 8-shot clip in 32 caliber, and 7-shot in 380 caliber
Barrel: 3 ½"
Sights: Fixed
Finish: Blued; plastic grips
Length overall: 6"
Approximate wt.: 22 to 24 oz.
Comments: Official pistol of the Italian Armed Forces from 1934 until 1951 in 380 caliber. Still sold commercially and used by Italian police. Lanyard loop on left side. Model 935 was discontinued in 1958.
Estimated Value: Excellent: $190.00
Very good: $150.00

Beretta Cougar

Beretta Cougar

Caliber: 380 ACP (9mm short)
Action: Semi-automatic; exposed hammer
Magazine: 7-shot clip
Barrel: 3 ½"
Sights: Fixed
Finish: Blued or chrome; plastic grips
Length overall: 6"
Approximate wt: 22 oz.
Comments: A post-World War II version of the Model 934 (1934). Those imported into the United States have the "Cougar" name on pistol. Some of the later models are maked "P.B. 1966". Add $10.00 for chrome.
Estimated Value: Excellent: $200.00
Very good: $160.00

Beretta Model 934 (1934) 380 and 935 (1935) 32

Beretta Model 948 Plinker

Caliber: 22 long rifle
Action: Semi-automatic; exposed hammer
Magazine: 7-shot clip
Barrel: 3 ½", 6"
Sights: Fixed
Finish: Blued; plastic grips
Length overall: 6" or 8 ½"
Approximate wt.: 16 - 18 oz.
Comments: Made from 1948 to 1958. Similar to the 1934/35 series except: 22 caliber; aluminum alloy frame. Replaced by the "Jaguar". The 6-inch barrel extends beyond the slide about 3 inches.
Estimated Value: Excellent: $140.00
Very good: $115.00

Beretta Model 70 Puma

Caliber: 32 ACP (7.65mm); 380 ACP
Action: Semi-automatic; exposed hammer
Magazine: 7-shot clip
Barrel: 3 ½"
Sights: Fixed
Finish: Blued or nickel; plastic wrap around grip
Length overall: 6 ½"
Approximate wt: 15 oz.
Comments: Post-World War II (1946) version of the Model 935 (1935). Aluminum alloy frame was used to reduce weight. Those imported into the United States have "PUMA" designation. Also made with steel frame. Discontinued. Add $15.00 for nickel finish.
Estimated Value: Excellent: $130.00
Very good: $105.00

Beretta Model 70 Puma

Handguns

Beretta Models 71 & 72 Jaguar

Caliber: 22 long rifle
Action: Semi-automatic; exposed hammer
Magazine: 7-shot clip
Barrel: 3½" (Model 71) and 6" (Model 72)
Sights: Fixed
Finish: Blued; wrap around plastic grip
Length overall: 6¼" or 8¾"
Approximate wt.: 16 - 18 oz.
Comments: Importation to the United States started in 1956. The light weight was obtained by using aluminum alloy receiver. Similar in appearance to the "Puma" except the 6" barrel extends beyond the slide about 3". Discontinued.
Estimated Value: Excellent: $135.00
Very good: $110.00

Beretta Model 949 Olympic

Beretta Model 951 (1951)

Beretta Models 71 & 72 Jaguar

Beretta Model 70S

Beretta Model 70S

Caliber: 380 ACP (9mm short); 22 long rifle
Action: Semi-automatic; exposed hammer
Magazine: 7-shot clip in 380, 8 shot in 22
Barrel: 3½"
Sights: Fixed
Finish: Blued; 2-piece wrap around plastic grip
Length overall: 6¼"
Approximate wt: 24 oz.
Comments: Compact pistol imported from Italy.   taly.
Estimated Value: New (retail): $235.00
Excellent: $175.00
Very good: $140.00

Beretta Model 949 Olympic

Caliber: 22 short, 22 long rifle
Action: Semi-automatic; exposed hammer
Magazine: 5-shot clip
Barrel: 8¾" with compensator muzzle brake
Sights: Rear adjustable for windage; front adjustable for elevation
Finish: Blued; checked walnut grips with thumb rest
Length overall: 12½"
Approximate wt.: 38 oz.
Comments: Also called the 949C, it was designed for use in Olympic rapid-fire matches and designated 949LR. Both models have been discontinued.
Estimated Value: Excellent: $300.00
Very good: $240.00

Beretta Model 951 (1951)

Caliber: 9mm Parabellum (Luger)
Action: Semi-automatic; exposed hammer
Magazine: 8-shot clip
Barrel: 4½"
Sights: Fixed
Finish: Blued; plastic wrap around grip
Length overall: 8"
Approximate wt.: 31 oz.
Comments: First produced in 1950 and adopted by Italian Army and Navy. Basic 1934 model features except it has aluminum alloy receiver. Also known as Brigadier model.
Estimated Value: Excellent: $275.00
Very good: $225.00

Beretta Minx M2

Beretta Model 70T

Beretta Minx M2 Model 950 B

Caliber: 22 short
Action: Semi-automatic; exposed hammer
Magazine: 7-shot clip
Barrel: 2½"
Sights: Fixed
Finish: Blued or nickel; plastic grips
Length overall: 4½"
Approximate wt: 10 oz.
Comments: Made from 1956 to present. Imported from 1956 to 1968. Aluminum alloy frame with a hinged barrel that tips up at chamber end. Can be used as single shot by removing magazine and tipping up barrel to load. Reintroduced in 1979, manufactured in the United States. Add $15.00 for nickel finish.
Estimated Value: New (retail): $149.95
Excellent: $115.00
Very good: $ 90.00

Beretta Model 70T

Caliber: 32 ACP (7.65mm)
Action: Semi-automatic; exposed hammer
Magazine: 9-shot clip
Barrel: 6"
Sights: Adjustable rear; blade front
Finish: Blued; plastic wrap around grip
Length overall: 9½"
Approximate wt.: 20 oz.
Comments: Imported from Italy. Target length barrel extends beyond front of slide.
Estimated Value: Excellent: $170.00
Very good: $135.00

Beretta Model 101

Same as 70T except: 22 caliber long rifle; 10-shot magazine.
Estimated Value: Excellent: $175.00
Very good: $140.00

Beretta Minx M-4 Model 950C

Beretta Jetfire Model 950B

Beretta Model 76

Beretta Minx M-4 Model 950C

Same as Minx M-2 except: 4" barrel; overall length is 6"; approximate weight 12 oz. Add $15.00 for nickel finish.
Estimated Value: Excellent: $115.00
Very good: $ 90.00

Beretta Jetfire Model 950B

Same as Minx M-2 except: 25 ACP (6.35mm) caliber; 7-shot magazine. Add $15.00 for nickel finish.
Estimated Value: New (retail): $149.95
Excellent: $115.00
Very good: $ 90.00

Beretta Model 76

Caliber: 22 long rifle
Action: Semi-automatic; exposed hammer
Magazine: 10-shot clip
Barrel: 6"
Sights: Adjustable rear, blade front
Finish: Blued; 2-piece wrap around plastic or wood grip
Length overall: 9½"
Approximate wt.: 35 oz.
Comments: Imported from Italy. Competition-type heavy barrel. Add $15.00 for wood grip
Estimated Value: New (retail): $285.00
Excellent: $215.00
Very good: $170.00

Handguns

Beretta Model DA 380

Caliber: 380 ACP (9mm short)
Action: Double action; semi-automatic; exposed round spur hammer
Magazine: 13-shot clip
Barrel: 3 ¾ "
Sights: Fixed
Finish: Blued; smooth walnut grips
Length overall: 6 ½ "
Approximate wt.: 23 oz.
Comments: This pistol features magazine release and safety release for either right or left hand.
Estimated Value: Excellent: $225.00
          Very good: $180.00

Beretta Model 90

Caliber: 32 ACP (7.65mm)
Action: Double action; semi-automatic; exposed hammer
Magazine: 8-shot clip
Barrel: 3 5/8", stainless steel
Sights: Fixed
Finish: Blued; plastic wrap around grip
Length overall: 6 ¾ "
Approximate wt.: 20 oz.
Comments: It has loaded chamber indicator and a sighting rib on the slide.
Estimated Value: Excellent: $190.00
          Very good: $160.00

Beretta Model DA 380

Beretta Model 90

Beretta Model 92

Beretta Model 81

Beretta Model 92

Caliber: 9mm Parabellum
Action: Semi-automatic; double and single action
Magazine: 15 shot clip
Barrel: 5"
Sights: Fixed
Finish: Blued; plastic or smooth wood grips
Length overall: 8 ½ "
Approximate wt.: 33 oz.
Comments: Introduced in the late 1970's. Add $25.00 for wood grips.
Estimated Value: New (retail): $470.00
          Excellent: $355.00
          Very good: $285.00

Beretta Model 81

Caliber: 32 ACP
Action: Semi-automatic; dounle and single action
Magazine: 12 shot clip
Barrel: 3 ¾ "
Sights: Fixed
Finish: Blued; plastic or smooth wood grips
Length overall: 6 ¾ "
Approximate wt.: 23 ½ oz.
Comments: Introduced in the late 1970's. Add $20.00 for wood grips.
Estimated Value: New (retail): $335.00
          Excellent: $255.00
          Very good: $205.00

Beretta Model 84

Similar to the Model 81 in 380 caliber (9mm short); 13 shot clip; add $20.00 for wood grips.
Estimated Value: New (retail): $335.00
          Excellent: $255.00
          Very good: $205.00

Browning Model 1910

Browning Nomad

Browning Model 1935
Hi Power

Browning 25 Pocket

Caliber: 25 ACP (6.35mm)
Action: Semi-automatic; concealed hammer
Magazine: 6-shot clip
Barrel: 2 1/8"
Sights: Fixed
Finish: Blued, hard rubber grip; nickel plated, light weight, plastic pearl grips; Renaissance engraved, Nacolac pearl grips.
Length overall: 4"
Approximate wt.: 8 to 10 oz.
Comments: A post-World War II modification of the FN Browning Baby Automatic pistol, it was lightened and grip safety was removed Imported into the U.S. from 1954 to 1968. Pistols imported into the U.S. and Canada usually do not have FN trademark.

Estimated Value:	Blue	Nickel	Renaissance
Excellent:	$175.00	$200.00	$475.00
Very good:	$150.00	$175.00	$400.00

Browning Model 1910

Caliber: 380 ACP (9mm short)
Action: Semi-automatic; concealed hammer
Magazine: 6-shot clip
Barrel: 3 ½"
Sights: Fixed
Finish: Blued, hard rubber grips; Renaissance engraved, Nacolac pearl grips
Length overall: 6"
Approximate wt.: 21 oz.
Comments: Basic design of the 1900 model FN Browning, with the appearance streamlined and a grip safety added. Imported from 1954 to 1968. Pistols imported into the U.S. and Canada usually do not have the FN trademark.

Estimated Value:	Blue	Renaissance
Excellent:	$190.00	$625.00
Very good:	$155.00	$500.00

Browning Nomad

Caliber: 22 long rifle
Action: Semi-automatic; concealed hammer
Magazine: 10-shot clip
Barrel: 4½" or 6¾'"
Sights: Removable blade front, adjustable rear sight
Finish: Blued, plastic grips
Length overall: 9" and 11¼"
Approximate wt.: 26 to 28 oz.
Comments: Made from 1963 to 1973. It has an alloy frame.

Estimated Value: Excellent:	$135.00
Very good:	$110.00

Browning Model 1935 Hi Power

Caliber: 9mm Parabellum
Action: Semi-automatic; exposed hammer
Magazine: 13-shot clip
Barrel: 4 5/8"
Sights: Fixed or adjustable rear sight
Finish: Blued or nickel; checkered walnut grips; Renaissance engraved, Nacolac pearl grips
Length overall: 7¾"
Approximate wt: 34 oz.
Comments: Imported into the U.S. from 1954 to present. Some were manufactured in Canada beginning in 1943. These have alloy frames for weight reduction. Pistols imported into the U.S. from Belgium usually do not have FN trademark. Add $40.00 for adjustable rear sight; Add $60.00 for nickel finish.

Estimated Value:	New (retail):	$409.95
	Excellent:	$310.00
	Very good:	$250.00

Browning Renaissance Engraved Cased Set

Contains one each of the following:
BROWNING 25 AUTOMATIC PISTOL
BROWNING MODEL 1910 380 AUTOMATIC PISTOL
BROWNING MODEL 1935 HI POWER AUTOMATIC PISTOL
in a special walnut carrying case. Each pistol is Renaissance Engraved with Nacolac pearl grips. Imported into the U.S. from 1954 through 1968.

Estimated Value: Excellent:	$2,500.00
Very good:	$2,000.00

Handguns

Browning Challenger

Browning International Medalist

Caliber: 22 long rifle
Action: Semi-automatic; hammerless
Magazine: 10 shot clip
Barrel: 5 15/16" heavy, counter weight
Sights: Fixed, non-reflective
Finish: Blued; wide walnut grips; adjustable hand stop
Length overall: 11 ¾"
Approximate wt.: 46 oz.
Comments: A target pistol introduced in 1980.
Estimated Value: New (retail): $575.00
Excellent: $435.00
Very good: $350.00

Browning International Medalist

Browning Model BDA 380

Browning Model BDA 45

Browning Model BDA 380

Caliber: 380 ACP
Action: Semi-automatic; exposed hammer; double and single
Magazine: 12 shot staggered row clip
Barrel: 3 ¾"
Sights: Adjustable square notch rear, blade front
Finish: Blued; smooth walnut grips, bronze medallion
Length overall: 6 ¾"
Approximate wt.: 23 oz.
Comments: Introduced in the late 1970's.
Estimated Value: New (retail): $314.95
Excellent: $235.00
Very good: $185.00

Browning Challenger, Challenger II

Caliber: 22 long rifle
Action: Semi-automatic; concealed hammer
Magazine: 10-shot clip
Barrel: 4 ½" or 6 ¾"
Sights: Removable blade front, adjustable rear
Finish: Blued, checkered walnut grips; Gold model (gold inlaid) finely figured walnut grips. Renaissance engraved finely figured walnut grips.
Length overall: 9 3/16" and 11 7/16"
Approximate wt.: 36 to 38 oz.
Comments: Blued model made from 1963 to 1974. Gold model and Renaissance model introduced in 1971. All steel construction. Now called Challenger II.

Estimated Value:	Blue	Gold	Renaissance
New (retail:	$199.95		
Excellent:	$150.00	$420.00	$400.00
Very good:	$120.00	$350.00	$320.00

Browning Medalist

Caliber: 22 long rifle
Action: Semi-automatic; concealed hammer
Magazine: 10-shot clip
Barrel: 6 ¾", ventilated rib
Sights: Removable blade front, adjustable micrometer rear
Finish: Blued, checkered walnut grips with thumb rest; Gold model (gold inlaid) finely figured and carved walnut grips with thumb rest; Renaissance Model engraved, finely figured and carved walnut grips with thumb rest.
Length overall: 11 ¾"
Approximate wt.: 45 oz.
Comments: All steel construction, made from 1963 to 1974. Gold model and Renaissance model introduced in 1971.

Estimated Value:	Blue	Gold Model	Renaissance
Excellent:	$280.00	$550.00	$575.00
Very good:	$230.00	$475.00	$480.00

Browning Model BDA 45

Caliber: 45 ACP
Action: Semi-automatic; exposed hammer; built in safety block; double and single
Magazine: 7 shot clip
Barrel: 4 ½"
Sights: Adjustable square notch rear, blade front
Finish: Blued; black checkered plastic grips
Length overall: 7 ¾"
Approximate wt.: 29 oz.
Comments: A handgun with a built-in safety feature: the tripper must be pulled for the gun to fire. Introduced in the late 1970's.
Estimated Value: New (retail): $349.95
Excellent: $265.00
Very good: $210.00

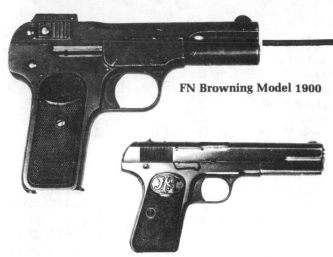

FN Browning Model 1900

FN Browning Model 1903 Military

FN Browning Model 1900

Caliber: 32 ACP (7.65mm)
Action: Semi-automatic; concealed hammer
Magazine: 7-shot clip
Barrel: 4"
Sights: Fixed
Finish: Blued; hard rubber grips with FN trademark
Length overall: 6¾"
Approximate wt.: 22 oz.
Comments: John Browning's first commercially successful pistol. This was the beginning for the .32 automatic cartridge, which is called 7.65 Browning pistol cartridge in the rest of the world. The 1900 was sold commercially throughout the world and was also used by police and military in countries such as Belgium, Russia China, and France. Made from 1900 to 1912.
Estimated Value: Excellent: $125.00
Very good: $100.00

FN Browning Model 1903 Military

Caliber: 9mm Browning long
Action: Semi-automatic; concealed hammer
Magazine: 7-shot clip
Barrel: 5"
Sights: Fixed
Finish: Blued, hard rubber grips with FN trademark
Length overall: 8"
Approximate wt.: 33 oz.
Comments: Made from 1903 to 1939. Lanyard ring on left grip.
Estimated Value: Excellent: $150.00
Very good: $125.00

FN Browning 6.35mm Pocket

Caliber: 25 ACP (6.35mm)
Action: Semi-automatic; concealed hammer; grip safety
Magazine: 6-shot clip
Barrel: 2"
Sights: Fixed
Finish: Blued; hard rubber grips with FN trademark
Length overall: 4½"
Approximate wt.: 13 oz.
Comments: Made from 1905 to 1947.
Estimated Value: Excellent: $160.00
Very good: $130.00

FN Browning Model 1910

FN Browning Model 1922

FN Browning 6.35mm Pocket

FN Browning Model 1910

Caliber: 32 ACP (7.65mm), 380 ACP (9mm short)
Action: Semi-automatic; concealed hammer
Magazine: 7-shot clip in 32 ACP, 6-shot clip in 380
Barrel: 3½"
Sights: Fixed
Finish: Blued, hard rubber grips with FN trademark
Length overall: 6"
Approximate wt.: 21 oz.
Comments: The basic design of the Model 1900 except it has streamlined appearance and grip safety. Made from 1910 to date.
Estimated Value: Excellent: $160.00
Very good: $125.00

FN Browning Model 1922 Military and Police

Caliber: 32 ACP (7.65mm), 380ACP (9mm short)
Action: Semi-automatic; concealed hammer
Magazine: 9-shot clip in 32; 8 shot clip in 380
Barrel: 4½"
Sights: Fixed
Finish: Blued; hard rubber grips with FN trademark
Length overall: 7"
Approximate wt.: 24 oz.
Comments: Identical to Model 1910 except it has longer grip frame, longer magazine and longer barrel. Made from 1922 to date. Lanyard ring on the left grip.
Estimated Value: Excellent: $175.00
Very good: $140.00

Handguns

FN Browning Baby

Caliber: 25 ACP (6.35mm)
Action: Semi-automatic; concealed hammer
Magazine: 6-shot clip
Barrel: 2 1/8"
Sights: Fixed
Finish: Blued, hard rubber grips with FN trademark
Length overall: 4"
Approximate wt.: 10 oz.
Comments: Made from 1940 to date. All steel construction, similar to Browning 25 Pocket Automatic Pistol, imported into U.S. from 1954 to 1968.
Estimated Value: Excellent: $175.00
Very good: $150.00

FN Browning Model 1935

FN Browning Baby

FN Browning Model 1935 Hi Power

Caliber: 9mm Parabellum
Action: Semi-automatic; exposed hammer
Magazine: 13-shot staggered line clip
Barrel: 4 5/8"
Sights: Fixed or adjustable
Finish: Blued or parkerized with checkered walnut or plastic grips
Length overall: 7¾"
Approximate wt.: 34 oz.
Comments: Production of this model by John Inglis Co. of Canada began in 1943. Some of these were produced with an alloy frame to reduce weight. Also during World War II Model 1935 was produced under German supervision for military use. The quality of the German pistol was poorer than those made before or after the war. A smaller version was also made with shorter barrel, slide and 10-shot clip from 1937 to 1940.

Estimated Value:	FN	German(superv.)	Canadian
Excellent:	$265.00	$220.00	$310.00
Very good:	$215.00	$190.00	$250.00

Budischowsky

Budischowsky TP-70

Budischowsky TP-70 Automatic Pistol

Caliber: 22 long rifle, 25 ACP
Action: Double action; semi-automatic; exposed hammer
Magazine: 6-shot clip
Barrel: 2½"
Sights: Fixed
Finish: Stainless steel; checkered plastic grips
Length overall: 4¾"
Approximate wt.: 12 oz.
Comments: All stainless steel construction. Manual & magazine safeties.
Estimated Value: Excellent: $130.00
Very good: $110.00

CZ

CZ Model 22 (1922)

Caliber: 380 ACP (9mm short)
Action: Semi-automatic; exposed hammer with shielding on both sides
Magazine: 8-shot clip
Barrel: 3½"
Sights: Fixed
Finish: Blued
Length overall: 6"
Approximate wt.: 22 oz.
Comments: Made in Czechoslovakia in the 1920's.
Estimated Value: Excellent: $175.00
Very good: $140.00

CZ Model 22 (1922)

CZ Model 1936 Pocket
Caliber: 25 ACP (6.35mm)
Action: Double action semi-automatic; slide does not cock hammer; (hammer is cocked and released by the trigger) shielded exposed hammer
Magazine: 8-shot clip
Barrel: 2 ½"
Sights: Fixed
Finish: Blued; plastic grips
Length overall: 4 ¾"
Approximate wt.: 14 oz.
Comments: Made from 1936 to present. U.S. importation discontinued in 1968.
Estimated Value: Excellent: $130.00
Very good: $110.00

CZ Model 38 (1938)
Caliber: 380 ACP (9mm short)
Action: Double action; semi-automatic
Magazine: 9-shot clip
Barrel: 3 ¾"
Sights: Fixed
Finish: Blued; plastic grips
Length overall: 7"
Approximate wt.: 28 oz.
Comments: Made in the late 1930's.
Estimated Value: Excellent: $155.00
Very good: $130.00

CZ Model 1945 Pocket
Same as CZ Model 1936 except for minor modifications.
Estimated Value: Excellent: $120.00
Very good: $100.00

CZ Model 50 (1950)
Caliber: .32 ACP (7.65mm)
Action: Double action semi-automatic; exposed hammer
Magazine: 8-shot clip
Barrel: 3 1/8"
Sights: Fixed
Finish: Blued, plastic grips
Length overall: 6 ½"
Approximate wt: 25 oz.
Comments: No longer imported into the U.S.
Estimated Value: Excellent: $165.00
Very good: $135.00

CZ "Duo" Pocket
Caliber: 25 ACP (6.35mm)
Action: Semi-automatic; concealed hammer
Magazine: 6-shot clip
Barrel: 2 1/8"
Sights: Fixed
Finish: Blued; plastic grips
Length overall: 4 ½"
Approximate wt: 15 oz.
Comments: Importation into the U.S. was discontinued in 1968.
Estimated Value: Excellent: $150.00
Very good: $125.00

CZ Model 27 (1927)
Caliber: 32 ACP (7.65mm)
Action: Semi-automatic; exposed hammer with shielding on both sides
Magazine: 8-shot clip
Barrel: 4"
Sights: Fixed
Finish: Blued; plastic grips
Length overall: 6 ½"
Approximate wt.: 25 oz.
Comments: This pistol usually bears the CZ mark, but World War II version may have the name Bohmische Waffenfabrik on top of slide
Estimated Value: Excellent: $165.00
Very good: $130.00

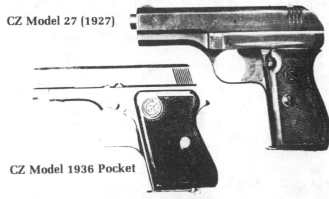

CZ Model 27 (1927)

CZ Model 1936 Pocket

CZ Model 38 (1938)

CZ Model 1945 Pocket

CZ Model 50 (1950)

CZ "Duo" Pocket

Charter Arms

Charter Arms Bulldog
Caliber: 44 Special, 357 magnum
Action: Single and double
Cylinder: 5-shot, swing-out
Barrel: 3", 4", 6"
Sights: Fixed
Finish: Blued; oil finished, checkered walnut, Bulldog grips
Length overall: 7½"(3" barrel)
Approximate wt.: 19 oz.
Comments: Made from 1971 to present.
Estimated Value: New (retail): $168.00
            Excellent: $125.00
            Very good: $100.00

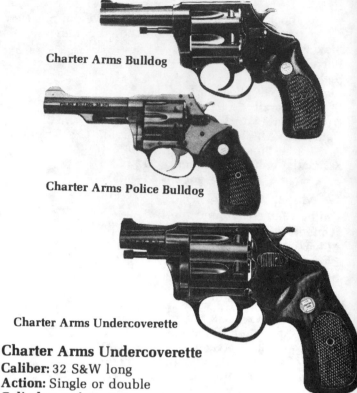

Charter Arms Bulldog

Charter Arms Police Bulldog

Charter Arms Police Bulldog
Caliber: 38 Special
Action: Single and double
Cylinder: 6-shot swing-out
Barrel: 4"
Sights: Fixed front, adjustable rear
Finish: Blued; checkered walnut Bulldog grips
Length overall: 8½"
Approximate wt.: 21 oz.
Comments: Production began in 1976.
Estimated Value: New (retail): $175.00
            Excellent: $140.00
            Very good: $115.00

Charter Arms Undercover
Caliber: 38 Special
Action: Single or double
Cylinder: 5-shot, swing out
Barrel: 2" or 3"
Sights: Fixed
Finish: Blued or nickel; oil finished, plain or hand checkered walnut grips
Length overall: 6¼" or 7 3/8"
Approximate wt: 16 or 17 oz.
Comments: Made from 1965 to present. Add $7.00 for checkered walnut Bulldog grips, add $15.00 for nickel.
Estimated Value: New (retail): $149.00
            Excellent: $110.00
            Very good: $ 90.00

Charter Arms Undercoverette

Charter Arms Undercoverette
Caliber: 32 S&W long
Action: Single or double
Cylinder: 6-shot, swing-out
Barrel: 2"
Sights: Fixed
Finish: Blued; oil finished, plain walnut grips
Length overall: 6¼"
Approximate wt.: 16½ oz.
Comments: Made from 1970 to present. Add $9 for checkered walnut Bulldog grips. Also called Undercover.
Estimated Value: New (retail): $149.00
            Excellent: $110.00
            Very good: $ 90.00

Charter Arms Pathfinder
Caliber: 22 long rifle, 22 magnum
Action: Single or double
Cylinder: 6-shot, swing-out
Barrel: 3" or 6"
Sights: Adjustable rear and partridge-type front on serrated ramp
Finish: Blued; oil finish, plain or hand checkered walnut Bulldog grips.
Length overall: 7 1/8" (3" barrel)
Approximate wt: 19 oz.
Comments: Made from 1970 to present. Add $9.00 for checkered walnut Bulldog grips. Add $15.00 for magnum; Add $10.00 for 6 inch barrel.
Estimated Value: New (retail): $168.00
            Excellent: $125.00
            Very good: $100.00

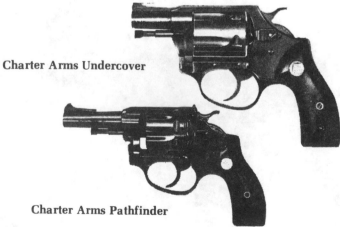

Charter Arms Undercover

Charter Arms Pathfinder

Charter Arms Target Bulldog

Charter Arms Pocket Target

Charter Arms Pocket Target
Caliber: 22 short, long, long rifle
Action: Single and double; exposed hammer
Cylinder: 6 shot swing out
Barrel: 3"
Sights: Adjustable snag free rear, ramp front
Finish: Blued; plain grips or checkered walnut Bulldog grips.
Length overall: 7 1/8"
Approximate wt.: 19 oz.
Comments: Introduced in the late 1960's.
Estimated Value: Excellent: $120.00
Very good: $100.00

Charter Arms Bulldog Tracker
Caliber: 357 magnum
Action: Double and single
Cylinder: 5 shot swing out
Barrel: 6"
Sights: Adjustable rear, ramp front
Finish: Blued; checkered walnut square butt grips
Length overall: 11"
Approximate wt.: 27 ½ oz.
Comments: Introduced in 1980.
Estimated Value: New (retail): $179.00
Excellent: $135.00
Very good: $110.00

Charter Arms Target Bulldog
Similar to the Bulldog with a 4" barrel; shrouded ejector rod; adjustable rear sight. Introduced in the late 1970's. Add $5.00 for 44 Special.
Estimated Value: New (retail): $189.00
Excellent: $150.00
Very good: $120.00

Colt

Colt Model 1900
Caliber: 38 ACP
Action: Semi-automatic; exposed spur hammer
Magazine: 7-shot clip
Barrel: 6"
Sights: Fixed
Finish: Blued; plain walnut grips
Length overall: 9"
Approximate wt.: 35 oz.
Comments: Combination safety and rear sight. Rear sight is pressed down to block hammer from firing pin. One of the first automatic pistols made in the U.S. and first automatic pistol made by Colt. Made from 1900 to 1902. No slide lock.
Estimated Value: Excellent: $550.00 - $1,000.00
Very good: $400.00 - $ 800.00

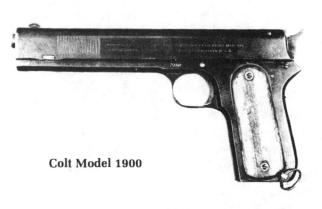

Colt Model 1900

Colt Model L (1902)
Similar to Colt Model 1900 except: no safety; round back hammer; hard rubber grips. Made from 1902 to 1907.
Estimated Value: Excellent: $525.00
Very good: $400.00

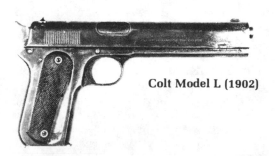

Colt Model L (1902)

Handguns

Colt Model M (380) 1st Issue Pocket
Caliber: 380 ACP (9mm short)
Action: Semi-automatic
Magazine: 7-shot clip
Barrel: 3¾"
Sights: Fixed
Finish: Blued or nickel; hard rubber or walnut checkered grips
Length overall: 6¾"
Approximate wt.: 24 oz.
Comments: Made from 1908 to 1911. Slide lock safety and grip safety. Barrel lock bushing at muzzle.
Estimated Value: Excellent: $275.00
Very good: $200.00

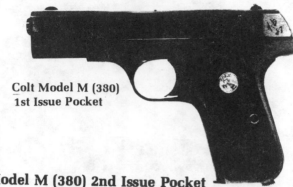

Colt Model M (380)
1st Issue Pocket

Colt Model M (380)
2nd Issue Pocket

Colt Model L (1902) Military

Colt Model L (1903) Pocket

Colt Model 1905 Military
Caliber: 45 ACP
Action: Semi-automatic
Magazine: 7-shot clip
Barrel: 5"
Sights: Fixed
Finish: Blued; checkered walnut grips
Length overall: 8½"
Approximate wt.: 34 oz.
Comments: Made from 1905 to 1912. Similar to model 1902 .38 caliber automatic pistol. First 45 caliber military automatic pistol made by Colt. Slide stop but no safety except some experimental models with short grip safety. Round hammer 1905 to 1908; after 1908 spur type hammer. Approximately 5,000 produced. NOTE: Some were fitted and equipped with a short-stock holster. These are scarce collectors items and valued much higher.
Estimated Value: Excellent: $650.00 - $1,200.00
Very good: $400.00 - $1,000.00

Colt Model M (380) 2nd Issue Pocket
Similar to first Model M (38) except: without barrel lock bushing and other minor changes. Made from 1911 to 1926. Add $200.00 for Military Model.
Estimated Value: Excellent: $260.00
Very good: $210.00

Colt Model M (380) 3rd Issue Pocket
Similar to 2nd Issue Model M (380) except: it has safety disconnector, which prevents cartridge in chamber from being fired if magazine is removed. Made from 1926 to 1941.
Estimated Value: Excellent: $265.00
Very good: $225.00

Colt Model L (1902) Military
Same as Colt Model L (1902) except: longer grips (more square at bottom) with lanyard ring; 8-shot magazine; weighs 37 oz. Made from 1902 to 1928. Spur type hammer used after 1907.
Estimated Value: Excellent: $400.00 - $1,000.00
Very good: $300.00 - $ 850.00

Colt Model L (1903) Pocket
Caliber: 38 ACP
Action: Semi-automatic; exposed hammer
Magazine: 7-shot clip
Barrel: 4½"
Sights: Fixed
Finish: Blued; checkered hard rubber grips
Length overall: 7½"
Approximate wt.: 31 oz.
Comments: Made from 1903 to 1927. Round type hammer to 1908, then changed to spur type hammer; no slide lock or safety.
Estimated Value: Excellent: $300.00
Very good: $250.00

Colt Model 1905 Military

Colt Model M (32) 1st Issue Pocket
Caliber: 32 ACP (7.65mm)
Action: Semi-automatic; concealed hammer
Magazine: 8-shot clip
Barrel: 3¾"
Sights: Fixed
Finish: Blued or nickel; hard rubber or checkered walnut grips
Length overall: 6¾"
Approximate wt.: 25 oz.
Comments: Made from 1903 to 1911. Slide lock safety and grip safety. Barrel lock bushing at muzzle.
Estimated Value: Excellent: $250.00
Very good: $210.00

Colt Model M (32) 1st Issue Pocket

Colt Model M (32) 2nd Issue Pocket

Colt Model M (32) 2nd Issue Pocket
Similar to 1st issue Model M (32) except: without barrel lock bushing and other minor modifications. Made from 1911 to 1926. Add $150.00 for Military Model.
Estimated Value: Excellent: $240.00
Very good: $200.00

Colt Model M (32) 3rd Issue Pocket
Similar to 2nd Issue Model M (32) except: safety disconnector, which prevents cartridge in chamber from being fired if magazine is removed. Made from 1926 to 1941.
Estimated Value: Excellent: $235.00
Very good: $190.00

Colt Model M (32)
3rd Issue Pocket

Colt Model N Pocket
Caliber: 25 ACP
Action: Semi-automatic; concealed striker instead of hammer
Magazine: 6-shot clip
Barrel: 2"
Sights: Fixed
Finish: Blued or nickel; hard rubber or checkered walnut
Length overall: 4½"
Approximate wt: 14 oz.
Comments: Made from 1908 to 1941. Magazine safety disconnector added in 1916 about serial number 141,000. All models have thumb safety and grip safety. Add $200.00 for Military Model.
Estimated Value: Excellent: $225.00
Very good: $175.00

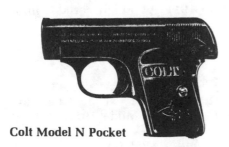

Colt Model N Pocket

Colt Junior Pocket Model 0-6
Caliber: 22 short, 25 ACP
Action: Semi-automatic; exposed round spur hammer
Magazine: 6-shot clip
Barrel: 2 1/8"
Sights: Fixed
Finish: Blued; checkered walnut grips
Length overall: 4½"
Approximate wt.: 13 to 14 oz.
Comments: Made in Spain by Astra (Uneta Y Compania, Guernica, Spain) for Colt as a replacement for the Model N which was discontinued in 1941. Imported from about 1958 to 1968.
Estimated Value: Excellent: $175.00
Very good: $140.00

Colt Junior Pocket Model 0-6

Handguns

Colt Government Model 1911

Caliber: 45 ACP
Action: Semi-automatic; exposed spur hammer
Magazine: 7-shot clip
Barrel: 5"
Sights: Fixed
Finish: Blued, nickel and parkerized or similar finish; checkered walnut grips
Length overall: 8½"
Approximate wt.: 39 oz.
Comments: Slide lock, thumb safety and grip safety. Adopted as a military side arm in 1911 in U.S. Made from 1911 to present with some modifications. Changed to Model 1911A1 in 1925. Military models are marked "U.S. Army", "U.S. Navy", or "U.S. Marines" and "United States Property" Colt licensed other firms to produce this pistol during both World Wars.

Estimated Value: Excellent: $325.00
Very good: $255.00

Colt Government Model 1911A1

Colt Government Model 1911

Colt Government Model 1911A1

Same as Government Model 1911 except: the grip safety tang was lengthened (to stop the hammer bite on fleshy hands); the trigger was shortened (to allow stubby fingers better control); the back strap below the grip safety was arched (for better instinctive pointing); and the sights were made larger & squared (to improve sight picture. Also the grips were made of checkered walnut or plastic. The 1911 A1 was made from 1925 to present. Change started about serial number 650000 in military model.

Estimated Value: Excellent: $275.00
Very good: $230.00

Colt Commercial Model 1911

Colt Commercial Model 1911 A1

Colt Commercial Model 1911

Same as Government Model 1911 except: not marked with military makings. The letter "C" is used in serial numbers. Blued or nickel finish. Made from 1911 to 1926 then changed to 1911 A1 about serial number C130000.

Estimated Value: Excellent: $300.00
Very good: $250.00

Colt Commercial Model 1911 A1

Same as Commercial Model 1911 except it has same modifications as the Government Model 1911 A1. Made from 1925 to 1970.

Estimated Value: Excellent: $265.00
Very good: $200.00

Colt 1911 (made by North American Arms Co.)

Same general specifications as 1911 Colt except: Made by North American Arms Co. in World War I period. About 100 made; company markings and serial number on slide.

Estimated Value: Excellent: $4,000.00
Very good: $3,000.00

Colt 1911 Springfield Armory N.R.A.

Same general specifications as 1911 Colt except: approximately 100 were made prior to World War I and sold through the Director of Civilian Marksmanship and have N.R.A. markings on frame.

Estimated Value: Excellent: $1600.00
Very good: $1400.00

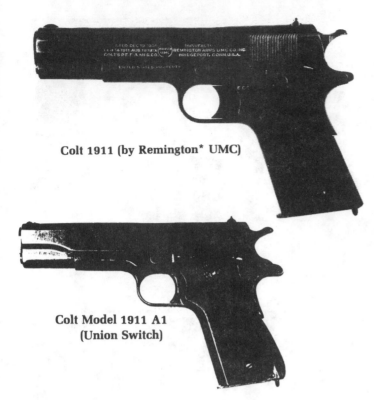

Colt 1911 (by Remington* UMC)

Colt Model 1911 A1
(Union Switch)

Colt 1911 (by Springfield Armory)

Same general specifications as 1911 Colt except: approximately 26,000 produced. Eagle motif and flaming bomb on frame and slide. Made in World War I period.

Estimated Value: Excellent: $550.00
Very good: $450.00

Colt 1911 (by Remington * UMC)

Same general specifications as 1911 Colt except: approximately 22,000 produced in World War I period. Inspector stamps B or E.

Estimated Value: Excellent: $450.00
Very good: $350.00

Colt 1911 A1 (by Singer Manufacturing Co.)

Same general specifications as 1911 A1 Colt except: approximately 500 made; blued finish; slide marked S.M. Co.; JKC inspector marking.

Estimated Value: Excellent: $2500.00
Very good: $2200.00

COLT 1911 A1 pistols were also produced during WWII by Union Switch & Signal Company, Remington Rand, Inc. and Ithaca Gun Company, Inc. Generally the estimated values of these pistols are about the same as the 1911 A1 pistol produced by Colt.

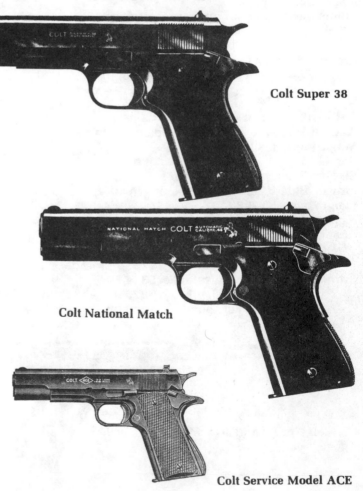

Colt Super 38

Colt National Match

Colt Service Model ACE

Colt Super 38

Same as Colt Commercial Model 1911 A1 except: caliber is 38 super ACP; magazine is 9-shot clip. Made from about 1928 to 1970.

Estimated Value: Excellent: $250.00
Very good: $200.00

Colt Super 38 Match

Same as Colt Super except: adjustable rear sight; hand honed action; match grade barrel. Made from about 1932 to 1940.

Estimated Value: Excellent: $350.00
Very good: $300.00

Colt National Match

Same as Colt Commercial Model 1911 A1 except: adjustable rear sight; hand honed action; match grade barrel. Made from 1932 to 1940.

Estimated Value: Excellent: $325.00
Very good: $275.00

Colt Service Model ACE

Similar to Colt National Match except: 22 caliber long rifle; 10-shot clip; weighs about 42 oz. It has a "floating chamber" that makes the recoil much greater than normal 22 caliber. Made from 1938 to mid 1940's.

Estimated Value: Excellent: $635.00
Very good: $525.00

Handguns

Colt Gold Cup National Match

Same as the Colt Commercial Model 1911 A1 except: hand fitted slide; enlarged ejection port; adjustable rear sight; adjustable trigger stop; new bushing design; checkered walnut grips; match grade barrel; flat grip below safety like model 1911. Made from about 1957 to 1970.

Estimated Value: Excellent: $275.00
                  Very good: $225.00

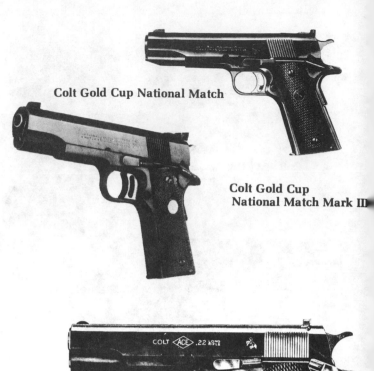

Colt Gold Cup National Match

Colt Gold Cup
National Match Mark III

Colt Gold Cup National Match Mark III

Similar to Colt Gold Cup National Match except: chambered for 38 Special mid-range wad cutter only. Operates with fixed barrel rather than locked breech. Made from 1960 to 1974.

Estimated Value: Excellent: $300.00
                  Very good: $225.00

Colt Ace Target

Caliber: 22 long rifle
Action: Semi-automatic; exposed spur hammer
Magazine: 10-shot clip
Barrel: 4¾"
Sights: Adjustable rear sight
Finish: Blued; checkered walnut or plastic grip
Length overall: 8¼"
Approximate wt.: 38oz.
Comments: Similar in appearance to the 1911 A1 and has same safety features. Made from about 1931 to 1941.

Colt Ace Target

Estimated Value: Excellent: $595.00
                  Very good: $500.00

Colt Ace (current)

Caliber: 22 long rifle
Action: Semi-automatic; exposed spur hammer
Magazine: 10 shot clip
Barrel: 5"
Sights: Fixed rear, ramp style front
Finish: Blued; checkered walnut grips
Length overall: 8 3/8"
Approximate wt.: 42 oz.
Comments: A full size automatic similar to the Colt Government MK IV/Series 70 in 22 long rifle. Produced from 1979 to present.

Estimated Value: New (retail): $324.50
                  Excellent: $270.00
                  Very good: $220.00

Colt Ace (current)

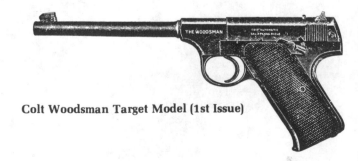

Colt Woodsman Target Model (1st Issue)

Colt Woodsman Target Model (1st Issue)

Caliber: 22 long rifle (regular velocity)
Action: Semi-automatic; concealed hammer
Magazine: 10-shot clip
Barrel: 6½"
Sights: Adjustable
Finish: Blued; checkered walnut grips
Length overall: 10½"
Approximate wt.: 28 oz.
Comments: This model not strong enough for Hi-speed cartridge, until a strong heat treated housing was produced about serial number 83790. Thumb safety only. Made from about 1915 to 1932.

Estimated Value: Excellent: $270.00
                  Very good: $200.00

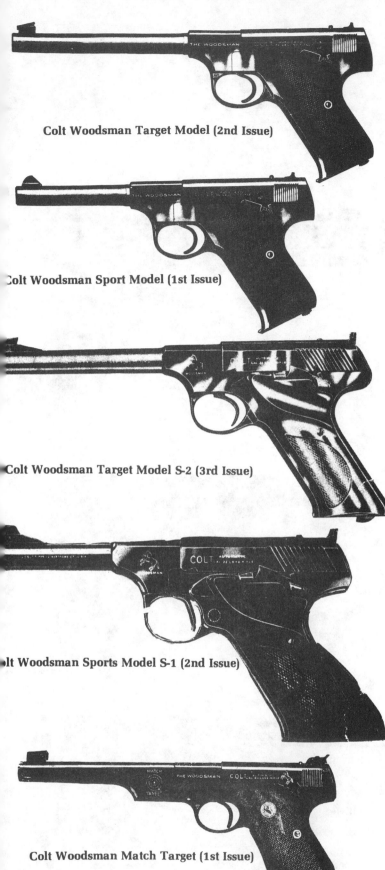

Colt Woodsman Target Model (2nd Issue)

Colt Woodsman Sport Model (1st Issue)

Colt Woodsman Target Model S-2 (3rd Issue)

lt Woodsman Sports Model S-1 (2nd Issue)

Colt Woodsman Match Target (1st Issue)

Colt Woodsman Target Model (2nd Issue)

Same as Colt Woodsman Target Model 1st Issue except: heavier tapered barrel and stronger housing for using either the 22 long rifle regular or Hi-speed cartridges. Made from about 1932 to 1945. Approximate wt: 29 oz.

Estimated Value: Excellent: $300.00
Very good: $225.00

Colt Woodsman Sport Model (1st Issue)

Caliber: 22 long rifle
Action: Semi-automatic; concealed hammer
Magazine: 10-shot clip
Barrel: 4½'' tapered barrel
Sights: Adjustable
Finish: Blued; checkered walnut grips
Length overall: 8½''
Approximate wt.: 27 oz.
Comments: Same as Colt Woodsman Target Model (2nd Issue) except shorter. Made from about 1933 to late 1940's.

Estimated Value: Excellent: $275.00
Very good: $220.00

Colt Woodsman Target Model S-2 (3rd Issue)

Similar to Colt Woodsman Target Model (2nd Issue) except: longer grips with thumb rest, larger thumb safety; slide stop; magazine disconnector; slide stays open when magazine is empty; checkered walnut or plastic grips. Approximate wt: 32 oz. Made from 1948 to late 1970's.

Estimated Value: Excellent: $180.00
Very good: $140.00

Colt Woodsman Sports Model S-1 (2nd Issue)

Same as Colt Woodsman Target Model S-2 (3rd Issue) except: 4½'' barrel, 9'' overall length; approximate wt. is 30 oz. Made from about 1948 to late 1970's.

Estimated Value: Excellent: $175.00
Very Good: $135.00

Colt Woodsman Match Target (1st Issue)

Caliber: 22 long rifle
Action: Semi-automatic; concealed hammer
Magazine: 10-shot clip
Barrel: 6½''; slightly tapered with flat sides
Sights: Adjustable rear
Finish: Blued; checkered walnut, one-piece grip with extended sides
Length overall: 11''
Approximate wt.: 36 oz.
Comments: Made from about 1938 to 1942.

Estimated Value: Excellent: $500.00
Very good: $425.00

Handguns

Colt Model S-4 Targetsman

Similar to Colt Woodsman Target Model (3rd Issue) except: cheaper made adjustable rear sight and does not have automatic slide stop. Made from about 1959 to late 1970's.

Estimated Value: Excellent: **$160.00**
                 Very good: **$130.00**

Colt Model S-4 Targetsman

Colt Woodsman Match Target Model S-3

Caliber: 22 long rifle
Action: Semi-automatic; concealed hammer
Magazine: 10-shot clip
Barrel: 4½'', 6''
Sights: Adjustable rear
Finish: Blued; checkered walnut grips with thumb rest
Length overall: 9'', 10½''
Approximate wt.: 36 to 39 oz.
Comments: Made from about 1948 to late 1970's. Flat sided weight added to full length of barrel. It has a slide stop and magazine safety.

Estimated Value: Excellent: **$200.00**
                 Very good: **$150.00**

Colt Woodsman
Match Target Model S-3

Colt Challenger Model

Caliber: 22 long rifle
Action: Semi-automatic; concealed hammer
Magazine: 10-shot clip
Barrel: 4½'', 6''
Sights: Fixed
Finish: Blued; checkered plastic grips
Length overall: 9'', 10½''
Approximate wt.: 30 to 32 oz. (depending on length)
Comments: Same basic design as Colt Woodsman Target Model (3rd Issue) except: slide doesn't stay open when magazine is empty; no magazine safety. Made from about 1950 to 1955.

Estimated Value: Excellent: **$165.00**
                 Very good: **$140.00**

Colt Challenger Model

Colt Huntsman Model S-5

Caliber: 22 long rifle
Action: Semi-automatic; concealed hammer
Magazine: 10-shot clip
Barrel: 4½'', 6''
Sights: Fixed
Finish: Blued; checkered walnut grips
Length overall: 9'', 10½''
Approximate wt.: 31 to 32 oz.
Comments: Made from about 1955 to late 1970's.

Estimated Value: Excellent: **$150.00**
                 Very good: **$125.00**

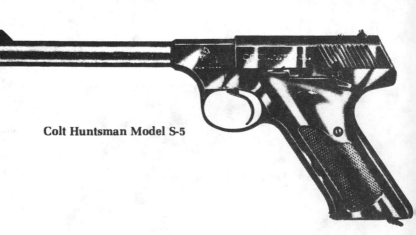

Colt Huntsman Model S-5

Colt Commander Light Weight

Colt Light Weight Commander

Caliber: 45 ACP
Action: Semi-automatic; exposed round spur hammer
Magazine: 7 shot clip
Barrel: 4¼"
Sights: Fixed
Finish: Blued; checkered or smooth walnut grips
Length overall: 7¾"
Approximate wt: 27 oz.
Comments: Same design as Gov. 1911 A1 model except: shorter and lighter; rounded spur hammer. Receiver and frame made of aluminum alloy. Made from 1949 to present. An all steel model was introduced in 1971 and is known as Combat Commander Model. It has either flat or arched mainspring housing. Add $10.00 for Combat. Add $12.00 for nickel finish.

Estimated Value: New (retail): $295.95
Excellent: $235.00
Very good: $190.00

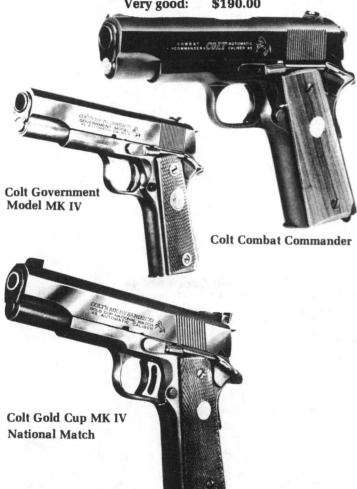

Colt Government Model MK IV

Colt Combat Commander

Colt Gold Cup MK IV National Match

Colt NRA Centennial Gold Cup National Match

Similar to Colt Gold Cup MK IV except: 45 caliber only; inscribed Commemorative Model, 2500 made in 1971. Original price was $250.00 each. Estimated value is $500.00 in mint condition with case.

Colt Combat Commander

Caliber: 9mm Parabellum, 38 Super ACP, 45 ACP
Action: Semi-automatic; exposed round spur hammer
Magazine: 9 shot clip in 9mm and 38 Super; 7 shot clip in 45 ACP
Barrel: 4¼"
Sights: Fixed
Finish: Blued or nickel (in 45 caliber only); checkered walnut grips
Length overall: 7 7/8"
Approximate wt.: 37 oz.
Comments: Same design as the Government 1911 A-1 except: shorter and lighter; round spur hammer; made from about 1971 to present with all steel frame and flat or arched mainspring housing. Add $5.00 for 9mm and $14.00 for nickel finish.

Estimated Value: New (retail): $299.95
Excellent: $240.00
Very good: $200.00

Colt Government Model MK IV / Series 70

Caliber: 9mm Luger, 38 Super ACP, 45 ACP
Action: Semi-automatic; exposed spur hammer
Magazine: 9-shot clip in 9mm and 38; 7-shot clip in 45
Barrel: 5"
Sights: Fixed
Finish: Blued or nickel; smooth or checkered walnut grips
Length overall: 8½"
Approximate wt: 38 to 39 oz.
Comments: Made from about 1970 to present. Add $10.00 for 38 Super and $5.00 for 9mm.

Estimated Value: New (retail): $299.95
Excellent: $240.00
Very good: $200.00

Colt Gold Cup MK IV National Match (Series 70)

Caliber: 38 Special MId-Range, 45 ACP
Action: Semi-automatic; exposed spur hammer
Magazine: 9-shot clip in 38, 7-shot in 45
Barrel: 5"
Sights: Adjustable rear for wind and elevation
Finish: Blued; checkered walnut with gold medallion
Length overall: 8¾"
Approximate wt: 39 oz.
Comments: Arched or flat housing below grip safety. Adjustable trigger stop, hand fitted slide, and improved barrel bushing. Made from about 1970 to present.

Estimated Value: New (retail): $399.95
Excellent: $320.00
Very good: $260.00

Handguns

Colt World War I Commemorative

Colt World War II Commemorative

Colt World War II Commemorative Series Engraved Replicas of Government Model 1911 A1 45 Automatic Pistol

Estimated Value is for mint, unused condition with original case.

	Date Issued	Total Made	Orig. Cost	Est. Value
European Theater	1970	11500	$ 250	**$ 450.00**
Pacific Theater	1970	11500	$ 250	**$ 450.00**

Colt World War I Commemorative Series Engraved Replicas of Government Model 1911 45 Automatic Pistol

Estimated Value is for mint unused condition with original case.

	Date Issued	Total Made	Orig. Cost	Est. Value
Chateau Thierry (Standard)	1967	7400	$ 200	$ 500
Chateau Thierry (Deluxe)	1967	75	$ 500	$1400
Chateau Thierry (Spec. Deluxe)	1967	25	$1000	$3000
Belleau Wood (Standard)	1968	7400	$ 200	$ 475
Belleau Wood (Deluxe)	1968	75	$ 500	$1350
Belleau Wood (Spec. Deluxe)	1968	25	$1000	$2800
Battle of 2nd Marne (Standard)	1968	7400	$ 220	$ 450
Battle of 2nd Marne (Deluxe)	1968	75	$ 500	$1300
Battle of 2nd Marne (Spec. Deluxe)	1968	25	$1000	$2600
Meuse-Argonne (Standard)	1969	7400	$ 220	$ 425
Meuse-Argonne (Deluxe)	1969	75	$ 500	$1250
Meuse-Argonne (Spec. Deluxe)	1969	25	$1000	$2500

Colt Lightning Model

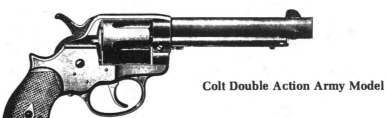

Colt Double Action Army Model

Colt Lightning Model

Caliber: 38 Centerfire, 41 Centerfire
Action: Single and double
Cylinder: 6-shot; 2/3 fluted; side load; loading gate
Barrel: 2½", 3½", 4½", 6"
Sights: Fixed
Finish: Blued or nickel; hard rubber birds head grips
Length overall: 7½" to 11"
Approximate wt.: 26 to 30 oz.
Comments: Made from 1877 to 1912, with and without side rod ejector. This was the first double action revolver made by Colt.

Estimated Value: Excellent: $375.00
Very good: $290.00

Colt Double Action Army Model

Caliber: 38-40, 44-40, 45 Colt
Action: Single or double action
Cylinder: 6-shot; 2/3 fluted; side load
Barrel: 3½" and 4" without side rod ejector. 4¾"; 5½" and 7½" with the side rod ejector
Sights: Fixed
Finish: Blued or nickel; hard rubber or checkered walnut grips.
Length overall: 8½" to 12½"
Approximate wt.: 35 to 39 oz.
Comments: Made from 1877 to 1910. Lanyard loop in butt; also called "Double Action Frontier". Similar to Lightning Model except larger.

Estimated Value: Excellent: $450.00
Very good: $375.00

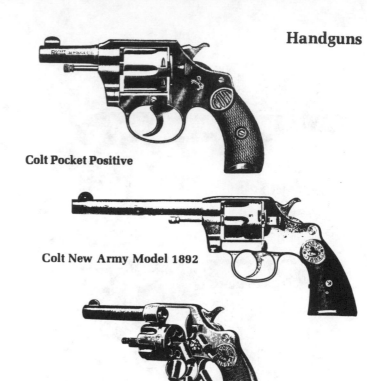

Colt Double Action Philippine Model
Same as Colt Double Action Army Model except: larger trigger guard and trigger. It was made originally for the Army in Alaska but was sent to the Philippines instead.
Estimated Value: Excellent: $500.00
Very good: $400.00

Colt New Army Model 1892
Caliber: 38 Colt short and long, 41 Colt short and long, 38 Special added in 1904, 32-20 added in 1905
Action: Single and double
Cylinder: 6-shot; 2/3 fluted; swing out; simultaneous hand ejector
Barrel: 3''; 4½''; 6''
Sights: Fixed
Finish: Blued or nickel; hard rubber or walnut grips
Length overall: 8¼'' to 11¼''
Approximate wt.: 29 to 32 oz.
Comments: Made from 1892 to 1908. Lanyard swivel attached to butt in 1901. All calibers on 41 caliber frame.
Estimated Value: Excellent: $275.00
Very good: $200.00

Colt New Navy Model 1892
Similar to Colt New Army Model 1892 except: has double cylinder notches and locking bolt. Sometimes called New Army 2nd issue.
Estimated Value: Excellent: $300.00
Very good: $225.00

Colt Army Model 1903
Same as Colt New Army Model 1892 except: modified grip design (smaller & shaped better); bore is slightly smaller in each caliber to increase accuracy.
Estimated Value: Excellent: $250.00
Very good: $200.00

Colt New Pocket
Caliber: 32 short and long Colt
Action: Single and double action
Cylinder: 6-shot; swing out; simultaneous ejector
Barrel: 2½'', 3½'' and 6''
Sights: Fixed
Finish: Blued or nickel; hard rubber grips
Length overall: 6½'' to 10½''
Approximate wt.: 15 to 18 oz.
Comments: Made from about 1895 to 1905.
Estimated Value: Excellent: $240.00
Very good: $200.00

Colt Pocket Positive
Similar to the New Pocket with the positive locking system of the Police Positive; 32 short and long S&W cartridges or 32 Colt Police Positive. Made from the early 1900's to just prior to World War II.
Estimated Value: Excellent: $185.00
Very good: $150.00

Colt Pocket Positive

Colt New Army Model 1892

Colt New Navy Model 1892

Colt Army Model 1903

Colt New Pocket

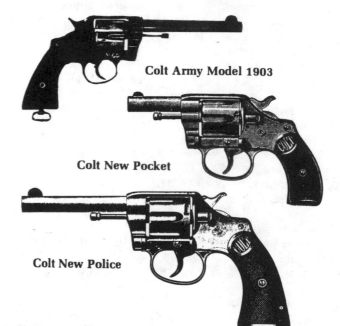

Colt New Police

Colt New Police
Caliber: 32 Colt short and long, 32 Colt New Police (S&W long)
Action: Single or double
Cylinder: 6-shot; swing out; simultaneous ejector
Barrel: 2½'', 4'', and 6''
Sights: Fixed
Finish: Blued or nickel; hard rubber grips
Length overall: 6½'' to 10''
Approximate wt.: 16 to 18 oz.
Comments: Built on same frame as New Pocket except larger grips. Made from about 1896 to 1905.
Estimated Value: Excellent: $260.00
Very good: $220.00

Handguns

Colt Bisley Model

Colt Bisley Flat-Top Model

Colt New Service

Caliber: 38 Special, 357 magnum (Introduced about 1936), 38-40, 44-40, 44 Russian, 44 Special, 45 ACP, 45 Colt, 450 Eley, 455 Eley, and 476 Eley

Action: Single or double

Cylinder: 6-shot; swing out; simultaneous ejector

Barrel: 4'', 5'', & 6'' in 357 and 38 Special, 4½'', 5½'', & 7½'' in other calibers. 4½'' in 45 ACP (Model 1917 Revolver made for U.S. Government during World War II.

Sights: Fixed

Finish: Blued or nickel; checkered walnut grips

Length overall: 9¼'' to 12¾''

Approximate wt.: 39 to 44 oz.

Comments: Made from about 1898 to 1942. The above calibers were made sometime during this period.

Estimated Value:	357 Magnum	1917 Model	Others
Excellent:	$375.00	$300.00	$325.00
Very good:	$300.00	$240.00	$265.00

Colt New Service Target

Caliber: Originally made for 44 Russian, 450 Eley, 455 Eley and 476 Eley. Later calibers were made for 44 Special, 45 Colt, and 45 ACP

Action: Single or double

Cylinder: 6-shot; swing out; simultaneous ejector

Barrel: 6'' and 7''

Sights: Adjustable target sights

Finish: Blued; checkered walnut grips

Length overall: 11¼'' and 12¾''

Approximate wt.: 40 to 42 oz.

Comments: A target version of the New Service revolver with hand finished action. Made from about 1900 to 1939.

Estimated Value: Excellent: $480.00
Very good: $380.00

Colt New Police Target

Same as Colt New Police except: 6-inch barrel only; blued finish and target sights. This is a target version of the New Police Model, made from 1896 to 1905.

Estimated Value: Excellent: $275.00
Very good: $225.00

Colt Bisley Model

Caliber: 32 long centerfire, 32-20 WCF, 38 long Colt CF, 38-40 WCF, 41 long Colt CF, 44 S&W Russian, 44-40 WCF, 45 Colt, 455 Eley

Action: Single action

Cylinder: 6-shot; half flute; side load

Barrel: 4¾''; 5½''; 7½'' with side rod ejector

Sights: Fixed

Finish: Blued with case hardened frame and hammer; hard rubber checkered grips

Length overall: 10¼'' to 13''

Approximate wt.: 36 to 40 oz.

Comments: Developed from the original Single Action Army Revolver by changing the trigger, hammer, and grips. Made from 1897 to 1912.

Estimated Value: Excellent: $425.00
Very good: $325.00

Colt Bisley Flat-Top Model

Similar to Colt Bisley Model except: frame over the cylinder has a flat top; the longer barrel models were referred to as target models; wood & ivory grips as well as hard rubber; target adjustable sights or regular fixed sights. Short barrel models sometimes referred to as the Pocket Bisley. It usually had fixed sights and no side rod ejector.

Estimated Value: Excellent: $825.00
Very good: $650.00

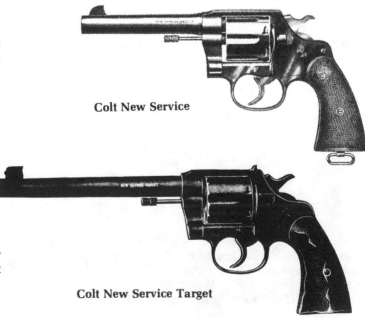

Colt New Service

Colt New Service Target

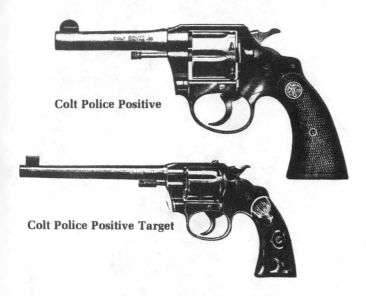

Colt Police Positive

Colt Police Positive Target

Colt Officers Model Target (1st Issue)

Colt Marine Corps Model 1905

Colt Police Positive Special

Colt Police Positive

Caliber: 32 short & long Colt (discontinued in 1915) 32 Colt New Police (32 S&W long) 38 New Police (38 S&W long)
Action: Single or double
Cylinder: 6-shot; swing-out; simultaneous ejector
Barrel: 2½", 4", 5", and 6"
Sights: Fixed
Finish: Blued or nickel; hard rubber or checkered walnut grips
Length overall: 6½" to 10½"
Approximate wt.: 18 to 22 oz.
Comments: This is an improved version of the New Police with the Positive Lock feature (This prevents the firing pin from contacting the cartridge until the trigger is pulled); made from 1905 to 1943.
Estimated Value: Excellent: $180.00
Very good: $145.00

Colt Police Positive Target

Same as Colt Police Positive except: 22 caliber long rifle from 1910 to 1932 and 22 long rifle regular or hi-speed after 1932, 22 Winchester rim fire from 1910 to 1935; blued finish; 6-inch barrel only; adjustable target sights; checkered walnut grips. Approximate wt. 22 to 26 oz.
Estimated Value: Excellent: $290.00
Very good: $225.00

Colt Officers Model Target (1st Issue)

Caliber: 38 Special
Action: Single or double
Cylinder: 6-shot; 2/3 fluted; swing-out; simultaneous ejector
Barrel: 6"
Sights: Adjustable
Finish: Blued; checkered walnut grip
Length Overall: 10½"
Approximate wt.: 34 oz.
Comments: Hand finished action. Made from about 1904 to 1908.
Estimated Value: Excellent: $310.00
Very good: $250.00

Colt Marine Corps Model 1905

Caliber: 38 Colt short and long, 38 Special
Action: Single or double
Cylinder: 6-shot; 2/3 fluted; swing out; simultaneous hand ejector
Barrel: 6"
Sights: Fixed
Finish: Blued or nickel; hard rubber or walnut
Length overall: 10½"
Approximate wt.: 32 oz.
Comments: Made from 1905 to 1908. Lanyard ring in butt; the grip is smaller and more rounded at the butt, than the Army or Navy Models. Also sometimes called model 1907.
Estimated Value: Excellent: $560.00
Very good: $470.00

Colt Police Positive Special

Caliber: 32-20 (discontinued in 1942), 32 New Police (S&W long), 38 Special
Action: Single or double
Cylinder: 6-shot; swing out; simultaneous ejector
Barrel: 4", 5" or 6"
Sights: Fixed
Finish: Blued or nickel; checkered rubber, plastic or walnut grips
Length overall: 8¾" to 10¾"
Approximate wt.: 23 to 28 oz.
Comments: Made from about 1907 to the late 1970's.
Estimated Value: Excellent: $175.00
Very good: $150.00

Handguns

Colt New Service Model 1909

Caliber: 32-20, 38 Special, 38-40, 41 Colt short and long, 44 Russian, 44-40, 45 Colt
Action: Single or double
Cylinder: 6-shot; 2/3 fluted; swing-out; simultaneous hand ejector
Barrel: 4", 4½", 5", 6"
Sights: Fixed
Finish: Blued or nickel; hard rubber or walnut grips
Length overall: 9¼" to 11¼"
Approximate wt.: 32 to 34 oz.
Comments: Made from 1909 to 1928. Adopted by U.S. armed forces in 1909 until 1911. (Automatic became the standard sidearm.) Also called "Army Special".
Estimated Value: Excellent: $250.00
Very good: $200.00

Colt Officers Model Target (2nd Issue)

Caliber: 22 long rifle (regular) 1930-32; 22 long rifle (Hi-Speed) 1932-49; 32 Police Positive 1932-42, 38 Special 1908 to 1949
Action: Single or Double
Cylinder: 6-shot; 2/3 fluted; swing out; simultaneous hand ejector
Barrel: 6" in 22 caliber and 32 Police Positive, 4", 4½", 5", 6", and 7½" in 38 Special
Sights: Adjustable rear
Finish: Blued; checkered walnut grips
Length overall: 9¼" to 12¾"
Approximate wt.: 32 to 40 oz.
Comments: Hand finished action, tapered barrel. Made from about 1908 to 1949 .
Estimated Value: Excellent: $325.00
Very good: $250.00

Colt Camp Perry (1st Issue)

Caliber: 22 short, long or long rifle
Action: Single
Cylinder: 1-shot; swing-out flat steel block instead of cylinder with rod ejector
Barrel: 10"
Sights: Adjustable front for elevation and adjustable rear for windage
Finish: Blued, checkered walnut grips with medallion
Length overall: 14"
Approximate wt.: 35 oz.
Comments: Built on Officers Model frame. Made from about 1926 to 1934.
Estimated Value: Excellent: $600.00
Very good: $500.00

Colt Camp Perry (2nd Issue)

Same as 1st issue except: 8" barrel (heavier); shorter hammer fall; overall length 12"; approximate wt. 34 oz., chamber is embedded for cartridge head to make it safe to use 22 long rifle Hi-Speed cartridges. Made from about 1934 to 1941.
Estimated Value: Excellent: $675.00
Very good: $550.00

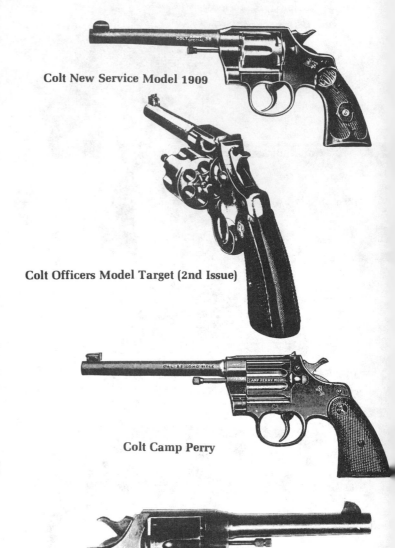

Colt New Service Model 1909

Colt Officers Model Target (2nd Issue)

Colt Camp Perry

Colt Army Model 1917

Colt Army Model 1917

Caliber: 45 ACP or 45 ACP rim cartridges
Action: Single or double
Cylinder: 6-shot; fluted; swing out; simultaneous hand ejector; used semi-circular clips to hold rimless case of 45 ACP
Barrel: 5½"; round tapered
Sights: Fixed
Finish: Blued; oil-finished walnut grips
Length overall: 10¾"
Approximate wt.: 40 oz.
Comments: Made from 1917 to 1928.
Estimated Value: Excellent: $240.00
Very good: $195.00

Colt Detective Special

Colt Bankers Special

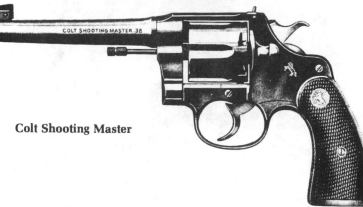

Colt Shooting Master

Colt Bankers Special

Caliber: 22 short, long & long rifle (Reg., or Hi-Speed) 38 New Police (S&W long)
Action: Single or double
Cylinder: 6-shot; swing out; simultaneous ejector
Barrel: 2"
Sights: Fixed
Finish: Blued; checkered walnut grips
Length overall: 6½"
Approximate wt.: 19 to 23 oz.
Comments: Same as Police Positive except 2-inch barrel only and rounded grip after 1933. Made from about 1928-40.

Estimated Value:	.22 Cal.	.38 Cal.
Excellent:	$600.00	$400.00
Very good:	$500.00	$325.00

Colt Shooting Master

Caliber: 38 Special, 357 magnum (introduced in 1936), 44 Special, 45 ACP, 45 Colt
Action: Single or double
Cylinder: 6-shot; swing out; simultaneous ejector
Barrel: 6"
Sights: Adjustable target sights
Finish: Blued; checkered walnut grips
Length overall: 11¼"
Approximate wt.: 42-44 oz.
Comments: A deluxe target revolver based on the New Service revolver. Made from about 1932 to 1940.

Estimated Value:	Excellent:	$500.00
	Very good:	$425.00

Colt Detective Special (Model D-1)

Caliber: 32 New Police (S&W Long) 38 Special
Action: Single or double
Cylinder: 6-shot; swing-out; simultaneous ejector
Barrel: 2" or 3"; 3" barrel dropped in 1970's
Sights: Fixed
Finish: Blued or nickel; checkered walnut grips with rounded or square butt
Length overall: 6¾" or 7¾"
Approximate wt: 21 oz.
Comments: Made from about 1926 to present. With or without hammer shroud.

Estimated Value:		blue	Nickel
	New (retail):	$259.95	$279.95
	Excellent:	$210.00	$225.00
	Very good:	$170.00	$180.00

Colt Official Police (Model E-1)

Caliber: 22 long rifle (reg) introduced in 1930; 22 long rifle (Hi-Speed) introduced in 1932; 32-20, made from about 1928 to 42; 38 Special made from 1928 to 1969; 41 long Colt, made from 1928 to 1930.
Action: Single or double
Cylinder: 6-shot; fluted; swing-out; simultaneous ejector
Barrel: 4" and 6" in 22 caliber, 4", 5", and 6" in 32-20, 2", 4", 5", and 6" in 41 caliber
Sights: Fixed
Finish: Blued or nickel; checkered walnut or checkered plastic grips
Length overall: 7¼" to 11¼"
Approximate wt.: 30 to 38 oz.
Comments: 41 caliber frame in all calibers. A refined version of the New Service Model 1909 which was discontinued in 1928. Made from about 1928 to 1970.

Estimated Value:	Excellent:	$220.00
	Very good:	$175.00

Colt Commando

Similar to Colt Official Police (Model E-1) except: made to Government specifications in 38 Special only; sand-blasted blued finished; produced for the Government. Made from 1942 to 1945.

Estimated Value:	Excellent:	$230.00
	Very good:	$180.00

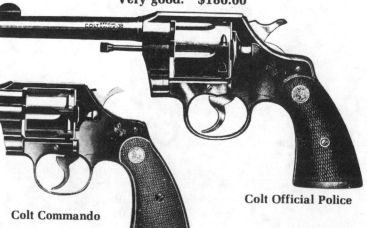

Colt Official Police

Colt Commando

Handguns

Colt Officers Model Special

Caliber: 22 long rifle (regular and Hi-Speed), 38 Special
Action: Single or double
Cylinder: 6-shot; 2/3 fluted; swing-out; simultaneous ejector
Barrel: 6"
Sights: Adjustable for windage and elevation
Finish: Blued; checkered plastic grips
Length overall: 11¼"
Approximate wt.: 42 oz. in 22 caliber, 38 oz. in 38 caliber
Comments: Replaced the officers Model Target (2nd issue) as target arm; heavier non-tapered barrel and re-designed hammer. Made from 1949 to 1953.
Estimated Value: Excellent: $220.00
Very good: $185.00

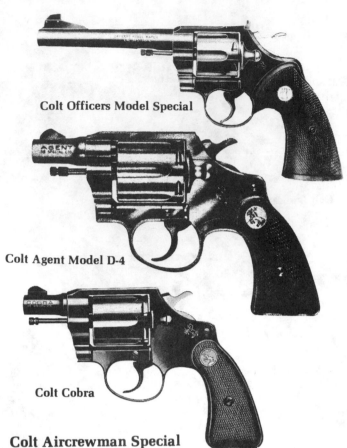

Colt Officers Model Special

Colt Agent Model D-4

Colt Cobra

Colt Cobra Model D-3

Caliber: 22 short & long rifle, 32 New Police (S&W long), 38 special
Action: Single or double
Cylinder: 6-shot; swing out; simultaneous ejector;
Barrel: 2", 3", 4", and 5"
Sights: Fixed
Finish: Blued or nickel; checkered walnut grip
Length overall: 6 5/8" to 9 5/8"
Approximate wt.: 16 to 22 oz.
Comments: Frame is made of a light alloy, but cylinder is steel. Made from 1950 to late 1970.

Estimated Value:	Blue	Nickel
Excellent:	$175.00	$200.00
Very good:	$135.00	$155.00

Colt Agent Model D-4

Caliber: 38 Special
Action: Single or double
Cylinder: 6-shot; swing-out; simultaneous ejector
Barrel: 2"
Sights: Fixed
Finish: Blued; checkered walnut grips
Length overall: 6¾"
Approximate wt.: 14 oz.
Comments: Frame made of lightweight alloy. Made from 1955 to late 1970's. Also available with hammer shroud.
Estimated Value: Excellent: $175.00
Very good: $140.00

Colt Viper

Colt Aircrewman Special

Caliber: 38 Special
Action: Single or double
Cylinder: 6-shot; swing-out; simultaneous ejector; aluminum alloy
Barrel: 2"
Sights: Fixed
Finish: Blued; checkered walnut grips
Length overall: 6¾"
Approximate wt.: 14 oz.
Comments: A rare lightweight special revolver developed by Colt at the request of U.S. Air Force during the Korean War. They were recalled in 1960.
Estimated Value: Excellent: $600.00
Very good: $500.00

Colt Viper

Caliber: 38 Special
Action: Single and double
Cylinder: 6 shot swing-out
Barrel: 4"
Sights: Fixed rear, ramp front
Finish: Blued or nickel; checkered walnut wrap around grips
Length overall: 8 5/8"
Approximate wt.: 20 oz.
Comments: Lightweight aluminum alloy frame, shrouded ejector rod. Made in the late 1970's. Add $20.00 for nickel model.
Estimated Value: Excellent: $175.00
Very good: $135.00

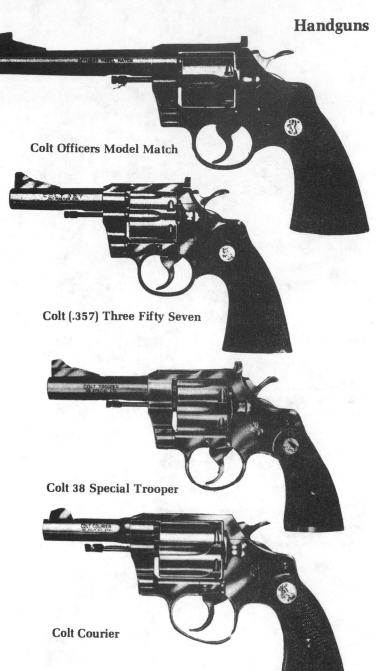

Colt Officers Model Match

Colt (.357) Three Fifty Seven

Colt 38 Special Trooper

Colt Courier

Colt Border Patrol

Caliber: 38 Special
Action: Single or double
Cylinder: 6-shot; swing-out; simultaneous ejector
Barrel: 4''
Sights: Fixed; Baughman quick draw front sight
Finish: Blued; checkered walnut grips
Length overall: 8¾''
Approximate wt.: 34 oz.
Comments: In 1952 about 400 were produced for a branch of the US Treasury Dept. The barrel is marked on left side ''Colt Border Patrol''.
Estimated Value: Excellent: $625.00
Very good: $525.00

Colt Officers Model Match

Caliber: 22 long rifle, 38 Special
Action: Single or double
Cylinder: 6-shot; 2/3 fluted; swing out; simultaneous ejector
Barrel: 6''
Sights: Adjustable for windage and elevation
Finish: Blued; checkered walnut grips
Length overall: 11¼''
Approximate wt.: 42 oz. in 22 caliber;; 38 oz. in 38 caliber
Comments: Has heavy tapered barrel and wide hammer spur. Made from about 1953 to 1970.
Estimated Value: Excellent: $235.00
Very good: $190.00

Colt (.357) Three Fifty Seven

Caliber: 357 magnum and 38 Special
Action: Single or double
Cylinder: 6-shot; swing out; simultaneous ejector
Barrel: 4'' and 6''
Sights: Adjustable rear sight
Finish: Blued; checkered walnut grips
Length overall: 9¼'' and 11¼''
Approximate wt.: 36 to 39 oz.
Comments: Made from about 1953 to 1962. It was replaced by Trooper Model.
Estimated Value: Excellent: $200.00
Very good: $170.00

Colt 38 Special Trooper

Caliber: 22, 38 Special
Action: Single or double
Cylinder: 6-shot; swing out; simultaneous ejector
Barrel: 4'' or 6''
Sights: Adjustable rear and quick draw front
Finish: Blued or nickel; checkered walnut square butt grips
Length overall: 9¼'' and 11¼''
Approximate wt.: 36 to 43 ounces
Comments: Made from about 1953 until 1962.
Estimated Value: Excellent: $190.00
Very good: $160.00

Colt Courier

Caliber: 22 short, long and long rifle, 32 New Police (S&W long)
Action: Single or double
Cylinder: 6-shot; swing out; simultaneous ejector; Made of lightweight alloy
Barrel: 3''
Sights: Fixed
Finish: Dual tone blue; checkered plastic grips
Length overall: 7½''
Approximate wt.: 14 to 20 oz.
Comments: Frame and cylinder made of lightweight alloy. Made in 1954 and 1955 only. A limited production revolver.
Estimated Value: Excellent: $600.00
Very good: $525.00

Handguns

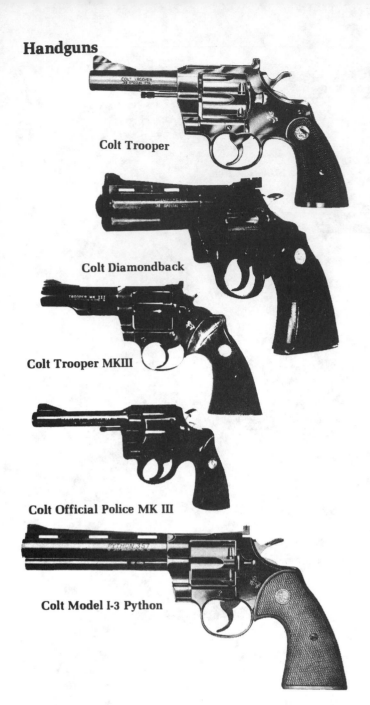

Colt Trooper

Colt Diamondback

Colt Trooper MKIII

Colt Official Police MK III

Colt Model I-3 Python

Colt Model I-3 Python, New Police Python, Python

Caliber: 357 magnum, 38 Special
Action: Single or double
Cylinder: 6-shot swing out; simultaneous ejector
Barrel: 2½", 4", 6" or 8" in 1980. Ventilated rib.
Sights: Adjustable rear (For windage and elevation)
Finish: Blued or nickel; checkered walnut target grips
Length overall: 7¼" to 13¼"
Approximate wt: 39 to 44 oz.
Comments: Made from about 1955 to present. Also called New Police Python, and currently Python. Add $15.00 for 8" barrel.

Estimated Value:	Blue	Nickel
New (retail):	$454.50	$473.50
Excellent:	$365.00	$380.00
Very good:	$300.00	$315.00

Colt Trooper

Caliber: 357 magnum, 38 Special
Action: Single or double
Cylinder: 6-shot; swing out; simultaneous ejector
Barrel: 4" or 6"
Sights: Adjustable rear and quick draw front
Finish: Blued or nickel; checkered walnut, square butt grips
Length overall: 9¼" and 11¼"
Approximate wt.: 34 to 38 oz.
Comments: Made from about 1953 to 1969. Replaced by Trooper MKIII.

Estimated Value: Excellent:	$200.00
Very good:	$165.00

Colt Diamondback

Caliber: 22, 22 WMR, 38 Special
Action: Single or double
Cylinder: 6-shot swing out; simultaneous ejector
Barrel: 2½", 4", 6" ventilated rib; 2½" dropped in late 1970's.
Sights: Adjustable rear
Finish: Blued or nickel; checkered walnut, square butt grips
Length overall: 7½", 9"
Approximate wt: 26 to 32 oz.
Comments: Made from 1967 to present.

Estimated Value:	Blue	Nickel
New (retail):	$308.00	$315.00
Excellent:	$250.00	$260.00
Very good:	$200.00	$210.00

Colt Trooper MKIII

Caliber: 357 magnum, 38 Special; 22 LR & 22 WMR Added in 1979
Action: Single or double
Cylinder: 6-shot swing out; simultaneous ejector
Barrel: 4", 6" and 8" in 1980.
Sights: Adjustable rear
Finish: Blued or nickel; checkered walnut grips
Length overall: 9½", 11½", and 13½"
Approximate wt: 39 to 42 oz.
Comments: Made from about 1969 to present; wide target typer trigger and hammer; Add $6.00 for 8" barrel.

Estimated Value:	Blue	Nickel
New (retail):	$288.95	$312.95
Excellent:	$230.00	$250.00
Very good:	$185.00	$200.00

Colt Official Police MK III

Caliber: 38 Special
Action: Single or double
Cylinder: 6-shot; swing-out; simultaneous ejector
Barrel: 4", 5" and 6"
Sights: Fixed
Finish: Blued; checkered walnut, square butt grips
Length overall: 9¼", 10¼", and 11¼"
Approximate wt.: 34 to 36 oz.
Comments: Made from about 1970 to late 1970's

Estimated Value: Excellent:	$175.00
Very good:	$140.00

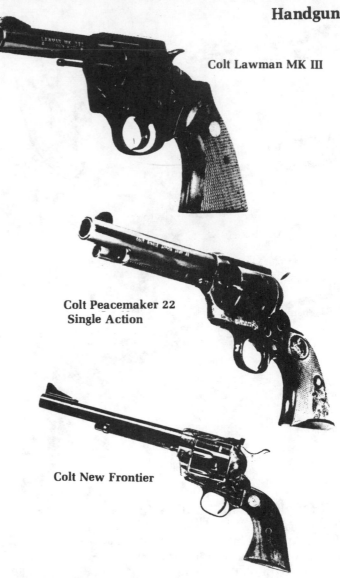

Colt Lawman MK III

olt Lawman MK III

aliber: 357 magnum and 38 Special
ction: Single or double
ylinder: 6-shot; swing out; simultaneous ejector
arrel: 2'' or 4'', heavy barrel
ights: Fixed
inish: Blued or nickel; checkered walnut grip
ength overall: 7¼'', 9¼''
pproximate wt.: 36 and 39 oz.
omments: Made from 1970 to present.

stimated Value:	Blue	Nickel
New (retail):	$245.00	$260.00
Excellent:	$195.00	$210.00
Very good:	$160.00	$170.00

Colt Peacemaker 22
Single Action

Colt Peacemaker 22 Single Action

Caliber: 22, 22 WRF (magnum) when equipped with dual cylinder
Action: Single
Cylinder: 6-shot; side load; loading gate; under barrel ejector rod
Barrel: 4¾'', 6'', and 7½''
Sights: Fixed
Finish: Blued barrel and cylinder; case hardened frame; black composite rubber grips
Length overall: 9 5/8'' to 12¾''
Approximate wt.: 29 to 33 oz.
Comments: All steel, 22 caliber version of the 45 caliber Peacemaker. Made from 1972 to late 1970's. Add $6.00 for 7½'' barrel (Buntline Model).

Estimated Value:	Excellent:	$135.00
	Very good:	$115.00

Colt New Frontier

Colt New Frontier

This is the same handgun as the Colt Peacemaker 22 SA except: equipped with a ramp front sight, and adjustable rear sight; flat top frame. Add $6.00 for 7½'' barrel (Buntline Model).

Estimated Value:	Excellent:	$150.00
	Very good:	$130.00

Colt Single Action Army

Caliber: 357 magnum, 38 Special, 44 Special, 45 Colt
Action: Single action
Cylinder: 6-shot; side load; loading gate; under barrel ejector rod
Barrel: 4¾'', 5½'', and 7½''
Sights: Fixed
Finish: Blued with case hardened frame; composite rubber grips; Nickel with checkered walnut grips
Length overall: 10 1/8'' to 12 7/8''
Approximate wt: 37 to 43 oz.
Comments: A revival of the Single Action Army Revovler, which was discontinued in 1941. The serial numbers start at 1001 SA. The letters SA were added to the serial numbers when production was resumed. Made from about 1955 to present. Add $7.00 for a 7½'' barrel.

Estimated Value:	Blue	Nickel
New (retail):	$399.95	$462.95
Excellent:	$300.00	$360.00
Very good:	$250.00	$295.00

Colt Single Action Army

Handguns

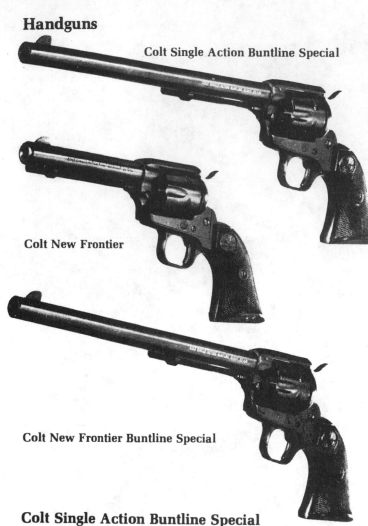

Colt Single Action Buntline Special

Colt New Frontier

Colt New Frontier Buntline Special

Colt Single Action Buntline Special

This is basically the same revolver as the Colt Single Action Army Revolver (1955 Model) except it is 45 Colt caliber only. The barrel is 12 inches; the gun has an overall length of 17½ inches; weighs about 42 ounces. It was made from about 1957 until 1975. Available again in 1980. Add $65.00 for nickel finish.

Estimated Value: New (retail): $422.95
Excellent: $335.00
Very good: $270.00

Colt New Frontier

This is the same handgun as the Colt Single Action Army revolver except: frame is flat topped; finish is high polished; ramp front sight and adjustable rear sight (wind and elevation); blued and case hardened finish; smooth walnut grips. This is a target version of the SA Army, made from about 1961 to present in 44-40, 44 Spec., and 45 Colt caliber only.

Estimated Value: New (retail): $475.95
Excellent: $380.00
Very good: $310.00

Colt New Frontier Buntline Special

This revolver is the same as the Colt New Frontier (1961 Model) except: 45 caliber only; 12 inch barrel; 17½ inches overall; weighs 42 ounces. Made from 1962 until 1967.

Estimated Value: Excellent: $390.00
Very good: $310.00

Colt Frontier Scout

Caliber: 22 and 22 WRF (interchangeable cylinder)
Action: Single action
Cylinder: 6-shot side load; loading gate; under barrel ejector rod
Barrel: 4¾" or 9½" (Buntline Scout)
Sights: Fixed
Finish: Blued or nickel; plastic or wood grips
Length overall: 9 5/16" to 14¼"
Approximate wt.: 24 to 34 oz.
Comments: Single Action Army replica ¾ scale size in 22 caliber. Made with bright alloy frame and blued steel frame from about 1958 until 1972. Add $10.00 for interchangeable cylinder, $10.00 for nickel finish, $10.00 for Buntline Scout.

Estimated Value: Excellent: $110.00
Very good: $ 90.00

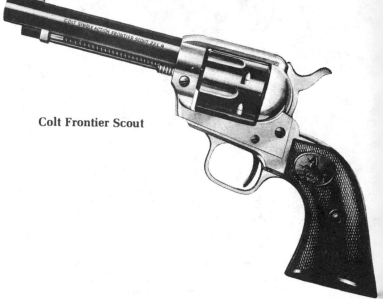

Colt Frontier Scout

Colt Commemorative Models

These guns are the same as the Colt Single Action Army and the Colt Frontier Scout Models except production was limited and they were inscribed to commemorate certain historical events. Estimated values are for mint unfired revolvers with original containers or cases.

S.A.A. Colt Commemoratives

Year	Inscription	Approx. Prod.	List Price	Est. Value
1961	Colt 125th Anniv. SAA 45	7375	$150.00	$ 600.00
1963	West Va. Statehood SAA 45	600	$150.00	$ 650.00
	Arizona Territorial Centennial SAA 45	1250	$150.00	$ 575.00
	Carolina Charter Tercentenary 22/45 combo	250	$240.00	$ 850.00
	H., Cook 1 to 100 22/45 combo	100	$275.00	$ 950.00

Year		Approx. Prod.	List Price	Est. Value
1964	Cherry's Sporting Goods 35th Anniv. 22/45 combo	100	$275.00	$1100.00
	Nevada Statehood Centennial SAA 45	1690	$150.00	$ 550.00
	Nevada Statehood Centennial 22/45 combo	190	$240.00	$ 775.00
	Nevada Statehood Cent. 22/45 combo with extra engraved cylinder	575	$350.00	$1000.00
	Nevada "Battle Born" SAA 45	80	$175.00	$1200.00
	Nevada "Battle Born" 22/45 combo	20	$265.00	$1600.00
	Montana Territorial Cent. SAA 45	850	$150.00	$ 600.00
	New Jersey Tercentenary SAA 45	250	$150.00	$ 675.00
	St. Louis Bicentennial SAA 45	450	$150.00	$ 550.00
	St. Louis Bicentennial 22/45 combo	250	$240.00	$ 800.00
	Pony Express Presentation SAA 45	100	$250.00	$ 825.00
	Chamizal Treaty SAA 45	50	$170.00	$1200.00
	Chamizal Treaty 22/45 combo	50	$280.00	$1600.00
	Col. Sam Colt Sesquicentennial Presentation SAA 45	4750	$225.00	$ 600.00
	Col. Sam Colt Sesquicentennial Deluxe Presentation	200	$500.00	$1650.00
	Col. Sam Colt Sesquicentennial Special Deluxe Presentation SAA 45	50	$1000.00	$3200.00
	Wyatt Earp Buntline SAA 45	150	$250.00	$1400.00
1965	Joaquin Murietta 22/45 combo	100	$350.00	$1000.00
	Old Fort Des Moines Reconstruction SAA 45	100	$170.00	$ 600.00
	Old Fort Des Moines Reconstruction 22/45 combo	100	$290.00	$ 900.00
	Appomattox Centennial SAA 45	250	$150.00	$ 650.00
	Appomattox Centennial 22/45 combo	250	$240.00	$ 850.00
1966	General Meade SAA 45	200	$165.00	$ 600.00
	Abercrombie & Fitch "Trailblazer" NY SAA 45	200	$275.00	$1650.00
	Calif. Gold Rush SAA 45	130	$175.00	$ 800.00
	Abercrombie & Fitch "Trailblazer", Chicago SAA 45	100	$275.00	$1700.00
	Abercrombie & Fitch "Trailblazer, San Francisco SAA 45	200	$275.00	$1600.00
1967	Lawman Series - Bat Masterson SAA 45	500	$180.00	$ 600.00
	Alamo SAA 45	550	$165.00	$ 600.00
	Alamo 22/45 combo	200	$265.00	$ 900.00
1968	Lawman Series - Pat Garrett SAA 45	500	$220.00	$ 600.00
1969	Lawman Series - Wild Bill Hickock SAA 45	500	$220.00	$ 600.00
1970	Texas Ranger SAA 45	1000	$650.00	$1200.00
	Lawman Series - Wyatt Earp SAA 45	500	$395.00	$1000.00
	Missouri Sesquicentennial SAA 45	500	$225.00	$ 575.00
1971	NRA Centennial SAA 45 or	4100	$250.00	$ 500.00
	NRA Centennial SAA 357 Mag.	2400	$250.00	$ 550.00
1974	Peacemaker Centennial 44-40	1500	$300.00	$475.00
	Peacemaker Centennial U.S. 45	1500	$300.00	$475.00
	Peacemaker Centennial cased pair, 44-40 & 45	500	$625.00	$1250.00
1976	U.S. Bicentennial Set	1776	$1695.00	$2200.00
1978	U.S. Cavalry 200th anniversary set, cased pair of 1860 Army percussion and accessories	3000	$995.00	$1050.00
1979	Ned Buntline 45 SAA	3000	$900.00	$900.00

Colt Frontier Scout Commemorative Models

Year	Inscription	Approx. Prod.	List Price	Est. Value
1961	Kansas Statehood	6200	$75.00	$300.00
	Pony Express Centennial	1000	$80.00	$450.00
1962	Columbus Ohio Sesquicentennial	200	$100.00	$500.00
	Fort Findlay, Ohio Sesquicentennial	110	$90.00	$550.00
	Fort Findlay, Cased pair (22 long rifle, 22 WRF)	20	$185.00	$2000.00
	New Mexico Golden Anniversary	1000	$180.00	$325.00
	West Virginia Statehood Centennial	3500	$75.00	$250.00

Handguns

1963				
	Arizona Territorial Cent.	5350	$75.00	$250.00
	Carolina Charter Tercentenary	300	$75.00	$350.00
	Fort Stephenson, Ohio Sesquicentennial	200	$75.00	$500.00
	Battle of Gettysburg Centennial	1020	$90.00	$300.00
	Idaho Territorial Centennial	900	$75.00	$350.00
	General J.H. Morgan Indiana Raid	100	$75.00	**$650.00**
1964	Nevada Statehood Cent.	3990	$75.00	$275.00
	Nevada "Battle Born"	980	$85.00	$300.00
	Montana Territorial Cent.	2250	$75.00	$250.00
	Wyoming Diamond Jubilee	2350	$75.00	$250.00
	General Hood Centennial	1500	$75.00	$250.00
	New Jersey Tercentary	1000	$75.00	$250.00
	St. Louis Bicentennial	800	$75.00	$250.00
	California Gold Rush	500	$80.00	$275.00
	Chamizal Treaty	450	$85.00	$300.00
1965	Kansas Cowtown Series Wichita	500	$85.00	$300.00
	Oregon Trail	1995	$75.00	$275.00
	Forty-Niner Miner	500	$85.00	$350.00
	Old Fort Des Moines Reconstruction	700	$90.00	$300.00
	Appomattox Centennial	1000	$75.00	$250.00
	General Meade Campaign	1200	$75.00	$275.00
	St. Augustine Quadricentennial	500	$85.00	$325.00
1966	Kansas Cowtown Series Dodge City	500	$85.00	$300.00
	Colorado Gold Rush	1350	$85.00	$250.00
	Oklahoma Territory	1350	$85.00	$250.00
	Dakota Territory	1000	$85.00	$250.00
	Kansas Cowtown Series Abilene	500	$95.00	$300.00
	Indiana Sesquicentennial	1500	$85.00	$250.00
1967	Lawman Series - Bat Masterson	3000	$90.00	$275.00
	Alamo	4200	$85.00	$250.00
	Kansas Cowtown Series Coffeyville	500	$95.00	$300.00
	Kansas Trail Series Chisholm Trail	500	$100.00	$250.00
1968	Nebraska Centennial	7500	$100.00	$250.00
	Kansas Trail Series Pawnee Trail	500	$110.00	$250.00
	Lawman Series - Pat Garret	3000	$110.00	$275.00
	General Nathan Bedford Forrest	3000	$110.00	$250.00

	Kansas Trail Series Santa Fe Trail	500	$120.00	$250.00
1969	Alabama Sesquicentennial	3000	$110.00	$250.00
	Golden Spike	11000	$135.00	$250.00
	Kansas Trail Series Shawnee Trail	500	$120.00	$275.00
	Arkansas Territory Sesquicentennial	3500	$110.00	$225.00
	Lawman Series - Wild Bill Hickock	3000	$117.00	$250.00
	California Bicentennial	5000	$135.00	$225.00
1970	Kansas Fort Series - Ft. Larned	500	$120.00	$250.00
	Kansas Fort Series - Ft. Hays	500	$130.00	$250.00
	Maine Sesquicentennial	3000	$120.00	$225.00
	Missouri Sesquicentennial	3000	$120.00	$225.00
	Kansas Fort Series - Ft. Riley	500	$130.00	$250.00
	Lawman Series - Wyatt Earp	3000	$120.00	$275.00
1971	Kansas Fort Series-Ft. Scott	500	$130.00	$225.00
1973	Florida Territorial Sesquicentennial	2000	$125.00	$220.00
	Arizona Ranger	3000	$135.00	$220.00
1977	2nd Amendment 22 caliber	3000	$194.95	$275.00

Colt Civil War Centennial Model

Caliber: 22 short
Action: Single action; single shot;
Barrel: 6"
Sights: Fixed
Finish: Blued; gold plated frame, grip frame and trigger guard; walnut grips
Length overall: 11¼"
Approximate wt.: 22 oz.
Comments: Approximately 24,100 were made in 1961. Estimated value is for mint unfired pistol in original case.

Est. Value	Orig. price	Est. value
Single pistol	**$32.50**	**$100.00**
Pair, consecutive nos.	**$70.00**	**$225.00**

Colt Civil War Centennial Model

Colt Rock Island Arsenal Centennial Pistol

Similar to Civil War Centennial Model except: approximately 550 made in 1962 to commemorate the Rock Island Arsenal Centennial in Illinois. Estimated value is for mint, unfired pistol in original case.

Orig. price	Est. value
$38.50	$200.00

Colt Derringer No. 4 (Replica of 1872)

Caliber: 22 short
Action: Single action; single shot; side swing barrel
Barrel: 2½"
Sights: Fixed
Finish: Gold finished frame; blued barrel, walnut grips. Also nickel plated with simulated ivory grips
Length overall: 5"
Approximate wt.: 8 oz.
Comments: Made from 1959 to 1963. A replica of the 41 caliber rim fire derringer No. 3.

Estimated Value:	Cased single	Cased pair
Mint, (unfired):	$100.00	$225.00
Excellent:	$ 50.00	$125.00
Very good:	$ 35.00	$ 90.00

Colt 1847 Walker Percussion

Caliber: 44 (cap & ball) black powder only
Action: Single action
Cylinder: 6 shot (percussion); engraved soldiers and Indians scene
Barrel: 9" round with loading lever under barrel
Sights: Fixed; German silver blade front, rear is notch in top of hammer
Finish: Case hardened color frame, hammer and loading lever; solid brass square back trigger guard; smooth one piece walnut grip; blued barrel and backstrap
Length overall: 15½"
Approximate wt.: 73 oz.
Comments: Made from the late 1970's to present; recommended load is 35 to 55 grains FFG or FFFG black powder; 451 to 457 pure lead ball; No. 11 percussion caps.

Estimated Value:	New (retail):	$446.95
	Excellent:	$335.00
	Very good:	$275.00

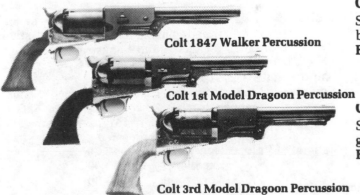

Colt 1847 Walker Percussion

Colt 1st Model Dragoon Percussion

Colt 3rd Model Dragoon Percussion

Colt Sheriff's Model Commemorative

A special limited production of the Sheriff's Model or Storekeeper's Model which was a single action 45 caliber with a 3" barrel and without an ejector rod. The original models were discontinued about 1927. About 475 blued commemorative pistols and about 25 nickel commemoratives were produced in 1961. The estimated value for the commemorative pistol is for mint unfired in original box or case.

	Orig. price	Est. value
Blue & Case Hardened	$130.00	$1000.00
Nickel	$140.00	$3500.00

Colt Derringer No. 4 Commemorative Models

Same as Derringer No. 4 except: production was limited and they are inscribed to commemorate certain historical events. Estimated value listed is for mint unfired derringer in original case.

		Approx. Prod.	Orig. Cost	Est. Value
1961	Genesco, IL, 125th Anniv.	100	$28.00	$450.00
1962	Fort McPherson, NE Cent.	300	$29.00	$350.00

Colt 1st Model Dragoon Percussion

Caliber: 44 (cap & ball) black powder only
Action: Single
Cylinder: 6 shot (percussion) unfluted; engraved with Ranger-Indians scene
Barrel: 7½" part octagon and part round
Sights: Fixed; German silver front, rear is notch in top of hammer
Finish: Blued with case hardened color frame and loading lever; brass backstrap and square back trigger guard; one piece smooth walnut grip
Length overall: 14"
Approximate wt.: 66 oz.
Comments: Made from the late 1970's to present; has oval bolt cuts in cylinder and short trigger; recommended load is 30 to 40 grains of FFG or FFFG black powder, 451 to 457 pure lead ball and No. 11 percussion caps.

Estimated Value:	New (retail):	$356.95
	Excellent:	$270.00
	Very good:	$215.00

Colt 2nd Model Dragon Percussion

Similar to the 1st Model Dragoon except: rectangular bolt cuts in cylinder.

Estimated Value:	New (retail):	$356.95
	Excellent:	$270.00
	Very good:	$215.00

Colt 3rd Model Dragoon Percussion

Similar to the 2nd Model Dragoon except: oval trigger guard and longer trigger.

Estimated Value:	New (retail):	$356.95
	Excellent:	$270.00
	Very good:	$215.00

Colt Baby Dragoon Percussion

Caliber:31 (cap & ball) black powder only
Action: Single
Cylinder: 5 shot (percussion) unfluted; engraved Ranger and Indian scene
Barrel: 4" round
Sights: Fixed brass pin front, rear sight in groove cut in top of hammer
Finish: Blued with case hardened color frame and hammer; silver plated square back trigger guard and backstrap
Length overall: 8¾"
Approximate wt.: 22 oz.
Comments: Re-introduced about 1979 and made to present. Recommended load is 10 to 15 grains of FFFG black powder, 321-325 pure lead ball and No. 10 percussion caps.

Estimated Value:	New (retail):	$322.50
	Excellent:	$250.00
	Very good:	$200.00

Colt 1860 Army Percussion

Caliber:44 (cap & ball) black powder only
Action: Single
Cylinder: 6 shot (percussion)/unfluted, engraved with naval scene
Barrel: 8" round with "creeping" type loading lever under barrel
Sights: Fixed; German silver front, rear is notch in top of hammer
Finish: Blued with case hardened color frame and loading lever; brass oval trigger guard; smooth one piece walnut grip
Length overall: 13¾"
Approximate wt.: 42 oz.
Comments: Made from the 1970's to present. Recommended load is 20 to 30 grains of FFG or FFFG black powder, 451 to 457 pure lead ball and No. 10 percussion caps.

Estimated Value:	New (retail):	$342.50
	Excellent:	$250.00
	Very good:	$200.00

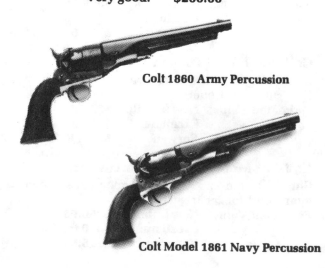

Colt 1860 Army Percussion

Colt Model 1861 Navy Percussion

Colt 1851 Navy Percussion

Caliber:36 (Cap and ball) Black powder only.
Action: Single action
Cylinder: 6-shot (percussion) unfluted; engraved cylinder (naval scene)
Barrel: 7½" octagon barrel; loading lever under barrel
Sights: Fixed; bead front sight; rear sight is groove cut in top of hammer.
Finish: Case hardened color frame and loading lever; blued barrel and cylinder; silver plated square back trigger guard and back strap; smooth walnut grips; cylinder has naval scene engraving
Length overall: 13"
Approximate wt: 42 oz.
Comments: A reissue of the 1851 Colt Navy Model produced by Colt for the black powder shooter. Made from late 1970's to present; recommended load 12 to 20 grains of FFFG black powder; .378 to .380 pure lead ball; No. 10 percussion caps.

Estimated Value:	New (retail):	$333.95
	Excellent:	$260.00
	Very good:	$210.00

Colt Navy Model 1851

Colt Model 1861 Navy Percussion

Caliber:36 (cap & ball) black powder only
Action: Single
Cylinder: 6 shot (percussion) unfluted engraved naval scene
Barrel: 7½" round with the "creeping" type loading lever under bottom
Sights: Fixed; German silver fixed front, rear is notch in top of hammer
Finish: Color case hardened frame, loading lever and hammer; blued barrel and cylinder; silver plated trigger guard and backstrap
Length overall: 13¾"
Approximate wt.: 42 oz.
Comments: Made from the 1970's to present. Recommended load is 20 to 30 grains of FFG or FFFG black powder, 451 to 457 pure lead ball and No. 10 percussion caps.

Estimated Value:	New (retail):	$342.50
	Excellent:	$250.00
	Very good:	$200.00

Colt Model 1862 Pocket Navy Percussion

Colt Model 1862 Pocket Police Percussion

Colt Model 1862 Pocket Navy Percussion

Caliber: 36 (cap & ball) black powder only
Action: Single
Cylinder: 5 shot (percussion); unfluted; engraved stage-coach scene
Barrel: 5½" octagon with hinged loading lever under bottom
Sights: Fixed brass pin front, rear is a notch cut in top of hammer
Finish: Blued with case hardened color frame, hammer, and loading lever; one piece smooth walnut grip
Length overall: 10 3/8"
Approximate wt.: 27 oz.
Comments: Re-introduced in the late 1970's. Recommended load is 12 to 20 grains of FFFG black powder, 378 to 380 pure lead ball and No. 10 percussion caps.

Estimated Value: New (retail): $313.50
Excellent: $240.00
Very good: $195.00

Colt Model 1862 Pocket Police Percussion

Caliber: 36 (cap & ball) black powder only
Action: Single
Cylinder: 5 shot (percussion) fluted
Barrel: 5½" round with "creeping" type loading lever under barrel
Sights: Fixed brass pin front, rear is notch cut in top of hammer
Finish: Blued with color case hardened frame, loading lever and hammer; silver plated oval trigger guard and backstrap; one piece smooth walnut grip
Length overall: 10 3/8"
Approximate wt.: 25 oz.
Comments: Re-introduced about 1979 and still available. Recommended load is 12 to 20 grains of FFFG black powder, 378 to 380 pure lead ball and No. 10 percussion caps.

Estimated Value: New (retail): $313.50
Excellent: $250.00
Very good: $200.00

Dan Wesson

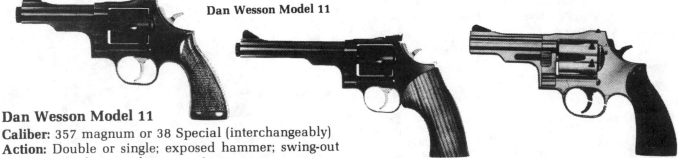

Dan Wesson Model 11

Dan Wesson Model 12

Dan Wesson Model 14

Dan Wesson Model 11

Caliber: 357 magnum or 38 Special (interchangeably)
Action: Double or single; exposed hammer; swing-out cylinder; simultaneous ejector
Cylinder: 6-shot swing-out
Barrel: 2½", 4", 6"; interchangeable barrels
Sights: Ramp front; fixed rear
Finish: Blued one piece changeable walnut grip
Length overall: 7¾" to 11¼"
Approximate wt.: 36 to 40 oz.
Comments: Made from about 1970 to 1974. Barrels and barrel cover (shroud) can be changed quickly by means of a recessed barrel nut; also one piece grip readily changeable to option styles.

Estimated Value: Excellent: $125.00
Very good: $100.00

Dan Wesson Model 12

Same as Model 11 except: target model with adjustable rear sight.

Estimated Value: Excellent: $130.00
Very good: $110.00

Dan Wesson Model 14, 14-2

Caliber: 357 magnum or 38 Special (interchangeably)
Action: Double or single; exposed hammer; swing-out cylinder; simultaneous ejector
Cylinder: 6-shot swing out
Barrel: 2½", 4", 6", 8" interchangeable barrels
Sights: Ramp front; fixed rear
Finish: Blued; one piece walnut grip
Length overall: 7¾" to 13¼"
Approximate wt.: 36 to 42 oz.
Comments: Made from about 1973 to present. A modified version of the Model 11, presently being called the 14-2 series. Prices increases as barrel length increases.

Estimated Value: New (retail): $180.95 - $201.95
Excellent: $140.00 $150.00
Very good: $110.00 $120.00

Handguns

Dan Wesson Model 15

Dan Wesson Model 9-2

Similar to Model 15 except Caliber 38 only.
Estimated Value: Excellent: $140.00
Very good: $110.00

Dan Wesson Model 15-2

Caliber: 357 magnum or 38 Special (interchangeably);
22S, L, LR after 1979
Action: Double or single; exposed hammer; swing-out
cylinder; simultaneous ejector
Cylinder: 6-shot; swing-out
Barrel: 2½", 4", 6", 8", 10", 12", 15" interchangeable
barrels. 22 caliber not available over 8".
Sights: Interchangeable colored front sight blade; adjustable rear sight with white outline
Finish: Blued; checkered wood target grips
Length overall: 7¾" to 13¼"
Approximate wt: 36 to 42 oz.
Comments: Made from about 1975 to present. Price increases as barrel length increases.
Estimated Value: New (retail): $232.90 - $339.95
Excellent: $175.00 - $250.00
Very good: $140.00 - $200.00

Dan Wesson Model 15-2H

Same as Model 15-2 except: has heavier bull barrel.
Estimated Value: New (retail): $255.45 - $370.95
Excellent: $190.00 - 275.00
Very good: $150.00 - 220.00

Dan Wesson Model 15-2V

Same as Model 15-2 except: has ventilated rib
assembly.
Estimated Value: New (retail): $257.45 - $376.15
Excellent: $190.00 - $280.00
Very good: $150.00 - $225.00

Dan Wesson Model 15-2 VH

Same as Mdoel 15-2 except: has heavier bull barrel with
ventilated rib assembly.
Estimated Value: New (retail): $278.30 - $407.65
Excellent: $205.00 - $300.00
Very good: $160.00 - $240.00

Dan Wesson Arms Pistol Pac

A carrying case containing revolver, 4 interchangeable
barrels (2½", 4", 6", & 8"), 2 interchangeable grips, & 4
colored front sight blades.

Model 14-2	New (retail):	$375.40
Model 15-2	New (retail)	$444.70
Model 15-2H	New (retail)	$520.10
Model 15-2 V	New (retail)	$532.35
Model 15-2 VH	New (retail)	$606.80

Dan Wesson Model 8-2

Similar to Model 14 except Caliber 38 only.
Estimated Value: Excellent: $140.00
Very good: $110.00

Dan Wesson Model 15

Similar to Model 14 except: adjustable rear sight. Made
from about 1973 to 1976.
Estimated Value: Excellent: $145.00
Very good: $115.00

Dan Wesson Model 15-2

Dan Wesson Model 15-2H

Dan Wesson Model 15-2V

Dan Wesson Model 15-VH

Dardick Magazine Pistol

Dardick 1100 - 11-shot
Dardick 1500 - 15-shot
Dardick 2000 - 20-shot

All models could be converted to a rifle by removing the barrel and fitting the frame into the rifle conversion kit.

Estimated Value:	Pistol with 22 & 38 caliber barrels
Excellent:	$360.00
Very good:	$250.00
	Pistol, 22 & 38 caliber barrels & rifle conversion kit
Excellent:	$625.00
Very good:	$550.00

Dardick Magazine Pistol

David Dardick developed a handgun, which resembles an automatic pistol, around a new type of cartridge called the "tround". The tround has a triangular case made of plastic. For the 38 caliber, the primer, powder, and bullets are loaded into the tround. The 22 caliber cartridges are simply placed in a plastic tround to adapt them to the feeding system. The firing pin position is changed to rim-fire by manually turning a screw in the frame. Therefore, the basic gun will shoot 22 caliber of 38 caliber by changing the barrel. The feeding system uses a three-legged star wheel which moves from magazine to firing position and dumps trounds through opening on right side. The feeding system is moved 120° with each pull of the trigger. The magazine is loaded by placing trounds in singly or by using 10-shot stripper clips. Production was started in 1959 at Hamden, Connecticut and stopped in 1960. All facilities, guns, and parts were auctioned to Numrich Arms in 1960. Approximately 40 guns were produced. The gun was made in three models and a rifle conversion kit. All models were made with two barrels (22 caliber and 38 caliber).

Detonics

Detonics Combat Master

Caliber: 45 ACP
Action: Semi-automatic; exposed hammer; single action
Magazine: 6 shot clip
Barrel: 3¼"
Sights: Fixed; some models have adjustable sights
Finish: Polished blue, matte blue, hard chrome, or satin nickel; checkered walnut grips
Length overall: 6¾"
Approximate wt.: 29 oz.
Comments: A lightweight compact combat 45 caliber pistol introduced in the late 1970's. Values are for standard model. Optional grades are considerably more expensive.

Detonics Combat Master

Estimated Value:	New (retail):	$369.00
	Excellent:	$275.00
	Very good:	$220.00

Fiala

Fiala Single Shot Magazine Pistol

Caliber: 22 short, long, & long rifle
Action: Hand operated slide action to chamber cartridge, cock striker, and eject empty case
Magazine: 10-shot clip
Barrel: 3", 7½", 20"
Sights: Target sight (adjustable rear sight)
Finish: Blued; plain wood grips
Length overall: 6¾"; 11¼"; or 23¾"
Approximate wt.: 27 to 44 oz.
Comments: Produced from about 1920 to 1923. A rare American pistol which had the appearance of an Automatic pistol. A shoulder stock was supplied for use with the 20" barrel.

	Pistol with 3" 7½" barrel	Pistol with all 3 barrels & shoulder stock
Estimated Value:		
Excellent:	$300.00	$675.00
Very good:	$250.00	$590.00

Fiala Single Shot Magazine Pistol

Great Western

Great Western Frontier

Great Western Double Barrel Derringer

Great Western Frontier
Caliber: 22 short, long, & long rifle, 357 magnum, 38 special, 44 magnum, 44 special, 45 Colt
Action: Single; hand ejector
Cylinder: 6-shot
Barrel: 4¾", 5½", 7½"; round barrel with ejector housing under barrel
Sights: Blade front; groove in top strap for rear sight
Finish: Blued; imitation stag grips
Length overall: 10 3/8" to 13 1/8"
Approximate wt.: 38 to 42 oz.
Comments: Replica of the Colt Single Action Revolver. Made from about 1951 to 1962. Values of these revolvers vary due to the poor quality of the early models. After 1955 they were also available in unassembled kit form. Values for factory-made models.
Estimated Value: Excellent: $140.00 - $225.00
Very good: $120.00 - $200.00

Great Western Double Barrel Derringer
Caliber: 38 S&W
Action: Single; double barrel; tip up to eject and load
Cylinder: None; barrels chambered for cartridges
Barrel: Superposed 3" double
Sights: Fixed
Finish: Blued; checkered plastic grips
Length overall: 4 7/8"
Approximate wt.: 14 oz.
Comments: Replica of the Remington Double Derringer. Made from about 1952 to 1962.
Estimated Value: Excellent: $110.00
Very good: $ 90.00

Harrington & Richardson

H & R Self Loading 25
Caliber: 25 ACP
Action: Semi-automatic; concealed hammer
Magazine: 6-shot clip
Barrel: 2"
Sights: None
Finish: Blued; hard rubber grips
Length overall: 4½"
Approximate wt.: 13 oz.
Comments: Approximately 20,000 produced from about 1912 to 1915.
Estimated Value: Excellent: $225.00
Very good: $185.00

H & R Self Loading 25

H & R Self Loading 32
Caliber: 32 ACP
Action: Semi-automatic; concealed hammer; grip safety
Magazine: 8-shot clip
Barrel: 3½"
Sights: Fixed
Finish: Blued; hard rubber grips
Length overall: 6½"
Approximate wt.: 22 oz.
Comments: A modified Webley & Scott designed pistol. Approximately 40,000 produced from about 1916 to 1939.
Estimated Value: Excellent: $200.00
Very good: $165.00

H & R Self Loading 32

H & R American

& R Young American

I & R Vest Pocket

H & R Automatic Ejecting Revolver

H & R Model 4

H & R Model 4
Caliber: 32 S&W, 32 S&W long, 38 S&W
Action: Double and single; exposed hammer; solid frame; side load
Cylinder: 6-shot in 32 caliber, 5-shot in 38 caliber, removable cylinder
Barrel: 2½", 4½", or 6" hexagon barrel
Sights: Fixed
Finish: Blued or nickel; hard rubber round butt grips
Length overall: 6½" to 10"
Approximate wt.: 14 to 18 oz.
Comments: Made from about 1904 to 1941.
Estimated Value: Excellent: $90.00
　　　　　　　　Very good: $75.00

H & R Model 5
Similar to model 4 except: 32 S&W caliber only; smaller frame and cylinder (5-shot); weighs 10-12 oz. Produced from about 1905 to 1939.
Estimated Value: Excellent: $90.00
　　　　　　　　Very good: $75.00

H & R Model 6
Similar to Model 5 except: 22 short, long, or long rifle; 7-shot cylinder; minor change in shape of top of frame at rear of cylinder. Made from about 1906 to 1941.
Estimated Value: Excellent: $95.00
　　　　　　　　Very good: $80.00

H & R American
Caliber: 32 S&W, 32 S&W long; 38 S&W
Action: Double and single; exposed hammer; solid frame; side load
Cylinder: 6-shot in 32 caliber; 5-shot in 38 caliber; removable cylinder
Barrel: 2½", 4½", or 6" hexagon barrel
Sights: Fixed
Finish: Blued or nickel; hard rubber round butt grips
Length overall: 6½" to 9¾"
Approximate wt.: 14 to 16 oz.
Comments: Made from about 1883 to 1941.
Estimated Value: Excellent: $90.00
　　　　　　　　Very good: $75.00

H & R Young American
Caliber: 22 short, long & long rifle, 32 S&W short
Action: Double and single; exposed hammer; solid frame; side load
Cylinder: 7-shot in 22 caliber; 5-shot in 32 caliber; removable cylinder
Barrel: 2", 4½", or 6" hexagon barrel
Sights: Fixed
Finish: Blued or nickel; hard rubber round butt grips
Length overall: 5½" to 9½"
Approximate wt.: 10 to 12 oz.
Comments: Made from about 1885 to 1941.
Estimated Value: Excellent: $85.00
　　　　　　　　Very good: $75.00

H & R Vest Pocket
Same as H & R Young American except: 1 1/8" barrel only; double action only; no spur on hammer; approx. wt. 8 oz. produced from about 1891 to 1941.
Estimated Value: Excellent: $90.00
　　　　　　　　Very good: $75.00

H & R Automatic Ejecting Revolver
Caliber: 32 S&W & 32 S&W long; 38 S&W
Action: Double and single; exposed hammer; hinged frame; top break
Cylinder: 6-shot in 32 caliber, 5-shot in 38 caliber, simultaneous automatic ejector
Barrel: 3¼", 4", 5" or 6" round barrel with rib
Sights: Fixed
Finish: Blued or nickel; hard rubber round butt grips
Length overall: 7¼" to 10"
Approximate wt.: 15 to 18 oz.
Comments: Manufactured from about 1891 to 1941.
Estimated Value: Excellent: $100.00
　　　　　　　　Very good: $ 80.00

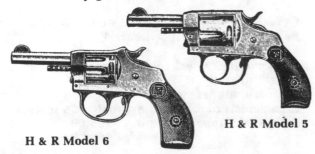

H & R Model 6

H & R Model 5

H & R Model 50

Same as Automatic Ejecting revolver except: double action only; concealed hammer; frame completely encloses hammer area. Made from about 1899 to 1941.

Estimated Value: Excellent: **$110.00**
Very good: **$ 90.00**

H & R Premier

Caliber: 22 short, long, & long rifle, 32 S&W
Action: Double and single; exposed hammer; hinged frame (small); top break
Cylinder: 7-shot in 22 caliber, 5-shot in 32 caliber; simultaneous automatic ejector.
Barrel: 2'', 3'', 4'', 5'', or 6'' round ribbed barrel
Sights: Fixed
Finish: Blued or nickel; hard rubber round butt grips
Length overall: 5¾'' to 9¾''
Approximate wt.: 12 to 16 oz.
Comments: Made from about 1895 to 1941.

Estimated Value: Excellent: **$115.00**
Very good: **$100.00**

H & R Model 40

Same as Premier except: double action only; concealed hammer; frame completely encloses hammer area; produced from about 1899 to 1941.

Estimated Value: Excellent: **$120.00**
Very good: **$100.00**

H & R Trapper Model

Same as Model 6 except: 6'' barrel; checkered square butt walnut grips. Made from about 1924 to 1942.

Estimated Value: Excellent: **$100.00**
Very good: **$ 80.00**

H & R Hunter Model (1926)

Same as Trapper Model except: 10'' barrel; weighs 18 oz. Made from about 1926 to 1930.

Estimated Value: Excellent: **$105.00**
Very good: **$ 85.00**

H & R Hunter Model (1930)

Similar to Hunter Model (1926) except: larger frame; 9-shot safety cylinder recessed chambers; weighs 26 oz. Made from about 1930 to 1941.

Estimated Value: Excellent: **$110.00**
Very good: **$ 90.00**

H & R Model 944

Caliber: 22 short, long, & long rifle, 22 WRF
Action: Double and single; exposed hammer; heavy hinged frame; top break
Cylinder: 9-shot; simultaneous automatic ejector
Barrel: 6'' round, ribbed barrel
Sights: Fixed
Finish: Blued; checkered, square butt, walnut grips
Length overall: 10''
Approximate wt.: 24 oz.
Comments: Produced from about 1925 to 1930.

Estimated Value: Excellent: **$95.00**
Very good: **$80.00**

H & R Model 50

H & R Premier

H & R Model 40

H & R Trapper Model

H & R Model 944

H & R Model 955

H & R Model 945

Same as Model 944 except: safety cylinder (recessed chambers). Made from about 1929 to 1941.
Estimated Value: Excellent: **$110.00**
Very good: **$ 90.00**

H & R Model 955

Same as Model 945 except: 10'' barrel; approximate wt. 28 oz. Made from about 1929 to 1941.
Estimated Value: Excellent: **$115.00**
Very good: **$ 95.00**

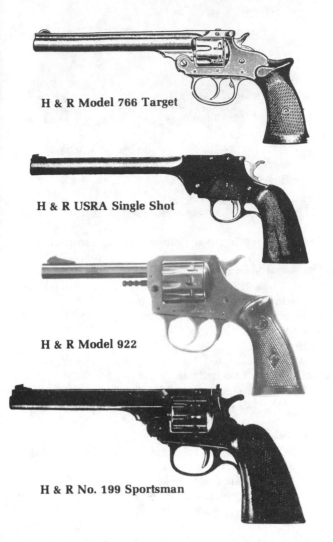

H & R Model 766 Target

H & R USRA Single Shot

H & R Model 922

H & R No. 199 Sportsman

H & R Model 923

Same as Model 922 except: nickel finish. Made from about 1930 to late 1970's.

Estimated Value: Excellent: $75.00
Very good: $60.00

H & R No. 199 Sportsman

Caliber: 22 short, long, & long rifle
Action: Double and single; exposed hammer; hinged frame; top break
Cylinder: 9-shot; simultaneous automatic ejector
Barrel: 6" round, ribbed
Sights: Adjustable target
Finish: Blued; checkered, square butt; walnut grips
Length overall: 11"
Approximate wt.: 27 oz.
Comments: Made from about 1931 to 1951.
Estimated Value: Excellent: $115.00
Very good: $ 95.00

H & R Defender 38

Similar to No. 199 Sportsman Model except: 38 S&W caliber; 4" or 6" barrel; fixed sights; plastic grips. Made from about 1933 to 1946.
Estimated Value: Excellent: $120.00
Very good: $100.00

H & R Model 766 Target

Caliber: 22 short, long, & long rifle, 22 WRF
Action: Double and single; exposed hammer; small hinged frame; top break
Cylinder: 7-shot; simultaneous automatic ejector
Barrel: 6" round ribbed
Sights: Fixed
Finish: Blued; checkered, square butt, walnut grips
Length overall: 10"
Approximate wt.: 16 oz.
Comments: Made from about 1926 to 1936.
Estimated Value: Excellent: $150.00
Very good: $120.00

H & R Ultra Sportsman

Caliber: 22 short, long, & long rifle
Action: Single; exposed hammer; hinged frame; top brake
Cylinder: 9-shot; simultaneous automatic ejector
Barrel: 6" round, ribbed
Sights: Adjustable target sights
Finish: Blued; checkered, square butt, walnut grips
Length overall: 10"
Approximate wt.: 30 oz.
Comments: Heavy frame; short cylinder; and wide hammer spur. Made from about 1928 to 1938.
Estimated Value: Excellent: $125.00
Very good: $110.00

H & R USRA Single Shot

Same as Ultra Sportsman except: single shot only (no cylinder); cartridge chamber in barrel; barrel fills in cylinder space; 7", 8", or 10" barrel lengths; approximate wt. 29 to 31 oz. Made from about 1928 to 1943.
Estimated Value: Excellent: $250.00
Very good: $220.00

H & R Model 922 Revolver

Caliber: 22 short, long, long rifle
Action: Double and single; exposed hammer; solid frame; side load
Cylinder: 9-shot removable cylinder
Barrel: 4", 6", or 10" octagon barrel in early models; later models had 2½", 4" or 6" round barrel
Sights: Fixed
Finish: Blued; checkered walnut on early models; or plastic grips on later models
Length overall: 8¼" to 14¼"
Approximate wt: 20 to 26 oz.
Comments: Made from about 1929 to late 1970's.
Estimated Value: Excellent: $70.00
Very good: $55.00

H & R Defender 38

Handguns

H & R Model 299 New Defender

Same as No. 199 Sportsman Model except: 2" barrel; 6¼" overall length. Made from about 1936 to 1941.
Estimated Value: Excellent: $100.00
                 Very good: $ 85.00

H & R No. 999 Deluxe Sportsman

Same as No. 199 Sportsman Model except: redesigned hammer and ventilated barrel rib in 1950's. Made from about 1936 to present. 32 caliber (6 shot cylinder) and 4" barrel available in 1979. Add $5.00 for 6" barrel.
Estimated Value: New (retail): $140.00
                 Excellent: $110.00
                 Very good: $ 90.00

H & R Bobby Model 15

Caliber: 32 S&W, 32 S&W long, 38 S&W
Action: Double and single; exposed hammer; hinged frame; top break
Cylinder: 6-shot in 32 caliber, 5-shot in 38 caliber; simultaneous automatic ejector
Barrel: 4" round ribbed
Sights: Fixed
Finish: Blued; checkered, square butt, walnut grips
Length overall: 9"
Approximate wt.: 23 oz.
Comments: Made from about 1941 to 1943.
Estimated Value: Excellent: $125.00
                 Very good: $100.00

H & R Model 632

Caliber: 32 S&W, 32 S&W long
Action: Double and single; exposed hammer; solid frame; side load
Cylinder: 6-shot removable
Barrel: 2½" or 4" round
Sights: Fixed
Finish: Blued; checkered tenite grips
Length overall: 6¾" to 8¼"
Approximate wt.: 19 to 21 oz.
Comments: 2½" barrel model has round butt grips. Made from about 1946 to present.
Estimated Value: New (retail): $74.50
                 Excellent: $55.00
                 Very good: $45.00

H & R Model 633

Same as Model 632 except: nickel finish; 2½" barrel only. Made from about 1946 to late 1970's.
Estimated Value: Excellent: $55.00
                 Very good: $45.00

H & R No. 999 Deluxe Sportsman

H & R Model 632

H & R Model 929 Side-Kick

Caliber: 22 short, long, long rifle
Action: Double and single; exposed hammer; solid frame
Cylinder: 9-shot swing out; simultaneous manual ejector
Barrel: 2½", 4", or 6" round
Sights: 2½" has fixed sights; 4" and 6" barrels have windage adjustable rear sight
Finish: Blued; checkered plastic grips
Length overall: 6¾" to 10¼"
Approximate wt.: 22 to 28 oz.
Comments: Made about 1956 to present.
Estimated Value: New (retail): $89.50
                 Excellent: $70.00
                 Very good: $55.00

H & R Model 930 Side-Kick

Same as Model 929 Side-Kick except: nickel finish; 2½" or 4" barrel. Still in production.
Estimated Value: New (retail): $94.50
                 Excellent: $75.00
                 Very good: $60.00

H & R Model 622

Caliber: 22 short, long, long rifle
Action: Double and single; exposed hammer; solid frame; side load
Cylinder: 6-shot removable
Barrel: 2½", 4", or 6" round
Sights: Fixed
Finish: Blued; checkered plastic grips
Length overall: 6¾" to 10¼"
Approximate wt.: 24 to 28 oz.
Comments: Made from about 1957 to present.
Estimated Value: New (retail): $69.50
                 Excellent: $50.00
                 Very good: $40.00

H&R Model 642

Similar to the Model 622 in 22 WMR caliber; 2½" or 4" barrel.
Estimated Value: New (retail): $74.50
                 Excellent: $55.00
                 Very good: $45.00

H & R Model 623

Sames as Model 622 except: nickel finish. Made from about 1957 to late 1970's.
Estimated Value: Excellent: $55.00
                 Very good: $45.00

H & R Model 622

H & R Model 929 Side-Kick

H & R Model 732 Guardsman

H & R Model 733 Guardsman

H & R Model 939 Ultra Sidekick

H & R Model 949 Forty-Niner

H & R Model 900

H & R Model 949 Forty-Niner

Caliber: 22 short, long & long rifle
Action: Double and single; exposed hammer; solid frame; side load and ejection
Cylinder: 9-shot
Barrel: 5½" round; ejector
Sights: Blade front sight; adjustable rear sight
Finish: Blued; smooth walnut, one-piece, western style grips
Length overall: 10¼"
Approximate wt.: 31 oz.
Comments: Made from about 1959 to present.
Estimated Value: New (retail): $89.50
          Excellent: $70.00
          Very good: $55.00

H & R Model 950 Forty-Niner

Same as Model 949 Forty-Niner revolver except nickel finish.
Estimated Value: New (retail): $94.50
          Excellent: $75.00
          Very good: $60.00

H & R Model 976

Similar to 949, with 7½" barrel, case hardened frame. Add $20.00 for nickel finish.
Estimated Value: New (retail): $99.50
             Excellent: $75.00
             Very good: $60.00

H & R Model 732 Guardsman

Caliber: 32 S&W, 32 S&W long
Action: Double and single; exposed hammer; solid frame
Cylinder: 6-shot swing out; simultaneous manual ejector
Barrel: 2½" or 4" round
Sights: Fixed
Finish: Blued; checkered plastic grips
Length overall: 6¾" to 8¼"
Approximate wt.: 23 to 26 oz.
Comments: Made from about 1958 to present.
Estimated Value: New (retail): $89.50
          Excellent: $70.00
          Very good: $55.00

H & R Model 733 Guardsman

Same as Model 732 Guardsman except: 2½" barrel; nickel finish; round butt grips. Made from about 1958 to present.
Estimated Value: New (retail): $94.50
          Excellent: $75.00
          Very good: $60.00

H & R Model 939 Ultra Sidekick & 940

Caliber: 22 short, long, long rifle
Action: Double and single; exposed hammer; solid frame
Cylinder: 9-shot swing out; simultaneous manual ejector
Barrel: 6", ventilated rib target barrel; bull barrel on 940
Sights: Ramp front; adjustable rear sight
Finish: Blued; checkered walnut grips with thumb rest
Length overall: 10½"
Approximate wt.: 33 oz.
Comments: Made from about 1958 to present.
Estimated Value: New (retail): $110.00
          Excellent: $ 85.00
          Very good: $ 70.00

H&R Model 903

Similar to the Model 939 with a solid heavy flat sided barrel and adjustable sights. Introduced in 1980.
Estimated Value: New (retail): $90.50
             Excellent: $70.00
             Very good: $55.00

H&R Model 603

Similar to the Model 903 in 22 magnum.
Estimated Value: New (retail): $90.50
             Excellent: $70.00
             Very good: $55.00

H&R Model 904

Similar to the Model 903 with a 6" heavy round barrel.
Estimated Value: New (retail): $90.50
             Excellent: $70.00
             Very good: $55.00

H&R Model 604

Similar to the Model 904 in 22 magnum.
Estimated Value: New (retail): $90.50
             Excellent: $70.00
             Very good: $55.00

Handguns

H & R Model 900
Caliber: 22 short, long, long rifle
Action: Double and single; exposed hammer; solid frame; side load
Cylinder: 9-shot removable
Barrel: 2½", 4" or 6"
Sights: Fixed
Finish: Blued; checkered plastic grips
Length overall: 6½" to 10"
Approximate wt.: 23 to 26 oz.
Comments: Made from about 1962 to 1973.
Estimated Value: Excellent: $60.00
            Very good: $50.00

H & R Model 901
Same as Model 900 except nickel finish. Made from about 1962 to 1963.
Estimated Value: Excellent: $65.00
             Very good: $55.00

H & R Model 925 Defender
Caliber: 38 S&W
Action: Double and single; exposed hammer; hinged frame; top break
Cylinder: 5-shot; simultaneous automatic ejector
Barrel: 2½" round, ribbed
Sights: Fixed front sight; adjustable rear sight
Finish: Blued; one-piece wrap around grip
Length overall: 6¾"
Approximate wt.: 22 oz.
Comments: Made from about 1964 to late 1970's.
Estimated Value: Excellent: $90.00
             Very good: $75.00

H & R Model 926
Caliber: 38 S&W
Action: Double and single; exposed hammer; hinged frame; top break
Cylinder: 5-shot; simultaneous automatic ejector
Barrel: 4"
Sights: Adjustable rear sight
Finish: Blued; checkered plastic, square butt grips
Length overall: 8¼"
Approximate wt.: 31 oz.
Comments: Made from about 1972 to late 1970's.
Estimated Value: Excellent: $95.00
             Very good: $80.00

H & R Model 666 Convertible
Caliber: 22 short, long & long rifle, 22 magnum (WMR) with extra interchangeable cylinder
Action: Double and single; exposed hammer; solid frame; side load
Cylinder: 6-shot removable; extra interchandeable cylinder so either cartridge can be used.
Barrel: 6" round
Sights: Fixed
Finish: Blued; black cycolac, square butt grips
Length overall: 10¼"
Approximate wt: 28 oz.
Comments: Made from about 1975 to late 1970's.
Estimated Value: Excellent: $70.00
             Very good: $55.00

H & R Model 926

H & R Model 649 Convertible

H & R Model 666 Convertible

H & R Model 649 Convertible
Caliber: 22 short, long & long rifle also, 22 magnum (WMR) with extra interchangeable cylinder
Action: Double and single; exposed hammer; solid frame; side load and ejection
Cylinder: 6-shot removable cylinder; single manual ejector; extra interchangeable cylinder
Barrel: 5½" round barrel; ejector rod housing under barrel
Sights: Blade front sight; adjustable rear sight
Finish: Blued barrel; satin finish frame; smooth western style, walnut grip
Length overall: 10¼"
Approximate wt.: 32 oz.
Comments: Western style; made from about 1975 to present.
Estimated Value: New (retail): $99.50
             Excellent: $75.00
             Very good: $60.00

H & R Model 650 Convertible
Same as Model 649 Convertible except nickel finish.
Estimated Value: New (retail): $115.00
             Excellent: $ 85.00
             Very good: $ 70.00

H & R Model 676 Convertible
Similar to Model 649 Convertible except: 4½", 5½", 7½" or 12" barrel; blued barrel with antique color cased frame; ejector finger rest at back of trigger guard; Still in production. Add $25.00 for 12" barrel model.
Estimated Value: New (retail): $115.00
             Excellent: $ 85.00
             Very good: $ 70.00

H&R Model 686
Similar to the Model 676 with ramp front sight, adjustable rear sight. Add $10.00 for 12" barrel.
Estimated Value: New (retail): $94.00
             Excellent: $75.00
             Very good: $60.00

Hartford Automatic Target

Hartford Single Shot

Caliber: 22 long rifle
Action: Single shot; hand operated; concealed hammer
Magazine: None
Barrel: 6¾"
Sights: Fixed front; rear dovetailed into slide
Finish: Matted finish on slide & frame; blued barrel; black rubber or walnut grips
Length overall: 10¾"
Approximate wt.: 37 oz.
Comments: Produced from about 1929 to 1930. Similar in appearance to the Hartford Automatic Target Pistol. Rights and properties of Hartford Arms were sold to High Standard Mfg. Co. in 1932.
Estimated Value: Excellent: $335.00
Very good: $275.00

Hartford Automatic Target

Caliber: 22 long rifle
Action: Semi-automatic; concealed hammer
Magazine: 10-shot clip
Barrel: 6¾"
Sights: Fixed front; rear sight dovetailed in slide
Finish: Blued; black rubber grips
Length overall: 10¾"
Approximate wt.: 32 oz.
Comments: Manufactured from about 1929 to 1930. Similar in appearance to Colt Woodsman and Hi Standard Model B Automatic Pistol. Rights and properties of Hartford Arms were sold to High Standard Mfg. Co. in 1932.
Estimated Value: Excellent: $270.00
Very good: $200.00

Hartford Repeating Pistol

Caliber: 22 long rifle
Action: Manual operation of slide after each shot to eject fired cartridge and feed another cartridge from magazine to chamber for next shot; concealed hammer
Magazine: 10-shot clip
Barrel: 6¾"
Sights: Fixed front; rear sight dovetailed into slide
Finish: Blued; black rubber grips
Length overall: 10¾"
Approximate wt.: 31 oz.
Comments: Made from about 1929 to 1930. Same general design and appearance as the Hartford Automatic target pistol. Rights and properties of Hartford Arms were sold to High Standard Mfg. in 1932.
Estimated Value: Excellent: $300.00
Very good: $240.00

High Standard

High Standard Model B

Caliber: 22 long rifle
Action: Semi-automatic; concealed hammer; thumb safety
Magazine: 10-shot clip
Barrel: 4½" or 6¾"
Sights: Fixed
Finish: Blued; hard rubber grips
Length overall: 8½" & 10¾"
Approximate wt: 30 to 34 oz.
Comments: Produced from about 1931 to 1942. Thumb safety.
Estimated Value: Excellent: $130.00
Very good: $100.00

High Standard Model HB

Same as Model B except: exposed hammer and no thumb safety. Made from about 1932 to 1942.
Estimated Value: Excellent: $140.00
Very good: $110.00

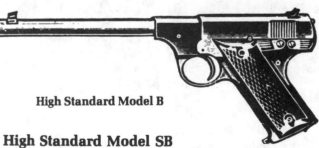

High Standard Model B

High Standard Model SB

Same as Model B except: 6¾" smooth bore for shooting 22 long rifle shot cartridges.
Estimated Value: Excellent: $135.00
Very good: $105.00

High Standard Model C

Same as Model B except: chambered for 22 shot cartridges. Manufactured from about 1932 to 1942.
Estimated Value: Excellent: $125.00
Very good: $100.00

Handguns

High Standard Model A

Caliber: 22 long rifle
Action: Semi-automatic; concealed hammer; thumb safety
Magazine: 10-shot clip
Barrel: 4½" or 6¾"
Sights: Adjustable target sights
Finish: Blued; checkered walnut grips
Length overall: 9¼" or 11¼"
Approximate wt.: 34 to 36 oz.
Comments: Produced from about 1937 to 1942.
Estimated Value: Excellent: $160.00
           Very good: $130.00

High Standard Model A

High Standard Model HA

Same as Model A except: exposed spur hammer and no thumb safety.
Estimated Value: Excellent: $165.00
           Very good: $135.00

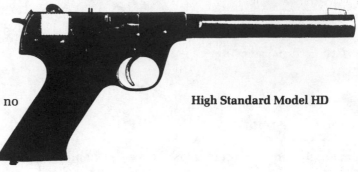

High Standard Model HD

High Standard Model D

Same as Model A except: heavier barrel; approximate weight 37 to 40 oz., depending on barrel length.
Estimated Value: Excellent: $160.00
           Very good: $130.00

High Standard Model HD

Same as Model D except: exposed spur hammer; no thumb safety.
Estimated Value: Excellent: $175.00
           Very good: $140.00

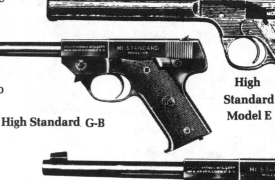

High Standard G-B

High Standard Model E

High Standard Model HDM or HD Military

Same as Model HD except it has thumb safety. Made from about 1941 to 1947, stamped "U.S. Property"
Estimated Value: Excellent: $225.00
           Very good: $185.00

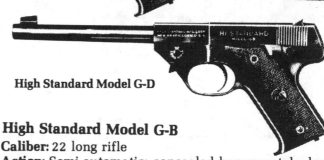

High Standard Model G-D

High Standard Model HD Military (Post War)

Same as Model HDM except it is not stamped "U.S. Property;" Made from about 1946 to 1951 (post World War II model).
Estimated Value: Excellent: $150.00
           Very good: $135.00

High Standard Model E

Similar to Model A except: extra heavy barrel; thumb rest grips. Approximate weight 39 to 42 oz.
Estimated Value: Excellent: $165.00
           Very good: $135.00

High Standard Model HE

Same as Model E except: exposed spur hammer; no thumb safety.
Estimated Value: Excellent: $175.00
           Very good: $140.00

High Standard Model G-B

Caliber: 22 long rifle
Action: Semi-automatic; concealed hammer; takedown model; interchangeable barrels; thumb safety.
Magazine: 10-shot clip
Barrel: 4½" and 6¾'
Sights: Fixed sights
Finish: Blued; checkered plastic grips
Length overall: 8½" and 10¾"
Approximate wt.: 34 to 36 oz.
Comments: Produced from about 1948 to 1951. Add $20.00 if pistol has both barrels.
Estimated Value: Excellent: $140.00
           Very good: $110.00

High Standard Model G-D

Same as Model G-B except: adjustable target sights; checkered walnut grips; approximate wt. 38 to 40 oz.; length overall about 9¼" to 11½". Add $20.00 if pistol has both barrels.
Estimated Value: Excellent: $170.00
           Very good: $140.00

High Standard Model G-380

High Standard Olympic 1st Model

High Standard Olympic ISU

High Standard Olympic 2nd Model

High Standard Sport-King 1st Model

High Standard Sport-King 1st Model
Caliber: 22 long rifle
Action: Semi-automatic; concealed hammer; takedown model with interchangeable barrel; thumb safety at top center of left grip
Magazine: 10-shot clip
Barrel: 4½" and/or 6¾"
Sights: Fixed
Finish: Blued; checkered plastic grips with thumb rest
Length overall: 9"; 11¼"
Approximate wt: 36 to 39 oz.
Comments: Manufactured from about 1951 to 1958. Add $20.00 for pistol with both barrels.
Estimated Value: Excellent: $125.00
Very good: $105.00

High Standard Model G-E
Same as Model G-D except: heavy barrel; thumb rest; walnut grips; approximate wt. 42 to 44 oz. Add $25.00 if pistol has both barrels.
Estimated Value: Excellent: $190.00
Very good: $155.00

High Standard Model G-380
Caliber: 380 ACP
Action: Semi-automatic; exposed spur hammer; thumb safety; barrel takedown mode
Magazine: 6-shot clip; bottom release
Barrel: 5"
Sights: Fixed; blade front and notched rear
Finish: Blued; checkered plastic grips
Length overall: 9"
Approximate wt.: 40 oz.
Comments: First of the barrel takedown models produced by High Standard. Manufactured from about 1944 to 1950.
Estimated Value: Excellent: $225.00
Very good: $180.00

High Standard Olympic 1st Model
Similar to Model G-E except: 22 short caliber; light alloy slide; made from about 1950 to 1951; approximate wt. 38 to 40 oz. Add $25.00 if pistol has both barrels.
Estimated Value: Excellent: $200.00
Very good: $160.00

High Standard Olympic 2nd Model
Similar to Olympic 1st Model except: thumb safety located at center top of left grip; plastic grips with thumb rest; produced from about 1951 to 1958. Add $20.00 if pistol has both barrels.
Estimated Value: Excellent: $180.00
Very good: $145.00

High Standard Olympic ISU
Caliber: 22 short
Action: Semi-automatic; concealed hammer; wide target trigger; anti-backlash trigger adjustment
Magazine: 10-shot clip
Barrel: 5½" bull barrel (1963-1966); 8" tapered barrel (1958-1964); 6¾" tapered barrel (1958-present); integral stabilizer and 2 removable weights
Sights: Ramp front; adjustable rear
Finish: Blued; checked walnut thumb rest grips
Length overall: 11¼" (6¾" barrel)
Approximate wt.: 40 to 41 oz.
Comments: Meets International Shooting Union Regulations; left or right hand grips; regular Hi-Standard style grip or the squared military style grip; military style has rear sight frame mounted. Made from about 1958 to late 1970's.
Estimated Value: Excellent: $230.00
Very good: $190.00

Handguns

High Standard Sport-King 2nd Model

Similar to Sport-King 1st Model except: made from about 1958 to late 1970's; interior changes; still has interchangeable barrel; blued or nickel finish; weighs 39 to 42 oz. Add $10.00 for nickel finish. Add $20.00 for pistol with both barrels.

Estimated Value: Excellent: $130.00
               Very good: $105.00

High Standard Sport-King 2nd Model

High Standard Lightweight Sport-King

Same as Sport-King 1st Model except: made from about 1954 to 1965; aluminum alloy frame (wt. 28 to 30 oz.). Add $15.00 for pistol with both barrels.

Estimated Value: Excellent: $120.00
               Very good: $ 95.00

High Standard Supermatic

Standard Tournament Model

Standard Citation Model

**Supermatic Standard Citation
and Military Citation Model**

High Standard Supermatic Series

Caliber: 22 long rifle
Action: Semi-automatic; concealed hammer; thumb safety; takedown model with interchangeable barrels
Magazine: 10-shot clip
Barrel: 4½", 5½", 6¾", 7¼", 8", 10"
Sights: Ramp front, adjustable rear
Finish: Blued; checkered plastic or checkered wood grips with or without thumb rest
Length overall: 9¼" to 14¾"
Approximate wt.: 40 to 46 oz.
Comments: The 5¼" barrels are heavy (bull) barrels and the 7¼" barrels are heavy (bull) fluted barrels.
Estimated Value:

Standard Supermatic Model manufactured from about 1951 to 1958. 4¼" and/or 6¾" interchangeable barrels. Add $20.00 for pistols with both barrels.

           Excellent: $150.00
           Very good: $120.00

Standard Tournament Model made from about 1958 to 1963; 5½" bull barrel and/ or 6¾" regular barrel with stabilizer and 2 removable weights; adjustable trigger pull. Add $20.00 for pistol with both barrels.

           Excellent: $170.00
           Very good: $135.00

Standard Citation Model made from about 1959 to 1966; 5½" bull barrel or 6¾", 8" or 10" tapered barrel with stabilizer and 2 removable weights; adjustable trigger pull.

           Excellent: $180.00
           Very good: $150.00

Supermatic Standard Citation and Military Citation Model made from about 1965 to present; 5½" heavy (bull) or 7¼" heavy fluted barrel with military grip or standard grip. Add $20.00 for 7¼" barrel.

           New (retail): $286.00
           Excellent: $230.00
           Very good: $185.00

Supermatic Trophy Military Model

High Standard Flite-King 1st Model
Same as Sport-King 1st Model except: produced from about 1953 to 1958; aluminum alloy frame and slide (wt. 24 to 26 oz.) caliber - 22 short only. Add $20.00 for pistol with both barrels.
Estimated Value: Excellent: $125.00
Very good: $110.00

High Standard Flite-King 2nd Model
Same as Flite-King 1st Model Automatic except: made from about 1958 to 1965: all steel construction; caliber - 22 long rifle only. Add $20.00 for pistol with both barrels.
Estimated Value: Excellent: $140.00
Very good: $115.00

High Standard Field-King
Same as Sport-King 1st Model except: adjustable target sights; 6¾" heavy barrel (wt. about 44 oz.).
Estimated Value: Excellent: $135.00
Very good: $115.00

High Standard Dura-Matic
Caliber: 22 long rifle
Action: Semi-automatic; concealed hammer; takedown interchangeable barrel model
Magazine: 10-shot clip
Barrel: 4½", 6½"
Sights: Fixed
Finish: Blued; checkered plastic grips
Length overall: 8 7/8", 10 7/8"
Approximate wt.: 33 to 35 oz.
Comments: Manufactured from about 1954 to 1969.
Estimated Value: Excellent: $120.00
Very good: $100.00

High Standard Plinker
Caliber: 22 long rifle
Action: Semi-automatic; concealed hammer
Magazine: 10-shot clip
Barrel: 4½", 6½"
Sights: Fixed
Finish: Blued; checkered plastic grips
Length overall: 9" to 11"
Approximate wt.: 28 to 30 oz.
Comments: Made from about 1971 to 1974.
Estimated Value: Excellent: $100.00
Very good: $ 80.00

Supermatic Trophy Citation made from about 1959 to 1966; 5½" bull barrel or 7¼" fluted barrel
Excellent: $210.00
Very good: $170.00

Supermatic Trophy Military Model manufactured from about 1965 to present; 5½" bull barrel or 7¼" fluted barrel with square military style grip; adjustable trigger pull. Add $10.00 for 7¼" barrel.
New (retail): $304.00
Excellent: $225.00
Very good: $180.00

High Standard Brenner Commemorative
A highly engraved model of the Supermatic Military Trophy pistol with 5½" barrel. A limited number of 1000 were produced in 1972, and sold for $550.00 each.
Estimated Value - Unused and unfired condition $1,050.00

High Standard Flite-King 1st Model

High Standard Field-King

High Standard Dura-Matic

High Standard Plinker

Handguns

High Standard Sharpshooter

Caliber: 22 long rifle
Action: Semi-automatic; concealed hammer
Magazine: 9-shot clip
Barrel: 5½" heavy (bull) barrel
Sights: Ramp front; adjustable rear
Finish: Blued; checkered plastic grips
Length overall: 10"
Approximate wt.: 38 oz.
Comments: Produced from about 1971 to present.
Estimated Value: New (retail): $253.00
            Excellent: $195.00
            Very good: $150.00

High Standard Sharpshooter

High Standard Victor

High Standard Victor

Caliber: 22 long rifle
Action: Semi-automatic; concealed hammer; interchangeable barrel
Magazine: 10-shot clip
Barrel: 4½" or 5½" with solid or ventilated aluminum rib and barrel weights
Sights: Ramp front, adjustable rear
Finish: Blued; checkered walnut grips with thumb rest
Length overall: 8¾"; 9¾"
Approximate wt.: 38 oz.
Comments: Hi-Standard type grip or square military type grip. Manufactured from about 1972 to present.
Estimated Value: New (retail): $348.00
            Excellent: $260.00
            Very good: $210.00

High Standard Sentinel

High Standard Sentinel

Caliber: 22 short, long, or long rifle
Action: Double or single action; solid frame
Cylinder: 9-shot swing out; simultaneous manual ejector
Barrel: 3", 4", 6"
Sights: Fixed
Finish: Blued or nickel; checkered plastic grips
Length overall: 8" to 11"
Approximate wt.: 18 to 24 oz.
Comments: Made from about 1954 to 1974; aluminum alloy frame.
Estimated Value: Excellent: $80.00
            Very good: $65.00

High Standard Sentinel Deluxe

Same as Sentinel Revolver except: adjustable rear sight; checkered walnut square butt grip; wide trigger; 4" or 6" barrel only; made from about 1965 to 1974.
Estimated Value: Excellent: $90.00
            Very good: $75.00

High Standard Sentinel Snub

Same as Sentinel Revolver except: 2 3/8" barrel only; overall length 7½"; weighs 15 oz.'; checkered plastic birdshead grip (rounded butt). Produced from about 1956 to 1974. Some were made in pink, turquoise, and gold colored finish as well as blue and nickel.
Estimated Value: Excellent: $90.00
            Very good: $75.00

High Standard Sentinel Imperial

Same as Sentinel revolver except: ramp front sight; black or nickel finish; checkered walnut square butt grips. Made from about 1961 to 1965.
Estimated Value: Excellent: $85.00
            Very good: $70.00

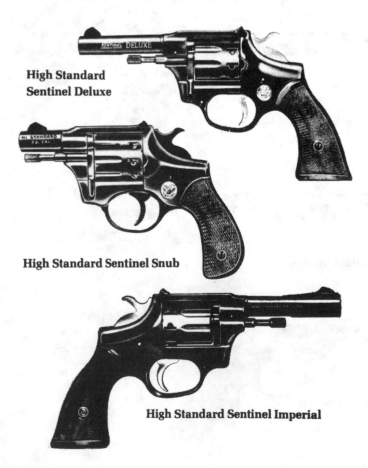

High Standard Sentinel Deluxe

High Standard Sentinel Snub

High Standard Sentinel Imperial

High Standard Longhorn

Caliber: 22 short, long, and long rifle
Action: Double and single; solid frame;
Cylinder: 9-shot swing-out; simultaneous manual ejector
Barrel: 4½" or 5½" (1961 to 1966); 9½" (1966 to 1971); dummy ejector housing under barrel
Sights: Blade front; fixed or adjustable rear
Finish: Blued; plastic grips; walnut grips on 9½" barrel model
Length overall: 10"; 11"; 15"
Approximate wt.: 26 to 32 oz.
Comments: Aluminum alloy frame. Made from about 1961 to 1971. Add $15.00 for 9½" barrel model.
Estimated Value: Excellent: $100.00
Very good: $ 80.00

High Standard Longhorn Combination

Similar to Longhorn revolver except: extra interchangeable cylinder in caliber 22 magnum; 9½" barrel only; smooth walnut grips. Made from about 1971 to present. Add $10.00 for adjustable rear sight.
Estimated Value: New (retail): $214.50
Excellent: $160.00
Very good: $125.00

High Standard Kit Gun

Caliber: 22 short, long and long rifle
Action: Double and single action; solid frame
Cylinder: 9-shot swing out; simultaneous manual ejector
Barrel: 4"
Sights: Ramp front sight, adjustable rear
Finish: Blued; checkered walnut grips
Length overall: 9"
Approximate wt.: 19 oz.
Comments: Aluminum alloy frame. Produced from about 1970 to 1973.
Estimated Value: Excellent: $75.00
Very good: $60.00

High Standard Double Nine

Caliber: 22 short, long and long rifle
Action: Double and single; solid frame
Cylinder: 9-shot; swing out with simultaneous manual ejector
Barrel: 5½"; dummy ejector housing under barrel
Sights: Blade front; fixed or adjustable rear
Finish: Blued or nickel; plastic grips
Length overall: 11"
Approximate wt.: 28 oz.
Comments: Aluminum alloy frame; a western style of the Sentinel revolvers. Made from about 1958 to 1971. Add $10.00 for nickel finish.
Estimated Value: Excellent: $100.00
Very good: $ 80.00

High Standard Double Nine Combination

Same as Double-Nine revolver except: extra interchangeable cylinder in caliber 22 magnum; smooth walnut grip; made from about 1971 to present; steel frame; weighs 32 oz. Add $10.00 for nickel finish or adjustable rear sight.
Estimated Value: New (retail): $210.50
Excellent: $160.00
Very good: $125.00

High Standard Natchez

Similar to Double-Nine revolver except: 4½" barrel only; 10" overall length; weighs 32 oz.; blued finish only; plastic ivory birdshead grips. Made from about 1961 to 1966.
Estimated Value: Excellent: $120.00
Very good: $100.00

High Standard Posse

Similar to Double-Nine revolver except: 3½" barrel without dummy ejector housing; 9" length overall; weighs 24 oz.; brass trigger guard and grip frame; blued finish only; smooth walnut grips. Made from about 1961 to 1966.
Estimated Value: Excellent: $110.00
Very good: $ 90.00

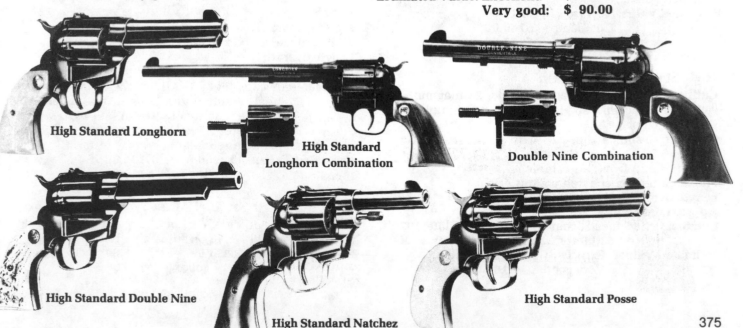

High Standard Longhorn

High Standard Longhorn Combination

Double Nine Combination

High Standard Double Nine

High Standard Natchez

High Standard Posse

Handguns

High Standard Hombre

Caliber: 22 short, long, and long rifle
Action: Double and single; solid frame
Cylinder: 9-shot swing out; simultaneous ejector
Barrel: 4½"
Sights: Blade front, adjustable rear
Finish: Blued or nickel; smooth walnut grip
Length overall: 10"
Approximate wt.: 26 oz.
Comments: Steel frame; manufactured from about 1972 to 1974. Add $5.00 for nickel finish.
Estimated Value: Excellent: $100.00
Very good: $ 80.00

High Standard Durango

Caliber: 22 short, long and long rifle
Action: Double and single; solid frame
Cylinder: 9-shot; swing out with simultaneous ejector
Barrel: 4½"; 5½"; dummy ejector housing under barrel
Sights: Blade front adjustable rear
Finish: Blued or nickel; smooth walnut grip
Length overall: 10"; 11"
Approximate wt.: 25 to 27 oz.
Comments: Produced from about 1972 to 1975.
Estimated Value: Excellent: $110.00
Very good: $ 90.00

High Standard High Sierra Combination

Caliber: 22 short, long, long rifle
Action: Double and single; solid frame
Cylinder: 9-shot swing out; two interchangeable cylinders
Barrel: 7" octagonal
Sights: Blade front; adjustable rear
Finish: Blued; smooth walnut grips
Length overall: 12½"
Approximate wt.: 38 oz.
Comments: Steel frame; gold plated trigger guard and backstrap. Made from about 1973 to present.
Estimated Value: New (retail): $214.50
Excellent: $160.00
Very good: $125.00

High Standard Camp Gun

Caliber: 22 short, long, and long rifle, 22 magnum
Action: Double and single; solid frame; simultaneous ejector
Cylinder: 9-shot, swing-out
Barrel: 6"
Sights: Ramp front; adjustable rear
Finish: Blued; checkered walnut grips
Length overall: 11"
Approximate wt: 31 oz.
Comments: Produced from about 1975 to late 1970's. Add $3.00 for 22 magnum caliber.
Estimated Value: Excellent: $130.00
Very good: $105.00

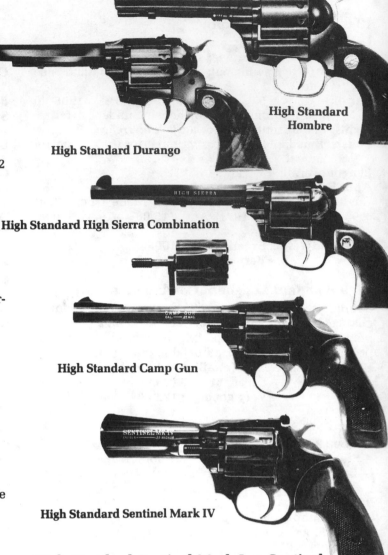

High Standard Hombre

High Standard Durango

High Standard High Sierra Combination

High Standard Camp Gun

High Standard Sentinel Mark IV

High Standard Sentinel Mark I or Sentinel

Caliber: 22 short, long, long rifle
Action: Double and single action; solid frame
Cylinder: 9-shot swingpout with simultaneous manual ejector
Barrel: 2", 4"
Sights: Ramp front; fixed or adjustable rear
Finish: Blued or nickel; smooth walnut grips
Length overall: 7", 9"
Approximate wt: 28 to 30 oz.
Comments: A completely redesigned and improved all steel version of the 22 caliber Sentinel. Produced from about 1974 to late 1970's. Add $10.00 for nickel finish and $10.00 for adjustable rear sight.
Estimated Value: Excellent: $135.00
Very good: $110.00

High Standard Sentinel Mark IV or Sentinel

Same as Sentinel Mark I except 22 magnum only. Add $10.00 for nickel finish or adjustable rear sight.
Estimated Value: Excellent: $135.00
Very good: $110.00

High Standard Sentinel Mark II

High Standard Sentinel Mark III

High Standard
22 Caliber Derringer

High Standard Sentinel Mark II

Caliber: 38 Special, 357 magnum
Action: Double and single; solid frame
Cylinder: 6-shot swing-out with simultaneous manual ejector
Barrel: 2½", 4", 6"
Sights: Ramp front; fixed rear
Finish: Blued; checkered walnut grips
Length overall: 7½" to 11"
Approximate wt.: 38 to 40 oz.
Comments: Heavy-duty all steel revolver. Made from about 1974 to late 1970's.
Estimated Value: Excellent: $150.00
Very good: $120.00

High Standard Sentinel Mark III

Similar to Sentinel Mark II except: deluxe trophy blue finish; checkered walnut wrap around grips; checkered back strap; adjustable rear sight.
Estimated Value: Excellent: $175.00
Very good: $135.00

High Standard Crusader

Caliber: 44 magnum, 45 Colt, 357 magnum
Action: Double and single
Cylinder: 6 shot
Barrel: 4½" in 45 Colt or 44 magnum; 6½" in 45 Colt, 44 magnum or 357 magnum; 8 3/8" in 45 Colt, 44 magnum, 357 magnum
Sights: Adjustable rear, ramp blade front
Finish: Blued; shrouded ejector rod; smooth walnut grips in 44 magnum, checkered walnut grips in 45 Colt and 357 magnum.
Length overall: 9 7/8"-14"
Approximate wt.: 43-52 oz.
Comments: A large frame handgun introduced in the late 1970's. Add $5.00 for 6½" barrel, $12.00 for 8 3/8" barrel.
Estimated Value: New (retail): $432.00
Excellent: $325.00
Very good: $260.00

High Standard 22 Caliber, Derringer

Caliber: 22 short, long and long rifle (1962 to present); 22 magnum rimfire (1963 to present)
Action: Double; concealed hammer; hammer block safety; front of trigger guard cut away for easy access to trigger.
Cylinder: None; 2-shot chambers in barrels
Barrel: 3½" double barrel (barrels superposed); dual ejection; cartridge chamber in each barrel.
Sights: Fixed
Finish: Blued; nickel; plastic grips (1962 to present); gold plated presentation model in walnut case (1965 to 1966).
Length overall: 5"
Approximate wt.: 11 oz.
Comments: Steel barrels; aluminum alloy frame. Manufactured from about 1962 to present.

Estimated Value:	Blued	Nickel
New (retail):	$130.00	$151.50
Excellent:	$100.00	$115.00
Very good:	$ 80.00	$ 95.00

Gold presentation models with case in unused condition:

1-derringer $180.00
2-derringer $375.00
(with consecutive numbers)

High Standard
Crusader Medium Frame

High Standard
Crusader

High Standard Crusader Medium Frame

Similar to the Crusader in 357 magnum only; 4½" or 6½" barrel; weight is 40 to 42 oz.; a smaller version of the Crusader. Add $7.00 for 6½" barrel.
Estimated Value: New (retail): $425.75
Excellent: $320.00
Very good: $255.00

Iver Johnson

Iver Johnson Safety Hammer

Iver Johnson Safety Hammer

Caliber: 22 short, long, and long rifle, 32 S&W, 32 S&W long, or 38 S&W

Action: Double and single; exposed hammer; hinged frame; top break style; simultaneous ejector; heavier frame for 32 and 38 caliber

Cylinder: 7-shot in 22 caliber, 6-shot in 32 caliber, 5-shot in 38 caliber

Barrel: 2″, 3″, 3¼″, 4″, 5″, 6″; round barrel with rib on top.

Sights: Fixed

Finish: Blued or nickel; hard rubber or wood grips; round or square butt grip.

Length overall: 6¾″ to 10¾″ (depending on barrel length)

Approximate wt.: 14 to 21 oz. (depening on caliber & barrel length)

Comments: Produced from about 1892 to 1950 with some improvements and minor changes.

Estimated Value: Excellent: $95.00
Very good: $75.00

Iver Johnson Safety Hammerless

Same as Safety Hammer model except: side plates of frame extended to enclose hammer; double-action only; concealed hammer. Made from aboiut 1895 to 1950.

Estimated Value: Excellent: $100.00
Very good: $ 80.00

Iver Johnson Target 9-shot Revolver

Similar to Model 1900 Target except: 9-shot cylinder; 6″or 10″ barrel; 10¾″ to 14¾″ length overall; weight 24 to 28 oz. Introduced about 1929 and discontinued in 1946.

Estimated Value: Excellent: $85.00
Very good: $70.00

Iver Johnson Supershot

Caliber: 22 short, long, long rifle

Action: Double and single; exposed hammer; hinged frame; top break style; simultaneous ejector

Cylinder: 7-shot; 9-shot

Barrel: 6″; round barrel with solid rib on top

Sights: Fixed

Finish: Blued; checkered walnut grip (one piece)

Length overall: 10¾″

Approximate wt.: 25 oz.

Comments: Some have adjustable finger rest behind trigger guard. Made from about 1929 to 1949.

Estimated Value: Excellent: $85.00
Very good: $70.00

Iver Johnson Sealed Eight Supershot

Similar to Supershot Revolver except: 8-shot cylinder recessed for cartridge head; 10″ barrel length; 10¾″ to 14¾″ overall lengths; adjustable rear sight. Made from about 1931 to 1957.

Estimated Value: Excellent: $100.00
Very good: $ 80.00

Iver Johnson Model 1900

Iver Johnson Safety Hammerless

Iver Johnson Model 1900

Caliber: 22 short, long, long rifle, 32 S&W, 32 S&W long, 38 S&W

Action: Double and single; exposed hammer; solid frame; side load

Cylinder: 7-shot in 22 caliber, 6-shot in 32 caliber, 5-shot in 38 caliber, removable cylinder

Barrel: 2½″, 4½″, 6″; octagon barrel

Sights: Fixed

Finish: Blued or nickel; hard rubber grips

Length overall: 7″ to 10¾″ (depending on barrel length)

Approximate wt.: 11 oz. to 19 oz.

Comments: Manufactured from about 1900 to 1947.

Estimated Value: Excellent: $80.00
Very good: $65.00

Iver Johnson Model 1900 Target

Same as Model 1900 except: 22 caliber only; 6″ or 9″ barrel length; length overall 10¾″ to 13¾″; approximate wt. 22 to 26 oz.; checkered walnut grips; blued finish only. Made from about 1925 to 1942.

Estimated Value: Excellent: $90.00
Very good: $70.00

Iver Johnson Model 1900 Target

Iver Johnson Sealed Eight Supershot

Iver Johnson Sealed Eight Target

Caliber: 22 short, long, long rifle
Action: Double and single; exposed hammer; solid frame; side load
Cylinder: 8-shot; cylinder recessed for cartridge head; removable
Barrel: 6", 10"; octagon barrel
Sights: Fixed
Finish: Blued; checkered walnut grip (one piece)
Length overall: 10¾"; 14¾"
Approximate wt.: 24 to 28 oz.
Comments: Produced from about 1931 to 1957.
Estimated Value: Excellent: $110.00
Very good: $ 90.00

Iver Johnson Sealed Eight Target

Iver Johnson Champion

Caliber: 22 short, long, long rifle
Action: Single; exposed hammer; hinged frame; top break style; simultaneous ejector
Cylinder: 8-shot; cylinder recessed for cartridge head.
Barrel: 6"
Sights: Adjustable target sights
Finish: Blued; checkered walnut grips (one piece)
Length overall: 10¾"
Approximate wt.: 28 oz.
Comments: Manufactured from about 1938 to 1948. Adjustable finger rest behind trigger guard.
Estimated Value: Excellent: $110.00
Very good: $ 90.00

Iver Johnson Trigger Cocking Target

Same as Champion Revolver except the trigger cocks the hammer on the first pull, then releases the hammer to fire the revolver on the second pull. Made from about 1940 to 1947.
Estimated Value: Excellent: $120.00
Very good: $100.00

Iver Johnson Armsworth Model 855

Caliber: 22 short, long, long rifle
Action: Single-action; exposed hammer; hinged frame; top break style; simultaneous ejector
Cylinder: 8-shot; chambers recessed for cartridge head
Barrel: 6"
Sights: Adjustable front and rear sights
Finish: Blued; checkered walnut grips (one piece)
Length overall: 10¾"
Approximate wt.: 30 oz.
Comments: Adjustable finger rest behind trigger guard; made from about 1954 to 1957.
Estimated Value: Excellent: $110.00
Very good: $ 90.00

Iver Johnson Sealed Eight Protector

Caliber: 22 short, long, long rifle
Action: Double and single; exposed hammer; hinged frame; top break style; simultaneous ejector
Cylinder: 8-shot; cylinder recessed for cartridge head
Barrel: 2½"
Sights: Fixed
Finish: Blued; checkered walnut grips
Length overall: 7½"
Approximate wt.: 20 oz.
Comments: Some had adjustable finger rest behind trigger guards. Made from about 1933 to 1949.
Estimated Value: Excellent: $115.00
Very good: $ 95.00

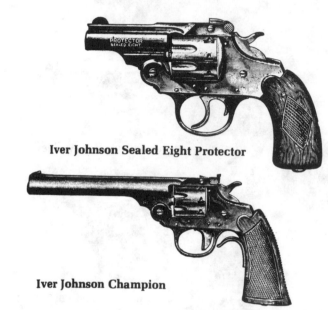

Iver Johnson Sealed Eight Protector

Iver Johnson Champion

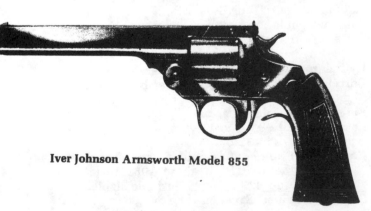

Iver Johnson Trigger Cocking Target

Iver Johnson Armsworth Model 855

Handguns

Iver Johnson Supershot Model 844

Iver Johnson Model 55 S-A Cadet

Iver Johnson Model 50A Sidewinder

Iver Johnson Model 55S Cadet

Iver Johnson Supershot Model 844

Similar to Armsworth Model 855 except: double and single action; 4½" or 6" barrel lengths; 9¼" to 10¾" overall length. Introduced about 1955, discontinued about 1957.

Estimated Value: Excellent: $100.00
               Very good: $ 80.00

Iver Johnson Model 50A Sidewinder

Caliber: 22 short, long, long rifle
Action: Double and single; exposed hammer; solid frame; side load with loading gate; removable cylinder
Cylinder: 8-shot; recessed chambers
Barrel: 4½", 6" ejector rod under barrel
Sights: Fixed or adjustable
Finish: Blued; plastic grip
Length overall: 9¾" to 11¼"
Approximate wt: 32 oz.
Comments: Frontier style double action revolver. Manfactured from about 1961 to late 1970's. Add $20.00 for adjustable sights.
Estimated Value: Excellent: $65.00
               Very good: $55.00

Iver Johnson Model 50A Sidewinder Convertible

Same as Model 50A Sidewinder except: extra interchangeable cylinder for 22 magnum (WRM) cartridges. Add $10.00 for adjustable sights.
Estimated Value: Excellent: $70.00
               Very good: $60.00

Iver Johnson Model 55S Cadet

Caliber: 22 short, long, long rifle, 32 S&W, 38 S & W
Action: Double and single; solid frame; exposed hammer; side load.
Cylinder: 8-shot in 22 caliber, 5-shot in 32 and 38 caliber; removable cylinder
Barrel: 2½"
Sights: Fixed
Finish: Blued; plastic round butt grips
Length overall: 7"
Approximate wt: 24 oz.
Comments: Made from about 1954 to 1961.
Estimated Value: Excellent: $60.00
               Very good: $50.00

Iver Johnson Model 55 S-A Cadet

Similar to Model 55S Cadet except: addition of loading gate about 1962; also in calibers 22 WRM magnum and 38 Special. Made from about 1962 to late 1970's.
Estimated Value: Excellent: $65.00
               Very good: $55.00

Iver Jonhson Model 55

Caliber: 22 short, long, long rifle
Action: Double and single; exposed hammer; solid frame; side load
Cylinder: 8-shot; chambers recessed for cartridge head; removable cylinder; unfluted cylinder
Barrel: 4½", 6"
Sights: Fixed
Finish: Blued; checkered walnut grip
Length overall: 9¼" to 10¾"
Approximate wt.: 22 to 24 oz.
Comments: Made from about 1955 to 1961.
Estimated Value: Excellent: $60.00
               Very good: $50.00

Iver Johnson Model 55A Target

Same as Model 55 Revolver except: fluted cylinder; loading gate at loading port; checkered plastic grip. Introduced about 1962. Made to late 1970's.
Estimated Value: Excellent: $65.00
               Very good: $55.00

Iver Johnson Model 57

Same as Model 55 Revolver except: adjustable front and rear sights; checkered plastic grip. Made from about 1955 to 1961.
Estimated Value: Excellent: $70.00
               Very good: $60.00

Iver Johnson Model 57A Target

Same as Model 55 Revolver except: fluted clyinder; adjustable front and rear sight; checkered plastic grips; loading gate at loading port. Made from about 1962 to late 1970's.

Estimated Value: Excellent: **$75.00**
Very good: **$60.00**

Iver Johnson Model 66 Trailsman

Caliber: 22 short, long, long rifle; 32 S&W, 38 S&W
Action: Double and single; exposed hammer; hinged frame; break top style; simuntaneous manual ejector under barrel; rebounding type hammer
Cylinder: 8-shot in 22 caliber, 5-shot in 32 and 38 caliber; recessed chambers
Barrel: 2¾", 6"; rib on top of barrel
Sights: Adjustable
Finish: Blued; checkered walnut or plastic grip; round butt on 2¾" barrel; square butt on 2¾" barrel
Length overall: 7", 11"
Approximate wt.: 28 to 32 oz.
Comments: 2¾" barrel snub model made from about 1961 to 1971. 6" barrel model made from about 1958 to 1975.

Estimated Value: Excellent: **$75.00**
Very good: **$60.00**

Iver Johnson Model 57A

Iver Johnson Model 66 Trailsman

Iver Johnson Model 67 Viking

Same as Model 66 Trailsman except: hammer safety device; 4½" or 6" barrel lengths. Made from 1964 to 1975.

Estimated Value: Excellent: **$80.00**
Very good: **$65.00**

Iver Johnson Model 67S Viking

Same as Model 67 except: 2¾" barrel length; overall length 7"; approximate wt. 25 oz.

Estimated Value: Excellent: **$75.00**
Very good: **$60.00**

Iver Johnson Model 67S Viking

Iver Johnson Bulldog

Caliber: 22 short, long, long rifle; 38 special
Action: Double and single; exposed hammer; solid frame; side load with loading gate
Cylinder: 8-shot in 22 caliber, 5-shot in 38 caliber; recessed chambers
Barrel: 2½", 4", heavy duty ribbed
Sights: Adjustable
Finish: Blued; plastic grips; round butt or square butt
Length overall: 6½", 9"
Approximate wt: 26 oz. to 30 oz.
Comments: Produced from about 1974 to late 1970's. Add $2.00 for 4" barrel model. Add $10.00 for 38 caliber.

Estimated Value: Excellent: **$80.00**
Very good: **$65.00**

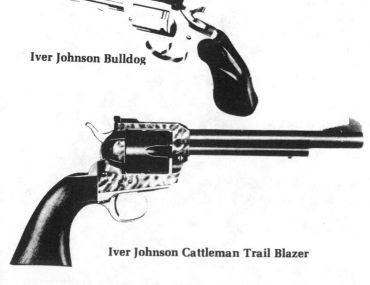

Iver Johnson Bulldog

Iver Johnson Cattleman Trail Blazer

Iver Johnson Cattleman Trail Blazer

Caliber: 22 short, long, long rifle; 22 magnum (WRM)
Action: Single; solid frame; exposed hammer; side load with loading gate
Cylinder: 6-shot; 2 interchangeable cylinders
Barrel: 5½"; 6"; manual ejector rod under barrel
Sights: Ramp front; adjustable rear
Finish: Blued, case hardened frame, brass backstrap & trigger guard; smooth walnut grip
Length overall: 11¼" to 12¼"
Approximate wt: 38 to 40 oz.
Comments: Made from about 1974 to late 1970's. Prices include both cylinders

Estimated Value: Excellent: **$125.00**
Very good: **$100.00**

Handguns

Iver Johnson Cattleman Magnum

Caliber: 38 Special & 357 magnum, 45 long Colt, 44 Special & 44 magnum

Action: Single; solid frame; exposed hammer; side load with loading gate

Cylinder: 6-shot

Barrel: 4¾", 5½", 7½" (357 magnum & 44 LC) 4¾", 6", 7½" (44 magnum); manual ejector rod under barrel

Sights: Blade front; fixed rear

Finish: Blued, case hardened frame; brass back strap & trigger guard; smooth walnut grips

Length overall: 10½" to 13¼"

Approximate wt: 38 to 46 oz.

Comments: Made from about 1974 to late 1970's; Add $25.00 for 44 magnum.

Estimated Value: Excellent: $150.00
Very good: $120.00

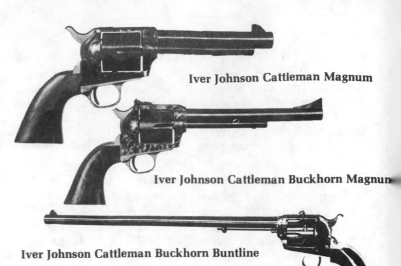

Iver Johnson Cattleman Magnum

Iver Johnson Cattleman Buckhorn Magnum

Iver Johnson Cattleman Buckhorn Buntline

Iver Johnson Cattleman Buckhorn Magnum

Same as Cattleman Magnum except: ramp front sight and adjustable rear sight. Add $25.00 for 12" barrel; Add $25.00 for 44 magnum.

Estimated Value: Excellent: $160.00
Very good: $130.00

Iver Johnson Cattleman Buckhorn Buntline

Same as Cattleman Buckhorn Magnum except: 18" barrel length only; grip back strap is cut for shoulder stock attachment; smooth walnut attachable shoulder stock; overall length without shoulder stock 24" and 36½" with shoulder stock; approximate wt. is 56 oz. without shoulder stock; shoulder stock wt. approximately 30 oz. Prices include stock. Add $25.00 for 44 magnum.

Estimated Value:

Excellent: $300.00
Very good: $240.00

Iver Johnson X300 Pony

Iver Johnson Sportsman

Iver Johnson X300 Pony

Caliber: 380

Action: Double and single; semi-automatic; exposed hammer

Magazine: 6 shot clip

Barrel: 3"

Sights: Adjustable rear, blade front

Finish: Blued or nickel; checkered wood grips

Length overall: 6"

Approximate wt.: 29 oz.

Comments: Currently available. Add $12.00 for nickel finish.

Estimated Value: New (retail): $216.00
Excellent: $165.00
Very good: $135.00

Iver Johnson Rookie

Caliber: 38 Special

Action: Double and single

Cylinder: 5 shot fluted

Barrel: 4"

Sights: Fixed

Finish: Blued or nickel; plastic grips

Length overall: 9"

Approximate wt.: 29 oz.

Comments: Made from the mid to late 1970's.

Estimated Value: Excellent: $75.00
Very good: $55.00

Iver Johnson Sportsman

Similar to the Rookie in 22 long rifle caliber; 4¾" or 6" barrel; blued finish; made in the mid 1970's.

Estimated Value: Excellent: $75.00
Very good: $55.00

Iver Johnson Deluxe Target

Similar to the Sportsman with adjustable sights.

Estimated Value: Excellent: $80.00
Very good: $60.00

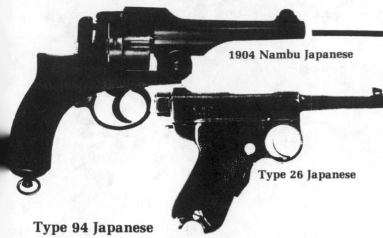

1904 Nambu Japanese

Type 26 Japanese

Type 26 Japanese

Caliber: 9mm rimmed pistol
Action: Double only; top break; hammer without cocking spur
Cylinder: 6-shot; automatic ejector
Barrel: 4¾"
Sights: Blade front & "V" notch rear
Finish: Blued; checkered 1 piece round grip
Length overall: 9½"
Approximate wt.: 32 oz.
Comments: Made from about 1893 to 1914.
Estimated Value: Excellent: $150.00
**   Very good: $120.00**

1904 Nambu Japanese

Caliber: 8mm bottle-neck Japanese
Action: Semi-automatic; grip-safety below trigger guard
Magazine: 8-shot clip
Barrel: 4¾"
Sights: Barley corn front; notched tangent rear
Finish: Blued; checkered wood grips
Length overall: 9"
Approximate wt.: 32 oz.
Comments: Made from about 1904 to 1925. Usually has a slot cut in rear of grip to accommodate shoulder stock holster.
Estimated Value: Excellent: $650.00
**   Very good: $575.00**

Type 94 Japanese

Caliber: 8mm bottle-necked Japanese
Action: Semi-automatic
Magazine: 6-shot clip
Barrel: 3¾"
Sights: Barley corn front; square notch rear
Finish: Blued; checkered grips
Length overall: 7¼"
Approximate wt.: 28 oz.
Comments: Produced from about 1934 to 1945. Made for export but was used as a service pistol during World War II. Most show evidence of poor manufacture.
Estimated Value: Excellent: $290.00
**   Very good: $240.00**

Type 57 New Nambu Japanese

Caliber: 9mm Parabellum; 45 ACP
Action: Semi-automatic; recoil operated
Magazine: 8-shot clip
Barrel: 4½"
Sights: Fixed
Finish: Blued; checkered grips
Length overall: 7¾"
Approximate wt.: 2 1/8"
Comments: A modified copy of the U.S. 1911 A1 produced by the firm of Shin Chuo Kogyo K.K. since World War II. Magazine catch at bottom of grip and doesn't have the grip safety.
Estimated Value: Excellent: $200.00
**   Very good: $160.00**

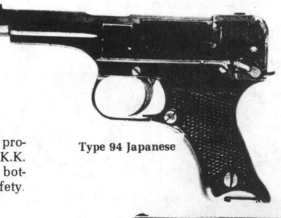

Type 94 Japanese

Type 57B New Nambu Japanese

Caliber: 32 ACP (7.65mm Browning)
Action: Semi-automatic; blow back operated
Magazine: 8-shot clip
Barrel: 3"
Sights: Fixed
Finish: Blued; checkered grips
Length overall: 6¼"
Approximate wt.: 20 oz.
Comments: A modified copy of the Browning M 1910 pistol produced by firm of Shin Chuo Kogyo K.K. after World War II.
Estimated Value: Excellent: $140.00
**   Very good: $110.00**

Type 57B New Nambu Japanese

Type 57 New Nambu Japanese

Handguns

Baby Nambu Japanese

Caliber: 7mm bottle-neck Japanese cartridge
Action: Semi-automatic; grip safety below trigger guard
Magazine: 7-shot clip
Barrel: 3¼"
Sights: Barly corn front, V notch rear.
Finish: Blued; checkered wood grips.
Approximate wt.: 24 oz.
Comments: This is a smaller version of the 1904 Nambu.
Estimated Value: Excellent: $800.00
Very good: $675.00

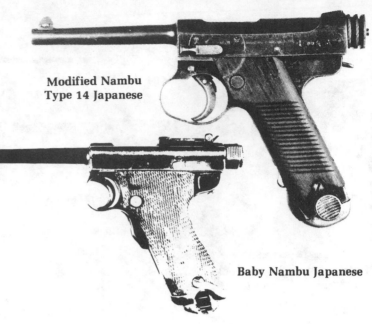

Modified Nambu
Type 14 Japanese

Baby Nambu Japanese

Nambu Type 14 Japanese

Caliber: 8mm bottle-necked Japanese
Action: Semi-automatic; manual safety
Magazine: 8-shot clip
Barrel: 4¾"
Sights: Barley corn front; undercut notch rear
Finish: Blued; grooved wood grips
Length overall: 9"
Approximate wt.: 32 oz.
Comments: A modified form of the 1904 Nambu introduced about 1925 and produced until about 1945.
Estimated Value: Excellent: $390.00
Very good: $325.00

Modified Nambu Type 14 Japanese

Similar to Nambu Type 14 except: it has enlarged trigger guard to allow use of a heavy gloves and a spring mounted in lower front of grip to hold magazine more securely.
Estimated Value: Excellent: $300.00
Very good: $250.00

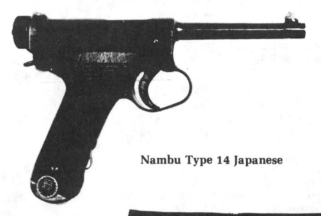

Nambu Type 14 Japanese

Lignose

Lignose Einhand
Model 2A Pocket

Lignose Model 2 Pocket

Lignose Einhand
Model 3A Pocket

Lignose Einhand Model 2A Pocket

Similar specifications as Model 2 except: designed for one-hand operation hence the name Einhand (one hand). Slide can be retracted to load and cock hammer, by using the trigger finger to pull back the front part of the trigger guard.
Estimated Value: Excellent: $185.00
Very good: $150.00

Lignose Einhand Model 3A Pocket

Same as Model 2A except: longer grip and uses 9-shot clip.
Estimated Value: Excellent: $215.00
Very good: $175.00

Lignose Model 2 Pocket

Caliber: 25 ACP (6.35mm)
Action: Semi-automatic; concealed hammer; thumb safety at top rear of left grip
Magazine: 6-shot clip
Barrel: 2 1/8"
Sights: Fixed
Finish: Blued; checkered hard rubber grips
Length overall: 4¾"
Approximate wt.: 15 oz.
Comments: Operation principle based on the 1906 Browning 25 caliber automatic pocket pistol; production started about 1920. Made in Germany. Early models marked "Bergmann".
Estimated Value: Excellent: $120.00
Very good: $100.00

Llama Model IX

Llama Model IIIA

Llama Model IIIA

Caliber: 380 ACP
Action: SEmi-automatic; manual and grip safety; exposed hammer
Magazine: 7-shot clip
Barrel: 3 11/16"
Sights: Partridge front; adjustable rear
Finish: Blued; chrome; chrome engraved; plastic grips
Length overall: 6¼"
Approximate wt: 1½ lbs.
Comments: Produced from about 1951 to late 1970's, ventilated rib on top of slide. Add $40.00 for chrome and $50.00 for engraved.
Estimated Value: Excellent: $170.00
Very good: $140.00

Llama Model VIII

Caliber: 9mm Luger, 38 Super ACP
Action: Semi-automatic; manual grip and safety; exposed hammer
Magazine: 9-shot clip
Barrel: 5"
Sights: Fixed front; adjustable rear
Finish: Blued; chrome; chrome engraved; checkered wood or simulated pearl grips
Length overall: 8½"
Approximate wt: 39 oz.
Comments: Produced from about 1953 to late 1970's; Add $40.00 for chrome and $50.00 for engraved
Estimated Value: Excellent: $220.00
Very good: $175.00

Llama Model XI

Caliber: 9mm Luger
Action: Semi-automatic; manual safety; no grip saftey; round exposed hammer
Magazine: 8-shot clip
Barrel: 4 7/8"
Sights: Fixed
Finish: Blued; chrome; checkered plastic grips with modified thumb rest
Length overall: 8"
Approximate wt: 34 oz.
Comments: Produced from about 1951 to late 1970's.With some minor modifications. Add $40.00 for chrome.
Estimated Value: Excellent: $200.00
Very good: $160.00

Llama Model IX

Caliber: 45 ACP
Action: Semi-automatic; locked breech; exposed hammer; manual safety
Magazine: 7-shot clip
Barrel: 5"
Sights: Fixed
Finish: Blued; checkered wood grips
Length overall: 8½"
Approximate wt.: 39 oz.
Comments: Manufactured from about 1936 to 1952.
Estimated Value: Excellent: $160.00
Very good: $130.00

Llama Model IXA

Similar to Model IX except; ventilated rib on slide; modified and improved version; also in chrome and chrome engraved finish; made from about 1952 to the late 1970's; Add $40.00 for chrome and $50.00 for engraved.
Estimated Value: Excellent: $220.00
Very good: $175.00

Llama Model I

Caliber: 32 ACP (7.65mm)
Action: Semi-automatic; blow back type; exposed hammer
Magazine: 8-shot clip
Barrel: 4"
Sights: Fixed
Finish: Blued; wood grips
Length overall: 6½"
Approximate wt.: 25 oz.
Comments: Made from about 1935 to 1941.
Estimated Value: Excellent: $110.00
Very good: $ 90.00

Llama Model II

Similar to Model I except: 7-shot clip; caliber 380 ACP (9mm short). Made from about 1935 to 1941.
Estimated Value: Excellent: $120.00
Very good: $100.00

Llama Model III

A modified version of the Model II. Produced from about 1947 to 1954.
Estimated Value: Excellent: $140.00
Very good: $110.00

Llama Model VIII

Llama Model XI

Handguns

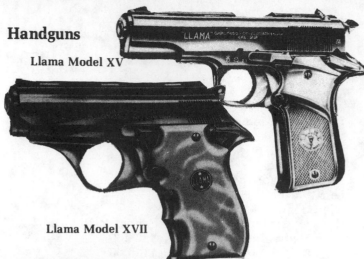

Llama Model XV

Llama Model XVII

Llama Standard Automatic Large Frame

Similar to the Model VIII and IXA. Currently produced. Add $50.00 for chrome.

Estimated Value: New (retail): $316.95
Excellent: $240.00
Very good: $195.00

Llama Standard Automtic Small Frame

Similar to the Models XV, XA, and IIIA. Currently produced.

Estimated Value: New (retail): $244.95
Excellent: $190.00
Very good: $155.00

Llama Martial

Caliber: 22 short, long, long rifle
Action: Double; solid frame; swing-out cylinder; simultaneous ejector
Cylinder: 6-shot swing out with thumb latch on left side of frame
Barrel: 6" in 22 caliber and 4" and 6" in 38 Special; ventilated rib
Sights: Target sights
Finish: Blued; chrome; chrome engraved; checkered wood or simulted pearl
Length overall: 9¼" to 11¼"
Approximate wt: 35 to 40 oz.
Comments: Produced from about 1969 to late 1970's; Add $25.00 for chrome and $25.00 for engraved

Estimated Value: Excellent: $160.00
Very good: $130.00

Llama Comanche, I

Caliber: 22 short, long, long rifle
Action: Double; simultaneous hand ejector; solid frame; swingpout cylinder
Cylinder: 6-shot swing out with thumb latch on left side of frame
Barrel: 6" with ventilated rib
Sights: Ramp front; adjustable rear
Finish: Blued; checkered walnut target grips
Length overall: 9¼"
Approximate wt: 36 oz.
Comments: Made from about 1978 to present; Add $75.00 for chrome.

Estimated Value: New (retail): $266.95
Excellent: $200.00
Very good: $160.00

Llama Model XV

Caliber: 22 long rifle
Action: Semi-automatic; blow back type; exposed hammer; grip & manual safety
Magazine: 9-shot clip
Barrel: 3 11/16"
Sights: Partridge type, fixed
Finish: Blued; chrome; chrome engraved; checkered wood grips
Length overall: 6¼"
Approximate wt: 18 oz.
Comments: A smaller version of the 1911 A1 Colt 45 ACP; made from about 1955 to late 1970's; Add $40.00 for chrome and $50.00 for engraved.

Estimated Value: Excellent: $165.00
Very good: $135.00

Llama Model XA

Same as model XV except: caliber 32 ACP; 8-shot magazine. Add $40.00 for chrome.

Estimated Value: Excellent: $160.00
Very good: $130.00

Llama Model XVII

Caliber: 22 short
Action: Semi-automatic; exposed hammer with round spur; manual safety
Magazine: 6-shot clip
Barrel: 2 3/8"
Sights: Fixed
Finish: Blued; chrome; plastic grips
Length overall: 4½"
Approximate wt: 14 oz.
Comments: No longer imported into U.S.A., because of 1968 gun control law. Also known as Executive Model. Add $20.00 for Chrome.

Estimated Value: Excellent: $125.00
Very good: $105.00

Llama Model XVIII

Same as model XVII except: 25 ACP caliber only; no longer imported into U.S.A. Add $20.00 for chrome.

Estimated Value: Excellent: $125.00
Very good: $105.00

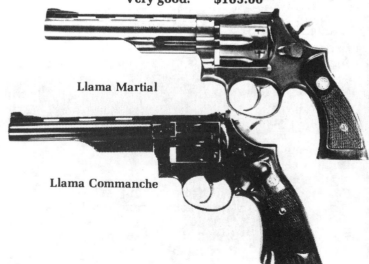

Llama Martial

Llama Commanche

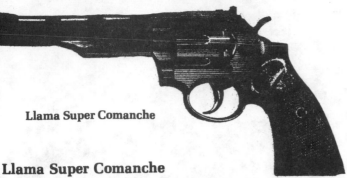

Llama Super Comanche

Llama Comanche II

Similar to the Comanche I in 38 Special with a 4'' or 6'' barrel. Introduced in 1973.

Estimated Value: New (retail): $266.95
Excellent: $200.00
Very good: $160.00

Llama Super Comanche

A heavier version of the Comanche for 44 magnum cartridges; 6'' barrel only.

Estimated Value: New (retail): $414.95
Excellent: $320.00
Very good: $260.00

Llama Comanche III

Similar to the Comanche II in 357 magnum caliber. Add $75.00 for satin chrome finish

Estimated Value: New (retail): $266.95
Excellent: $200.00
Very good: $160.00

MAB

MAB Model B

Similar to Model A except: top part of front section of slide cut away for empty cartridges to eject at top. Manufactured from about 1932 to 1966 (never imported into U.S.A.).

Estimated Value: Excellent: $125.00
Very good: $100.00

MAB Model C

Caliber: 32 ACP, 380 ACP
Action: Semi-automatic; concealed hammer; grip safety and manual safety
Magazine: 7-shot in 32 ACP, 6-shot in 380 ACP
Barrel: 3¼''
Sights: Fixed
Finish: Blued; checkered hard rubber grips
Length overall: 6¼''
Approximate wt.: 23 oz.
Comments: Production started about 1933. Importation into U.S.A. stopped in 1968.

Estimated Value: Excellent: $130.00
Very good: $110.00

MAB Model A

Caliber: 25 ACP (6.35mm)
Action: Semi-automatic; concealed hammer; manual safety; blow back design
Magazine: 6-shot slip
Barrel: 2½''
Sights: Fixed front; no rear
Finish: Blued; checkered hard rubber or plastic grips
Length overall: 4½''
Approximate wt.: 18 oz.
Comments: Resembles Browning Model 1906 vest pocket pistol. Production started about 1924, imported into U.S.A. as WAC Model A or Le Defendeur; importation stopped in 1968.

Estimated Value: Excellent: $120.00
Very good: $100.00

MAB Model A

MAB Model D

MAB Model C

MAB Model D

Caliber: 32 ACP, 380 ACP
Action: Semi-automatic; concealed hammer; grip safety and manual safety.
Magazine: 9-shot in 32 ACP, 8-shot in 380 ACP
Barrel: 4''
Sights: Fixed
Finish: Blued; checkered hard rubber grips
Length overall: 7''
Approximate wt.: 25 oz.
Comments: Imported into U.S.A. as WAC Model D or MAB Le Gendarme; manufacture started about 1932; importing discontinued in 1968.

Estimated Value: Excellent: $150.00
Very good: $125.00

Handguns

MAB Model F

Caliber: 22 long rifle
Action: Semi-automatic; concealed hammer; manual safety; blow back design
Magazine: 9-shot clip
Barrel: 4½", 6", 7"
Sights: Fixed
Finish: Blued; checkered grips
Length overall: 8½" to 11"
Approximate wt.: 23 oz.
Comments: Production began in 1950. Imported into U.S.A. under WAC trademark (importing stopped in 1968).
Estimated Value: Excellent: $130.00
Very good: $110.00

MAB Model R

Caliber: 22 long rifle, 32 ACP, 380 ACP, 9mm Parabellum
Action: Semi-automatic; exposed hammer; manual safety
Magazine: 9-shot in 22 caliber, 8-shot in 32 ACP, 7-shot in 380 ACP, 7 or 14-shot in 9mm
Barrel: 4½" or 7½" in 22; 4" in other calibers
Sights: Fixed
Finish: Blued checkered grips
Length overall: 7" to 10½"
Approximate wt.: 25 oz.
Comments: This model was never imported into U.S.A.
Estimated Value: Excellent: $120.00
Very good: $100.00

MAB Model F

MAB Model R

MAB Model E

Caliber: 25 ACP (6.35mm)
Action: Semi-automatic; concealed hammer; manual safety and grip safety
Magazine: 10-shot clip
Barrel: 4"
Sights: Fixed
Finish: Blued; checkered plastic grips
Length overall: 7"
Approximate wt.: 24 oz.
Comments: Production started about 1949; importation into U.S.A. discontinued in 1968. Imported into U.S.A. as WAC Model E.
Estimated Value: Excellent: $125.00
Very good: $100.00

MAB Model P

Caliber: 9mm Parabellum
Action: Semi-automatic; exposed hammer with round spur; recoil operated with locking breech; manual safety
Magazine: 8-shot clip; 15-shot staggered row clip
Barrel: 4½"
Sights: Blade front; notch rear
Finish: Blued; checkered grips
Length overall: 8"
Approximate wt.: 25 oz.
Comments: Still in production; bears a resemblance to the Browning model 1935.
Estimated Value: Excellent: $225.00
Very good: $180.00

MAB Model P

MAB Model E

Mauser

Mauser WTP Model 1 Vest Pocket

Caliber: 25 ACP
Action: Semi-automatic; concealed hammer
Magazine: 6-shot clip
Barrel: 2 3/8"
Sights: Fixed
Finish: Blued; hard rubber grips
Length overall: 4¼"
Approximate wt.: 12 oz.
Comments: Made from about 1923 to 1939.
Estimated Value: Excellent: $190.00
Very good: $150.00

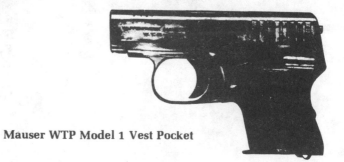

Mauser WTP Model 1 Vest Pocket

Mauser WTP Model 2 Vest Pocket

Similar to Model 1 except: curved back strap & trigger guard; smaller size - 2" barrel and about 4" overall length; approximate wt. - 10 oz. Produced from about 1939 to 1942 and from about 1950 to present.
Estimated Value: Excellent: $200.00
**   Very good: $160.00**

Mauser Model HSC Pocket Pistol

Caliber: 32 ACP, 380 ACP (1918 to present)
Action: Semi-automatic; double action; exposed hammer
Magazine: 8-shot clip
Barrel: 3 3/8"
Sights: Fixed
Finish: Blued or nickel; checkered wood grips
Length overall: 6¼"
Approximate wt.: 21 oz.
Comments: Produced from about 1938 to World War II and from about 1968 to present. Add $20.00 for nickel finish.

Estimated Value:	pre-WWII	1968 - Present
Excellent:	$220.00	$195.00
Very good:	$175.00	$150.00

Mauser WTP Model 2 Vest Pocket

Mauser Model HSC Pocket Pistol

Mauser Military Model
(Broomhandle Mauser)

Mauser Model 1934 Pocket

Mauser Military Model (Broomhandle Mauser)

Caliber: 7.63 Mauser; 9mm Luger Parabellum (during World War I, marked with a large figure 9-cut in the wooden grip), 9mm Mauser
Action: Semi-automatic; exposed hammer; selective fire introduced in 1930 - selective lever on "N" operated as normal semi-automatic, and on "R" operated as a machine pistol with fully automatic fire.
Magazine: 5 to 10-shot box magazine standard; 5 to 20-shot magazine on selective fire models.
Barrel: 5½" standard; also manufactured with other barrel lengths
Sights: Adjustable for elevation
Finish: Blued; checkered wood, serrated wood, carved wood, smooth wood, or hard rubber grips
Length overall: 12" with 5½" barrel
Approximate wt.: 43 oz. with 5½" barrel
Comments: Manufactured from about 1896 to 1918 and from about 1922 to 1937 with minor changes and improvements. Also produced with a shoulder stock holster (wood).
Estimated Value: Excellent: $750.00 - $2,500.00
**   Very good: $600.00 - $2,000.00**

Mauser Automatic Pocket

Caliber: 25 ACP, 32 ACP
Action: Semi-automatic; concealed hammer
Magazine: 9-shot clip in 25 ACP, 8-shot clip in 32 ACP
Barrel: 3" (25 ACP); 3½" (32 ACP)
Sights: Fixed
Finish: Blued; checkered walnut or hard rubber grips
Length overall: 5½" (25 ACP); 6" (32 ACP)
Approximate wt.: 22 oz.
Comments: 25 ACP model made from about 1910 to 1939. 32 ACP model made from about 1914 to 1934.
Estimated Value: Excellent: $175.00
**   Very good: $140.00**

Mauser Model 1934 Pocket

Similar to automatic Pocket Pistol except: larger one-piece wooden wrap around grip which covered the back strap; made from about 1934 to 1939; 32 ACP only.
Estimated Value: Excellent: $190.00
**   Very good: $150.00**

Remington 41 Caliber Double Derringer

Remington 41 Caliber Double Derringer
Caliber: 41 caliber rim fire
Action: Single; visible hammer with safety position; sheath trigger; manual extractors.
Cylinder: None; 2-shot double barrel
Barrel: 3" superposed double barrel ribbed top barrel; barrels swing up to load and extract cartridges.
Sights: Blade front; groove in frame rear
Finish: Blued or nickel plated; plain or engraved; round butt grips made of metal, walnut, rose wood, hard rubber, ivory, or pearl.
Length overall: 4 7/8"
Approximate wt.: 11 oz.
Comments: Approximately 132,000 were produced about 1866 to 1935. Serial numbers were repeated on these pistols, so the best way to estimate the age of a pistol is by the markings. They were marked as follows:
1866-1869- no extractors; left side of barrel E. REMINGTON & SONS. ILION, N.Y.; right side of barrel ELLIOT'S PATENT DEC. 12, 1865.
1869-1880- left side of barrel - ELLIOT'S PATENT DEC 12 1865; right side of barrel - E. REMINGTON & SONS, ILION, N.Y.
1880-1888- Barrel rib top - E. REMINGTON & SONS. ILION N.Y. ELLIOT'S PATENT DEC. 12th 1865
1888-1910- Barrel rib top - REMINGTON ARMS CO. ILION N.Y.
1910-1935- Barrel rib top - REMINGTON ARMS U.M.C. CO. ILION, N.Y.
In 1934 the Double Derringer was called Model No. 95.

Estimated Value:

Plain models	Excellent:	$350.00 - $550.00
	Very good:	$300.00 - $500.00
Presentation models	Excellent:	$450.00 - $700.00
	Very good:	$400.00 - $600.00

Remington Model 1891, Single-Shot Target
Caliber: 22, 25, 32RF, 32 S&W CF
Action: Single
Cylinder: None; single-shot with rolling breechblock for rim fire or center fire calibers
Barrel: 8", 10", 12"; half-octagon
Sights: Dovetail, German silver front and adj. "V" notch rifle rear
Finish: Blued barrel; case hardened frame; oil finished walnut grips and fore-end.
Length overall: 12" to 16" (depending on barrel length)
Approximate wt.: 40 to 45 oz.
Comments: Made from about 1891 to 1901 in light target calibers. Serial number on side of frame under grip.
Estimated Value: Excellent: $900.00
Very good: $750.00

Remington Model 1901, De-Luxe (S-S) Target
Caliber: 22 short or long rifle, 44 Russian CF.
Action: Single
Cylinder: None; single-shot with rolling breech-block for rim fire or center fire cartridges.
Barrel: 9" round; 10" half octagon
Sights: Ivory bead front; adj. "V" rear
Finish: Blued barrel and frame; checkered walnut grips and fore-end
Length overall: 13" to 14"
Approximate wt.: 36 to 44 oz.
Comments: Manufactured from about 1901 to 1909. Approximately 700 produced.
Estimated Value: Excellent: $825.00
Very good: $700.00

Remington Experimental 45 Caliber
An estimated value hasn't been placed on this pistol, since it is not known how many were produced or how they were marked. They were similar to the REMINGTON MODEL 51 AUTOMATIC PISTOL except: in 45 caliber, larger, and had an exposed spur hammer. They were made for U.S. Government test purposes about 1917.

Remington US Model 1911 and 1911 A1
These were pistols made by Remington, on the Colt Patent, for the U.S. Government during World War I & World War II. See "Colt Government Model 1911 and 1911 A1" for prices.

Remington Model 1891, Single-Shot Target

Remington Model 1901, De-Luxe (S-S) Target

Remington Model 51

Caliber: 32 ACP, 380 ACP
Action: Semi-automatic; concealed hammer
Magazine: 8-shot in 32 caliber, 7-shot in 380 caliber
Barrel: 3 ¼"
Sights: Fixed
Finish: Blued; hard rubber grips
Length overall: 6 5/8"
Approximate wt.: 20 oz.
Comments: Made from about 1920 to 1934. Approximately 69,000 were produced in 32 and 380 calibers.
Estimated Value: Excellent: $250.00
Very good: $200.00

Remington Model XP-100 Long Range

Caliber: 221 Remington "Fire Ball"
Action: Bolt action; single shot; thumb safety
Cylinder: None; single shot
Barrel: 10 ½" round steel with ventilated rib
Sights: Blade front; adjustable rear
Finish: Blued with bright polished bolt & handle; brown checkered nylon (zytel) one-piece grip and fore-end. Fore-end has cavity for adding balance weights.
Length overall: 16 ¾"
Approximate wt.: 60 oz.
Comments: Produced from about 1963 to present. Receiver is drilled and tapped for scope mount.
Estimated Value: New (retail): $274.95
Excellent: $210.00
Very good: $165.00

Remington Model XP-100 Silhouette

Similar to the Model XP-100 with a 15" barrel and in 7mm Benchrest Remington caliber. Introduced in 1980.
Estimated Value: New (retail): $299.95
Excellent: $235.00
Very good: $195.00

Remington Model XP-100 Silhouette

Remington Model XP-100 Long Range

Remington Model 51

Ruger

Ruger Standard Automatic

Caliber: 22 long rifle
Action: Semi-automatic; concealed hammer; thumb safety
Magazine: 9-shot clip
Barrel: 4 ¾" or 6"; tapered round barrel
Sights: Partridge type front; dove-tail rear
Finish: Blued; checkered hard rubber or walnut grips
Length overall: 8 ¾"; 10"
Approximate wt.: 36 to 38 oz.
Comments: Introduced about 1949 and still in production. (Sturm Ruger Company was formed about 1949). Red eagle insignia on grip used until 1951, then changed to black eagle insignia, after death of Alex Sturm.

Estimated Value:

Red eagle insignia (collector's item)	Excellent:	$300.00
	Very good:	$250.00
Black eagle insignia (made after 1951)	New (retail):	$109.00
	Excellent:	$ 85.00
	Very good:	$ 70.00

Ruger Standard Automatic

Ruger Mark I Target

Ruger Mark I Target

Similar to Ruger Standard Automatic except: adjustable sights; 6" tapered barrel.
Estimated Value: New (retail): $140.00
Excellent: $100.00
Very good: $ 80.00

391

Ruger Mark I Bull Barrell

Ruger Single-Six

Ruger New Model Super Single-Six Convertible

Stainless Steel Ruger New Model Super Single-Six Convertible

Ruger New Model Super Single-Six Convertible

Similar to Ruger Convertible Super Single-Six except: improved version featuring wide trigger; heavy stronger lock works; transfer bar firing pin protector; new interlocking mechanism; other improvements. Made from about 1973 to present.
Estimated Value: New (retail): $141.50
                    Excellent: $105.00
                    Very good: $ 85.00

Stainless Steel Ruger New Model Super Single-Six Convertible

Same as Ruger New Model Super Single-Six Convertible Revolver except: all stainless steel construction except sights (blued). 5½" or 6½" barrel only. Made from about 1976 to present. Prices for guns with both cylinders.
Estimated Value: New (retail): $201.00
                    Excellent: $150.00
                    Very good: $120.00

Ruger Mark I Bull Barrel

Same as Ruger Mark I Target Pistol except: barrel length - 5½"; overall length 9½"; untapered heavier barrel. Made from about 1963 to present.
Estimated Value: New (retail): $140.00
                    Excellent: $110.00
                    Very good: $ 90.00

Ruger Single-Six

Caliber: 22 short, long, long rifle, 22 WMR (after 1959)
Action: Single
Cylinder: 6-shot half fluted; flat loading gate from 1954 to 1957 then changed to fit the contour of the frame.
Barrel: 4 5/8", 5½", 6½", 9½"; ejector rod under barrel
Sights: Blade front; rear sight dovetailed and can be tapped to left or right
Finish: Blued; checkered hard rubber or smooth walnut grips
Length overall: 10", 10 7/8", 11 7/8", 14 7/8"
Approximate wt.: 32 to 36 oz.
Comments: The grip frame is made of aluminum alloy and the frame is made of chrome molybdenum steel; produced from about 1953 to 1973.
Estimated Value: Excellent: $125.00
                    Very good: $100.00

Ruger Lightweight Single-Six

Same as Ruger Single-Six except: made in 22 short, long, & long rifle only; 4 5/8" barrel; 10" overall length; weighs 23 oz.; cylinder and frame made of lightweight alloy. Produced from about 1956 to 1958.
Estimated Value: Excellent: $120.00
                    Very good: $100.00

Ruger Convertible Single-Six

Same as Ruger Single-Six revolver except: furnished with two cylinders - one chambered for 22 and the other chambered for 22 WMR. Manufactured from about 1961 to 1973. Prices for guns with both cylinders.
Estimated Value: Excellent: $130.00
                    Very good: $100.00

Ruger Convertible Super Single-Six

Same as Ruger Convertible Single-Six except: ramp front sight; adjustable rear sight with protective ribs on frame to protect rear sight; 5½" or 6½" barrel only. Made from about 1964 to 1973. Prices for guns with both cylinders.
Estimated Value: Excellent: $135.00
                    Very good: $105.00

Ruger New Model Blackhawk

Ruger Super Blackhawk 44 Magnum

Ruger Blackhawk 357 Convertible

Ruger Blackhawk 357 Magnum

Caliber: 357 magnum and 38 Special interchangeably
Action: Single
Cylinder: 6-shot
Barrel: 4 5/8"; 6½"; round barrel with ejector rod under barrel
Sights: Ramp front and adjustable rear sight
Finish: Blued; checkered hard rubber or smooth walnut wood grips
Length overall: 10 1/8"; 12"
Approximate wt.: 35 to 40 oz.
Comments: Made from about 1955 to 1973. In 1961 the frame was modified to a heavier frame with integral ribs on top to protect rear sight and slight grip alterations to improve the comfort of the "hold".

Estimated Value:	Pre-1961	After 1961
Excellent:	$140.00	$150.00
Very good:	$110.00	$120.00

Ruger Blackhawk 357 Convertible

Same as Ruger Blackhawk 357 Magnum Revolver except: Fitted with extra interchangeable cylinder for 9mm Parabellum cartridges. Manufactured from about 1967 to 1973.

Estimated Value:	Excellent:	$160.00
	Very good:	$135.00

Ruger New Model Blackhawk

Similar to Ruger Blackhawk 357 Revolver except: improved version, featuring wide trigger; stronger lock works; transfer bar firing pin protector, new interlocking mechanism; other improvements. Made from about 1973 to present in 30 carbine, 41 magnum, 357 magnum and 45 Colt.

Estimated Value:	New (retail):	$179.75
	Excellent:	$135.00
	Very good:	$110.00

Ruger Stainless Steel New Model Blackhawk 357

Same as Ruger New Model Blackhawk Revolver except: all stainless steel construction except sights (blued). Made from about 1976 to present.

Estimated Value:	New (retail):	$196.90
	Excellent:	$150.00
	Very good:	$115.00

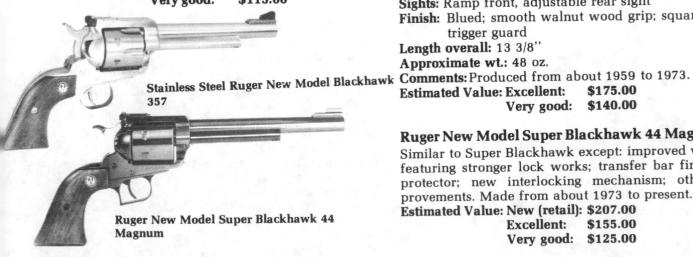

Stainless Steel Ruger New Model Blackhawk 357

Ruger New Model Super Blackhawk 44 Magnum

Ruger New Model Blackhawk Convertible

Same as Ruger New Model Blackhawk Revolver except: fitted with extra interchangeable cylinders for .357 magnum and 9mm Parabellum cartridges; 45 Colt and 45 ACP cartridges; made from about 1973 to present.

Estimated Value:	New (retail):	$196.90
	Excellent:	$145.00
	Very good:	$115.00

Ruger Blackhawk 44 Magnum

Caliber: 44 magnum and 44 S&W Special interchangeably
Action: Single
Cylinder: 6-shot heavy fluted cylinder
Barrel: 6½"; ejector rod under barrel
Sights: Ramp front; adjustable rear sight
Finish: Blued; smooth walnut grips
Length overall: 12½"
Approximate wt.: 40 oz.
Comments: Produced from about 1956 to 1962.

Estimated Value:	Excellent:	$200.00
	Very good:	$175.00

Ruger Super Blackhawk 44 Magnum

Caliber: 44 magnum, 44 S&W Special interchangeably
Action: Single
Cylinder: 6-shot heavy non-fluted cylinder
Barrel: 7½"; ejector rod under cylinder
Sights: Ramp front, adjustable rear sight
Finish: Blued; smooth walnut wood grip; square back trigger guard
Length overall: 13 3/8"
Approximate wt.: 48 oz.
Comments: Produced from about 1959 to 1973.

Estimated Value:	Excellent:	$175.00
	Very good:	$140.00

Ruger New Model Super Blackhawk 44 Magnum

Similar to Super Blackhawk except: improved version, featuring stronger lock works; transfer bar firing pin protector; new interlocking mechanism; other improvements. Made from about 1973 to present.

Estimated Value:	New (retail):	$207.00
	Excellent:	$155.00
	Very good:	$125.00

Ruger Blackhawk 41 Magnum

Ruger Blackhawk 30 Caliber

Ruger Blackhawk 41 Magnum
Caliber: 41 magnum
Action: Single
Cylinder: 6-shot
Barrel: 4 5/8"; 6½"
Sights: Ramp front; adjustable rear sight
Finish: Blued; smooth walnut grips
Length overall: 10¾"; 12 1/8"
Approximate wt.: 35 to 38 oz.
Comments: Produced from about 1965 to 1973.
Estimated Value: Excellent: $160.00
Very good: $130.00

Ruger New Model Blackhawk 41 Magnum
Similar to Blackhawk 41 Magnum except: improved version, featuring stronger lock works; transfer bar firing pin protector; new interlocking mechanism; other improvements. Made from about 1973 to present.
Estimated Value: New (retail): $179.75
Excellent: $135.00
Very good: $105.00

Ruger Blackhawk 45 Caliber
Caliber: 45 long Colt
Action: Single
Cylinder: 6-shot
Barrel: 4 5/8"; 7½"; round barrel with ejector rod under barrel
Sights: Ramp front and adjustable rear
Finish: Blued; smooth walnut grips
Length overall: 10 1/8"; 13 1/8"
Approximate wt.: 38 to 40 oz.
Comments: Made from about 1970 to 1973. Replaced by New Model Blackhawk in 1973.
Estimated Value: Excellent: $140.00
Very good: $110.00

Ruger Blackhawk 45 Caliber Convertible
Same as Blackhawk 45 Caliber revolver except: fitted with extra interchangeable cylinder for 45 ACP cartridges. Made from about 1970 to 1973. Replaced by New Model Blackhawk in 1973.
Estimated Value: Excellent: $150.00
Very good: $120.00

Ruger Blackhawk 30 Caliber
Caliber: 30 U.S. Carbine (M1)
Action: Single
Cylinder: 6-shot
Barrel: 7½"
Sights: Ramp front; adjustable rear sight
Finish: Blued; smooth walnut wood grips
Length overall: 13 1/8"
Approximate wt.: 39 oz.
Comments: Made from about 1968 to 1973. A good companion hand gun for the M1 carbine (30 caliber)
Estimated Value: Excellent: $175.00
Very good: $140.00

Ruger Redhawk

Ruger Redhawk
Caliber: 44 Rem. magnum
Action: Double and single
Cylinder: 6 shot swing out
Barrel: 7½", shrouded ejector rod under barrel
Sights: Adjustable rear, blade front
Finish: Stainless steel; checkered walnut grips
Length overall: 13"
Approximate wt.: 52 oz.
Comments: A heavy frame 44 magnum revolver introduced in 1979.
Estimated Value: New (retail): $325.00
Excellent: $260.00
Very good: $210.00

Ruger Bearcat

Caliber: 22 short, long, or long rifle
Action: Single
Cylinder: 6-shot; non-fluted engraved
Barrel: 4" round with ejector rod
Sights: Fixed
Finish: Blued; smooth walnut grips
Length overall: 8 7/8"
Approximate wt.: 17 oz.
Comments: Alloy frame; coil springs, and non-fluted engraved cylinder. Manufactured from about 1958 to 1972.
Estimated Value: Excellent: $130.00
Very good: $110.00

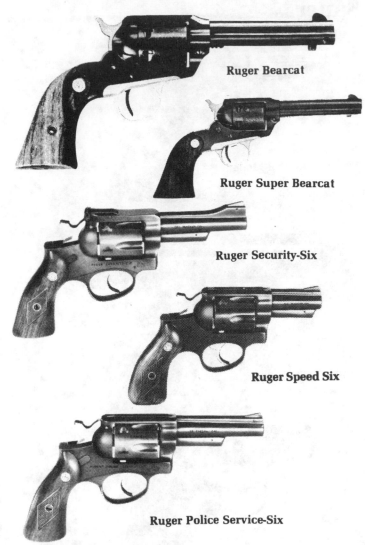

Ruger Bearcat

Ruger Super Bearcat

Ruger Security-Six

Ruger Speed Six

Ruger Police Service-Six

Ruger Super Bearcat

Same as Ruger Bearcat revolver except: all steel construction and made from about 1971 to 1975.
Estimated Value: Excellent: $125.00
Very good: $100.00

Ruger Security-Six 357 Magnum

Caliber: 357 magnum and 38 Special
Action: Double and single
Cylinder: 6-shot swing out
Barrel: 2¾"; 4"; 6"
Sights: Adjustable sights
Finish: Blued or stainless steel; square butt, checkered walnut grips
Length overall: 8"; 9¼"; 11¼"
Approximate wt: 32 to 35 oz.
Comments: Made from 1972 to present. A solid frame revolver with swing-out cylinder. Stainless steel model made from about 1975 to present. Add $16.00 for heavy barrel.

Estimated Value:	Blued	Stainless Steel
New (retail):	$192.00	$212.00
Excellent:	$135.00	$145.00
Very good:	$110.00	$115.00

Ruger Speed-Six

Similar to Security-Six 357 Magnum revolver except: round butt style grips and in calibers 9mm parabellum, 38 special and 357 magnum. Fixed sights only. Made from about 1975 to late 1970's. Add $16.00 for 9mm.

Estimated Value:	Blued	Stainless Steel
New (retail):	$148.00	$162.00
Excellent:	$120.00	$140.00
Very good:	$100.00	$120.00

Ruger Hawkeye Single Shot

Ruger Police Service-Six

Similar to Speed-Six revolver except: square butt style grips. Made from about 1976 to present. Add $16.00 for 9mm.

Estimated Value:	Blued	Stainless Steel
New (retail):	$148.00	$162.00
Excellent:	$120.00	$140.00
Very good:	$100.00	$120.00

Ruger Hawkeye Single Shot

Caliber: 256 magnum
Action: Single; single shot
Cylinder: None; rotating breech block to load chamber, which is part of the barrel
Barrel: 8½"; chamber in barrel; under barrel ejector rod
Sights: Adjustable target sights
Finish: Blued; smooth walnut grips
Length overall: 14½"
Approximate wt.: 44 oz.
Comments: The Hawkeye is built on the Ruger 44 magnum frame and resembles a revolver in appearance. Made from about 1963 to 1966.
Estimated Value: Excellent: $400.00
Very good: $325.00

Sauer 1913 (Old Model)

Sauer 1930 Model

Sauer WTM Pocket

Sauer 1938 Model (Model H)

Caliber: 32 ACP (7.65mm)
Action: Double; semi-automatic; concealed hammer; lever on left side permitted hammer to be cocked or uncocked by the thumb; also could be fired by pulling trigger in double action style.
Magazine: 7-shot clip
Barrel: 3¼ ''
Sights: Fixed
Finish: Blued; checkered plastic grips
Length overall: 6¼ ''
Approximate wt.: 26 oz.
Comments: Some models made with alloy slide (approximately 18 oz. in weight); war time models (WWII) inferior to earlier models; made from about 1938 to 1944.

Estimated Value:	pre-War models	war-time models
Excellent:	$190.00	$175.00
Very good:	$150.00	$140.00

Sauer 1913 (Old Model)

Caliber: 32 ACP (7.65 mm); 25 ACP (6.5 mm)
Action: Semi-automatic; concealed hammer
Magazine: 7-shot clip
Barrel: 3''
Sights: Fixed
Finish: Blued; checkered hard rubber grips
Length overall: 5 7/8''
Approximate wt.: 32 oz.
Comments: Produced from about 1913 to 1930.
Estimated Value: Excellent: $150.00
Very good: $120.00

Sauer 1930 Model

Similar to Sauer 1913 (Old Model) except: improved version with main difference being the improved grip design which provides a better hold; some models made with indicator pins to show when they were cocked; some models made with alloy slide & receiver (approximately 15 oz.) Made from about 1930 to 1938.
Estimated Value: Excellent: $175.00
Very good: $140.00

Sauer WTM Pocket

Caliber: 25 ACP (6.5mm)
Action: Semi-automatic; concealed hammer
Magazine: 6-shot clip
Barrel: 2 1/8''
Sights: Fixed
Finish: Blued; checkered hard rubber grips
Length overall: 4 1/8''
Approximate wt.: 18 oz.
Comments: Produced from about 1924 to 1928. Fluted slide with top ejection port.
Estimated Value: Excellent: $180.00
Very good: $145.00

Sauer 1928 Model Pocket

Similar to Sauer WTM Pocket Pistol except: smaller in size; 2'' barrel and about 3 7/8'' overall; made from about 1928 to 1938.
Estimated Value: Excellent: $190.00
Very good: $155.00

Sauer 1938 Model (Model H)

Savage Model 1907

Savage Model 1915

Savage Model 1917

Savage Model 1917

Caliber: 32 ACP, 380 ACP
Action: Semi-automatic; exposed spur cocking lever; thumb safety
Magazine: 10-shot in 32 caliber, 9-shot in 380 caliber, wider magazine than previous models, this allows for cartridges to be staggered in a double row.
Barrel: 3¾" in 32 caliber; 7" in 380 caliber
Sights: Fixed
Finish: Blued; hard rubber grips
Length Overall: 6½" (32 cal.), 7" (380 cal.)
Approximate wt.: 24 oz.
Comments: Produced from about 1918 to 1928. Approximately 28,000 made in 32 caliber and 126,000 in 380 caliber. Wide frame with flared grips and the slide has small vertical gripping serrations.
Estimated Value: Excellent: $240.00
    Very good: $200.00

Savage Model 101 Single Shot

Caliber: 22 short, long, long rifle
Action: Single; single shot
Cylinder: None; the false cylinder is the chamber part of the barrel
Barrel: 5½" alloy steel; swings out to load; ejector rod under barrel
Sights: Blade front & notched-bar rear
Finish: Blued barrel; painted one-piece aluminum alloy frame; compressed impregnated wood grips
Length overall: 9½"
Approximate wt.: 20 oz.
Comments: A single shot pistol built to resemble a single action frontier revolver. Made from about 1960 to 1968.
Estimated Value: Excellent: $90.00
    Very good: $75.00

Savage Model 1905 Military Type

Caliber: 45 ACP
Action: Semi-automatic; blow-back design, grip safety; exposed cocking lever
Magazine: 8-shot clip
Barrel: 5¼"
Sights: Fixed
Finish: Blued, checkered walnut grips
Length overall: 9"
Approximate wt.: 36 oz.
Comments: Approximately 200 were produced from about 1908 to 1911 and sold to U.S. Government Ordnance Dept. for tests, but lost to competition.
Estimated Value: Excellent: $1,500.00
    Very good: $1,200.00

Savage Model 1907

Caliber: 32 ACP, 380 ACP (after 1912)
Action: Semi-automatic; exposed rounded or spur cocking lever
Magazine: 10-shot in 32 caliber, 9-shot in 380 caliber
Barrel: 3¾" in 32 caliber; 4¼" in 380 caliber
Sights: Fixed
Finish: Blued, metal, hard rubber, or wood grips
Length overall: 6½" (32 caliber); 7" (380 caliber)
Approximate wt.: 20 oz.
Comments: Manufactured from about 1908 to 1920, with improvements and some changes in 1909, 1914, and 1918. Some military models with lanyard loop were made of the 1912 variety and sold from 1915 to 1917.
Estimated Value: Excellent: $265.00
    Very good: $220.00

Savage Model 1915

Caliber: 32 ACP, 380 ACP
Action: Semi-automatic; concealed hammer
Magazine: 10-shot in 32 caliber, 9-shot in 380 caliber
Barrel: 3¾" (32 caliber); 4¼" (380 caliber)
Sights: Fixed
Finish: Blued; hard rubber grips
Length overall: 6½" (32 caliber), 7" (380 caliber)
Approximate wt.: 22 oz.
Comments: Manufactured from about 1915 to 1917. Approximately 6,500 were produced in 32 caliber and approximately 2350 were produced in 380 caliber.
Estimated Value: Excellent: $300.00
    Very good: $250.00

Savage Model 101 Single Shot

Sheridan

Sheridan Knockabout

Caliber: 22 short, long, long rifle
Action: Single; exposed hammer
Magazine: None; single shot
Barrel: 5"; tip up barrel
Sights: Fixed
Finish: Blued; checkered plastic grips
Length overall: 6¾"
Approximate wt.: 21 oz.
Comments: An inexpensive single shot pistol which resembles an automatic pistol. Made from about 1953 to 1962. Approximately 20,000 produced.
Estimated Value: Excellent: $70.00
Very good: $55.00

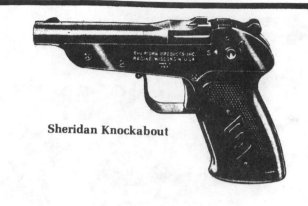

Sheridan Knockabout

Smith & Wesson

Smith & Wesson Model 32 Automatic

Smith & Wesson Model 35 Automatic

Smith & Wesson Model 32 Automatic

Caliber: 32 ACP
Action: Semi-automatic; concealed hammer; grip safety located in front of grip below trigger guard
Magazine: 7-shot clip
Barrel: 3½"; barrel is fixed to the frame; the slide fits into guides on the barrel
Sights: Fixed
Finish: Blued; smooth walnut grips
Length overall: 6½"
Approximate wt.: 24 oz.
Comments: Serial numbers are a separate series beginning at number 1. Approximately 958 produced from about 1924 to 1937.
Estimated Value: Excellent: $900.00
Very good: $650.00

Smith & Wesson Model 35 Automatic

Caliber: 35 S&W automatic
Action: Semi-automatic; concealed hammer; grip safety located in front of grip below trigger guard; manual safety at rear of left grip.
Magazine: 7-shot clip
Barrel: 3½"; barrel hinged to rear of frame
Sights: Fixed
Finish: Blued or nickel; smooth walnut grips
Length overall: 6½"
Approximate wt.: 22 oz.
Comments: Serial numbers are a separate series beginning at number 1; approximately 8350 were produced from about 1913 to 1921.
Estimated Value: Excellent: $450.00
Very good: $360.00

Smith & Wesson Model 39

Caliber: 9mm Luger Parabellum
Action: Double-action; semi-automatic; exposed hammer; thumb safety
Magazine: 8-shot clip
Barrel: 4"
Sights: Ramp front sight; rear sight adjustable for windage
Finish: Blued or nickel; checkered walnut grips
Length overall: 7½"
Approximate wt.: 28 oz.
Comments: Made from about 1954 to present; normally pistol has aluminum alloy frame; approximately 925 pistols were produced with steel frames sometime prior to 1966. Add $22.00 for nickel finish.

	Alloy frame	Steel frame
Estimated Value: New (retail):	$245.00	
Excellent:	$195.00	$950.00
Very good:	$155.00	$850.00

Smith & Wesson Model 39

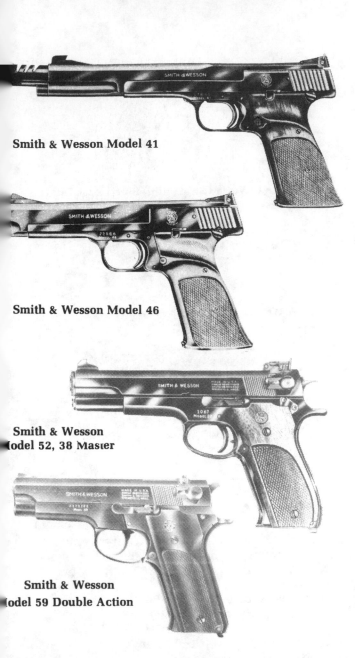

Smith & Wesson Model 41

Smith & Wesson Model 46

Smith & Wesson Model 52, 38 Master

Smith & Wesson Model 59 Double Action

Smith & Wesson Model 41

Caliber: 22 short, 22 LR (not interchangeably)
Action: Semi-automatic; concealed hammer; thumb safety
Magazine: 10-shot clip
Barrel: 5½''; 7 3/8''
Sights: Adjustable
Finish: Blued; checkered walnut grips with thumb rest
Length overall: 8 5/8'' to 10½''
Approximate wt.: 40 to 44 oz.
Comments: Made from about 1957 to present.
Estimated Value: New (retail): $294.00
  Excellent: $235.00
  Very good: $190.00

Smith & Wesson Model 46

Similar to Model 41 except: 22 long rifle caliber only; plastic grips with thumb rest. Made from about 1957 to 1966.
Estimated Value: Excellent: $220.00
  Very good: $175.00

Smith & Wesson Model 52, 38 Master

Caliber: 38 Special (mid-range wadcutter only)
Action: Semi-automatic; exposed hammer; thumb safety
Magazine: 5-shot clip
Barrel: 5''
Sights: Adjustable rear sights
Finish: Blued; checkered walnut grips
Length overall: 8 5/8''
Approximate wt.: 42 oz.
Comments: Made from about 1961 to present.
Estimated Value: New (retail): $471.00
  Excellent: $375.00
  Very good: $300.00

Smith & Wesson Model 61 Escort

Caliber: 22 long rifle
Action: Semi-automatic; concealed hammer; thumb safety
Magazine: 5-shot clip
Barrel: 2 1/8''
Sights: Fixed
Finish: Blued or nickel; checkered plastic grips
Length overall: 4¾''
Approximate wt.: 14 oz.
Comments: Manufactured from about 1970 to 1973.
  Add $10.00 for nickel finish.
Estimated Value: Excellent: $150.00
  Very good: $125.00

Smith & Wesson Model 61 Escort

Smith & Wesson Model 59 Double Action

Caliber: 9mm Luger Parabellum
Action: Double action; semi-automatic; exposed hammer; thumb safety
Magazine: 14-shot staggered column clip
Barrel: 4''
Sights: Ramp front; rear sight adjustable for windage
Finish: Blued or nickel; checkered high impact molded nylon
Length overall: 7½''
Approximate wt.: 28 oz.
Comments: Similar to model 39 except back of grip is straight and grip is wider to accommodate the thicker, staggered column magazine. Introduced about 1973 and still in production. Add $23.00 for nickel finish.
Estimated Value: New (retail): $294.00
  Excellent: $235.00
  Very good: $190.00

Handguns

Smith & Wesson Straightline Single Shot Target
Caliber: 22 short, long, long rifle
Action: Single; exposed striker (hammer)
Magazine: None; single shot
Barrel: 10"; cartridge chamber in barrel; barrel pivots to left to eject and load
Sights: Target sights
Finish: Blued; walnut grips
Length overall: 11½"
Approximate wt.: 35 oz.
Comments: Pistol resembles automatic pistol in appearance; sold with metal case, screwdriver and cleaning rod. Made from about 1925 to 1937. Add $50.00 for original case and accessories.
Estimated Value: Excellent: $600.00
Very good: $510.00

Smith & Wesson No. 3 Single Action New Model
Caliber: 44 S&W Russian center fire
Action: Single; exposed hammer; hinged frame (top break); simultaneous auto ejector
Cylinder: 6-shot
Barrel: 4", 5", 6", 6½", 7½" or 8" ribbed
Sights: Fixed or target
Finish: Blued or nickel; round butt, hard rubber or checkered walnut grips
Length overall: 9" to 13"
Approximate wt.: 36 to 40 oz.
Comments: An improved version of the S&W Russian single action revolver. Approximately 36,000 were manufactured from about 1878 to 1908. Sometimes called Single Action Russian Model.
Estimated Value: Excellent: $600.00
Very good: $510.00

Smith & Wesson No. 3 New Model Double Action
Similar to No. 3 Single Action New Model except: double and single action; 4", 5", 6" & 6½" barrel; overall length 9 to 11½"; sometimes listed as S&W 1881 Navy Revolver; rear of trigger guard is square; made from about 1881 to 1908.
Estimated Value: Excellent: $330.00
Very good: $270.00

Smith & Wesson 38 Double Action

Smith & Wesson Straightline Single Shot Target

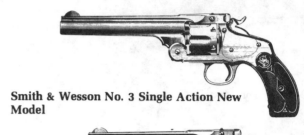
Smith & Wesson No. 3 Single Action New Model

Smith & Wesson No. 3 New Model Double Action

Smith & Wesson Double Action 44 Wesson Favorite
Similar to No. 3 Single Action New Model except: double and single action; 5" barrel only; lighter barrel and frame. Made from about 1882 to 1883 (approximately 1200 produced.)
Estimated Value: Excellent: $1,800.00
Very good: $1,200.00

Smith & Wesson 32 Double Action
Caliber: 32 S&W center fire
Action: Single and double; exposed hammer; hinged frame (top break)
Cylinder: 5-shot; simultaneous ejector
Barrel: 3" 1880 to 1882; 3", 3½", 6", 8" & 10" 1882 to 1909; 3", 3½" & 6" 1909 to 1919.
Sights: Fixed
Finish: Blued or nickel; round butt, hard rubber grips
Length overall: 7¼" to 14¼"
Approximate wt.: 23 to 28 oz.
Comments: Manufactured from about 1880 to 1919 in five modifications or issues; rear of trigger guard is square.

Estimated Value -

Issue	Dates	Quantity	Excellent	Very Good
1st	1880		$350.00	$300.00
2nd	1880-1882	22,000	$190.00	$150.00
3rd	1882-1889	21,200	$200.00	$160.00
4th	1889-1909	239,500	$150.00	$125.00
5th	1909-1919	44,600	$180.00	$150.00

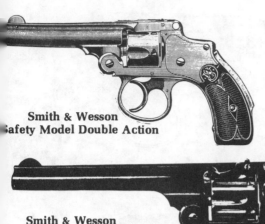

Smith & Wesson
Safety Model Double Action

Smith & Wesson
No. 3 Single Action Frontier

Smith & Wesson
Double Action Frontier

Smith & Wesson Perfected 38

Caliber: 38 S&W center fire
Action: Double and single; exposed hammer; hinged frame (top break, but also has side latch)
Cylinder: 5-shot; simultaneous ejector
Barrel: 3¼", 4", 5", & 6"
Sights: Fixed
Finish: Blued or nickel; round butt, hard rubber grip
Length overall: 7½" to 10¼"
Approximate wt.: 24 to 30 oz.
Comments: Similar to earlier 38 double action revolvers except: heavier frame; a side latch along with the top latch; improved lock work. Approximately 58,400 were produced from about 1909 to 1920.
Estimated Value: Excellent: $270.00
**   Very good: $220.00**

Smith & Wesson Single Action Target

Caliber: 32-44 S&W, 38-44 S&W
Action: Single; exposed hammer; hinged frame (top break)
Cylinder: 6-shot; simultaneous ejector
Barrel: 6½"
Sights: Target
Finish: Blued or nickel; round butt; hard rubber or checkered walnut grips
Length overall: 11"
Approximate wt.: 38 to 40 oz.
Comments: One of the first handguns to prove that a short-barrel arm could be a really accurate weapon. Made from 1887 to 1910.
Estimated Value: Excellent: $545.00
**   Very good: $485.00**

Smith & Wesson 38 Double Action

Caliber: 38 S&W
Action: Double and single; exposed hammer; hinged frame; top break style; back of trigger guard squared.
Cylinder: 5-shot; simultaneous ejector
Barrel: 3¼", 4",5" or 6"
Sights: Fixed
Finish: Blued or nickel; round butt; hard rubber grips
Length overall: 7½" to 10¼"
Approximate wt.: 20 to 24 oz.
Comments: Made from about 1880 to 1910 with some improvements and minor changes.
Estimated Value: Excellent: $215.00
**   Very good: $180.00**

Smith & Wesson Safety Model Double Action

Caliber: 32 S&W, 38 S&W
Action: Double only; concealed hammer with frame enclosing it; hinged frame; top break style; grip safety on rear of grip frame
Cylinder: 5-shot; simultaneous ejector
Barrel: 2", 3", or 3½" in 32 caliber; 2", 3¼", 4", 5" or 6" in 38 caliber; rib on top
Sights: Fixed
Finish: Blued or nickel; hard rubber or checkered walnut grips
Length overall: 5¾" to 9¾"
Approximate wt.: 15 to 20 oz.
Comments: Sometimes listed as the Safety Hammerless, New Department Model. Made from about 1887 to 1941. About 5 changes and improvements were made from 1887-1940.
Estimated Value: Excellent: $300.00
**   Very good: $245.00**

Smith & Wesson No. 3 Single Action Frontier

Caliber: 44, 40 Winchester rifle cartridge
Action: Single; exposed hammer; hinged frame (top break)
Cylinder: 6-shot; simultaneous auto ejector
Barrel: 4", 5" & 6½"
Sights: Fixed or target
Finish: Blued or nickel; round butt, hard rubber or checkered walnut grips
Length overall: 8½" to 11"
Approximate wt.: 38 to 42 oz.
Comments: Approximately 2,000 manufactured from about 1885 to 1908.
Estimated Value: Excellent: $950.00
**   Very good: $850.00**

Smith & Wesson Double Action Frontier

Similar to No. 3 Single Action Frontier except: double and single action; rear of trigger guard is square. Made from about 1886 to 1908 (approximately 15,000 were produced).
Estimated Value: Excellent: $330.00
**   Very good: $285.00**

Handguns

Smith & Wesson 1891 Single Action
Caliber: 38 S&W center fire
Action: Single; exposed hammer; hinged frame (top break)
Cylinder: 5-shot; simultaneous ejector
Barrel: 3¼", 4", 5" & 6"
Sights: Fixed
Finish: Blued or nickel; round butt, hard rubber grips
Length overall: 6¾" to 9½"
Approximate wt.: 34 to 38 oz. (depending on barrel length)
Comments: This revolver was also available with an accessory single shot target barrel in 22 caliber, 32 caliber, or 38 caliber and 6", 8" and 10" lengths. Made from 1891 to 1911. Approximately 26,000 were produced.

Smith & Wesson 1891 Single Action

Estimated Value:

	Revolver	Revolver and single shot barrel
Excellent:	$560.00	$925.00
Very good:	$500.00	$850.00

Smith & Wesson Mexican Model
Caliber: 38 S&W center fire
Action: Single; exposed hammer; hinged frame (top break); spur trigger
Cylinder: 5-shot; simultaneous ejector
Barrel: 3¼", 4", 5", & 6"
Sights: Fixed
Finish: Blued or nickel; round butt, hard rubber grips
Length overall: 7¾" to 10½"
Comments: Similar to Model 1891 except: it has a spur trigger; doesn't have half-cock notch on the hammer. Approximately 2,000 manufactured from about 1891 to 1911.

Estimated Value: Excellent: $950.00
Very good: $850.00

Smith & Wesson Military & Police Winchester 32-20

Smith & Wesson Model 1 Hand Ejector
Caliber: 32 S&W long
Action: Double and single; exposed hammer; first Smith & Wesson solid frame revolver; longer top strap over cylinder than later models
Cylinder: 6-shot; swing-out cylinder; simultaneous manual ejector
Barrel: 3¼", 4¼", or 6"
Sights: Fixed
Finish: Blued or nickel; round butt; hard rubber grips
Length overall: 8 to 10¾"
Approximate wt.: 20 to 24 oz.
Comments: First model produced by Smith & Wesson with solid frame; Made from about 1896 to 1903.

Estimated Value: Excellent: $215.00
Very good: $170.00

Smith & Wesson 1899 Hand Ejector
Caliber: 38 long Colt
Action: Double and single; exposed hammer; solid frame
Cylinder: 6-shot; swing out; simultaneous manual ejector; cylinder release on side of frame
Barrel: 4", 5", 6", or 6½"
Sights: Fixed
Finish: Blued or nickel; checkered hard rubber or walnut round butt grips
Length overall: 9" to 11½"
Approximate wt.: 22 to 26 oz.
Comments: Made for police, Army, Navy, and commercial use; forerunner of the military and police models. Made from about 1899 to 1902 (approximately 21,000 produced). Army and Navy versions have lanyard swivel in butt and 6" or 6½" barrel lengths.

Estimated Value: Excellent: $270.00
Very good: $225.00

Smith & Wesson Military & Police Winchester 32-20
Similar to Model 1899 except: caliber 32-20 only; improvements and changes similar to Model 10 Military & Police revolvers over the years produced from about 1899 to 1940.

Estimated Value: Excellent: $250.00
Very good: $200.00

Smith & Wesson Model M Hand Ejector

1891 Single Shot Target Pistol

New Century Triple Lock

Smith & Wesson 44 Hand Ejector

Smith & Wesson Model 30 Hand Ejector

Smith & Wesson 44 Hand Ejector

Similar to New Century Triple Lock except: cylinder crane lock eliminated; 44 Smith & Wesson Special, 44 Smith & Wesson Russian, or 45 Colt calibers; 45 Colt caliber made in 6½" barrel only; other calibers in 4", 5", 6" length. Made from about 1915 to 1937.

Estimated Value: Excellent: **$360.00**
                        Very good: **$310.00**

Smith & Wesson Model 30 Hand Ejector

Caliber: 32 Smith & Wesson and 32 Smith & Wesson long
Action: Double and single; exposed hammer; solid frame
Cylinder: 6-shot; swing-out; simultaneous manual ejector; cylinder release on left side of frame
Barrel: 2" (1949 to 1975), 3", 4" or 6"
Sights: Fixed
Finish: Blued or nickel; checkered hard rubber or checkered walnut round butt grips
Length overall: 6" to 10"
Approximate wt.: 16 to 20 oz.
Comments: Manufactured from about 1903 to 1975 with many improvements and minor changes over the years.
Estimated Value: Excellent: **$165.00**
                        Very good: **$130.00**

Smith & Wesson Model M Hand Ejector

Caliber: 22 short, long, long rifle
Action: Double and single; exposed hammer; solid frame
Cylinder: 9-shot; swing-out; simultaneous manual ejector
Barrel: 2¼" (1902-1911); 3", 3½" (1906-1911) or 6" (1911-1921)
Sights: Fixed or adjustable (available after 1911)
Finish: Blued or nickel; checkered hard rubber round butt grips (1902-1911); checkered hard rubber square butt grips (1911-1921)
Length overall: 5¾" to 10½"
Approximate wt.: 10 to 14 oz.
Comments: Cylinder latch release on left side of frame 1902 to 1906; cylinder latch under barrel 1906 to 1921. Made from about 1902 to 1921, sometimes called Lady Smith.
Estimated Value: Excellent: **$630.00**
                        Very good: **$585.00**

Smith & Wesson 1891 Single Shot Target Pistol

Caliber: 22 short, long, long rifle
Action: Single; exposed hammer; hinged frame (top break)
Cylinder: None; single shot
Barrel: 10"
Sights: Adjustable target
Finish: Blued; hard rubber square butt grips
Length overall: 13½"
Appproximate wt.: 25 oz.
Comments: Produced from about 1905 to 1909.
Estimated Value: Excellent: **$300.00**
                        Very good: **$250.00**

Smith & Wesson Perfected Single Shot

Similar to Model 1891 Single Shot except: double and single action; checkered walnut square butt grips; made from about 1909 to 1923; the U.S. Olympic team of 1920 used this model pistol, therefore, it is sometimes designated "Olympic Model." Add $125.00 for Olympic Models.

Estimated Value: Excellent: **$330.00**
                        Very good: **$290.00**

Smith & Wesson New Century Triple Lock

Caliber: 44 S&W Special, 450 Eley, 45 Colt, or 455 Mark II British
Action: Double and single; exposed hammer; solid frame
Cylinder: 6-shot swing-out; simultaneous hand ejector; called triple lock because of lock on cylinder crane as well as the usual locks under barrel and at rear of cylinder.
Barrel: 4", 5", 6½" or 7½" tapered round
Sights: Fixed
Finish: Blued or nickel; checkered walnut square butt grips
Length overall: 9¼" to 12¾"
Approximate wt.: 36 to 41 oz.
Comments: Approximately 20,000 made from about 1908 to 1915; about 5,000 of these were made for the British Army.
Estimated Value: Excellent: **$600.00**
                        Very good: **$525.00**

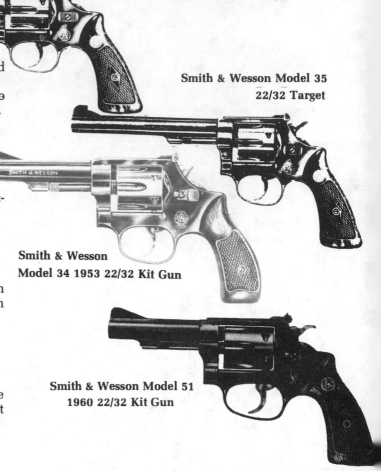

Smith & Wesson 22/32 Target

Smith & Wesson Model 35
22/32 Target

Smith & Wesson
Model 34 1953 22/32 Kit Gun

Smith & Wesson Model 51
1960 22/32 Kit Gun

Smith & Wesson 22/32 Target Revolver

Caliber: 22 short, long, long rifle
Action: Double and single; exposed hammer; solid frame
Cylinder: 6-shot swing-out; recessed chamber (1935 to 1953); cylinder release on left side of frame.
Barrel: 6"
Sights: Adjustable target sights
Finish: Blued; checkered square butt walnut grips
Length overall: 10½"
Approximate wt.: 24 oz.
Comments: Frame design similar to Model 30 hand ejector model. Made from about 1911-1953.
Estimated Value: Excellent: $240.00
     Very good: $190.00

Smith & Wesson 22/32 1935 Kit Gun

Same as 22/23 Target except: 4" barrel; overall length 8"; weight about 21 oz; round butt grips. Made from about 1935 to 1953.
Estimated Value: Excellent: $210.00
     Very good: $170.00

Smith & Wesson Model 35 22/32 Target

Similar to 22/32 target except: newer type adjustable rear sight; S&W magna-type target grips; weight about 25 oz. Produced from about 1953 to 1974.
Estimated Value: Excellent: $225.00
     Very good: $185.00

Smith & Wesson Model 34 1953 22/32 Kit Gun

Similar to 22/32 Kit Gun except: 2" or 4" barrel; round or square butt grips; blued or nickel finish. Made from about 1953 to present. Add $13.00 for nickel finish.
Estimated Value: New (retail): $185.00
     Excellent: $150.00
     Very good: $120.00

Smith & Wesson Model 43 1955 22/32 Kit Gun

Same as Model 34 1953 22/32 Kit Gun except: 3½" barrel only; lighter alloy frame; approximately 15 oz. weight; square butt grips. Made from about 1954 to 1974.
Estimated Value: Excellent: $150.00
     Very good: $125.00

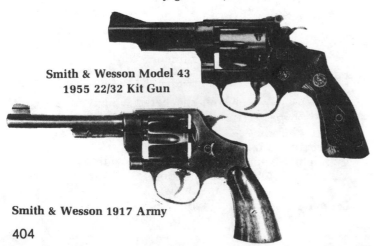

Smith & Wesson Model 43
1955 22/32 Kit Gun

Smith & Wesson 1917 Army

Smith & Wesson Model 51 1960 22/32 Kit Gun

Same as Model 43 1953 22/32 Kit Gun except: chambered for 22 magnum (WRM) only; all steel construction; approximately 24 oz. weight. Manufactured from about 1960 to 1974.
Estimated Value: Excellent: $180.00
     Very good: $150.00

Smith & Wesson 1917 Army

Caliber: 45 auto rim cartridge and 45 ACP (by using two 3 round steel half moon clips to hold the cartridge heads.
Action: Double and single; exposed hammer; solid frame
Cylinder: 6-shot swing out; simultaneous manual ejector; release on left side of frame
Barrel: 5½"
Sights: Fixed
Finish: Blued; smooth or checkered walnut square butt grips.
Length overall: 10¾"
Approximate wt.: 37 oz.
Comments: Approximately 175,000 made for U.S. Government from about 1917 to 1919. Then made for commercial sale from about 1919 to 1941. U.S. Government models had a dull blue finish and smooth grips.

Estimated Value:	Military	Commercial
Excellent:	$240.00	$270.00
Very good:	$195.00	$225.00

Smith & Wesson
Model 22 1950 Army

Smith & Wesson
1926 Model 44 Military

Smith & Wesson
1926 Model 44 Target

Smith & Wesson
Model 21 1950 44 Military

Smith & Wesson
Model 24 1950 44 Target

Smith & Wesson
Model 25 1955 45 Target

Smith & Wesson Model 22 1950 Army

Similar to 1917 Army except: made after World War II;
minor changes; made from about 1950 to 1967.

Estimated Value: Excellent: **$250.00**
                  Very good: **$205.00**

Smith & Wesson 1926 Model 44 Military

Caliber: 44 S&W Special
Action: Double and single; exposed hammer; solid
        frame
Cylinder: 6-shot swing-out simultaneous manual ejec-
        tor; cyclinder release on left side of frame
Barrel: 4", 5" or 6½"
Sights: Fixed
Finish: Blued or nickel; checkered square butt walnut
        grips
Length overall: 9¼" to 11¾"
Approximate wt.: 40 oz.
Comments: Manufactured from about 1926 to 1941.
Estimated Value: Excellent: **$300.00**
                  Very good: **$265.00**

Smith & Wesson 1926 Model 44 Target

Same as 1926 Model Military except: 6½" barrel only;
adjustable target sights; blued finish only. Made from
about 1926 to 1941.

Estimated Value: Excellent: **$330.00**
                  Very good: **$280.00**

Smith & Wesson Model 21 1950 44 Military

Similar to 1926 Model Military Revolver except: made
after World War II; minor changes. Produced from
about 1950 to 1967.

Estimated Value: Excellent: **$310.00**
                  Very good: **$265.00**

Smith & Wesson Model 24 1950 44 Target Revolver

Similar to 1926 Model 44 Target except made after
World War II; minor changes; ribbed barrel. Made from
about 1950 to 1967.

Estimated Value: Excellent: **$350.00**
                  Very good: **$300.00**

Smith & Wesson Model 25 1955 45 Target, 1955-5

Same as Model 24 1950 44 Target except: caliber 45
ACP; made from about 1955 to date. Add $20.00 for 45
Colt.

Estimated Value: **New (retail):**   **$356.00**
                  Excellent: **$285.00**
                  Very good: **$230.00**

Smith & Wesson Model 20 Heavy Duty

Caliber: 38 Special
Action: Double and single; exposed hammer; solid
        frame
Cylinder: 6-shot swing-out; simultaneous ejector;
        release on left side of frame
Barrel: 4", 5", or 6½"
Sights: Fixed
Finish: Blued or nickel; checkered walnut square butt
        grips
Length overall: 9 3/8" to 11 7/8"
Approximate wt.: 38 to 41 oz.
Comments: Made from about 1930 to 1967.
Estimated Value: Excellent: **$260.00**
                  Very good: **$215.00**

Smith & Wesson Model 20 Heavy Duty

Handguns

Smith & Wesson Model 23 Outdoorsman Revolver

Similar to Model 20 Heavy Duty except: target version; 6½" barrel only; ribbed barrel after 1950; approximately 42 oz. wt.; blued finish; adjustable target sights. Produced from about 1930 to 1967.

Estimated Value: Excellent: $350.00
Very good: $285.00

Smith & Wesson Military & Police

Caliber: 38 Special
Action: Double and single; exposed hammer; solid frame
Cylinder: 6-shot swing-out; simultaneous ejector; release on left side of frame
Barrel: 2" (after 1933); 4", 5", 6" or 6½" (1902-1915)
Sights: Fixed
Finish: Blued or nickel; checkered hard rubber or checkered walnut round or square butt grips
Length overall: 7" to 11½"
Approximate wt.: 26 to 32 oz.
Comments: Manufactured from about 1902 to 1942 with improvements and minor changes. Basic frame is known as S&W K frame Model. Add $10.50 for nickel finish. Also know as 1902 Model and 1905 Model M & P.

Estimated Value: Excellent: $135.00
Very good: $110.00

Smith & Wesson Model 10 Military & Police

Similar to 38 M & P and Victory Mdoels with an improved hammer throw. Made from about 1948 to present. Add $10.50 for nickel, $12.00 for heavy barrel.

Estimated Value: New (retail): $143.00
Excellent: $115.00
Very good: $ 90.00

Smith & Wesson Victory Model

Same as Model 10 Military & Police except: sand blasted or brushed parkerized finish; smooth square butt grips with lanyard ring; made from about 1941 to 1946 for the U.S. Government during World War II; usually 38 Special caliber, but some termed 38-200 were made for the British Forces.

Estimated Value: Excellent: $180.00
Very good: $145.00

Smith & Wesson Model 13 M & P

Smith & Wesson Model 65 M&P

Smith & Wesson Model 23 Outdoorsman

Smith & Wesson Model 10

Smith & Wesson Model 64

Smith & Wesson Model 12
Military & Police Airweigh

Smith & Wesson Model 13 M & P

Similar to the Model 10 Military and Police in 357 magnum caliber and heavy barrel; add $15.00 for nickel.

Estimated Value: New (retail): $156.50
Excellent: $130.00
Very good: $105.00

Smith & Wesson Model 65 M&P

Similar to the Model 13 with a satin stainless steel finish.

Estimated Value: New (retail): $173.00
Excellent: $145.00
Very good: $120.00

Smith & Wesson Model 64 Military & Police

Same as Model 10 Military & Police Revolver except: 4" barrel only; satin finish stainless steel construction; made from about 1972 to present.

Estimated Value: New (retail): $162.00
Excellent: $135.00
Very good: $125.00

Smith & Wesson Model 12 Military & Police Airweight

Same as Model 10 Military & Police except: light alloy frame; 2" barrel only; approximate wt. 18 oz; made from about 1952 to present. Add $25.00 for nickel finish.

Estimated Value: New (retail): $185.00
Excellent: $150.00
Very good: $120.00

Smith & Wesson 38 Military & Police Target

Same as Model 10 Military & Police except: 6" barrel only; approximate wt. 33 oz.; checkered walnut grips; adjustable target sights; produced from about 1924 to 1941.

Estimated Value: Excellent: $210.00
Very good: $170.00

Smith & Wesson K-32 Target

Similar to S&W 38 Military & Police Target except: caliber 32 S&W, 32 S&W long, and 32 Colt New Police; heavier barrel; approximate wt. 34 oz. Introduced about 1940; discontinued about 1941.

Estimated Value: Excellent: $540.00
Very good: $480.00

Smith & Wesson Model 27 357 Magnum

Caliber: 357 magnum and 38 Special
Action: Double and single; exposed hammer; solid frame
Cylinder: 6-shot swing-out; recessed chambers; simultaneous manual ejector; release on left side of frame
Barrel: 3½", 5", 6", 6½", or 8 3/8" ribbed
Sights: Adjustable target
Finish: Blued or nickel; checkered walnut grips
Length overall: 7 7/8" to 14¼"
Approximate wt: 42 to 47 oz.
Comments: Made from about 1935 to present. Made from 1935 to 1938 on special orders (worth more). Add $12.00 for 8 3/8" barrel.

Estimated Value: New (retail): $376.00
Excellent: $300.00
Very good: $240.00

Smith & Wesson Model 28 Highway Patrolman

Similar to Model 27 357 Magnum except: 4" or 6" barrel; ramp front sight and adjustable rear sight; blued finish. Made from about 1954 to date. Add $15.00 for target grips.

Estimated Value: New (retail): $222.00
Excellent: $190.00
Very good: $150.00

Smith & Wesson Model K-22 Outdoorsman

Caliber: 22 short, long, long rifle
Action: Double and single action; exposed hammer; solid frame
Cylinder: 6-shot swing out; simultaneous manual ejector; release on left side of frame
Barrel: 6"
Sights: Fixed or target sights
Finish: Blued or nickel; checkered walnut grips
Length overall: 11½"
Approximate wt.: 35 oz.
Comments: Made from about 1931 to 1942.

Estimated Value: Excellent: $240.00
Very good: $210.00

Smith & Wesson Model 31 Regulation Police

Caliber: 32 S&W, 32 Colt New Police
Action: Double and single; exposed hammer; solid frame
Cylinder: 6-shot swing out; simultaneous manual ejector; release on left side of frame
Barrel: 2" (1949 - present); 3", 3¼", 4", 4¼" or 6"
Sights: Fixed
Finish: Blued or nickel; checkered square butt walnut grips
Length overall: 6½" to 10½"
Approximate wt.: 17 to 20 oz.
Comments: Made from about 1917 to present. Add $14.00 for nickel finish.

Estimated Value: New (retail): $179.00
Excellent: $145.00
Very good: $115.00

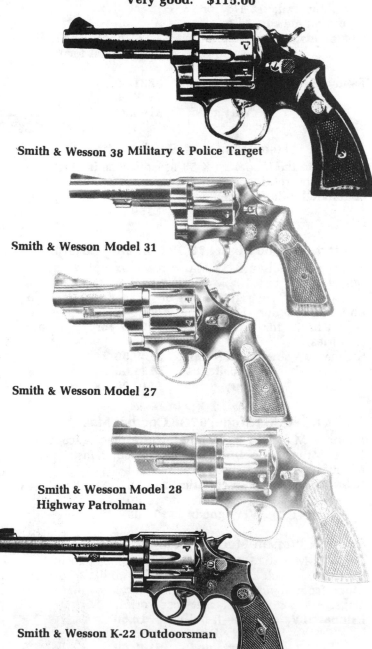

Smith & Wesson 38 Military & Police Target

Smith & Wesson Model 31

Smith & Wesson Model 27

Smith & Wesson Model 28 Highway Patrolman

Smith & Wesson K-22 Outdoorsman

Handguns

Smith & Wesson K-22 Masterpiece
Same as K-22 Outdoorsman except: improved version; better adjustable rear sight; short cocking action; anti-backlash trigger; made from about 1942 to 1947.
Estimated Value: Excellent: $330.00
Very good: $270.00

Smith & Wesson Model 14 K-38 Masterpiece
Caliber: 38 Special
Action: Double and single; or single action only; exposed hammer; solid frame
Cylinder: 6-shot swing-out; simultaneous manual ejector; release on left side of frame
Barrel: 6" or 8 3/8"
Sights: Partridge front sight; click adjustable rear sight
Finish: Blued; checkered square butt walnut grips
Length overall: 11 1/8" or 13½"
Approximate wt: 36 to 38 oz.
Comments: Made from about 1947 to present. Add $10.00 for 8 3/8" barrel, $40.00 for target accessories.
Estimated Value: New (retail): $221.50
Excellent: $175.00
Very good: $140.00

Smith & Wesson Model 14 Single Action
Similar to the Model 14 K-38 Masterpiece in single action; 6" barrel; blued only.
Estimated Value: Excellent: $185.00
Very good: $150.00

Smith & Wesson Model 15 38 Combat Masterpiece
Same as Model 14 K-38 Masterpiece except: 2" or 4" barrel; 7 1/8" or 9 1/8" overall; approximate wt. 34 oz.; quick draw front sight; blued or nickel finish; double and single action. Made from about 1950 to present. Add $12.00 for nickel finish, $17.00 for target accessories.
Estimated Value: New (retail): $169.50
Excellent: $135.00
Very good: $110.00

Smith & Wesson Model 67 38 Combat Masterpiece
Same as Model 15 38 Combat Masterpiece except: 4" barrel only; satin finish stainless steel construction. Manufactured from about 1972 to date.
Estimated Value: New (retail): $212.50
Excellent: $170.00
Very good: $135.00

Smith & Wesson Model 19 357 Combat Magnum
Same as Model 15 38 Combat Masterpiece except: 2", 4" or 6" barrel; caliber 357 magnum and 38 Special. Made from about 1956 to present; round or square butt grips. Add $25.00 for target accessories.
Estimated Value: New (retail): $216.50
Excellent: $175.00
Very good: $140.00

Smith & Wesson Model Regulation Police Target
Similar to Smith & Wesson Model 31 Regulation Police except: 6" barrel only; adjustable target sights; made from about 1917 to 1940; blued finish.
Estimated Value: Excellent: $180.00
Very good: $145.00

Smith & Wesson Model 32 Terrier
Similar to Model 33 Regulation Police revolver except: 2" barrel only; 6½" overall length. Manufactured from about 1936 to 1974.
Estimated Value: Excellent: $170.00
Very good: $140.00

Smith & Wesson Model 33 Regulation Police Revolver
Same as S&W Model 31 Regulation Police except: 38 caliber S&W and 38 Colt New Police; 5-shot cylinder capacity. Produced from about 1917 to 1974.
Estimated Value: Excellent: $170.00
Very good: $140.00

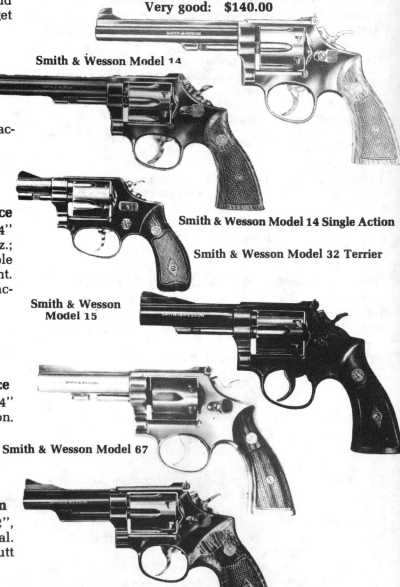

Smith & Wesson Model 14

Smith & Wesson Model 14 Single Action

Smith & Wesson Model 32 Terrier

Smith & Wesson Model 15

Smith & Wesson Model 67

Smith & Wesson Model 19

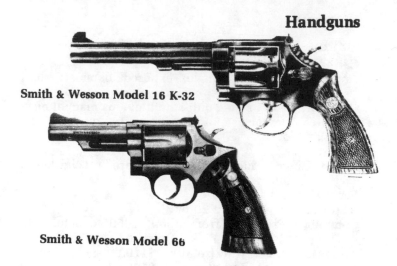

Smith & Wesson Model 16 K-32

Smith & Wesson Model 66 357 Combat Magnum

Same as Model 19 357 Combat Magnum except: 2 ½" or 4" barrel; satin finish stainless steel. Produced from about 1972 to present.

Estimated Value: New (retail): $231.50
               Excellent: $185.00
               Very good: $150.00

Smith & Wesson Model 16 K-32 Masterpiece

Same as Model 14 K-38 Masterpiece except: 32 S&W long, and 32 Colt Police caliber; 6" barrel only; double and single action. Made from about 1947 to 1974.

Estimated Value: Excellent: $230.00
               Very good: $185.00

Smith & Wesson Model 66

Smith & Wesson 17 K-22 Masterpiece

Smith & Wesson Model 48

Smith & Wesson Model 57

Smith & Wesson Model 58

Smith & Wesson Model 17 K-22 Masterpiece

Same as Model 14 K-38 Masterpiece except: 22 short, long, long rifle caliber; double and single action. Made from about 1947 to present; approx. wt. 40 oz. Add $10.00 for 8 3/8" barrel, $30.00 for target accessories.

Estimated Value: New (retail): $222.50
               Excellent: $180.00
               Very good: $145.00

Smith & Wesson Model 18 22 Combat Masterpiece

Same as Model 17 K-22 Masterpiece except: 4" barrel; 9 1/8" overall length; approximate wt. 38 oz. Made from about 1950 to date. Add $17.00 for target accessories.

Estimated Value: New (retail): $205.00
               Excellent: $165.00
               Very good: $130.00

Smith & Wesson Model 48 K-22 Magnum Masterpiece

Same as Model 17 K-22 Masterpiece except: 22 magnum (WMRF) caliber; also available with auxiliary cylinder for 22 short, long & long rifle. Made from about 1948 to present. Add $11.00 for 8 3/8" barrel. Add $30.00 for auxiliary 22 short, long & long rifle cylinder.

Estimated Value: New (retail): $237.00
               Excellent: $190.00
               Very good: $150.00

Smith & Wesson Model 57 41 Magnum Revolver

Caliber: 41 magnum
Action: Double and single; exposed hammer; solid frame
Cylinder: 6-shot swing-out; simultaneous manual ejector; release on left side of frame
Barrel: 4", 6" or 8 3/8" ribbed
Sights: Ramp front, adjustable rear
Finish: Blued or nickel; checkered wood grips
Length overall: 9 3/8" to 13¾"
Approximate wt: 38 to 42 oz.
Comments: Manufactured from about 1964 to present. Add $12.00 for 8 3/8" barrel.

Estimated Value: New (retail): $376.00
               Excellent: $300.00
               Very good: $240.00

Smith & Wesson Model 58 41 Military & Police

Similar to Model 57 41 magnum except: 4" barrel only; fixed sights; no rib on barrel. Made from about 1964 to late 1970's. Add $10.00 for nickel finish.

Estimated Value: Excellent: $200.00
               Very good: $160.00

Handguns

Smith & Wesson Model 36 Chiefs Special

Caliber: 38 Special
Action: Double and single; exposed hammer; solid frame
Cylinder: 5-shot swing-out; simultaneous manual ejector; release on left side of frame
Barrel: 2" or 3"
Sights: Fixed
Finish: Blued or nickel; round or square butt checkered walnut grips
Length overall: 6½" to 7¾"
Approximate wt: 19 to 20 oz.
Comments: Produced from about 1950 to date. Add $14.00 for nickel finish
Estimated Value: New (retail): $170.50
Excellent: $135.00
Very good: $110.00

Smith & Wesson
Model 36 Chiefs Special

Smith & Wesson
Model 37 Airweight

Smith & Wesson Model 60 Chiefs
Special Stainless Steel

nith & Wesson Model 40
Centennial Hammerless

Smith & Wesson Model 42
Centennial Airweight

Smith & Wesson Model 3
Bodyguard Airweight

Smith & Wesson Model 37 Airweight Chiefs Special

Same as Model 36 Chiefs Special except: light alloy frame; approximate wt. is 13 to 14 oz. Made from about 1954 to present. Add $25.00 for nickel finish.
Estimated Value: New (retail): $189.50
Excellent: $150.00
Very good: $125.00

Smith & Wesson Model 60 Chiefs Special Stainless

Same as Model 36 Chiefs Special except: Satin-finished stainless steel construction 2" barrel only; round butt grip; approximate wt. 20 oz. Made from about 1965 to date.
Estimated Value: New (retail): $207.50
Excellent: $180.00
Very good: $155.00

Smith & Wesson Model 40 Centennial Hammerless

Similar to Model 36 Chiefs Special except: concealed hammer; frame extends over hammer area; 2" barrel; double action only; grip safety located on rear of grip. Made from about 1952 to 1974.
Estimated Value: Excellent: $180.00
Very good: $145.00

Smith & Wesson Model 42 Centennial Airweight

Same as Model 40 Centennial except: light alloy frame; approximate wt. 13 oz. Made from about 1954 to 1974.
Estimated Value: Excellent: $180.00
Very good: $145.00

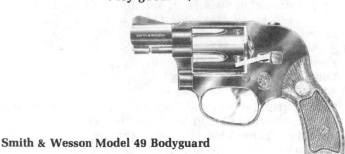

Smith & Wesson Model 49 Bodyguard

Smith & Wesson Model 38 Bodyguard Airweight

Same as Model 36 Chiefs Special except: light alloy frame; shrouded hammer (frame extends up side of hammer until only top of spur is exposed); approximate wt. - 15 oz.; 2" barrel only. Produced from about 1955 to present. Add $25.00 for nickel finish.
Estimated Value: New (retail): $197.50
Excellent: $160.00
Very good: $125.00

Smith & Wesson Model 49 Bodyguard

Same as Model 38 Bodyguard Airweight except: steel frame; approximate wt. 21 oz. Manufactured about 1959 to date. Add $13.00 for nickel finish.
Estimated Value: New (retail): $183.50
Excellent: $145.00
Very good: $120.00

Smith & Wesson Model 53

Smith & Wesson Model 29

Smith & Wesson Model 63

Smith & Wesson Model 63 1977 22/32 Kit Gun

Caliber: 22 long rifle
Action: Double and single; exposed hammer
Cylinder: 6 shot swing-out
Barrel: 4"
Sights: Adjustable micrometer square notch rear, red ramp front
Finish: Stainless steel, satin finish; checkered walnut grips
Length overall: 9 3/8"
Approximate wt.: 24½ oz.
Comments: Currently produced.
Estimated Value: New (retail): $216.00
Excellent: $180.00
Very good: $145.00

Smith & Wesson Model 53 22 Jet Magnum

Caliber: 22 Remington Jet center-fire and 22 short, long, & long rifle by using chamber inserts and repositioning floating firing pin of hammer.
Action: Double and single; exposed hammer; solid frame
Cylinder: 6-shot swing-out; simultaneus manual ejector; cylinder release on left side of frame
Barrel: 4", 6", or 8 3/8"
Sights: Ramp front; adjustable rear
Finish: Blued; checkered walnut target grips
Length overall: 9¼" to 13 5/8"
Approximate wt.: 38 to 42 oz.
Comments: Produced from about 1961 to 1974. Could be fitted with 22 caliber cylinder.
Estimated Value: Excellent: $360.00
Very good: $290.00

Smith & Wesson Model 29 44 Magnum

Caliber: 44 magnum
Action: Double and single; exposed hammer; solid frame
Cylinder: 6-shot swing-out; simultaneous manual ejector; release on left side of frame
Barrel: 4", 6½", or 8 3/8" ribbed
Sights: Ramp front; adjustable rear
Finish: Blued or nickel; checkered wood grips
Length overall: 9 3/8" to 13¾"
Approximate wt.: 44 to 49 oz.
Comments: Made from about 1956 to present. Add $12.00 for 8 3/8" barrel
Estimated Value: New (retail): $376.00
Excellent: $310.00
Very good: $295.00

Smith & Wesson Model 629

Similar to the Model 29 with a satin stainless steel finish.
Estimated Value: New (retail): $421.00
Excellent: $345.00
Very good: $285.00

Star

Star Model 1919 Pocket

Star Model 1919 Pocket

Caliber: 25 ACP (6.35mm)
Action: Semi-automatic; exposed hammer
Magazine: 8-shot clip
Barrel: 2 5/8"
Sights: Fixed
Finish: Blued; checkered wood grips
Length overall: 4 7/8"
Approximate wt.: 16 oz.
Comments: Produced from about 1919 to 1934; distinguished by the safety at the top rear of the slide.
Estimated Value: Excellent: $125.00
Very good: $100.00

Star Model CO Pocket

Star Model CO Pocket

Improved version of the 1919 Model; doesn't have the safety at top rear of slide; safety in front of left grip; plastic grips; some engraved nickel plated models produced. Made from about 1934 to 1957. Add $20.00 for engraved nickel model.
Estimated Value: Excellent: $160.00
Very good: $130.00

Handguns

Star Model H

Similar to Model CO pistol except: caliber 32 ACP; 9-shot clip; approximate wt. 20 oz.; produced from about 1934 to 1941.

Estimated Value: Excellent: $130.00
Very good: $105.00

Star Model HN

Same as Model H except: caliber 380 ACP; 6-shot clip.

Estimated Value: Excellent: $140.00
Very good: $115.00

Star Model E Pocket

Caliber: 25 ACP (6.35mm)
Action: Semi-automatic; exposed hammer
Magazine: 6-shot clip
Barrel: 2"
Sights: Fixed
Finish: Blued; checkered grips
Length overall: 4"
Approximate wt.: 10 oz.
Comments: Small compact pocket pistol; safety located in front of left grip; no longer in production.

Estimated Value: Excellent: $150.00
Very good: $125.00

Star Model F & FR

Caliber: 22 long rifle
Action: Semi-automatic; exposed hammer; manual safety at top rear or left grip
Magazine: 10-shot clip
Barrel: 4¼" (regular); 6" & 7" on Sport & Target models
Sights: Fixed; adjustable on Sport & Target models
Finish: Blued; chromed; chromed engraved; plastic grips
Length overall: 7¼" to 10"
Approximate wt.: 24 to 32 oz.
Comments: Model F made from about 1942 to 1968. Model FR is improved version made from about 1968 to late 1970's. Add $10.00 for chrome model.

Estimated Value: Excellent: $125.00
Very good: $100.00

Star Model I (Police Model)

Caliber: 32 ACP
Action: Semi-automatic; exposed hammer
Magazine: 9-shot clip
Barrel: 4¾"
Sights: Fixed
Finish: Blued; plastic grips
Length overall: 7½"
Approximate wt.: 25 oz.
Comments: Made from about 1934 to 1945; never imported into U.S.A.

Estimated Value: Excellent: $120.00
Very good: $100.00

Star Model A & AS

Caliber: 9mm Luger, 9mm Bergmann, 9mm Largo, 38 Super auto
Action: Semi-automatic; exposed hammer
Magazine: 8-shot clip
Barrel: 5"
Sights: Fixed
Finish: Blued; checkered walnut grips
Length overall: 8"
Approximate wt.: 35 oz.
Comments: This handgun resembles the 1911A1 Colt. Produced from about 1924 the late 1970's.

Estimated Value: Excellent: $180.00
Very good: $150.00

Star Model B

Similar to Model A except: barrel lengths 4¼" or 6½"; caliber 9mm Parabellum only; made from about 1924 to 1942.

Estimated Value: Excellent: $200.00
Very good: $160.00

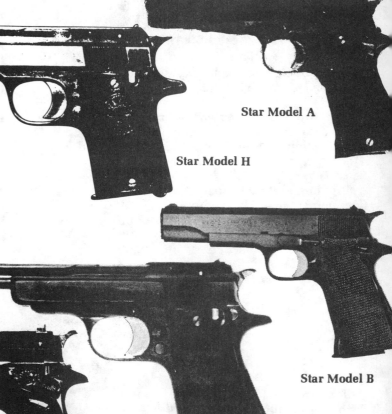

Star Model A

Star Model H

Star Model B

Star Model I (Police Model)

Star Model F & FR

Star Model IN

Same as Model I except: caliber 380 ACP; still in production; 8-shot clip.

Estimated Value: Excellent: $145.00
Very good: $115.00

Star Model M (Military)
Caliber: 380 ACP; 9mm Luger; 9mm Bergmann, 38 ACP, 45 ACP
Action: Semi-automatic; exposed hammer; manual safety
Magazine: 7-shot clip in 45 caliber, 8-shot clip in all other calibers
Barrel: 5"
Sights: Fixed
Finish: Blued; checkered grips
Length overall: 8½"
Approximate wt.: 36 oz.
Comments: A modified version of the U.S. Government Colt 1911 45 automatic, made from about 1935 to present. Not imported into U.S.A.
Estimated Value: Excellent: $175.00
Very good: $145.00

Star Model Super Star

Star Model Super SI

Star Model Super S
Same as Model S except: addition of disarming bolt; improved luminous sights; magazine safety; & indicator for number of unfired cartridges. This model was discontinued in 1954.
Estimated Value: Excellent: $200.00
Very good: $165.00

Star Model Super SI
Same as Model Super S except: caliber 32 ACP; 8-shot clip.
Estimated Value: Excellent: $185.00
Very good: $155.00

Star Model CU (Starlet)
Caliber: 25 ACP
Action: Semi-automatic; exposed hammer
Magazine: 8-shot clip
Barrel: 2 3/8"
Sights: Fixed
Finish: Blued or chromed slide and black, gray, gold, blue or green receiver; checkered plastic grips
Length overall: 4¾"
Approximate wt.: 12 oz.
Comments: Manufactured from about 1957 to present. Never imported into U.S.A. Manual safety catch at top rear of left grip. Alloy frame.
Estimated Value: Excellent: $120.00
Very good: $100.00

Star Model Super Star
Same as Model M except: 38 Super ACP, 9mm Parabellum, and 380 ACP only; addition of disarming bolt; improved sights; magazine safety; indicator for number of unfired cartridges. Made from about 1942 to 1954.
Estimated Value: Excellent: $180.00
Very good: $150.00

Star Model S
Caliber: 380 ACP
Action: Semi-automatic; exposed hammer; manual safety
Magazine: 7-shot clip
Barrel: 4"
Sights: Fixed
Finish: Blued; chromed; engraved; plastic grips
Length overall: 6½"
Approximate wt.: 20 oz.
Comments: A scaled-down modification of the Colt 1911 45 Automatic. Made from about 1941 to present; (not imported into U.S.A. since 1968).
Estimated Value: Excellent: $190.00
Very good: $160.00

Star Model S I
Same as Model S except: caliber 32 ACP; 8-shot clip
Estimated Value: Excellent: $175.00
Very good: $150.00

Star Model M (Military)

Star Model Super S

Handguns

Star Model DK (Starfire)

Caliber: 380 ACP
Action: Semi-automatic; exposed hammer; manual safety at top rear of left grip
Magazine: 6-shot clip
Barrel: 3"
Sights: Fixed
Finish: Blued; checkered plastic grips
Length overall: 5½"
Approximate wt.: 16 oz.
Comments: Made from about 1958 to present. Never imported into U.S.A.
Estimated Value: Excellent: $160.00
Very good: $125.00

Star Model Super SM

Caliber: 380 ACP
Action: Semi-automatic; exposed hammer
Magazine: 9-shot clip
Barrel: 4"
Sights: Blade front sight; rear sight adjustable for windage
Finish: Blued; chrome; checkered wood grips
Length overall: 6¾"
Approximate wt.: 21 oz.
Comments: Made from about 1970 to late 1970's. Add $15.00 for chrome model.
Estimated Value: Excellent: $150.00
Very good: $120.00

Star Model PD

Caliber: 45 ACP
Action: Semi-automatic; exposed hammer
Magazine: 8-shot clip
Barrel: 4"
Sights: Ramp front; adjustable rear
Finish: Blued; chrome; checkered wood grips
Approximate wt.: 25 oz.
Length overall: 7"
Comments: Made from about 1975 to present. Add $15.00 for chrome model.
Estimated Value: New (retail): $330.00
Excellent: $250.00
Very good: $20.00

Star Model BK, BKM

Caliber: 9mm Luger
Action: Semi-automatic; exposed hammer; manual thumb safety
Magazine: 8-shot clip
Barrel: 4½"
Sights: Fixed
Finish: Blued; chrome; checkered wood grips
Length overall: 7¼"
Approximate wt.: 22 oz.
Comments: Made from about 1970 to present. Alloy frame; resembles Colt 1911 45 ACP. Add $20.00 for chrome model.
Estimated Value: New (retail): $255.00
Excellent: $190.00
Very good: $150.00

Star Model HK (Lancer)

Basically same as Model CU Starlet except: caliber 22 long rifle; 3" barrel; 5½" overall length. Made from about 1955 to present.
Estimated Value: Excellent: $130.00
Very good: $110.00

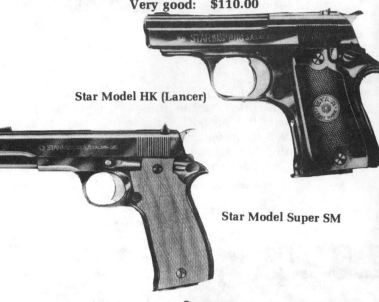

Star Model HK (Lancer)

Star Model Super SM

Star Model PD

Star Model BK

Star Model BM

Star Model BM

Similar to the Model BKM without alloy frame. Add $20.00 for chrome finish.
Estimated Value: New (retail): $255.00
Excellent: $195.00
Very good: $160.00

Sterling Model 283

Sterling Model 285

Sterling Model 300

Sterling Model 286

Sterling Model 302

Sterling Model 400 Automatic Pistol

Caliber: 380 ACP
Action: Semi-automatic; double action with exposed hammer; safety locks firing pin.
Magazine: 6-shot clip
Barrel: 3½"
Sights: Ramp front, adjustable rear sight
Finish: Blued or nickel; checkered grips
Length overall: 6½"
Approximate wt.: 24 oz.
Comments: All steel construction. Produced from about 1973 to late 1970's. Replaced by Mark II 400. Add $10.00 for nickel finish.

Estimated Value:		Blued
	Excellent:	$150.00
	Very good:	$120.00

Sterling Mark II 400

Similar to 400 except streamlined and lightweight. Add $10.00 for nickel plated finish and $50.00 for stainless steel.

Estimated Value:	New (retail):	$209.50
	Excellent:	$160.00
	Very good:	$125.00

Sterling Model 283

Caliber: 22 long rifle
Action: Semi-automatic; exposed hammer; adjustable trigger and a sear lock safety
Magazine: 10-shot clip
Barrel: 4½", 6" or 8" heavy bull barrel
Sights: Blade front, click adjustable rear
Finish: Blued; checkered plastic grips
Length overall: 9"; 10½" or 12½"
Approximate wt.: 36 to 40 oz.
Comments: All steel construction. Manufactured from about 1970 to 1972. Also known as Target 300 Model.

Estimated Value: Excellent:	$125.00
Very good:	$100.00

Sterling Model 284

Same as Model 283 automatic pistol except: lighter tapered barrel. Also known as Target 300L Model. Made from about 1970 to 1972.

Estimated Value: Excellent:	$110.00
Very good:	$ 90.00

Sterling Model 285

Same as Model 283 automatic pistol except: ramp front sight & fixed rear sight; made in 4½" heavy barrel only; non-adjustable trigger. Produced from about 1970 to 1972. Also known as Husky Model.

Estimated Value: Excellent:	$100.00
Very good:	$ 80.00

Sterling Model 286

Same as Model 283 automatic pistol except: ramp front sight and fixed rear sight; made in 4½" & 6" tapered barrel only; non-adjustable trigger; also known as Trapper Model. Made from about 1970 to 1972.

Estimated Value: Excellent:	$90.00
Very good:	$75.00

Sterling Model 300

Caliber: 25 ACP
Action: Semi-automatic blowback action; concealed hammer
Magazine: 6-shot clip
Barrel: 2½"
Sights: None
Finish: Blued; nickel or stainless steel (after 1975) with cycolac grips
Length overall: 4½"
Approximate wt.: 13 oz.
Comments: All steel construction. Manufactured from about 1972 to present. Add $10.00 for nickel finish and $20.00 for stainless steel.

Estimated Value: New (retail):	$104.95
Excellent:	$ 80.00
Very good:	$ 65.00

Sterling Model 302, 302S

Same as Model 300 Automatic Pistol except: caliber 22 long rifle. 302 S is stainless steel. Add $20.00 for stainless steel.

Estimated Value: New (retail):	$104.95
Excellent:	$ 80.00
Very good:	$ 65.00

Handguns

Sterling Model 400S

Similar to Model 400 except: constructed of stainless steel. Made from 1976 to late 1970's
Estimated Value: Excellent: $175.00
Very good: $140.00

Sterling Model 402

Similar to Model 400 automatic pistol except: caliber 22 long rifle; 8-shot clip magazine. Made from about 1973 to 1975. Add $10.00 for nickel finish.
Estimated Value: Excellent: $150.00
Very good: $120.00

Sterling Model 402

Sterling Model 400S

Stevens

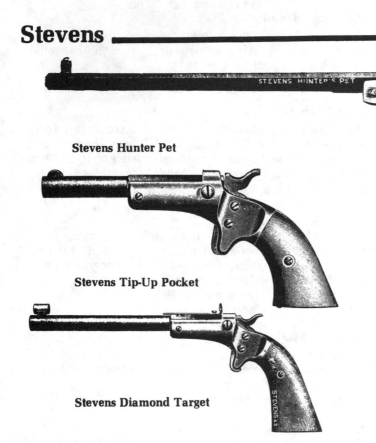

Stevens Hunter Pet

Stevens Tip-Up Pocket

Stevens Diamond Target

Stevens Diamond Target

Caliber: 22 RF long rifle (Black powder 1888-1912); 22 long rifle (Smokeless powder 1912-1915)
Action: Single; sheath trigger; tip-up barrel
Cylinder: None; single shot
Barrel: 6", 10"; part octagon
Sights: Globe or bead front; peep or adj. rear
Finish: Blued barrel; nickel plated iron frame to 1912. Varnished long walnut square grips.
Length overall: 9½" to 13½"
Approximate wt.: 10 to 13 oz.
Comments: Made from about 1888 to 1915. Marked J. STEVENS A. & T. CO. Approx 132,000 produced.
Estimated Value: Excellent: $200.00
Very good: $160.00

Stevens Hunter Pet

Caliber: 22 LR, 25 RF, 32 RF, 38 long RF, 44 long RF, 38-40, 44-40, 38-35, 44-50, 24 gauge
Action: Single with sheath trigger
Cylinder: None; single shot with pivoted barrel
Barrel: 18", 20", 22", or 24" octagon and half octagon
Sights: Adjustable for elevation; also some had Steven's Vernier peep sight attached to back strap
Finish: Blued barrel; nickel plated frame and detachable skeleton stock; smooth, varnished walnut, square butt grips.
Length overall: 22" to 28"
Approximate wt.: 5¾ lbs.
Comments: Serial numbers in 4000 to 13000 range. Approximately 8000 produced from about 1888 to 1907.

Estimated Value:

With Stock
Excellent: $390.00
Very good: $300.00

Stevens Tip-Up Pocket

Caliber: 22 short RF, 30 RF (to 1902)
Action: Single with sheath trigger
Cylinder: None; single shot with tip-up barrel
Barrel: 3½"; part octagon
Sights: Blade front; notch in frame rear
Finish: Blued barrel; nickel plated frame to 1912; blued frame after 1912; varnished walnut square butt grips
Length overall: 6¼"
Approximate wt.: 10 oz.
Comments: Produced from about 1888 to 1915. Marked J. Stevens A. & T. Co.
Estimated Value: Excellent: $160.00
Very good: $125.00

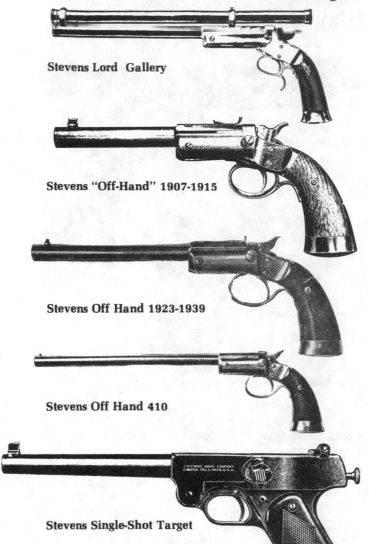

Stevens Lord Gallery

Stevens "Off-Hand" 1907-1915

Stevens Off Hand 1923-1939

Stevens Off Hand 410

Stevens Single-Shot Target

Stevens Lord Gallery

Caliber: 22 long rifle, 25 RF (smokeless powder)
Action: Single; tip up barrel
Cylinder: None; single shot
Barrel: 10"; octagon at breech - rest of barrel round
Sights: Bead front; wind gauge rear
Finish: Blued barrel; nickel plated frame; varnished, checkered walnut grips; trigger guard with outer finger spur and inner curl.
Length overall: 14"
Approximate wt.: 3 lb.
Comments: Made from about 1898 to 1908 with serial numbers probably above 4,000.
Estimated Value: Excellent: $210.00
**   Very good: $170.00**

Stevens "Off-Hand" 1907-1915

Caliber: 22 long rifle, 25 RF, smokeless powder
Action: Single; tip up barrel
Cylinder: None; single shot
Barrel: Octagon breech; 6"; 8"; & 10"
Sights: Bead front; stepped elevator rear
Finish: Blued barrel; plated frame; varnished walnut grips with base butt cap; blued frame after 1912.
Length overall: 9¼" to 13¼"
Approximate wt.: 24 to 28 oz.
Comments: Manufactured from about 1907 to 1915. Marked J. STEVENS A. & T. CO.
Estimated Value: Excellent: $275.00
**   Very good: $235.00**

Stevens Off Hand 1923-1939

Caliber: 22 long rifle
Action: Single; tip up barrel
Cylinder: None; single shot
Barrel: Octagon breech; 6", 8", 10" & 12¼"
Sights: Bead front; rear adj. for elevation
Finish: Blued barrel & frame also plated frame; walnut grips with butt cap
Length overall: 9¼" to 15½"
Approximate wt.: 24 to 34 oz.
Comments: Made in the mid 1920's to late 1930's.
Estimated Value: Excellent: $240.00
**   Very good: $200.00**

Stevens Off Hand 410

Caliber: 410 gauge (2½")
Action: Single; tip-up barrel
Cylinder: None; single shot
Barrel: Octagon breech; choked 8" or 12¼" barrel
Sights: Shot gun front sight
Finish: Blued barrel & frame also plated frame; walnut grips with butt cap
Length overall: 11¼" to 15½"
Approximate wt.: 23 to 25 oz.
Comments: Manufactured from about 1925 to 1935. Marked J. STEVENS ARMS COMPANY
Estimated Value: Excellent: $240.00
**   Very good: $200.00**

Stevens Single-Shot Target

Caliber: 22 long rifle
Action: Single; tip up barrel; round knurled cocking piece
Cylinder: None; single shot
Barrel: Round; 8"
Sights: Partridge front; adj. wind-gauge rear
Finish: Blued (Blackish blue color); black composition checkered grips
Length overall: 11½"
Approximate wt.: 37 oz.
Comments: A target single shot pistol with configuration of an automatic pistol. Made from about 1919 to 1942. Approximately 10,000 produced. The 1919 pistols had serial numbers from 1 to approximately 5,000 range with Pat. App'd For on barrel. After 1920 marked Pat'd April 27. 1920. All pistols marked J. STEVENS ARMS COMPANY.
Estimated Value: Excellent: $220.00
**   Very good: $160.00**

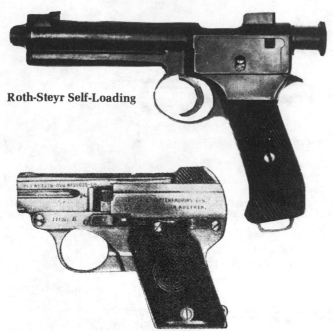

Roth-Steyr Self-Loading

Steyr Vest Pocket (Baby) Automatic

Steyr Model 1909 Pocket Automatic Pistol

Caliber: 32 ACP
Action: Semi-automatic; concealed hammer; blow-back action; early models have no extractor (empty case is blown out by gas after the breech-block is pushed open by firing); barrel can be tipped down for cleaning, using as single shot pistol, or for removing unfired cartridge.
Magazine: 7-shot clip
Barrel: 3 ½"
Sights: Fixed
Finish: Blued; checkered wood grips
Length overall: 6 ½"
Approximate wt.: 23 oz.
Comments: Made in both Austria and Belgium. The Austrian variety was a finer pistol from the standpoint of manufacture and reliability.
Estimated Value:

    Early Model
    Excellent: $145.00
    Very good: $120.00

    Later model (w/extractor)
    Excellent: $175.00
    Very good: $150.00

Steyr-Solothurn Pocket Model Automatic Pistol

Similar to the Steyr model 1909 except: a modified version; uses extractors to remove empty cases; production started about 1934 from Solothurn factory in Switzerland.
Estimated Value: Excellent: $150.00
                Very good: $125.00

Roth-Steyr Self-Loading Pistol

Caliber: 8mm Roth-Steyr
Action: Semi-automatic; concealed striker; locked breech design uses rotation of barrel by cam action to unlock barrel when fired; the striker is cocked by the recoil, but the trigger action has to pull it further back before it will release to fire.
Magazine: 10-shot non-detachable; usually loaded by a charger from the top.
Barrel: 5 1/8"
Sights: Fixed
Finish: Blued; checkered wood grips
Length overall: 9 1/8"
Approximate wt.: 36 oz.
Comments: Adopted by the Austro-Hungarian Cavalry in 1907. This is one of the earliest forms of successful locked-breech pistols.
Estimated Value: Excellent: $90.00
                Very good: $75.00

Steyr Vest Pocket (Baby) Automatic Pistol

Caliber: 25 ACP
Action: Semi-automatic; concealed hammer; blow-back action; early models have no extractor (empty case is blown out by gas after the breech block is pushed open by firing); barrel can be tipped down for cleaning, using as a single shot pistol, or for removing unfired cartridges.
Magazine: 6-shot clip
Barrel: 2"
Sights: Fixed
Finish: Blued; hard rubber, checkered grips
Length overall: 4 ½"
Approximate wt.: 12 oz.
Comments: First manufactured about 1908.
Estimated Value:

    Early Model
    Excellent: $140.00
    Very good: $115.00

    Later model (with extractor)
    Excellent: $150.00
    Very good: $125.00

Steyr-Solothurn Pocket Model Automatic

Steyr Model 1912 Military Automatic

Steyr Nazi-Proofed

Steyr Model 1912 Military
Caliber: 9mm Steyr
Action: Semi-automatic; exposed hammer; short-recoil; locked breech action (barrel rotates to unlock breech when gun is fired)
Magazine: 8-shot non-detatchable; loaded from top singly or by using a strip clip
Barrel: 5"
Sights: Fixed
Finish: Blued; checkered wood grips
Length overall: 8½"
Approximate wt.: 33 oz.
Comments: Made from about 1911 until after World War I; also referred to as Model 1911 or Steyr-Hahn; adopted by the Austro-Hungarian Army in 1912.
Estimated Value: Excellent: $175.00
Very good: $150.00

Steyr Nazi-Proofed
Same as Steyr Model 1912 except: Converted to fire the 9mm Luger cartridge during World War II and marked "P-08".
Estimated Value: Excellent: $210.00
Very good: $180.00

Thompson Center

Thompson Center Contender
Caliber: 22 short, long, long rifle; 22 WMR, 5mm Remington, 22 Hornet, 22 Remington jet, 221 Fireball, 222 Remington, 256 Winchester magnum, 30 M1 carbine, 30-30 special, 357 magnum, 9mm Luger, 45 ACP, 45 Colt, 44 magnum, and other wildcat calibers
Action: Single; frame accomodates any caliber barrel; hammer adjusts to rim fire or center fire; adjustable trigger pull
Cylinder: None; single shot
Barrel: 8¾", 10", 14". The 357 magnum, 45 Colt, and 44 magnum, barrels have detachable chokes for use with shot shells
Sights: Ramp front, adjustable rear
Finish: Blued; checkered walnut grips and fore end
Length overall: 12½" to 17¾"
Approximate wt.: 38 to 60 oz.
Comments: Introduced about 1967, still being produced; Add $10.00 for ventilated rib; Add $11.00 for super "14" receiver and add $9.00 for super "14" barrel.

Thompson Center Contender

Estimated Value:	Rec.(only)	Bar.(only)	Complete
New (retail):	$135.00	$90.00	$225.00
Excellent:	$ 95.00	$70.00	$175.00
Very good:	$ 85.00	$60.00	$150.00

Walther

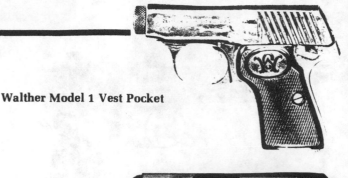

Walther Model 1 Vest Pocket

Caliber: 25 ACP
Action: Semi-automatic; concealed hammer
Magazine: 6-shot clip
Barrel: 2''
Sights: Fixed
Finish: Blued; checkered hard rubber grips
Length overall: 4¼''
Approximate wt.: 10 oz.
Comments: Top section of slide is cut away from behind front sight to breech block face. Made from about 1908 to 1912.
Estimated Value: Excellent: $220.00
Very good: $175.00

Walther Model 1 Vest Pocket

Walther Model 2 Vest Pocket

Similar to Model 1 except: slide fully encloses the barrel; ejector port right side of slide; overall length 4¼ inches; approximate wt. 12 ounces. Produced from about 1909 to 1915.
Estimated Value: Excellent: $195.00
Very good: $160.00

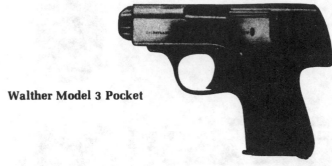

Walther Model 3 Pocket

Walther Model 3 Pocket

Caliber: 32 ACP
Action: Semi-automatic; concealed hammer
Magazine: 6-shot clip
Barrel: 2 5/8''
Sights: Fixed
Finish: Blued; checkered hard rubber grips
Length overall: 5''
Approximate wt.: 17 oz.
Comments: Produced from about 1910 to 1928; ejector port on left side of slide.
Estimated Value: Excellent: $230.00
Very good: $190.00

Walther Model 4 Pocket

Walther Model 4 Pocket

Similar to Model 3 except: larger in overall size; 3½ inch barrel; 6 inches overall; longer grip; 8-shot clip; a slide extension connected to forward end of the slide. Produced from about 1910 to 1918.
Estimated Value: Excellent: $225.00
Very good: $180.00

Walther Model 5 Vest Pocket Pistol

Similar to Model 2 except: improved version with a better finish. Produced from about 1913 to 1920.
Estimated Value: Excellent: $200.00
Very good: $160.00

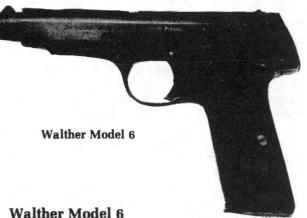

Walther Model 6

Walther Model 5 Vest Pocket Pistol

Walther Model 6

Caliber: 9mm Parabellum
Action: Semi-automatic; concealed hammer
Magazine: 8-shot clip
Barrel: 4¾''
Sights: Fixed
Finish: Blued; hard rubber grips
Length overall: 8¼''
Approximate wt.: 33 ounces.
Comments: Produced from about 1915 to 1917; ejection port on right side of slide.,
Estimated Value: Excellent: $275.00
Very good: $225.00

Walther Model 7 Pocket

Caliber: 25 ACP
Action: Semi-automatic; concealed hammer
Magazine: 8-shot clip
Barrel: 3"
Sights: Fixed
Finish: Blued; checkered hard rubber grips
Length overall: 5 ¼"
Approximate wt.: 13 ounces.
Comments: Introduced in 1917, discontinued in 1918. Ejection port on right side of slide.
Estimated Value: Excellent: $225.00
Very good: $185.00

Walther Model 7 Pocket

Walther Model 8 Pocket

Walther Model 8 Pocket

Caliber: 25 ACP
Action: Semi-automatic; concealed hammer
Magazine: 8-shot clip
Barrel: 2 7/8"
Sights: Fixed
Finish: Blued; checkered plastic grips
Length overall: 5 1/8"
Approximate wt.: 13 ounces.
Comments: Produced from about 1920 to 1945. Earlier models had takedown catch but later models used trigger guard as slide lock; a variety of special styles were made, such as nickel or gold plated, engraved finishes with pearl or ivory grips. Special plated and engraved styles worth more.
Estimated Value: Excellent: $200.00
Very good: $160.00

Walther Model 9 Vest Pocket

Walther Model PP

Walther Model 8 Lightweight Pocket

Same as Model 8 except: aluminum alloy used for frame, making it lighter; approximate wt. 9 ounces.
Estimated Value: Excellent: $220.00
Very good: $175.00

Walther Model 9 Vest Pocket

Caliber: 25 ACP
Action: Semi-automatic; concealed hammer
Magazine: 6-shot clip
Barrel: 2"
Sights: Fixed
Finish: Blued; checkered plastic grips
Length overall: 4"
Approximate wt.: 9 ½ oz.
Comments: Produced from about 1921 to 1945; a variety of special styles were made, such as nickel or gold plated engraved finishes with pearl or ivory grips; top section of slide from front sight to breech block face is cut away. Special plated and engraved styles worth more.
Estimated Value: Excellent: $230.00
Very good: $185.00

Walther Model PP

Caliber: 22 long rifle, 25 ACP, or 380 ACP
Action: Double action semi-automatic; exposed hammer; thumb safety that drops the hammer on blocked firing pin
Magazine: 8-shot clip
Barrel: 3 ¾"
Sights: Fixed
Finish: Blued; checkered plastic or checkered wood grips; steel back strap
Length overall: 6 9/16"
Approximate wt.: 24 oz.
Comments: Made from about 1929 to 1945; also nickel, silver and gold plated engraved models with ivory and pearl grips were produced; first commercially successful double action automatic pistol; initially made in 32 ACP but later made in 22, 25, and 380 calibers; the center fire calibers were made with and without a signal pin to indicate a round in the chamber; World War II models had poorer finish and workmanship. Special plated and engraved models worth more.

Estimated Value:	Regular Model	WWII Model
	$335.00	$230.00
Very good:	$270.00	$180.00

Handguns

Walther Model PPK

Same as Model PP except: 3 ¼ " barrel; 5 15/16" overall length; 7-shot magazine; approximate wt. 19 oz.; one-piece wrap around grip. Produced from about 1931 to 1945.

Estimated Value:	Regular Model	WWII Model
Excellent:	$350.00	$275.00
Very good:	$280.00	$215.00

Walther Models PP & PPK Lightweight

Same as Models PP & PPK except: lighter weight due to aluminum alloy frame.

Estimated Value: Excellent: $360.00
Very good: $285.00

Walther Presentation Models PP & PPK

Same size as regular Models PP & PPK in 32 caliber; not made to be fired because they were constructed of soft aluminum alloy.

Estimated Value: Excellent: $400.00 - $600.00

Walther Model PPK/S

Same as Model PPK except: larger size to meet U.S.A. Treasury Dept. specifications for importation into U.S.A.; the PPK/S uses the slide and barrel of PPK Model mounted on the PP Model frame; overall length is about 6 inches; 8-shot magazine. Add $20.00 for 22 long rifle.

Estimated Value: New (retail): $495.00
Excellent: $375.00
Very good: $300.00

Walther Model P-5

Caliber: 9mm Parabellum
Action: Double action, semi-automatic; exposed hammer
Magazine: 8 shot clip
Barrel: 3 ½ "
Sights: Adjustable rear, blade front
Finish: Blued; plastic grips
Length overall: 7"
Approximate wt.: 28 oz.
Comments: Introduced in 1980.
Estimated Value: New (retail): $860.00
Excellent: $650.00
Very good: $520.00

Walther Model PPK/S American

Caliber: 380 ACP
Action: Double action, semi-automatic; exposed hammer
Magazine: 7 shot clip
Barrel: 3 ¼ "
Sights: Fixed
Finish: Blued or stainless steel; plastic grips
Length overall: 6"
Approximate wt.: 23 oz.
Comments: An American built model of the Walther PPK/S, introduced in the late 1970's.
Estimated Value: New (retail): $265.00
Excellent: $200.00
Very good: $160.00

Walther Model P-5

Walther Model PPK/S

Walther Model PPK

Walther Model PP

Walther Model PP Auto

Same as pre-War II Model PP except being produced in West Germany from about 1955 to date. Add $20.00 for 22 caliber.

Estimated Value: New (retail): $505.00
Excellent: $375.00
Very good: $300.00

Walther Model PPK Auto

Same as pre-War II Model PPK except being produced in West Germany from about 1955 to date. Importation into U.S.A. discontinued in 1968 due to restrictions imposed by the U.S. Treasury Dept.

Estimated Value: Excellent: $385.00
Very good: $310.00

Walther Model PPK Lightweight

Same as Model PPK except: lighter weight due to use of aluminum alloy frame; not made in 380 caliber; importation discontinued in 1968.

Estimated Value: Excellent: $390.00
Very good: $315.00

Walther Model P-38 IV

Similar to the P-38 with strengthened slide, no dust cover and steel reinforced frame; adjustable rear sight.
Estimated Value: New (retail): $690.00
Excellent: $525.00
Very good: $420.00

Walther Model P-38 K

Similar to the Model P-38 IV with a 2¾" barrel.
Estimated Value: New (retail): $690.00
Excellent: $525.00
Very good: $420.00

Walther Model HP

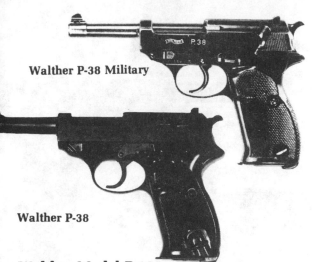

Walther P-38 Military

Walther P-38

Walther Model P-38 IV

Walther Model P-38

Same as P-38 Military Model except: improved workmanship; use of aluminum alloy in construction of frame; calibers 22 long rifle, 30 Luger and 9mm Luger; approximate wt. 28 ox.; add $30.00 for 22 caliber.
Estimated Value: 30 Luger or 9mm Luger
New (retail): $660.00
Excellent: $500.00
Very good: $400.00

Walther Model HP

Caliber: 9mm Luger
Action: Double action semi-automatic; exposed hammer
Magazine: 8-shot clip
Barrel: 5"
Sights: Fixed
Finish: Blued; checkered walnut or plastic grips
Length overall: 8 3/8"
Approximate wt.: 35 oz.
Comments: Well-made pistol, produced from about 1937 to 1945.
Estimated Value: Excellent: $600.00
Very good: $500.00

Walther Model P-38 Military

Similar to Model HP except: modified version of the Model HP adopted as the Official German service arm in 1938 and produced until about 1945. A poorer quality mass produced military pistol; some of the war time models were of very loose fit and very rough finish.
Estimated Value: Excellent: $350.00
Very good: $300.00

Webley

Webley 1906 Model Vest Pocket

Webley 1909 Model Vest Pocket

Webley 1906 Model Vest Pocket

Caliber: 25 ACP
Action: Semi-automatic; exposed hammer; grip safety in front of grip
Magazine: 6-shot clip
Barrel: 2 1/8"
Sights: None
Finish: Blued; checkered hard rubber grips
Length overall: 4¾"
Approximate wt.: 12 oz.
Comments: Made from about 1906 to 1940.
Estimated Value: Excellent: $160.00
Very good: $120.00

Webley & Scott 1909 Model Vest Pocket

Similar to 1906 Model except: ejection port in top of slide; concealed hammer; has fixed front and rear sights mounted on slide. Made from 1909 to 1940.
Estimated Value: Excellent: $175.00
Very good: $140.00

Handguns

Webley & Scott 1906 Model Police

Caliber: 32 ACP; 380 ACP
Action: Semi-automatic; exposed hammer
Magazine: 8-shot in 32 ACP, 7-shot in 380 ACP
Barrel: 3½"
Sights: Fixed; police version has rear sight and civilian model has a groove for rear sight
Finish: Blued; checkered hard rubber grips
Length overall: 6¼"
Approximate wt.: 20 oz.
Comments: Made from about 1905 to 1940; with or without grip safety.
Estimated Value: Excellent: $150.00
Very good: $120.00

Webley & Scott 9mm Military & Police

Caliber: 9mm Browning long
Action: Semi-automatic; exposed hammer; grip safety
Magazine: 8-shot clip
Barrel: 5¼"
Sights: Fixed
Finish: Blued; checkered plastic grips
Length overall: 8"
Approximate wt.: 32 oz.
Comments: Made from about 1909 to 1930.
Estimated Value: Excellent: $420.00
Very good: $350.00

Webley & Scott Mark I

Caliber: 455 Webley self-loading
Action: Semi-automatic; exposed hammer; grip safety
Magazine: 7-shot clip
Barrel: 5"
Sights: Fixed front; movable rear
Finish: Blued; checkered hard rubber or checkered walnut grips
Length overall: 8½"
Approximate wt.: 39 oz.
Comments: Adopted by British Royal Navy and Marines in 1913; made from about 1911 to 1931.
Estimated Value: Excellent: $275.00
Very good: $225.00

Webley & Scott Mark I No. 2

Similar to Mark I except: a slightly different version with fitted shoulder stock and adjustable rear sight; issued to the British Royal Flying Corps in 1915. Prices for gun with shoulder stock.
Estimated Value: Excellent: $650.00
Very good: $600.00

Webley & Scott 38

Similar to Mark I except: a smaller modified version with concealed hammer; 8-shot magazine; 38 ACP caliber; made from about 1910 to 1930.
Estimated Value: Excellent: $225.00
Very good: $200.00

Webley & Scott 1906 Model Police

Webley & Scott 9mm Military & Police

Webley & Scott Mark I

Webley & Scott Mark I No. 2

Webley & Scott 1909 Model Single Shot Target

Webley & Scott 1909 Model Single Shot Target

Caliber: 22 short, long, long rifle
Action: Single-action; exposed hammer; hinged frame; tip-up barrel, trigger guard also barrel release.
Cylinder: None; single shot; chamber in barrel
Barrel: 10" round
Sights: Fixed; later models have adjustable rear sight
Finish: Blued; hard rubber or wood grips
Length overall: 15"
Approximate wt.: 35 oz.
Comments: Target pistol; made from about 1909 to 1965 with improvements made in 1938, 1952 and 1956.
Estimated Value: Excellent: $225.00
Very good: $185.00

Webley & Scott 1911 Model Single Shot

Caliber: 22 short, long, long rifle
Action: Manually operated slide to chamber cartridge; exposed hammer
Magazine: None; single shot
Barrel: 4½" or 9"
Sights: Adjustable
Finish: Blued; checkered hard rubber grips
Length overall: 6¼" to 10¾"
Approximate wt.: 20 to 24 oz.
Comments: Has the appearance of automatic pistol; built on the 32 caliber frame; made for police training arm; some had removable wooden shoulder stocks; only a few hundred were made. Produced from about 1925 to 1927.
Estimated Value: Excellent: $300.00
Very good: $250.00

Webley & Scott Mark III Government Model

Caliber: 450, 455, or 476 Webley
Action: Double and single-action; exposed hammer; hinged frame; top break; simultaneous ejector
Cylinder: 6-shot
Barrel: 4", 6", 7½"
Sights: Fixed, also adjustable rear
Finish: Blued; hard rubber or wood grips
Length overall: 9¼" to 12¾"
Approximate wt.: 36 to 40 oz.
Comments: Made from about 1896 to 1928.
Estimated Value: Excellent: $150.00
Very good: $120.00

Webley & Scott Match Invader Single Shot Target

Similar to 1909 Model Single Shot Target except; also in caliber 32 S&W long, 38 S&W or 38 Special; approximate wt. 33 ounces. Made from about 1952 to 1965.
Estimated Value: Excellent: $175.00
Very good: $150.00

Webley & Scott Mark III Government Model

Webley & Scott Police & Civilian Pocket

Webley & Scott Pocket Model Hammerless

Webley & Scott 1911 Model Single Shot

**Webley & Scott Match Invader
Single Shot Target**

Webley & Scott Mark III Police

Webley & Scott Mark III Police

Caliber: 38 S&W
Action: Double and single-action; exposed hammer; hinged frame; top break simultaneous ejector
Cylinder: 6-shot
Barrel: 3", 4", 5"
Sights: Fixed or adjustable rear
Finish: Blued; checkered hard rubber or walnut grips
Length overall: 8¼" to 10¼"
Approximate wt.: 19 to 22 oz.
Comments: Made from about 1897 to 1945.
Estimated Value: Excellent: $160.00
Very good: $120.00

Webley & Scott Pocket Model Hammerless

Caliber: 32 S&W
Action: Double action; concealed hammer; hinged frame; top break; simultaneous ejector
Cylinder: 6-shot
Barrel: 3½"
Sights: Fixed
Finish: Blued; hard rubber or wood grips
Length overall: 6½"
Approximate wt.: 18 oz.
Comments: The hammer is enclosed by the frame; made from about 1898-1940.
Estimated Value: Excellent: $150.00
Very good: $120.00

Webley & Scott Police & Civilian Pocket

Similar to Pocket Model Hammerless except: exposed hammer; double and single-action. Made from about 1901 to 1940.
Estimated Value: Excellent: $130.00
Very good: $110.00

Webley Mark IV Police Model

Caliber: 38 S&W
Action: Double and single-action; exposed hammer; hinged frame; top break simultaneous ejector
Cylinder: 6-shot
Barrel: 4", 5", or 6"
Sights: Fixed or adjustable
Finish: Blued; checkered wood or plastic grips
Length overall: 8 1/8" to 10 1/8"
Approximate wt.: 24 to 29 oz.
Comments: Made from about 1927 to present.
Estimated Value: Excellent: $150.00
Very good: $120.00

Webley Mark IV Police Model

Webley Mark IV War Model

Similar to Mark IV Police Model except: made during World War II (from about 1940 to 1945) with poor finish and fitting.
Estimated Value: Excellent: $165.00
Very good: $130.00

Webley Mark IV

Webley Mark IV Pocket Model

Similar to Mark IV Police Model except: calibers 32 S&W, 32 S&W long, or 38 S&W, barrel length 3"; approximate wt. 24 oz.; overall length 7 1/8".
Estimated Value: Excellent: $160.00
Very good: $125.00

Webley Mark IV Pocket Model

Webley Mark IV Target Model

Similar to Mark IV Police Model except: caliber 22 short, long, & long rifle only; adjustable rear sight; barrel length 6"; approximate wt. 32 oz. Made from about 1931 to 1968.
Estimated Value: Excellent: $180.00
Very good: $150.00

Webley Mark IV

Webley Mark VI British Service

Caliber: 455 Webley
Action: Double and single-action; hinged frame; break top simultaneous ejector
Cylinder: 6-shot
Barrel: 4", 6" or 7½"
Sights: Fixed
Finish: Blued; checkered hard rubber or wood grips
Length overall: 9¼" to 12¾"
Approximate wt.: 34 to 39 oz.
Comments: Made from 1915 to 1928.
Estimated Value: Excellent: $175.00
Very good: $140.00

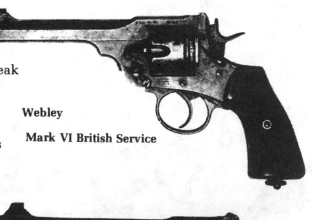

Webley Mark VI British Service

Webley Police Mark VI Target

Similar to Mark VI British except: caliber 22 short, long, and long rifle; barrel length 6" only; target sights; approximate wt. 40 oz.
Estimated Value: Excellent: $180.00
Very good: $145.00

Webley Mark VI Target

Glossary

ACP—Automatic Colt Pistol. This abbreviation is used to denote ammunition designed for semi-automatic pistols.

Action—The method by which a firearm is fed ammunition and fired; the portion of the firearm responsible for feeding ammunition and firing.

Adjustable choke—A muzzle attachment, either factory or manually installed, that allows the shooter to change the choke of his shotgun; several brands are available.

Autoloading—Semi-automatic action.

Automatic ejector—A device for extracting the fired case from the breech when the action is engaged.

Automatic safety—A safety that is put into action by reloading or cocking the firearm.

Barrel—The part of a gun through which the bullet or shot passes from breech to muzzle.

Barrel adapter—A device inserted into a barrel to change the gauge or caliber to a smaller size.

Barrel band—A metal ring encircling the barrel and forearm, found generally on carbines, lever actions or full length forearms.

Bead—A type of sight; a small round ball on top of barrel at the muzzle.

Beavertail—Wider than average.

Blowback—A semi-automatic action, that is operated by the pressure of the fired cartridge.

Blueing—A finishing treatment applied to the metal portions of firearms for lasting protection; named for the blue-black final appearance.

Glossary

Bolt action—An action, either repeating or single shot, that requires manual operation of the bolt handle to feed the chamber.

Box lock—An action, with few working parts, found in break-open firearms.

Box magazine—A box shaped magazine that stores the cartridges.

Breech—The rear end of the barrel where chamber is located.

Buck horn—A type of rear sight.

Bull barrel—An unusually thick and heavy barrel.

Butt plate—A sturdy piece attached to the rearmost section of the stock to protect the wood of the stock.

Buttstock—The stock.

Carbine—A rifle with a short barrel, generally 18"-20".

Case hardened—A treatment, using carbon and extreme heat, for strengthening metal parts; the treated portion takes on a multi-colored, hazy finish.

CB cap—A 22 caliber cartridge, shorter and less powerful than the 22 caliber short.

CF (Centerfire)—A cartridge in which the primer is located in the center of the base.

Chamber—The portion of the firearm that supports the cartridge during firing.

Checkering—Pattered lines cut into the wood of grips and forearms or slide handles; it is decorative and at the same time provides a non-slip surface.

Cheekpiece—An extended area in the stock used for proper cheek positioning against the stock.

Choke—The design of a shotgun barrel that dictates the spread and pattern of shot leaving the barrel.

Choke Tube—A device that is inserted into the muzzle of a shotgun to alter the choke.

Clip—A removable magazine, inserted into a firearm, that holds the cartridges feeds them into the chamber.

Comb—The upper portion of the stock.

Compensator—A device attached to the muzzle or made into the barrel to reduce the upward swing of the barrel when fired.

Cylinder—A rotating cartridge holder used in a revolver, in which the chambers are located.

Damascus barrel—A type of barrel produced by welding small twisted pieces of iron and steel in a spiral; these barrels were thought to be stronger in the late 1800's.

Derringer—Small, short, one or two barrel handgun, easily concealed.

Double action—Designation of a handgun that can be discharged simply by pulling the trigger— manual cocking unnecessary.

Double barrel—A gun with two barrels, usually a shotgun, rifle or rifle/shotgun combination with barrels side by side or over and under.

Double set trigger—A device with a cocking trigger and a firing trigger, usually on target guns.

Dovetail—A groove by which the sight is attached to the barrel.

Ejector—A mechanism for removing, or partially removing empty cases from the gun.

Exposed hammer—A visible hammer that can be manually cocked.

Falling block—An action, found in some early single shots, in which the chamber closing mechanism moves vertically by moving a lever.

Firing Pin—The device that strikes the primer part of a cartridge to fire the cartridges.

Finish—The exterior appearance of a gun including type of wood, stock, forearm and type of metal; sights, decoration and added features.

Fixed Sights—Stationary sights; not movable.

Flash supressor—An instrument that reduces or hides muzzle flame or flash.

Fluted—A shallow groove or grooves found in some forearms and on revolver cylinders.

Forearm—The portion of the gun under the barrel that is gripped when firing; usually made of wood; the forearm can be in the form of a slide handle on slide action gun.

Front sight—The sight at the muzzle end of the barrel.

Gas operation—A type of action in which gas from a discharging cartridge is used to operate the action.

Grip safety—A safety located on the grip of a pistol.

Hammer—A spring powered piece that strikes the firing pin; it is actuated by the trigger.

Hammerless—A gun with a concealed hammer or stiking mechanism.

Handgun—A gun that is operated with one hand; revolver, single shot, or semi-automatic pistol.

Handguard—A piece that fits on top of the barrel to protect the hand from the heat of rapid fire; usually found on military type rifles.

Hooded sight—A sight with a protective cover.

Lanyard loop or ring—A metal ring on military handguns that is attached to a strap.

Lever action—A firearm in which the action is operated by the movement of a lever usually part of the trigger guard.

Loading gate—In revolvers a piece that swings open to allow loading; in a long gun a spring powered door that is forced open when loading cartridges into the magazine.

Long—The middle designation of a 22 caliber cartridge longer than a short, shorter than a long rifle.

Long rifle—The designation of a 22 caliber cartridge more powerful than a long.

Magazine—The portion of the gun that holds cartridges ready for feeding into the chamber; in repeating weapons only.

Magnum—A more powerful cartridge than the standard cartridge.

Micrometer—A highly accurate adjustable sight found mainly on target rifles.

Monte Carlo—A type of stock in which there is a rise at the forward portion; usually has a cheek piece.

Muzzle—Forward most end of the barrel.

Open Sight—A "notched" sight.

Palm rest—An adjustable handgrip found on match rifles.

Parkerizing—A matted, rust-resistant surface applied to metal with a phosphate solution; used on military firearms.

Partridge sights—A square notched rear sight and square post front sight.

Peep sight—A circular rear sight with a small hole that provides greater accuracy than open or notched sights.

Glossary

Pistol—Handgun; usually a semi-automatic handgun.

Pistol grip—The grip portion of a handgun; or a grip resembling that of a pistol built into the stock of a shotgun or rifle.

Pump—Slide-action.

Ramp Sight—A front sight that is positioned atop a ramp base.

Recoil pad—A rubber cushion attached to some shotguns and high powered rifles designed to reduce recoil impact on the shooter.

Repeating—Any rifle or shotgun that has a magazine and may be refired without reloading.

Revolver—A handgun, that has a rotating cylinder magazine.

Rib—A flat piece fitted on top of barrel to aid in sighting or add decor; may be ventilated, matt or solid.

RF (Rimfire)—A cartridge in which the firing primer is in the perimeter of the shell base or head.

Safety—A mechanism that prevents the gun from being fired.

Schnabel—A decorative lip at the end of a forearm.

Semi-automatic—An autoloading action in which cartridges are fed automatically; the trigger must be pressed for every desired discharge.

Short—A small 22 caliber cartridge.

Shotgun—A non-rifled long gun, designated by gauge, for firing shot shells.

Side Lever—A lever located on the side of a receiver that is tripped to open the gun.

Single action—The hammer must be cocked before the gun can be fired.

Single set trigger—A trigger that can be fired by heavy pull or put into another position to allow light pull.

Single trigger—A single trigger used to fire a double barrel shotgun; a selective single trigger is equipped with a lever that allows the shooter to chose the barrel to be discharged first; the non-selective trigger is always fired in the same, factory-set sequence.

Slide action—A pump action long arm. An action that requires a manual slide of the forearm section (slide handle) in order to complete the action cycle.

Sling—A removable strap usually attached to military, high powered hunting, and some target rifles or shotguns.

Snubnose—A revolver with a very short barrel.

Swivel—A metal loop through which is passed a sling for carrying; either detachable or stationary.

Takedown—A gun that can be easily taken apart for transport or storage.

Thumbhole—A feature found mostly on match rifles, a hole in the stock for the shooter's thumb.

Thumb lever—A lever atop the frame that is tripped to break open the firearm.

Thumb rest—Usually found on handgun grips, a place to rest thumb to provide better hold.

Trigger—The piece under the action that is pressed to open the firing mechanism.

Trigger guard—A metal barrier around the trigger for protection of the trigger.

Tubular magazine—A tube in which cartridges are stored end to end, ready to be transported to the chamber; can be under barrel or in stock.

Ventilated rib—A rib that is separated from the barrel by short posts.

WMR—Winchester magnum rim fire.

INDEX